STUDENT SOLUTIONS MANUAL

PATRICIA FOARD

ALGEBRA & TRIGONOMETRY
Third Edition

Blitzer

PEARSON

Prentice
Hall

Upper Saddle River, NJ 07458

Editor-in-Chief: Sally Yagan
Senior Acquisitions Editor: Eric Frank
Supplement Editor: Aja Shevelew
Assistant Managing Editor: John Matthews
Production Editor: Allyson Kloss
Supplement Cover Manager: Paul Gourhan
Supplement Cover Designer: Joanne Alexandris
Manufacturing Buyer: Ilene Kahn

© 2004 Pearson Education, Inc.
Pearson Prentice Hall
Pearson Education, Inc.
Upper Saddle River, NJ 07458

Pearson Prentice Hall® is a trademark of Pearson Education, Inc.

Printed in the United States of America

10 9 8 7 6 5 4 3 2

ISBN 0-13-149159-8

Pearson Education Ltd., *London*
Pearson Education Australia Pty. Ltd., *Sydney*
Pearson Education Singapore, Pte. Ltd.
Pearson Education North Asia Ltd., *Hong Kong*
Pearson Education Canada, Inc., *Toronto*
Pearson Educación de Mexico, S.A. de C.V.
Pearson Education—Japan, *Tokyo*
Pearson Education Malaysia, Pte. Ltd.
Pearson Education, *Upper Saddle River, New Jersey*

Table of Contents

Chapter P

Check Point Exercises

1. a. $\left|1-\sqrt{2}\right|$

Because $\sqrt{2} \approx 1.4$, the number inside the absolute value bars is negative. The absolute value of x when $x < 0$ is $-x$. Thus,

$$\left|1-\sqrt{2}\right|=-\left(1-\sqrt{2}\right)=\sqrt{2}-1$$

b. $\left|\pi-3\right|$

Because $\pi \approx 3.14$, the number inside the absolute value bars is positive. The absolute value of a positive number is the number itself. Thus, $\left|\pi-3\right|=\pi-3$.

c. $\dfrac{|x|}{x}$ if $x > 0$

If $x > 0$, then $|x| = x$. Thus,

$$\frac{|x|}{x}=\frac{x}{x}=1.$$

2. Because the distance between a and b is given by $|a-b|$, the distance between -4 and 5 is

$$|-4-5|=|-9|=9.$$

3. Begin by substituting 30 for x. Because $x = 30$, we will be finding the U.S. population 30 years after 1960, in the year 1990.

$2.35(30) + 179.5$
$= 250$

Thus, in 1990, the population of the United States was 250 million.

4. Simplify: $7(4x-3y) + 2(5x+y)$.

Use the distributive property to remove the parentheses. Then, multiply and group like terms. Finally combine like terms.

$7(4x-3y) + 2(5x+y)$.
$= 7 \cdot 4x - 7 \cdot 3y + 2 \cdot 5x + 2 \cdot y$
$= 28x - 21y + 10x + 2y$
$= (28x + 10x) + (2y - 21y)$
$= 38x - 19y$

Exercise Set P.1

For Exercises 1 and 3:

a. The natural numbers are used for counting, $\{1, 2, 3, 4, 5 \ldots\}$

b. The whole numbers add 0 to the set of natural numbers, $\{0, 1, 2, 3, 4, 5 \ldots\}$

c. The integers add the negative of the natural numbers to the set of whole numbers, $\{\ldots, \_5, \_4, \_3, \_2, \_1, 2, 3, 4, 5 \ldots\}$

d. The rational numbers can be expressed as an integer divided by a nonzero integer or a terminating or repeating decimal.,

e. The irrational numbers cannot be expressed as a quotient of integers or a terminating or repeating decimal.

1. a. $\sqrt{100}$

b. $0, \sqrt{100}$

c. $-9, 0, \sqrt{100}$

d. $-9, \dfrac{-4}{5}, 0, 0.25, 9.2, \sqrt{100}$

e. $\sqrt{3}$

3. a. $\sqrt{64}$

   b. $0,\ \sqrt{64}$

   c. $-11,\ 0,\ \sqrt{64}$

   d. $-11,\ \dfrac{-5}{6},\ 0,\ 0.75,\ \sqrt{64}$

   e. $\sqrt{5},\ \pi$

5. 0

7. Answers may vary.

9. True; -13 is to the left of -2 on the number line.

11. True; 4 is to the right of -7 on the number line.

13. True; $-\pi = -\pi$

15. $|300| = 300$

17. $|12 - \pi| = 12 - \pi$

19. $\left|\sqrt{2} - 5\right| = 5 - \sqrt{2}$

21. $\dfrac{-3}{|-3|} = \dfrac{-3}{3} = -1$

23. $||{-}3| - |{-}7|| = |3 - 7| = |{-}4| = 4$

25. $|x + y|;\ x = 2$ and $y = -5$
$|2 + (-5)| = |-3| = 3$

27. $|x| + |y| = |2| + |-5| = 2 + 5 = 7$

29. $\dfrac{y}{|y|} = \dfrac{-5}{|-5|} = \dfrac{-5}{5} = -1$

31. $|17 - 2| = |15| = 15$

33. $|5 - (-2)| = |7| = 7$

35. $|-4 - (-19)| = |15| = 15$

37. $|-1.4 - (-3.6)| = |2.2| = 2.2$

39. $5x + 7 = 5\,(4) + 7 = 27$

41. $4(x + 3) - 11 = 4[(-5) + 3] - 11$
$\qquad\qquad = 4(-2) - 11 = -19$

43. $\dfrac{5}{9}(F - 32) = \dfrac{5}{9}(77 - 32)$
$\qquad\qquad\quad = \dfrac{5}{9}(45)$
$\qquad\qquad\quad = 25$

45. $\dfrac{5(x + 2)}{2x - 14} = \dfrac{5(10 + 2)}{2(10) - 14}$
$\qquad\qquad\quad = \dfrac{5(12)}{6}$
$\qquad\qquad\quad = 5 \cdot 2$
$\qquad\qquad\quad = 10$

47. $\dfrac{2x + 3y}{x + 1};\ x = -2,\ y = 4$
$\quad = \dfrac{2(-2) + 3(4)}{-2 + 1} = \dfrac{-4 + 12}{-1} = \dfrac{8}{-1} = -8$

49. $6 + (-4) = (-4) + 6$; commutative property of addition

51. $6 + (2 + 7) = (6 + 2) + 7$; associative property of addition

53. $(2 + 3) + (4 + 5) = (4 + 5) + (2 + 3)$; commutative property of addition

55. $2(-8 + 6) = -16 + 12$; distributive property of multiplication over addition

57. $\dfrac{1}{x+3}(x+3)=1; x \neq -3$, inverse property of

    multiplication

59. $5(3x+4)-4=5\cdot3x+5\cdot4-4$
$$=15x+20-4$$
$$=15x+16$$

61. $5(3x-2)+12x=5\cdot3x-5\cdot2+12x$
$$=15x-10+12x$$
$$=27x-10$$

63. $7(3y-5)+2(4y+3)$
$$=7\cdot3y-7\cdot5+2\cdot4y+2\cdot3$$
$$=21y-35+8y+6$$
$$=29y-29$$

65. $5(3y-2)-(7y+2)=15y-10-7y-2$
$$=8y-12$$

67. $7-4[3-(4y-5)]=7-4[3-4y+5]$
$$=7-4[8-4y]$$
$$=7-32+16y$$
$$=16y-25$$

69. $-(-14x)=14x$

71. $-(2x-3y-6)=-2x+3y+6$

73. $\dfrac{1}{3}(3x)+[(4y)+(-4y)]=x+0$
$$=x$$

75. Yes; The order in which you put on your shoes does not matter.

77. Answers may vary.

79. $81-0.6x$, for $x=100$
    $=81-0.6(100)=21$
    $1900+100=2000$
    In 2000, approximately 21% of Americans will smoke.

81. a. $0.6(220-a)=0.6(220)-0.6(a)$
$$=132-0.6a$$

    b. Let $a=20$
        $0.6(220-a)=0.6(220-20)$
$$=0.6(200)$$
$$=120$$
        $132-0.6a=132-0.6(20)$
$$=132-12=120$$

83.–87. Answers may vary.

89. a. False; For example, 1.7 is a rational number and it is not an integer.

    b. False; All whole numbers, $0,1,2,3,\cdots\}$, are also integers.

    c. True; –7.5 is a rational number and it is not positive.

    d. False; $-\pi$ is an irrational number that is also negative.

    (c) is true.

91. $\sqrt{2}\approx1.4$
    $1.4<1.5$
    $\sqrt{2}<1.5$

93.
$$-\dfrac{3.14}{2}=-1.57$$
$$-\dfrac{\pi}{2}\approx-1.571$$
$$-1.57>-1.571$$
$$-\dfrac{3.14}{2}>-\dfrac{\pi}{2}$$

Section P.2

Check Point Exercises

1. $(-4)^3\cdot2^2=(-4)(-4)(-4)\cdot2\cdot2$
$$=-64\cdot4$$
$$=-256$$

2. a. $2^{-3}=\dfrac{1}{2^3}=\dfrac{1}{2\cdot2\cdot2}=\dfrac{1}{8}$

b. $\dfrac{1}{6^{-2}} = \dfrac{1}{\frac{1}{6^2}} = 6^2 = 36$

3. a. $3^3 \cdot 3^2 = 3^{3+2} = 3^5 = 243$

    b. $2^4 \cdot 2^{-7} = 2^{4+(-7)} = 2^{-3} = \dfrac{1}{2^3} = \dfrac{1}{8}$

    c. $x^{-5} \cdot x^{11} = x^{-5+11} = x^6$

4. a. $(3^3)^2 = 3^{3 \cdot 2} = 3^6 = 729$

  b. $(y^7)^4 = y^{7 \cdot 4} = y^{28}$

  c. $(x^{-4})^2 = x^{-4 \cdot 2} = x^{-8} = \dfrac{1}{x^8}$

5. a. $\dfrac{3^6}{3^4} = 3^{6-4} = 3^2 = 9$

  b. $\dfrac{x^5}{x^{12}} = x^{5-12} = x^{-7} = \dfrac{1}{x^7}$

  c. $\dfrac{y^2}{y^{-7}} = y^{2-(-7)} = y^{2+7} = y^9$

6. $(-4x)^3 = (-4)^3 x^3 = -64x^3$

7. a. $\left(\dfrac{3}{4}\right)^3 = \dfrac{3^3}{4^3} = \dfrac{27}{64}$

  b. $\left(-\dfrac{2}{y}\right)^5 = \dfrac{(-2)^5}{y^5} = \dfrac{-32}{y^5} = -\dfrac{32}{y^5}$

8. a. $(2x^3 y^6)^4 = (2)^4 (x^3)^4 (y^6)^4$
                 $= (2)^4 x^{3 \cdot 4} y^{6 \cdot 4}$
                 $= 16x^{12} y^{24}$

  b. $(-6x^3 y^6)^4 (3xy^3) = (-6)(3)x^2 xy^5 y^3$
      $= -18x^{2+1} y^{5+3}$
      $= -18x^3 y^8$

c. $\dfrac{100x^{12} y^2}{20x^{16} y^{-4}} = \left(\dfrac{100}{20}\right)\left(\dfrac{x^{12}}{x^{16}}\right)\left(\dfrac{y^2}{y^{-4}}\right)$
             $= 5x^{12-16} y^{2-(-4)}$
             $= 5x^{-4} y^6$
             $= \dfrac{5y^6}{x^4}$

d. $\left(\dfrac{5x}{y^4}\right)^{-2} = \dfrac{5^{-2} x^{-2}}{(y^4)^{-2}}$
           $= \dfrac{5^{-2} x^{-2}}{y^{-8}}$
           $= \dfrac{y^8}{5^2 x^2}$
           $= \dfrac{y^8}{25x^2}$

9. a. Express 7.4×10^9 in decimal notation by moving the decimal point in 7.4 nine places to the right.
$7.4 \times 10^9 = 7,400,000,000$

  b. Express 3.017×10^{-6} in decimal notation by moving the decimal point in 3.017 six places to the left.
$3.017 \times 10^{-6} = 0.000003017$

10. a. To express 7,410,000,000 in scientific notation, the decimal point needs to move nine places. The exponent on 10 is positive since 7,410,000,000 is greater than 10.
$7,410,000,000 = 7.41 \times 10^9$

  b. To express 0.000000092 in scientific notation, the decimal points needs to move eight places. The exponent on 10 is negative since 0.000000092 is between 0 and 1.
$0.000000092 = 9.2 \times 10^{-8}$

11. $\dfrac{3.6 \times 10^9}{2.8 \times 10^8}$

$= 1.286 \times 10$

$= 12.86$

The average American spent \$12.86 on full-fat ice cream.

Exercise Set P.2

1. $5^2 \cdot 2 = (5 \cdot 5) \cdot 2 = 25 \cdot 2 = 50$

3. $(-2)^6 = (-2)(-2)(-2)(-2)(-2)(-2) = 64$

5. $-2^6 = -2 \cdot 2 \cdot 2 \cdot 2 \cdot 2 \cdot 2 = -64$

7. $(-3)^0 = 1$

9. $-3^0 = -1$

11. $4^{-3} = \dfrac{1}{4^3} = \dfrac{1}{4 \cdot 4 \cdot 4} = \dfrac{1}{64}$

13. $2^2 \cdot 2^3 = 2^{2+3} = 2^5 = 2 \cdot 2 \cdot 2 \cdot 2 \cdot 2 = 32$

15. $(2^2)^3 = 2^{2 \cdot 3} = 2^6 = 2 \cdot 2 \cdot 2 \cdot 2 \cdot 2 \cdot 2 = 64$

17. $\dfrac{2^8}{2^4} = 2^{8-4} = 2^4 = 2 \cdot 2 \cdot 2 \cdot 2 = 16$

19. $3^{-3} \cdot 3 = 3^{-3+1} = 3^{-2} = \dfrac{1}{3^2} = \dfrac{1}{3 \cdot 3} = \dfrac{1}{9}$

21. $\dfrac{2^3}{2^7} = 2^{3-7} = 2^{-4} = \dfrac{1}{2^4} = \dfrac{1}{2 \cdot 2 \cdot 2 \cdot 2} = \dfrac{1}{16}$

23. $x^{-2}y = \dfrac{1}{x^2} \cdot y = \dfrac{y}{x^2}$

25. $x^0 y^5 = 1 \cdot y^5 = y^5$

27. $x^3 \cdot x^7 = x^{3+7} = x^{10}$

29. $x^{-5} \cdot x^{10} = x^{-5+10} = x^5$

31. $(x^3)^7 = x^{3 \cdot 7} = x^{21}$

33. $(x^{-5})^3 = x^{-5 \cdot 3} = x^{-15} = \dfrac{1}{x^{15}}$

35. $\dfrac{x^{14}}{x^7} = x^{14-7} = x^7$

37. $\dfrac{x^{14}}{x^{-7}} = x^{14-(-7)} = x^{14+7} = x^{21}$

39. $(8x^3)^2 = 8^2(x^3)^2 = 8^2 x^{3 \cdot 2} = 64x^6$

41. $\left(-\dfrac{4}{x}\right)^3 = \dfrac{(-4)^3}{x^3} = -\dfrac{64}{x^3}$

43. $(-3x^2 y^5)^2 = (-3)^2 (x^2)^2 \cdot (y^5)^2$

$= 9x^{2 \cdot 2} y^{5 \cdot 2}$

$= 9x^4 y^{10}$

45. $(3x^4)(2x^7) = 3 \cdot 2 x^4 \cdot x^7 = 6x^{4+7} = 6x^{11}$

47. $(-9x^3 y)(-2x^6 y^4) = (-9)(-2)x^3 x^6 y y^4$

$= 18x^{3+6} y^{1+4}$

$= 18x^9 y^5$

49. $\dfrac{8x^{20}}{2x^4} = \left(\dfrac{8}{2}\right)\left(\dfrac{x^{20}}{x^4}\right) = 4x^{20-4} = 4x^{16}$

51. $\dfrac{25a^{13} \cdot b^4}{-5a^2 \cdot b^3} = \left(\dfrac{25}{-5}\right)\left(\dfrac{a^{13}}{a^2}\right)\left(\dfrac{b^4}{b^3}\right)$

$= -5a^{13-2} b^{4-3}$

$= -5a^{11} b$

53. $\dfrac{14b^7}{7b^{14}} = \left(\dfrac{14}{7}\right)\left(\dfrac{b^7}{b^{14}}\right) = 2 \cdot b^{7-14} = 2b^{-7} = \dfrac{2}{b^7}$

55. $(4x^3)^{-2} = (4^{-2})(x^3)^{-2}$

$= 4^{-2} x^{-6}$

$= \dfrac{1}{4^2 x^6}$

$= \dfrac{1}{16x^6}$

57. $\dfrac{24x^3 \cdot y^5}{32x^7 y^{-9}} = \dfrac{3}{4}x^{3-7}y^{5-(-9)}$

$= \dfrac{3}{4}x^{-4}y^{14}$

$= \dfrac{3y^{14}}{4x^4}$

59. $\left(\dfrac{5x^3}{y}\right)^{-2} = \dfrac{5^{-2}x^{-6}}{y^{-2}} = \dfrac{y^2}{25x^6}$

61. $\left(\dfrac{-15a^4 b^2}{5a^{10}b^{-3}}\right)^3$

$= \left(\dfrac{-3b^{2-(-3)}}{a^{10-4}}\right)^3$

$= \left(\dfrac{-3b^5}{a^6}\right)^3$

$= \dfrac{-27b^{15}}{a^{18}}$

63. $\left(\dfrac{3a^{-5}b^2}{12a^3 b^{-4}}\right)^0 = 1$

65. $4.7 \times 10^3 = 4700$

67. $4 \times 10^6 = 4{,}000{,}000$

69. $7.86 \times 10^{-4} = 0.000786$

71. $3.18 \times 10^{-6} = 0.00000318$

73. $3600 = 3.6 \times 10^3$

75. $220{,}000{,}000 = 2.2 \times 10^8$

77. $0.027 = 2.7 \times 10^{-2}$

79. $0.000763 = 7.63 \times 10^{-4}$

81. $(2 \times 10^3)(3 \times 10^2) = (2 \times 3) \times (10^3 \times 10^2)$

$= 6 \times 10^{3+2}$

$= 6 \times 10^5$

$= 600{,}000$

83. $(4.1 \times 10^2)(3 \times 10^{-4}) = (4.1 \times 3) \times (10^2 \times 10^{-4})$

$= 12.3 \times 10^{2+(-4)}$

$= 12.3 \times 10^{-2}$

$= 0.123$

85. $\dfrac{12 \times 10^6}{4 \times 10^2} = \left(\dfrac{12}{4}\right) \times \left(\dfrac{10^6}{10^2}\right)$

$= 3 \times 10^{6-2}$

$= 3 \times 10^4$

$= 30{,}000$

87. $\dfrac{6.3 \times 10^3}{3 \times 10^5} = \left(\dfrac{6.3}{3}\right) \times \left(\dfrac{10^3}{10^5}\right)$

$= 2.1 \times 10^{3-5} = 2.1 \times 10^{-2}$

$= 0.021$

89. $\dfrac{480{,}000{,}000{,}000}{0.00012}$

$= \dfrac{4.8 \times 10^{11}}{1.2 \times 10^{-4}}$

$= 4 \times 10^{11-(-4)}$

$= 4 \times 10^{15}$

91. $\dfrac{0.00072 \cdot 0.003}{0.00024}$

$$= \frac{7.2 \times 10^{-4} \cdot 3 \times 10^{-3}}{2.4 \times 10^{-4}}$$

$$= \frac{21.6 \times 10^{-7}}{2.4 \times 10^{-4}}$$

$$= 9 \times 10^{-7-(-4)}$$

$$= 9 \times 10^{-3}$$

93. $\dfrac{1.9 \times 10^{12}}{2.8 \times 10^{8}}$

$$= 0.68 \times 10^{4}$$

$$= 6.8 \times 10^{3}$$

$$= 6800$$

Each U.S. citizen paid an average of $6800 in taxes.

95. $2.8 \times 10^{8} \cdot 4000$

$$= 2.8 \times 10^{8} \cdot 4 \times 10^{3}$$

$$= 11.2 \times 10^{11}$$

$$= 1.12 \times 10^{12}$$

The total spent on health care in the U.S. was $1.12 x 10¹².

97. $5.3 \times 10^{-23} \cdot 20000$

$$= 5.3 \times 10^{-23} \cdot 2 \times 10^{4}$$

$$= 10.6 \times 10^{-19}$$

$$= 1.06 \times 10^{-18}$$

The mass of 20,000 molecules of oxygen is 1.06 x 10⁻¹⁸ grams.

99.–105. Answers may vary.

107. a. False, $4^{-2} = \dfrac{1}{16} > 4^{-3} = \dfrac{1}{64}$

b. True, $5^{-2} = \dfrac{1}{25} > 2^{-5} = \dfrac{1}{32}$

c. False, $16 = (-2)^{4} \neq 2^{-4} = \dfrac{1}{16}$

d. False. $\dfrac{5^{2} \cdot 5^{-2}}{2^{5} \cdot 2^{-5}} = \dfrac{5^{2-2}}{2^{5-5}} = \dfrac{5^{0}}{2^{0}} = \dfrac{1}{1} = 1$

1 is not greater than 1

109. $b^{A} = MN, b^{C} = M, b^{D} = N$

$$b^{A} = b^{C} b^{D}$$

$$A = C + D$$

Section P.3

Check Point Exercises

1. a. Since $\sqrt{a^{2}} = |a|$,

$\sqrt{3^{2}} = 3.$

b. $\sqrt{x} \cdot \sqrt{10x} = \sqrt{x \cdot 10x}$

$$= \sqrt{10x^{2}}$$

$$= \sqrt{5 \cdot 2x^{2}}$$

$$= \sqrt{5x^{2}} \cdot \sqrt{2}$$

$$= 5x\sqrt{2}$$

2. a. $\sqrt{\dfrac{25}{16}} = \dfrac{\sqrt{25}}{\sqrt{16}} = \dfrac{5}{4}$

b. $\dfrac{\sqrt{50x^{3}}}{\sqrt{x}} = \sqrt{\dfrac{50x^{3}}{2x}}$

$$= \sqrt{25x^{2}}$$

$$= \sqrt{25x^{2}} \cdot \sqrt{}$$

$$= 5x\sqrt{}$$

3. a. $8\sqrt{13} + 9\sqrt{13} = (8+9)\sqrt{3}$

$$= 17\sqrt{13}$$

b. $\sqrt{17x} - 20\sqrt{17x}$
  $= 1\sqrt{17x} - 20\sqrt{17x}$
  $= (1 - 20)\sqrt{17x}$
  $= -19\sqrt{17x}$

4. a. $5\sqrt{27} + \sqrt{12}$
  $= 5\sqrt{9 \cdot 3} + \sqrt{4 \cdot 3}$
  $= 5 \cdot 3\sqrt{3} + 2\sqrt{3}$
  $= 15\sqrt{3} + 2\sqrt{3}$
  $= (15 + 2)\sqrt{3}$
  $= 17\sqrt{3}$

b. $6\sqrt{18x} - 4\sqrt{8x}$
  $= 6\sqrt{9 \cdot 2x} - 4\sqrt{4 \cdot 2x}$
  $= 6 \cdot 3\sqrt{2x} - 4 \cdot 2\sqrt{2x}$
  $= 18\sqrt{2x} - 8\sqrt{2x}$
  $= (18 - 8)\sqrt{2x}$
  $= 10\sqrt{2x}$

5. a. If we multiply numerator and denominator by $\sqrt{3}$, the denominator becomes $\sqrt{3} \cdot \sqrt{3} = \sqrt{9} = 3$. Therefore, multiply by 1, choosing $\dfrac{\sqrt{3}}{\sqrt{3}}$ for 1.
  $\dfrac{5}{\sqrt{3}} = \dfrac{5}{\sqrt{3}} \cdot \dfrac{\sqrt{3}}{\sqrt{3}} = \dfrac{5\sqrt{3}}{\sqrt{9}} = \dfrac{5\sqrt{3}}{3}$

b. The *smallest* number that will produce a perfect square in the denominator of $\dfrac{6}{\sqrt{12}}$ is $\sqrt{3}$ because $\sqrt{12} \cdot \sqrt{3} = \sqrt{36} = 6$. So multiply by 1, choosing $\dfrac{\sqrt{3}}{\sqrt{3}}$ for 1.
  $\dfrac{6}{\sqrt{12}} = \dfrac{6}{\sqrt{12}} \cdot \dfrac{\sqrt{3}}{\sqrt{3}} = \dfrac{6\sqrt{3}}{\sqrt{36}} = \dfrac{6\sqrt{3}}{6} = \sqrt{3}$

6. The denominator will not contain a radical if multiplied by $4 - \sqrt{5}$. Therefore, multiply

by 1, choosing $\dfrac{4 - \sqrt{5}}{4 - \sqrt{5}}$ for 1.

$\dfrac{8}{4 + \sqrt{5}} = \dfrac{8}{4 + \sqrt{5}} \cdot \dfrac{4 - \sqrt{5}}{4 - \sqrt{5}}$
$= \dfrac{8(4 - \sqrt{5})}{4^2 - (\sqrt{5})^2}$
$= \dfrac{8(4 - \sqrt{5})}{16 - 5}$
$= \dfrac{8(4 - \sqrt{5})}{11}$ or $\dfrac{32 - 8\sqrt{5}}{11}$

7. a. $\sqrt[3]{40} = \sqrt[3]{8 \cdot 5} = \sqrt[3]{8} \cdot \sqrt[3]{5} = 2\sqrt[3]{5}$

b. $\sqrt[5]{8} \cdot \sqrt[5]{8} = \sqrt[5]{64}$
  $= \sqrt[5]{2^2 \cdot 2}$
  $= 2\sqrt[5]{2}$

c. $\sqrt[3]{\dfrac{125}{27}} = \dfrac{\sqrt[3]{125}}{\sqrt[3]{27}} = \dfrac{5}{3}$

8. $3\sqrt[3]{81} - 4\sqrt[3]{3}$
  $= 3\sqrt[3]{27 \cdot 3} - 4\sqrt[3]{3}$
  $= 3 \cdot 3\sqrt[3]{3} - 4\sqrt[3]{3}$
  $= 9\sqrt[3]{3} - 4\sqrt[3]{3}$
  $= (9 - 4)\sqrt[3]{3}$
  $= 5\sqrt[3]{3}$

9. a. $81^{\frac{1}{2}} = \sqrt{81} = 9$

b. $27^{\frac{1}{3}} = \sqrt[3]{27} = 3$

c. $32^{-\frac{1}{5}} = \dfrac{1}{32^{\frac{1}{5}}} = \dfrac{1}{\sqrt[5]{32}} = \dfrac{1}{2}$

10. a. $4^{\frac{3}{2}} = (\sqrt{4})^3 = 2^3 = 8$

b. $32^{-\frac{2}{5}} = \dfrac{1}{32^{\frac{2}{5}}} = \dfrac{1}{(\sqrt[5]{32})^2} = \dfrac{1}{2^2} = \dfrac{1}{4}$

11. a. $\left(2x^{4/3}\right)\left(5x^{8/3}\right)$

$$= 2 \cdot 5 x^{4/3} \cdot x^{8.3}$$
$$= 10x^{12/3}$$
$$= 10x^{4}$$

b. $\dfrac{20x^4}{5x^{3/2}} = \left(\dfrac{20}{5}\right)\left(\dfrac{x^4}{x^{3/2}}\right)$

$$= 4x^{4-(3/2)}$$
$$= 4x^{(8/2)-(3/2)}$$
$$= 4x^{5/2}$$

12. $\sqrt[6]{x^3} = x^{3/6} = x^{1/2} = \sqrt{x}$

Exercise Set P.3

1. $\sqrt{36} = \sqrt{6^2} = 6$

3. $\sqrt{-36}$ is not a real number.

5. $\sqrt{(-13)^2} = |-13| = 13$

7. $\sqrt{50} = \sqrt{25 \cdot 2} = \sqrt{25}\sqrt{2} = 5\sqrt{2}$

9. $\sqrt{45x^2} = \sqrt{9x^2 \cdot 5}$

$$= \sqrt{9x^2}\sqrt{5}$$
$$= \sqrt{9}\sqrt{x^2}\sqrt{5}$$
$$= 3|x|\sqrt{5}$$

11. $\sqrt{2x} \cdot \sqrt{6x} = \sqrt{2x \cdot 6x}$

$$= \sqrt{12x^2}$$
$$= \sqrt{4x^2} \cdot \sqrt{3}$$
$$= 2x\sqrt{3}$$

13. $\sqrt{x^3} = \sqrt{x^2} \cdot \sqrt{x} = x\sqrt{x}$

15. $\sqrt{2x^2} \cdot \sqrt{6x} = \sqrt{2x^2 \cdot 6x}$

$$= \sqrt{2x^3}$$
$$= \sqrt{4x^2} \cdot \sqrt{3x}$$
$$= 2x\sqrt{3x}$$

17. $\sqrt{\dfrac{1}{81}} = \dfrac{\sqrt{1}}{\sqrt{81}} = \dfrac{1}{9}$

19. $\sqrt{\dfrac{49}{16}} = \dfrac{\sqrt{49}}{\sqrt{16}} = \dfrac{7}{4}$

21. $\dfrac{\sqrt{48x^3}}{\sqrt{3x}} = \sqrt{\dfrac{48x^3}{3x}} = \sqrt{6x^2} = 4x$

23. $\dfrac{\sqrt{50x^4}}{\sqrt{3x}} = \sqrt{\dfrac{50x^4}{3x}}$

$$= \sqrt{50x^3}$$
$$= \sqrt{25x^2} \cdot \sqrt{2x}$$
$$= 5x\sqrt{2x}$$

25. $\dfrac{\sqrt{200x^3}}{\sqrt{10x^{-1}}}$

$$= \sqrt{\frac{200x^3}{10x^{-1}}}$$

$$= \sqrt{20x^{3-(-1)}}$$

$$= \sqrt{20x^4}$$

$$= \sqrt{4 \cdot 5x^4}$$

$$= 2x^2 \sqrt{5}$$

27. $7\sqrt{3} + 6\sqrt{3} = (7+6)\sqrt{3} = 13\sqrt{3}$

29. $6\sqrt{17x} - 8\sqrt{17x} = (6-8)\sqrt{17x} = -2\sqrt{17x}$

31. $\sqrt{8} + 3\sqrt{2} = \sqrt{4 \cdot 2} + 3\sqrt{2}$
$$= 2\sqrt{2} + 3\sqrt{2}$$
$$= (2+3)\sqrt{2}$$
$$= 5\sqrt{2}$$

33. $\sqrt{50x} - \sqrt{8x} = \sqrt{25 \cdot 2x} - \sqrt{4 \cdot 2x}$
$$= 5\sqrt{2x} - 2\sqrt{2x}$$
$$= (5-2)\sqrt{2x}$$
$$= 3\sqrt{2x}$$

35. $3\sqrt{18} + 5\sqrt{50} = 3\sqrt{9 \cdot 2} + 5\sqrt{25 \cdot 2}$
$$= 3 \cdot 3\sqrt{2} + 5 \cdot 5\sqrt{2}$$
$$= 9\sqrt{2} + 25\sqrt{2}$$
$$= (9+25)\sqrt{2}$$
$$= 34\sqrt{2}$$

37. $3\sqrt{8} - \sqrt{32} + 3\sqrt{72} - \sqrt{75}$
$$= 3\sqrt{4 \cdot 2} - \sqrt{16 \cdot 2} + 3\sqrt{36 \cdot 2} - \sqrt{25 \cdot 3}$$
$$= 3 \cdot 2\sqrt{2} - 4\sqrt{2} + 3 \cdot 6\sqrt{2} - 5\sqrt{3}$$
$$= 6\sqrt{2} - 4\sqrt{2} + 18\sqrt{2} - 5\sqrt{3}$$
$$= 20\sqrt{2} - 5\sqrt{3}$$

39. $\dfrac{1}{\sqrt{7}} = \dfrac{1}{\sqrt{7}} \cdot \dfrac{\sqrt{7}}{\sqrt{7}} = \dfrac{\sqrt{7}}{7}$

41. $\dfrac{\sqrt{2}}{\sqrt{5}} = \dfrac{\sqrt{2}}{\sqrt{5}} \cdot \dfrac{\sqrt{5}}{\sqrt{5}} = \dfrac{\sqrt{10}}{5}$

43. $\dfrac{13}{3+\sqrt{11}} = \dfrac{13}{3+\sqrt{11}} \cdot \dfrac{3-\sqrt{11}}{3-\sqrt{11}}$
$$= \dfrac{13(3-\sqrt{11})}{3^2 - (\sqrt{11})^2}$$
$$= \dfrac{13(3-\sqrt{11})}{9-11}$$
$$= \dfrac{13(3-\sqrt{11})}{-2}$$

45. $\dfrac{7}{\sqrt{5}-2} = \dfrac{7}{\sqrt{5}-2} \cdot \dfrac{\sqrt{5}+2}{\sqrt{5}+2}$
$$= \dfrac{7(\sqrt{5}+2)}{(\sqrt{5})^2 - 2^2}$$
$$= \dfrac{7(\sqrt{5}+2)}{5-4}$$
$$= 7(\sqrt{5}+2)$$

47. $\dfrac{6}{\sqrt{5}+\sqrt{3}} = \dfrac{6}{\sqrt{5}+\sqrt{3}} \cdot \dfrac{\sqrt{5}-\sqrt{3}}{\sqrt{5}-\sqrt{3}}$
$$= \dfrac{6(\sqrt{5}-\sqrt{3})}{(\sqrt{5})^2 - (\sqrt{3})^2}$$
$$= \dfrac{6(\sqrt{5}-\sqrt{3})}{5-3}$$
$$= \dfrac{6(\sqrt{5}-\sqrt{3})}{2}$$
$$= 3(\sqrt{5}-\sqrt{3})$$

49. $\sqrt[3]{125} = \sqrt[3]{5^3} = 5$

51. $\sqrt[3]{-8} = \sqrt[3]{(-2)^3} = -2$

53. $\sqrt[4]{-16}$ is not a real number.

55. $\sqrt[4]{(-3)^4} = |-3| = 3$

57. $\sqrt[5]{(-3)^5} = -3$

59. $\sqrt[5]{\dfrac{1}{32}} = \sqrt[5]{\dfrac{1}{2^5}} = -\dfrac{1}{2}$

61. $\sqrt[3]{32} = \sqrt[3]{8 \cdot 4} = \sqrt[3]{8}\sqrt[3]{4} = 2 \cdot \sqrt[3]{4}$

63. $\sqrt[3]{x^4} = \sqrt[3]{x^3 \cdot x} = x \cdot \sqrt[3]{x}$

65. $\sqrt[3]{9} \cdot \sqrt[3]{6} = \sqrt[3]{54} = \sqrt[3]{27 \cdot 2} = \sqrt[3]{27}\sqrt[3]{2} = 3\sqrt[3]{2}$

67. $\dfrac{\sqrt[5]{64x^6}}{\sqrt[5]{2x}} = \sqrt[5]{\dfrac{64x^6}{2x}} = \sqrt[5]{32x^5} = 2x$

69. $4\sqrt[5]{2} + 3\sqrt[5]{2} = 7\sqrt[5]{2}$

71. $5\sqrt[3]{16} + \sqrt[3]{54} = 5\sqrt[3]{8 \cdot 2} + \sqrt[3]{27 \cdot 2}$
$$= 5 \cdot 2\sqrt[3]{2} + 3\sqrt[3]{2}$$
$$= 10\sqrt[3]{2} + 3\sqrt[3]{2}$$
$$= 13\sqrt[3]{2}$$

73. $\sqrt[3]{54xy^3} - y\sqrt[3]{128x}$
$$= \sqrt[3]{27 \cdot 2xy^3} - y\sqrt[3]{64 \cdot 2x}$$
$$= 3y\sqrt[3]{2x} - 4y\sqrt[3]{2x}$$
$$= -y\sqrt[3]{2x}$$

75. $\sqrt{2} + \sqrt[3]{8} = \sqrt{2} + 2$

77. $36^{1/2} = \sqrt{36} = 6$

79. $8^{1/3} = \sqrt[3]{8} = 2$

81. $125^{2/3} = \left(\sqrt[3]{125}\right)^2 = 5^2 = 25$

83. $32^{-4/5} = \dfrac{1}{32^{4/5}} = \dfrac{1}{2^4} = \dfrac{1}{16}$

85. $\left(7x^{1/3}\right)\left(2x^{1/4}\right) = 7 \cdot 2x^{1/3} \cdot x^{1/4}$
$$= 14 \cdot x^{1/3+1/4}$$
$$= 14x^{7/12}$$

87. $\dfrac{20x^{1/2}}{5x^{1/4}} = \left(\dfrac{20}{5}\right)\left(\dfrac{x^{1/2}}{x^{1/4}}\right)$
$$= 4 \cdot x^{1/2-1/4}$$
$$= 4x^{1/4}$$

89. $\left(x^{2/3}\right)^3 = x^{2/3 \cdot 3} = x^2$

91. $(25x^4y^6)^{1/2} = 25^{1/2}x^{4 \cdot 1/2}y^{6 \cdot 1/2} = 5x^2|y|^3$

93. $\dfrac{\left(3y^{\frac{1}{4}}\right)^3}{y^{\frac{1}{12}}} = \dfrac{27y^{\frac{3}{4}}}{y^{\frac{1}{12}}} = 27y^{\frac{3}{4}-\frac{1}{12}}$
$$= 27y^{\frac{8}{12}} = 27y^{\frac{2}{3}}$$

95. $\sqrt[4]{5^2} = 5^{2/4} = 5^{1/2} = \sqrt{5}$

97. $\sqrt[3]{x^6} = x^{6/3} = x^2$

99. $\sqrt[6]{x^4} = x^{4/6} = |x|^{2/3}$

101. $\sqrt[9]{x^6y^3} = x^{\frac{6}{9}}y^{\frac{3}{9}} = x^{\frac{2}{3}}y^{\frac{1}{3}} = \sqrt[3]{x^2y}$

103. $2\sqrt{5L}$ with $L = 40$ gives
$$2\sqrt{5 \cdot 40} = 2\sqrt{200}$$
$$= 2\sqrt{100 \cdot 2}$$
$$= 2 \cdot 10\sqrt{2}$$
$$= 20\sqrt{2}$$
The speed of the car prior to the accident was $20\sqrt{2}$ miles per hour.

105. $\dfrac{w}{h} = \dfrac{2}{\sqrt{5}-1}$

$\qquad = \dfrac{2}{\sqrt{5}-1} \cdot \dfrac{\sqrt{5}+1}{\sqrt{5}+1}$

$\qquad = \dfrac{2(\sqrt{5}+1)}{(\sqrt{5})^2 - 1^2}$

$\qquad = \dfrac{2(\sqrt{5}+1)}{5-1}$

$\qquad = \dfrac{2(\sqrt{5}+1)}{4}$

$\qquad = \dfrac{\sqrt{5}+1}{2}$

$\qquad \approx 1.62$

107. $\dfrac{7\sqrt{2 \cdot 2 \cdot 3}}{6} = \dfrac{7\sqrt{2^2 \cdot 3}}{6}$

$\qquad = \dfrac{7\sqrt{2^2}\sqrt{3}}{6}$

$\qquad = \dfrac{7 \cdot 2\sqrt{3}}{6}$

$\qquad = \dfrac{7}{3}\sqrt{3}$

109. $0.07d^{3/2} = 0.07 \cdot 9^{3/2}$

$\qquad = 0.07(\sqrt{9})^3$

$\qquad = 0.07 \cdot 3^3$

$\qquad = 0.07 \cdot 27$

$\qquad = 1.89$

The duration of a storm whose diameter is 9 miles is 1.89 hours.

111.–115. Answers may vary.

117. $\dfrac{73t^{\frac{1}{3}} - 28t^{\frac{2}{3}}}{t}$

For 1986, $t = 1$ $\dfrac{73(1)^{\frac{1}{3}} - 28(1)^{\frac{2}{3}}}{1}$ $= 45$	For 1987, $t = 2$ $\dfrac{73(2)^{\frac{1}{3}} - 28(2)^{\frac{2}{3}}}{2}$ $= 23.8$
For 1988, $t = 3$ $\dfrac{73(3)^{\frac{1}{3}} - 28(3)^{\frac{2}{3}}}{3}$ $= 15.7$	For 1989, $t = 4$ $\dfrac{73(4)^{\frac{1}{3}} - 28(4)^{\frac{2}{3}}}{4}$ $= 11.3$
For 1990, $t = 5$ $\dfrac{73(5)^{\frac{1}{3}} - 28(5)^{\frac{2}{3}}}{5}$ $= 8.6$	For 1991, $t = 6$ $\dfrac{73(6)^{\frac{1}{3}} - 28(6)^{\frac{2}{3}}}{2}$ $= 6.7$
For 1992, $t = 7$ $\dfrac{73(7)^{\frac{1}{3}} - 28(7)^{\frac{2}{3}}}{7}$ $= 5.3$	For 1993, $t = 8$ $\dfrac{73(8)^{\frac{1}{3}} - 28(8)^{\frac{2}{3}}}{8}$ $= 4.3$
For 1994, $t = 9$ $\dfrac{73(9)^{\frac{1}{3}} - 28(9)^{\frac{2}{3}}}{9}$ $= 3.4$	For 1995, $t = 10$ $\dfrac{73(10)^{\frac{1}{3}} - 28(10)^{\frac{2}{3}}}{10}$ $= 2.7$
For 1996, $t = 11$ $\dfrac{73(11)^{\frac{1}{3}} - 28(11)^{\frac{2}{3}}}{11}$ $= 2.2$	For 1997, $t = 12$ $\dfrac{73(12)^{\frac{1}{3}} - 28(12)^{\frac{2}{3}}}{12}$ $= 1.7$
For 1998 $t = 13$	For 1999, $t = 14$

$\dfrac{73(13)^{\frac{1}{5}}-28(13)^{\frac{2}{5}}}{13}$ $=1.3$	$\dfrac{73(14)^{\frac{1}{5}}-28(14)^{\frac{2}{5}}}{14}$ $=0.9$
For 2000, $t=15$ $\dfrac{73(15)^{\frac{1}{5}}-28(15)^{\frac{2}{5}}}{15}$ $=0.6$	For 2001, $t=16$ $\dfrac{73(16)^{\frac{1}{5}}-28(16)^{\frac{2}{5}}}{16}$ $=0.4$

119. a. False; $(-8)^{1/3}=\sqrt[3]{-8}=-2$, which is a real number.

    b. False; $\sqrt{x^2+y^2}\neq\sqrt{(x+y)^2}=x+y$, if $x+y\geq 0$.

    c. False; $\dfrac{1}{2}=8^{-1/3}\neq -2$

    d. True; $2^1=2^{1/2}2^{1/2}=2$

    (d) is true.

121. $\sqrt{\square\cdot x^{\square}}=5\cdot x^7$

    $\left(\square\cdot x^{\square}\right)^{1/2}=5\cdot x^7$

    Square both sides.

    $\square\cdot x^{\square}=25\cdot x^{14}$

    Let $\square=25$ and $\square=14$.

123. a. $3^{1/2}\;\boxed{}\;3^{1/3}$

    Square both sides. $3\;\boxed{}\;3^{2/3}=9^{1/3}$

    Raise to the third power on both sides.

    $3^3=27\;\boxed{>}\;\left(9^{1/3}\right)^3=9$

    b. $\sqrt{7}+\sqrt{18}\;\boxed{}\;\sqrt{7+18}$

    $\sqrt{7}+\sqrt{18}\;\boxed{}\;\sqrt{7+18}=\sqrt{25}=5$

    Square both sides.

    $(\sqrt{7}+\sqrt{18})^2=7+2\sqrt{126}+18$

    $=25+3\sqrt{14}\;\boxed{>}\;25$

13

Section P.4

Check Point Exercises

1. **a.** $(-17x^3 + 4x^2 - 11x - 5) + (16x^3 - 3x^2 + 3x - 15)$

   $= (-17x^3 + 16x^3) + (4x^2 - 3x^2) + (-11x + 3x) + (-5 - 15)$

   $= -x^3 + x^2 - 8x - 20$

   b. $(13x^2 - 9x^2 - 7x + 1) - (-7x^3 + 2x^2 - 5x + 9)$

   $= (13x^3 - 9x^2 - 7x + 1) + (7x^3 - 2x^2 + 5x - 9)$

   $= (13x^3 + 7x^3) + (-9x^2 - 2x^2) + (-7x + 5x) + (1 - 9)$

   $= 20x^3 - 11x^2 - 2x - 8$

2. $(5x - 2)(3x^2 - 5x + 4)$

   $= 5x(3x^2 - 5x + 4) - 2(3x^2 - 5x + 4)$

   $= 5x \cdot 3x^2 - 5x \cdot 5x + 5x \cdot 4 - 2 \cdot 3x^2 + 2 \cdot 5x - 2 \cdot 4$

   $= 15x^3 - 25x^2 + 20x - 6x^2 + 10x - 8$

   $= 15x^3 - 31x^2 + 30x - 8$

3. $(7x - 5)(4x - 3) = 7x \cdot 4x + 7x(-3) + (-5)4x + (-5)(-3)$

   $= 28x^2 - 21x - 20x + 15$

   $= 28x^2 - 41x + 15$

4. **a.** Use the special-product formula shown.

   $(A + B)(A - B) = A^2 - B^2$

   $(7x + 8)(7x - 8) = (7x)^2 - (8)^2$

   $= 49x^2 - 64$

   b. Use the special-product formula shown.

   $(A + B)(A - B) = A^2 - B^2$

   $(2y^3 - 5)(2y^3 + 5) = (2y^3 + 5)(2y^3 - 5) = (2y^3)^2 - (5)^2 = 4y^6 - 25$

5. **a.** Use the special-product formula shown.

   $(A + B)^2 = A^2 + 2AB + B^2$

   $(x + 10)^2 = x^2 + 2 \cdot x \cdot 10 + 10^2$

   $= x^2 + 20x + 100$

   b. Use the special-product formula shown.

   $(A + B)^2 = A^2 + 2AB + B^2$

   $(5x + 4)^2 = (5x)^2 + 2(5x)(4) + 4^2$

   $= 25x^2 + 40x + 16$

6. a. Use the special-product formula shown.
$$(A - B)^2 = A^2 - 2AB + B^2$$
$$(x - 9)^2 = x^2 - 2 \cdot x \cdot 9 + 9^2$$
$$= x^2 - 18x + 81$$

b. Use the special-product formula shown.
$$(A - B)^2 = A^2 - 2AB + B^2$$
$$(7x - 3)^2 = (7x)^2 - 2(7x)(3) + 3^2$$
$$= 49x^2 - 42x + 9$$

7. $(x^3 - 4x^2y + 5xy^2 - y^3) - (x^3 - 6x^2y + y^3)$
$$= (x^3 - 4x^2y + 5xy^2 - y^3) + (-x^3 + 6x^2y - y^3)$$
$$= (x^3 - x^3) + (-4x^2y + 6x^2y) + (5xy^2) + (-y^3 - y^3)$$
$$= 2x^2y + 5xy^2 - 2y^3$$

8. a. $(7x - 6y)(3x - y) = (7x)(3x) + (7x)(-y) + (-6y)(3x) + (-6y)(-y)$
$$= 21x^2 - 7xy - 18xy + 6y^2$$
$$= 21x^2 - 25xy + 6y^2$$

b. $(x^2 + 5y)^2 = (x^2)^2 + 2(x^2)(5y) + (5y)^2$
$$= x^4 + 10x^2y + 25y^2$$

Exercise Set P.4

1. Yes; $2x + 3x^2 - 5 = 3x^2 + 2x - 5$

3. No; The form of a polynomial involves addition and subtraction, not division.

5. $3x^2$ has degree 2
$-5x$ has degree 1
4 has degree 0
$3x^2 - 5x + 4$ has degree 2.

7. x^2 has degree 2
$-4x^3$ has degree 3
$9x$ has degree 1
$-12x^4$ has degree 4
63 has degree 0
$x^2 - 4x^3 + 9x - 12x^4 + 63$ has degree 4.

9. $(-6x^3 + 5x^2 - 8x + 9) + (17x^3 + 2x^2 - 4x - 13) = (-6x^3 + 17x^3) + (5x^2 + 2x^2) + (-8x - 4x) + (9 - 13)$
$$= 11x^3 + 7x^2 - 12x - 4$$

The degree is 3.

11. $(17x^3 - 5x^2 + 4x - 3) - (5x^3 - 9x^2 - 8x + 11) = (17x^3 - 5x^2 + 4x - 3) + (-5x^3 + 9x^2 + 8x - 11)$
$$= (17x^3 - 5x^3) + (-5x^2 + 9x^2) + (4x + 8x) + (-3 - 11)$$
$$= 12x^3 + 4x^2 + 12x - 14$$

The degree is 3.

13. $(5x^2 - 7x - 8) + (2x^2 - 3x + 7) - (x^2 - 4x - 3) = (5x^2 - 7x - 8) + (2x^2 - 3x + 7) + (-x^2 + 4x + 3)$
$$= (5x^2 + 2x^2 - x^2) + (-7x - 3x + 4x) + (-8 + 7 + 3)$$
$$= 6x^2 - 6x + 2$$

The degree is 2.

15. $(x + 1)(x^2 - x + 1) = x(x^2) - x \cdot x + x \cdot 1 + 1(x^2) - 1 \cdot x + 1 \cdot 1$
$$= x^3 - x^2 + x + x^2 - x + 1$$
$$= x^3 + 1$$

17. $(2x - 3)(x^2 - 3x + 5) = (2x)(x^2) + (2x)(-3x) + (2x)(5) + (-3)(x^2) + (-3)(-3x) + (-3)(5)$
$$= 2x^3 - 6x^2 + 10x - 3x^2 + 9x - 15$$
$$= 2x^3 - 9x^2 + 19x - 15$$

19. $(x + 7)(x + 3) = x^2 + 3x + 7x + 21 = x^2 + 10x + 21$

21. $(x - 5)(x + 3) = x^2 + 3x - 5x - 15 = x^2 - 2x - 15$

23. $(3x + 5)(2x + 1) = (3x)(2x) + 3x(1) + 5(2x) + 5 = 6x^2 + 3x + 10x + 5 = 6x^2 + 13x + 5$

25. $(2x - 3)(5x + 3) = (2x)(5x) + (2x)(3) + (-3)(5x) + (-3)(3)$
$$= 10x^2 + 6x - 15x - 9$$
$$= 10x^2 - 9x - 9$$

27. $(5x^2 - 4)(3x^2 - 7) = (5x^2)(3x^2) + (5x^2)(-7) + (-4)(3x^2) + (-4)(-7)$
$$= 15x^4 - 35x^2 - 12x^2 + 28$$
$$= 15x^4 - 47x^2 + 28$$

29. $(8x^5 + 3)(x^2 - 5) = (8x^5)(x^2) + (8x^5)(-5) + (3)(x^2) + (3)(-5)$
$$= 8x^5 - 40x^5 + 3x^2 - 15$$

31. $(x + 3)(x - 3) = x^2 - 3^2$
$$= x^2 - 9$$

33. $(3x+2)(3x-2) = (3x)^2 - 2^2$
$$= 9x^2 - 4$$

35. $(5-7x)(5+7x) = 5^2 - (7x)^2$
$$= 25 - 49x^2$$

37. $(4x^2+5x)(4x^2-5x) = (4x^2)^2 - (5x)^2$
$$= 16x^4 - 25x^2$$

39. $\left(1-y^5\right)\left(1+y^5\right) = (1)^2 - \left(y^5\right)^2 = 1 - y^{10}$

41. $(x+2)^2 = x^2 + 2 \cdot x \cdot 2 + 2^2 = x^2 + 4x + 4$

43. $(2x+3)^2 = (2x)^2 + 2(2x)(3) + 3^2$
$$= 4x^2 + 12x + 9$$

45. $(x-3)^2 = x^2 - 2 \cdot x \cdot 3 + 3^2 = x^2 - 6x + 9$

47. $(4x^2-1)^2$
$$= (4x^2)^2 - 2(4x^2)(1) + 1^2$$
$$= 16x^4 - 8x^2 + 1$$

49. $(7-2x)^2 = 7^2 - 2(7)(2x) + (2x)^2$
$$= 49 - 28x + 4x^2$$
$$= 4x^2 - 28x + 49$$

51. $(x+1)^3 = x^3 + 3 \cdot x^2 \cdot 1 + 3x \cdot 1^2 + 1^3$
$$= x^3 + 3x^2 + 3x + 1$$

53. $(2x+3)^3$
$$= (2x)^3 + 3 \cdot (2x)^2 \cdot 3 + 3(2x) \cdot 3^2 + 3^3$$
$$= 8x^3 + 36x^2 + 54x + 27$$

55. $(x-3)^3 = x^3 - 3 \cdot x^3 \cdot 3 + 3 \cdot x \cdot 3^2 - 3^3$
$$= x^3 - 9x^2 + 27x - 27$$

57. $(3x-4)^3 = (3x)^3 - 3(3x)^2 \cdot 4 + 3(3x) \cdot 4^2 - 4^3$
$$= 27x^3 - 108x^2 + 144x - 64$$

59. $(5x^2y - 3xy) + (2x^2y - xy) = (5x^2y + 2x^2y) + (-3xy - xy)$
$$= (5+2)x^2y + (-3-1)xy$$
$$= 7x^2y - 4xy \text{ is of degree 3.}$$

61. $(4x^2y + 8xy + 11) + (-2x^2y + 5xy + 2) = (4x^2y - 2x^2y) + (8xy + 5xy) + (11 + 2)$
$$= (4 - 2)x^2y + (8 + 5)xy + 13$$
$$= 2x^2y + 13xy + 13 \text{ is of degree 3.}$$

63. $(x^3 + 7xy - 5y^2) - (6x^3 - xy + 4y^2) = (x^3 + 7xy - 5y^2)$
$$= (x^3 - 6x^3) + (7xy + xy) + (-5y^2 - 4y^2)$$
$$= (1 - 6)x^3 + (7 + 1)xy + (-5 - 4)y^2$$
$$= -5x^3 + 8xy - 9y^2 \text{ is of degree 3.}$$

65. $(3x^4y^2 + 5x^3y - 3y) - (2x^4y^2 - 3x^3y - 4y + 6x) = (3x^4y^2 + 5x^3y - 3y) + (-2x^4y^2 + 3x^3y + 4y - 6x)$
$$= (3x^4y^2 - 2x^4y^2) + (5x^3y + 3x^3y) + (-3y + 4y) - 6x$$
$$= (3 - 2)x^4y^2 + (5 + 3)x^3y + (-3 + 4)y - 6x$$
$$= x^4y^2 + 8x^3y + y - 6x \text{ is of degree 6.}$$

67. $(x + 5y)(7x + 3y) = x(7x) + x(3y) + (5y)(7x) + (5y)(3y)$
$$= 7x^2 + 3xy + 35xy + 15y^2$$
$$= 7x^2 + 38xy + 15y^2$$

69. $(x - 3y)(2x + 7y) = x(2x) + x(7y) + (-3y)(2x) + (-3y)(7y)$
$$= 2x^2 + 7xy - 6xy - 21y^2$$
$$= 2x^2 + xy - 21y^2$$

71. $(3xy - 1)(5xy + 2) = (3xy)(5xy) + (3xy)(2) + (-1)(5xy) + (-1)(2)$
$$= 15x^2y^2 + 6xy - 5xy - 2$$
$$= 15x^2y^2 + xy - 2$$

73. $(7x + 5y)^2 = (7x)^2 + 2(7x)(5y) + (5y)^2 = 49x^2 + 70xy + 25y^2$

75. $(x^2y^2 - 3)^2 = (x^2y^2)^2 - 2(x^2y^2)(3) + 3^2 = x^4y^4 - 6x^2y^2 + 9$

77. $(x - y)(x^2 + xy + y^2) = x(x^2) + x(xy) + x(y^2) + (-y)(x^2) + (-y)(xy) + (-y)(y^2)$
$$= x^3 + x^2y + xy^2 - x^2y - xy^2 - y^3$$
$$= x^3 - y^3$$

79. $(3x + 5y)(3x - 5y) = (3x)^2 - (5y)^2 = 9x^2 - 25y^2$

81. $(7xy^2 - 10y)(7xy^2 + 10y) = (7xy^2)^2 - (10y)^2 = 49x^2y^4 - 100y^2$

83. $0.018x^2 - 0.757x + 9.047$ when $x = 40$ yields

$0.018(40)^2 - 0.757(40) + 9.047 = 28.8 - 30.28 + 9.047 = 7.567$

A person earning \$40,000 feels underpaid \$7567.

85. $-1.45x^2 + 38.52x + 470.78$ for $x = 25$ yields

$-1.45(25)^2 + 38.52(25) + 470.78 = 527.53$

Violent crimes for 2000 will be approximately 527.53 per 100,000 inhabitants.

87. Number of people still ill t weeks after January 1 = (Number of people who catch cold t weeks after January 1) – (Number of people who recover t weeks after January 1)

$= (5t - 3t^2 + t^3) - \left(t - t^2 + \dfrac{1}{3}t^3\right)$

$= (5t - 3t^2 + t^3) + \left(-t + t^2 - \dfrac{1}{3}t^3\right)$

$= (5t - t) + (-3t^2 + t^2) + \left(t^3 - \dfrac{1}{3}t^3\right)$

$= 4t - 2t^2 + \dfrac{2}{3}t^3$

89. $(x+3)(x+9) - (x+1)(x+5)$

$= (x^2 + 9x + 3x + 27) - (x^2 + 5x + x + 5)$

$= (x^2 + 12x + 27) - (x^2 + 6x + 5)$

$= (x^2 + 12x + 27) + (-x^2 - 6x - 6)$

$= (x^2 - x^2) + (12x - 6x) + (27 - 5)$

$= 6x + 22$

91.–97. Answers may vary.

99.

x	$0.0032x^3 + 0.023x^2$ $- 2.2477x + 61.1998$	Percentage of high school seniors who have used marijuana	x	$0.0032x^3 + 0.023x^2$ $- 2.2477x + 61.1998$	Percentage of high school seniors who have used marijuana
0	61.2	61.2% in 1980	11	43.5	43.5% in 1991
1	59.0	59.0% in 1981	12	43.1	43.1% in 1992
2	56.8	56.8% in 1982	13	42.9	42.9% in 1993
3	54.8	54.8% in 1983	14	43.0	43.0% in 1994
4	52.8	52.8% in 1984	15	43.5	43.5% in 1995
5	50.9	50.9% in 1985	16	44.2	44.2% in 1996
6	49.2	49.2% in 1986	17	45.4	45.4% in 1997

7	47.7	47.7% in 1987	18	46.9	46.9% in 1998
8	46.3	46.3% in 1988	19	48.7	48.7% in 1999
9	45.2	45.2% in 1989	20	51.0	51.0% in 1000
10	44.2	44.2% in 1990			

The trend decreases until 1993, then starts to increase.

101. $[(7x+5)+4y][(7x+5)-4y] = (7x+5)^2 - 4y^2$
$$= (7x)^2 + 2(7x)(5) + 5^2 - 16y^2$$
$$= 49x^2 + 70x + 25 - 16y^2$$

103. $(x+y)(x-y)(x^2+y^2) = (x^2-y^2)(x^2+y^2)$
$$= (x^2)^2 - (y^2)^2$$
$$= x^4 - y^4$$

Section P.5

Check Point Exercises

1. **a.** $10x^3 - 4x^2$
$$= 2x^2(5x) - 2x^2(2)$$
$$= 2x^2(5x - 2)$$

   b. $2x(x - 7) + 3(x - 7)$
$$= (x - 7)(2x + 3)$$

2. $x^3 + 5x^2 - 2x - 10$
$$= (x^3 + 5x^2) - (2x + 10)$$
$$= x^2(x + 5) - 2(x + 5)$$
$$= (x + 5)(x^2 - 2)$$

3. **a.** Find two numbers whose product is 40 and whose sum is 13. The required integers are 8 and 5. Thus,
$$x^2 + 13x + 40 = (x + 5)(x + 8) \text{ or } (x + 8)(x + 5)$$

   b. Find two numbers whose product is –14 and whose sum is –5. The required integers are –7 and 2. Thus,
$$x^2 - 5x - 14 = (x - 7)(x + 2) \text{ or } (x + 2)(x - 7).$$

4. Find two First terms whose product is $6x^2$.
$$6x^2 + 19x - 7 = (6x \quad)(x \quad)$$
$$6x^2 + 19x - 7 = (3x \quad)(2x \quad)$$

   Find two Last terms whose product is –7.
   The possible factors are 1(–7) and –1(7).

   Try various combinations of these factors to find the factorization in which the sum of the Outside and Inside products is 19x.

Possible Factors of $6x^2 + 19x - 7$	Sum of Outside and Inside Products (Should Equal 19x)
$(6x + 1)(x - 7)$	$-42x + x = -41x$
$(6x - 7)(x + 1)$	$6x - 7x = -x$
$(6x - 1)(x + 7)$	$42x - x = 41x$

$(6x + 7)(x - 1)$	$-6x + 7x = x$
$(3x + 1)(2x - 7)$	$-21x + 2x = -19x$
$(3x - 7)(2x + 1)$	$3x - 14x = -11x$
$(3x - 1)(2x + 7)$	$21x - 2x = 19x$
$(3x + 7)(2x - 1)$	$-3x + 14x = 11x$

Thus, $6x^2 + 19x - 7 = (3x - 1)(2x + 7)$ or $(2x + 7)(3x - 1)$.

5. Express each term as the square of some monomial. Then use the formula for factoring $A^2 - B^2$.

   a. $x^2 - 81 = x^2 - 9^2 = (x + 9)(x - 9)$

   b. $36x^2 - 25 = (6x)^2 - 5^2 = (6x + 5)(6x - 5)$

6. Express $81x^4 - 16$ as the difference of two squares and use the formula for factoring $A^2 - B^2$.
   $81x^4 - 16 = (9x^2)^2 - 4^2 = (9x^2 + 4)(9x^2 - 4)$

   The factor $9x^2 - 4$ is the difference of two squares and can be factored. Express $9x^2 - 4$ as the difference of two squares and again use the formula for factoring $A^2 - B^2$.
   $(9x^2 + 4)(9x^2 - 4) = (9x^2 + 4)\left[(3x)^2 - 2^2\right] = (9x^2 + 4)(3x + 2)(3x - 2)$

   Thus, factored completely,
   $81x^4 - 16 = (9x^2 + 4)(3x + 2)(3x - 2)$.

7. a. $x^2 + 14x + 49 = x^2 + 2 \cdot x \cdot 7 + 7^2 = (x + 7)^2$

   b. Since $16x^2 = (4x)^2$ and $49 = 7^2$, check to see if the middle term can be expressed as twice the product of $4x$ and 7. Since $2 \cdot 4x \cdot 7 = 56x$, $16x^2 - 56x + 49$ is a perfect square trinomial. Thus,
   $$16x^2 - 56x + 49 = (4x)^2 - 2 \cdot 4x \cdot 7 + 7^2$$
   $$= (4x - 7)^2$$

8. a. $x^3 + 1 = x^3 + 1^3$
   $$= (x + 1)(x^2 - x \cdot 1 + 1^2)$$
   $$= (x + 1)(x^2 - x + 1)$$

    b. $125x^3 - 8 = (5x)^3 - 2^3$

$$= (5x - 2)\left[(5x)^2 + (5x)(2) + 2^2\right.$$
$$= (5x - 2)(25x^2 + 10x + 4]$$

9. Factor out the greatest common factor.

$$3x^3 - 30x^2 + 75x = 3x\left(x^2 - 10x + 25\right)$$

Factor the perfect square trinomial.
$$3x\left(x^2 - 10x + 25\right) = 3x\left(x - 5\right)^2$$

10. Reorder to write as a difference of square.

$$x^2 - 36a^2 + 20x + 100 = \left(x^2 + 20x\_100\right) - 36a^2$$
$$= \left(x + 10\right)^2 - 36a^2$$
$$= \left(x + 10 - 6a\right)\left(x + 10 + 6a\right)$$

11. $x\left(x - 1\right)^{-\frac{1}{2}} + \left(x - 1\right)^{\frac{1}{2}}$

$$= \left(x - 1\right)^{-\frac{1}{2}}\left[x + \left(x - 1\right)^{\frac{1}{2} - \left(-\frac{1}{2}\right)}\right]$$

$$= \left(x - 1\right)^{-\frac{1}{2}}\left[x + \left(x - 1\right)\right]$$

$$= \left(x - 1\right)^{-\frac{1}{2}}\left(2x - 1\right)$$

Exercise Set P.5

    1. $18x + 27 = 9 \cdot 2x + 9 \cdot 3$
$$= 9(2x + 3)$$

    3. $3x^2 + 6x = 3x \cdot x + 3x \cdot 2$
$$= 3x(x + 2)$$

5. $9x^4 - 18x^3 + 27x^2$
$= 9x^2(x^2) + 9x^2(-2x) + 9x^2(3)$
$= 9x^2(x^2 - 2x + 3)$

7. $x(x+5) + 3(x+5) = (x+5)(x+3)$

9. $x^2(x-3) + 12(x-3) = (x-3)(x^2+12)$

11. $x^3 - 2x^2 + 5x - 10 = x^2(x-2) + 5(x-2)$
$= (x^2+5)(x-2)$

13. $x^3 - x^2 + 2x - 2 = x^2(x-1) + 2(x-1)$
$= (x-1)(x^2+2)$

15. $3x^3 - 2x^2 - 6x + 4 = x^2(3x-2) - 2(3x-2)$
$= (3x-2)(x^2-2)$

17. $x^2 + 5x + 6 = (x+2)(x+3)$

19. $x^2 - 2x - 15 = (x-5)(x+3)$

21. $x^2 - 8x + 15 = (x-5)(x-3)$

23. $3x^2 - x - 2 = (3x+2)(x-1)$

25. $3x^2 - 25x - 28 = (3x-28)(x+1)$

27. $6x^2 - 11x + 4 = (2x-1)(3x-4)$

29. $4x^2 + 16x + 15 = (2x+3)(2x+5)$

31. $x^2 - 100 = x^2 - 10^2 = (x+10)(x-10)$

33. $36x^2 - 49 = (6x)^2 - 7^2 = (6x+7)(6x-7)$

35. $9x^2 - 25y^2 = (3x)^2 - (5y)^2$
$= (3x+5y)(3x-5y)$

37. $x^4 - 16 = (x^2)^2 - 4^2$
$= (x^2+4)(x^2-4)$
$= (x^2+4)(x+2)(x-2)$

39. $16x^4 - 81 = (4x^2)^2 - 9^2$
$= (4x^2+9)(4x^2-9)$
$= (4x^2+9)[(2x)^2 - 3^2]$
$= (4x^2+9)(2x+3)(2x-3)$

41. $x^2 + 2x + 1 = x^2 + 2 \cdot x \cdot 1 + 1^2 = (x+1)^2$

43. $x^2 - 14x + 49 = x^2 - 2 \cdot x \cdot 7 + 7^2$
$= (x-7)^2$

45. $4x^2 + 4x + 1 = (2x)^2 + 2 \cdot 2x \cdot 1 + 1^2$
$= (2x+1)^2$

47. $9x^2 - 6x + 1 = (3x)^2 - 2 \cdot 3x \cdot 1 + 1^2$
$= (3x-1)^2$

49. $x^3 + 27 = x^3 + 3^3$

$\qquad = (x+3)(x^2 - x \cdot 3 + 3^2)$

$\qquad = (x+3)(x^2 - 3x + 9)$

51. $x^3 - 64 = x^3 - 4^3$

$\qquad = (x-4)(x^2 + x \cdot 4 + 4^2)$

$\qquad = (x-4)(x^2 + 4x + 16)$

53. $8x^3 - 1 = (2x)^3 - 1^3$

$\qquad = (2x-1)[(2x)^2 + (2x)(1) + 1^2]$

$\qquad = (2x-1)(4x^2 + 2x + 1)$

55. $64x^3 + 27 = (4x)^3 + 3^3$

$\qquad = (4x+3)[(4x)^2 - (4x)(3) + 3^2]$

$\qquad = (4x+3)(16x^2 - 12x + 9)$

57. $3x^3 - 3x = 3x(x^2 - 1) = 3x(x+1)(x-1)$

59. $4x^2 - 4x - 24 = 4(x^2 - x - 6)$

$\qquad = 4(x+2)(x-3)$

61. $2x^4 - 162 = 2(x^4 - 81)$

$\qquad = 2[(x^2)^2 - 9^2]$

$\qquad = 2(x^2 + 9)(x^2 - 9)$

$\qquad = 2(x^2 + 9)(x^2 - 3^2)$

$\qquad = 2(x^2 + 9)(x+3)(x-3)$

63. $x^3 + 2x^2 - 9x - 18 = (x^3 + 2x^2) - (9x + 18)$

$\qquad = x^2(x+2) - 9(x+2)$

$\qquad = (x^2 - 9)(x+2)$

$\qquad = (x^2 - 3^2)(x+2)$

$\qquad = (x-3)(x+3)(x+2)$

65. $2x^2 - 2x - 112 = 2(x^2 - x - 56)$

$\qquad = 2(x-8)(x+7)$

67. $x^3 - 4x = x(x^2 - 4)$

$\qquad = x(x^2 - 2^2)$

$\qquad = x(x-2)(x+2)$

69. $x^2 + 64$ is prime.

71.

$x^3 + 2x^2 - 4x - 8 = (x^3 + 2x^2) + (-4x - 8)$

$\qquad = x^2(x+2) - 4(x+2)$

$\qquad = (x^2 - 4)(x+2)$

$\qquad = (x^2 - 2^2)(x+2)$

$\qquad = (x-2)(x+2)(x+2)$

$\qquad = (x-2)(x+2)^2$

73. $y^5 - 81y = y(y^4 - 81)$

$\qquad = y[(y^2)^2 - 9^2]$

$\qquad = y(y^2 + 9)(y^2 - 9)$

$\qquad = y(y^2 + 9)(y^2 - 3^2)$

$\qquad = y(y^2 + 9)(y+3)(y-3)$

75. $20y^4 - 45y^2 = 5y^2(4y^2 - 9)$

$\qquad = 5y^2[(2y)^2 - 3^2]$

$\qquad = 5y^2(2y+3)(2y-3)$

77. $x^2 - 12x + 36 - 49y^2$

$\qquad = \left(x^2 - 12x + 36\right) - 49y^2$

$\qquad = \left(x-6\right)^2 - 49y^2$

$\qquad = \left(x-6-7y\right)(x-6+7y)$

79. $9b^2x - 16y - 16x + 9b^2y$

$\qquad = \left(9b^2x + 9b^2y\right) + \left(-16x - 16y\right)$

$\qquad = 9b^2\left(x+y\right) - 16\left(x+y\right)$

$\qquad = \left(x+y\right)\left(9b^2 - 16\right)$

$\qquad = \left(x+y\right)\left(3b-4\right)\left(3b+4\right)$

81. $x^2y - 16y + 32 - 2x^2$

$= \left(x^2y - 16y\right) + \left(-2x^2 + 32\right)$

$= y\left(x^2 - 16\right) - 2\left(x^2 - 16\right)$

$= \left(x^2 - 16\right)\left(y - 2\right)$

$= \left(x - 4\right)\left(x + 4\right)\left(y - 2\right)$

$= \left(x + 3\right)^{\frac{1}{2}}\left[1 - \left(x + 3\right)^{\frac{3}{2} - \frac{1}{2}}\right]$

$= \left(x + 3\right)^{\frac{1}{2}}\left[1 - \left(x + 3\right)\right]$

$= \left(x + 3\right)^{\frac{1}{2}}\left(-x - 2\right)$

$= -(x + 3)^{\frac{1}{2}}(x + 2)$

83. $2x^3 - 8a^2x + 24x^2 + 72x$

$= 2x\left(x^2 - 4a^2 + 12x + 36\right)$

$= 2x\left[\left(x^2 + 12x + 36\right) - 4a^2\right]$

$= 2x\left[\left(x + 6\right)^2 - 4a^2\right]$

$= 2x\left(x + 6 - 2a\right)\left(x + 6 + 2a\right)$

85. $x^{\frac{3}{2}} - x^{\frac{1}{2}} = x^{\frac{1}{2}}\left(x^{\frac{3}{2} - \frac{1}{2}}\right) - 1 = x^{\frac{1}{2}}\left(x - 1\right)$

87. $4x^{-\frac{2}{3}} + 8x^{\frac{1}{3}}$

$= 4x^{-\frac{2}{3}}\left(1 + 2x^{\frac{1}{3} - \left(-\frac{2}{3}\right)}\right) = 4x^{-\frac{2}{3}}\left(1 + 2x\right)$

$= \dfrac{4\left(x + 2x\right)}{x^{\frac{2}{3}}}$

89. $\left(x + 3\right)^{\frac{1}{2}} - \left(x + 3\right)^{\frac{3}{2}}$

91. $\left(x + 5\right)^{-\frac{1}{2}} - \left(x + 5\right)^{-\frac{3}{2}}$

$= \left(x + 5\right)^{-\frac{3}{2}}\left[\left(x + 5\right)^{-\frac{1}{2} - \left(-\frac{3}{2}\right)} - 1\right]$

$= \left(x + 5\right)^{-\frac{3}{2}}\left[\left(x + 5\right) - 1\right]$

$= \left(x + 5\right)^{-\frac{3}{2}}\left(x + 4\right)$

$= \dfrac{x + 4}{(x + 5)^{\frac{3}{2}}}$

93. $\left(4x - 1\right)^{\frac{1}{2}} - \dfrac{1}{3}\left(4x - 1\right)^{\frac{3}{2}}$

$$= (4x-1)^{\frac{1}{2}}\left[1-\frac{1}{3}(4x-1)^{\frac{3}{2}-\frac{1}{2}}\right]$$

$$= (4x-1)^{\frac{1}{2}}\left[1-\frac{1}{3}(4x-1)\right]$$

$$= (4x-1)^{\frac{1}{2}}\left[1-\frac{4}{3}x+\frac{1}{3}\right]$$

$$= (4x-1)^{\frac{1}{2}}\left(\frac{4}{3}-\frac{4}{3}x\right)$$

$$= (4x-1)^{\frac{1}{2}}\frac{4}{3}(1-x)$$

$$= \frac{-4(4x-1)(x-1)}{3}$$

95. a. $(x-0.4x)-0.4(x-0.4x)$

$$= (x-0.4x)(1-0.4)$$

$$= (0.6x)(0.6)$$

$$= 0.36x$$

b. No. it is selling at 36% of the original price.

97. $256 - 16t^2 = 16(16 - t^2) = 16(4 - t)(4 + t)$

99. $(3x)(3x) - 2 \cdot 2 = (3x)^2 - 2^2$
$$= (3x+2)(3x-2)$$

101.–107. Answers may vary.

109. $x^{2n} + 6x^n + 8 = \left(x^n + 4\right)\left(x^n + 2\right)$

111. $x^4 - y^4 - 2x^3 y + 2xy^3$

$$= \left(x^4 - y^4\right) + \left(-2x^3 y + 2xy^3\right)$$

$$= \left(x^2 - y^2\right)\left(x^2 + y^2\right) - 2xy\left(x^2 - y^2\right)$$

$$= \left(x^2 - y^2\right)\left(x^2 + y^2 - 2xy\right)$$

$$= (x-y)(x+y)\left(x^2 - 2xy + y^2\right)$$

$$= (x-y)(x+y)(x-y)^2$$

$$= (x-y)^3(x+y)$$

113. $x^2 + bx + 15$, $b = 16$, -16, 8 or -8

Section P.6

Check Point Exercises

1. a. The denominator would equal zero if $x = -5$, so -5 must be excluded from the domain.

b. $x^2 - 36 = (x+6)(x-6)$

The denominator would equal zero if $x = -6$ or $x = 6$, so -6 and 6 must both must be excluded from the domain.

2. a.
$$\frac{x^3 + 3x^2}{x+3} = \frac{x^2(x+3)}{x+3}$$
$$= \frac{x^2(x+3)}{x+3}$$
$$= x^2, \ x \neq -3$$

Because the denominator is $x + 3, \ x \neq -3$

b.
$$\frac{x^2 - 1}{x^2 + 2x + 1} = \frac{(x-1)(x+1)}{(x+1)(x+1)}$$
$$= \frac{x-1}{x+1}, x \neq -1$$

Because the denominator is $(x+1)(x+1), x \neq -1$

3.
$$\frac{x+3}{x^2-4} \cdot \frac{x^2-x-6}{x^2+6x+9}$$
$$= \frac{x+3}{(x+2)(x-2)} \cdot \frac{(x-3)(x+2)}{(x+3)(x+3)}$$
$$= \frac{x+3}{(x+2)(x-2)} \cdot \frac{(x-3)(x+2)}{(x+3)(x+3)}$$
$$= \frac{x-3}{(x-2)(x+3)}, \ x \neq -2, \ x \neq 2, \ x \neq -3$$

Because the denominator has factors of $x + 2, \ x - 2,$ and $x + 3, \ x \neq -2, \ x \neq 2,$ and $x \neq -3$.

4.
$$\frac{x^2 - 2x + 1}{x^3 + x} \div \frac{x^2 + x - 2}{3x^2 + 3}$$
$$= \frac{x^2 - 2x + 1}{x^3 + x} \cdot \frac{3x^2 + 3}{x^2 + x - 2}$$
$$= \frac{(x-1)(x-1)}{x(x^2+1)} \cdot \frac{3(x^2+1)}{(x+2)(x-1)}$$
$$= \frac{3(x-1)}{x(x+2)}, \ x \neq 0, \ x \neq -2, \ x \neq 1$$

For nonzero denominators, $x \neq 0, \ x \neq -2, \ x \neq 1$.

5.
$$\frac{x}{x+1} - \frac{3x+2}{x+1} = \frac{x-3x-2}{x+1}$$
$$= \frac{-2x-2}{x+1}$$
$$= \frac{-2(x+1)}{x+1}$$
$$= -2, x \neq -1$$

For a nonzero denominator, $x \neq -1$.

6.
$$\frac{3}{x+1} + \frac{5}{x-1}$$
$$= \frac{3x(x-1)+5(x+1)}{(x+1)(x-1)}$$
$$= \frac{3x-3+5x+5}{(x+1)(x-1)}$$
$$= \frac{8x+2}{(x+1)(x-1)}$$
$$= \frac{2(4x+1)}{(x+1)(x-1)} \quad \text{For a nonzero denominator, } x \neq -1 \text{ and } x \neq 1.$$
$$= \frac{2(4x+1)}{(x+1)(x-1)}, \; x \neq -1, \; x \neq 1$$

7. Factor each denominator completely.

$x^2 - 6x + 9 = (x-3)^2$

$x^2 - 9 = (x+3)(x-3)$

List the factors of the first denominator.

$x-3, \; x-3$

Add any unlisted factors from the second denominator.

$x-3, \; x-3, \; x+3$

The least common denominator is the product of all factors in the final list.

$(x-3)(x-3)(x+3)$ or $(x-3)^2(x+3)$

is the least common denominator.

8. Find the least common denominator.

$x^2 - 10x + 25 = (x-5)^2$

$2x - 10 = 2(x-5)$

The least common denominator is $2(x-5)(x-5)$.

Write all rational expressions in terms of the least common denominator.

$$\frac{x}{x^2 - 10x + 25} - \frac{x-4}{2x-10}$$

$$= \frac{x}{(x-5)(x-5)} - \frac{x-4}{2(x-5)}$$

$$= \frac{2x}{2(x-5)(x-5)} - \frac{(x-4)(x-5)}{2(x-5)(x-5)}$$

Add numerators, putting this sum over the least common denominator.

$$= \frac{2x-(x-4)(x-5)}{2(x-5)(x-5)}$$

$$= \frac{2x-(x^2-5x-4x+20)}{2(x-5)(x-5)}$$

$$= \frac{2x-x^2+5x+4x-20}{2(x-5)(x-5)}$$

$$= \frac{2x-x^2+5x+4x-20}{2(x-5)(x-5)}$$

$$= \frac{-x^2+11x-20}{2(x-5)(x-5)}$$

$$= \frac{-x^2+11x-20}{2(x-5)^2}, \; x \neq 5$$

9. $\dfrac{\frac{1}{x}-\frac{3}{2}}{\frac{1}{x}+\frac{3}{4}} = \dfrac{\frac{2}{2x}-\frac{3x}{2x}}{\frac{4}{4x}+\frac{3x}{4x}}, \; x \neq 0$

$$= \frac{\frac{2-3x}{2x}}{\frac{4+3x}{4x}}, \; x \neq \frac{-4}{3}$$

$$= \frac{2-3x}{2x} \div \frac{4+3x}{4x}$$

$$= \frac{2-3x}{2x} \cdot \frac{4x}{4+3x}$$

$$= \frac{2-3x}{4+3x} \cdot \frac{4}{2}$$

$$= \frac{2-3x}{4+3x} \cdot \frac{2}{1}$$

$$= \frac{2(2-3x)}{4+3x}, \; x \neq 0 \text{ and } x \neq \frac{-4}{3}$$

Exercise Set P.6

1. $\dfrac{7}{x-3}, \; x \neq 3$

3. $\dfrac{x+5}{x^2-25} = \dfrac{x+5}{(x+5)(x-5)}, \; x \neq 5, -5$

5. $\dfrac{x-1}{x^2+11x+10} = \dfrac{x-1}{(x+1)(x+10)}, \; x \neq -1, -10$

7. $\dfrac{3x-9}{x^2-6x+9} = \dfrac{3(x-3)}{(x-3)(x-3)}$

$$= \frac{3}{x-3}, \; x \neq 3$$

9. $\dfrac{x^2-12x+36}{4x-24} = \dfrac{(x-6)(x-6)}{4(x-6)} = \dfrac{x-6}{4}.$

$x \neq 6$

11. $\dfrac{y^2+7y-18}{y^2-3y+2} = \dfrac{(y+9)(y-2)}{(y-2)(y-1)} = \dfrac{y+9}{y-1},$

$y \neq 1, 2$

13. $\dfrac{x^2+12x+36}{x^2-36} = \dfrac{(x+6)^2}{(x+6)(x-6)} = \dfrac{x+6}{x-6},$

$x \neq 6, -6$

15. $\dfrac{x-2}{3x+9} \cdot \dfrac{2x+6}{2x-4} = \dfrac{x-2}{3(x+3)} \cdot \dfrac{2(x+3)}{2(x-2)}$

$$= \frac{2}{6} = \frac{1}{3}, \; x \neq 2, -3$$

17. $\dfrac{x^2-9}{x^2} \cdot \dfrac{x^2-3x}{x^2+x-12}$

$$= \frac{(x-3)(x+3)}{x^2} \cdot \frac{x(x-3)}{(x+4)(x-3)}$$

$$= \frac{(x-3)(x+3)}{x(x+4)}, \; x \neq 0, -4, 3$$

19. $\dfrac{x^2 - 5x + 6}{x^2 - 2x - 3} \cdot \dfrac{x^2 - 1}{x^2 - 4}$

$= \dfrac{(x-3)(x-2)}{(x-3)(x+1)} \cdot \dfrac{(x+1)(x-1)}{(x-2)(x+2)}$

$= \dfrac{x-1}{x+2}, \quad x \neq -2, -1, 2, 3$

21. $\dfrac{x^3 - 8}{x^2 - 4} \cdot \dfrac{x+2}{3x} = \dfrac{(x-2)(x^2 + 2x + 4)}{(x-2)(x+2)} \cdot \dfrac{x+2}{3x}$

$= \dfrac{x^2 + 2x + 4}{3x}, x \neq -2, 0, 2$

23. $\dfrac{x+1}{3} \div \dfrac{3x+3}{7} = \dfrac{x+1}{3} \div \dfrac{3(x+1)}{7}$

$= \dfrac{x+1}{3} \cdot \dfrac{7}{3(x+1)}$

$= \dfrac{7}{9}, \quad x \neq -1$

25. $\dfrac{x^2 - 4}{x} \div \dfrac{x+2}{x-2} = \dfrac{(x-2)(x+2)}{x} \cdot \dfrac{x-2}{x+2}$

$= \dfrac{(x-2)^2}{x}; x \neq 0, -2$

27.

$\dfrac{4x^2 + 10}{x-3} \div \dfrac{6x^2 + 15}{x^2 - 9}$

$= \dfrac{2(2x^2 + 5)}{x-3} \div \dfrac{3(2x^2 + 5)}{(x-3)(x+3)}$

$= \dfrac{2(2x^2 + 5)}{x-3} \cdot \dfrac{(x-3)(x+3)}{3(2x^2 + 5)}$

$= \dfrac{2(x+3)}{3}, \quad x \neq 3, -3$

29.

$\dfrac{x^2 - 25}{2x - 2} \div \dfrac{x^2 + 10x + 25}{x^2 + 4x - 5}$

$= \dfrac{(x-5)(x+5)}{2(x-1)} \div \dfrac{(x+5)^2}{(x+5)(x-1)}$

$= \dfrac{(x-5)(x+5)}{2(x-1)} \cdot \dfrac{(x+5)(x-1)}{(x+5)^2}$

$= \dfrac{x-5}{2}, \quad x \neq 1, -5$

31.

$\dfrac{x^2 + x - 12}{x^2 + x - 30} \cdot \dfrac{x^2 + 5x + 6}{x^2 - 2x - 3} \div \dfrac{x+3}{x^2 + 7x + 6}$

$= \dfrac{(x+4)(x-3)}{(x+6)(x-5)} \cdot \dfrac{(x+2)(x+3)}{(x+1)(x-3)} \cdot \dfrac{(x+6)(x+1)}{x+3}$

$= \dfrac{(x+4)(x+2)}{x-5}$

$x \neq -6, -3, -1, 3, 5$

33. $\dfrac{4x+1}{6x+5} + \dfrac{8x+9}{6x+5} = \dfrac{4x+1+8x+9}{6x+5}$

$= \dfrac{12x+10}{6x+5}$

$= \dfrac{2(6x+5)}{6x+5} = 2, \quad x \neq -\dfrac{5}{6}$

35. $\dfrac{x^2 - 2x}{x^2 + 3x} + \dfrac{x^2 + x}{x^2 + 3x} = \dfrac{x^2 - 2x + x^2 + x}{x^2 + 3x}$

$= \dfrac{2x^2 - x}{x^2 + 3x}$

$= \dfrac{x(2x-1)}{x(x+3)}$

$= \dfrac{2x-1}{x+3}, \quad x \neq 0, -3$

37.

$$\frac{4x-10}{x-2} - \frac{x-4}{x-2} = \frac{4x-10-(x-4)}{x-2}$$
$$= \frac{4x-10-x+4}{x-2}$$
$$= \frac{3x-6}{x-2}$$
$$= \frac{3(x-2)}{x-2}$$
$$= 3, \ x \neq 2$$

39. $\dfrac{x^2+3x}{x^2+x-12} - \dfrac{x^2-12}{x^2+x-12}$

$$= \frac{x^2+3x-(x^2-12)}{x^2+x-12}$$
$$= \frac{x^2+3x-x^2+12}{x^2+x-12}$$
$$= \frac{3x+12}{x^2+x-12}$$
$$= \frac{3(x+4)}{(x+4)(x-3)}$$
$$= \frac{3}{x-3}, \ x \neq 3, -4$$

41. $\dfrac{3}{x+4} + \dfrac{6}{x+5} = \dfrac{3(x+5)+6(x+4)}{(x+4)(x+5)}$

$$= \frac{3x+15+6x+24}{(x+4)(x+5)}$$
$$= \frac{9x+39}{(x+4)(x+5)}, \ x \neq -4, -5$$

43. $\dfrac{3}{x+1} - \dfrac{3}{x} = \dfrac{3x-3(x+1)}{x(x+1)}$

$$= \frac{3x-3x-3}{x(x+1)} = -\frac{3}{x(x+1)}, \ x \neq -1, 0$$

45. $\dfrac{2x}{x+2} + \dfrac{x+2}{x-2} = \dfrac{2x(x-2)+(x+2)(x+2)}{(x+2)(x-2)}$

$$= \frac{2x^2-4x+x^2+4x+4}{(x+2)(x-2)}$$
$$= \frac{3x^2+4}{(x+2)(x-2)}, \ x \neq -2, 2$$

47. $\dfrac{x+5}{x-5} + \dfrac{x-5}{x+5}$

$$= \frac{(x+5)(x+5)+(x-5)(x-5)}{(x-5)(x+5)}$$
$$= \frac{x^2+10x+25+x^2-10x+25}{(x-5)(x+5)}$$
$$= \frac{2x^2+50}{(x-5)(x+5)}, \ x \neq -5, 5$$

49. $\dfrac{4}{x^2+6x+9} + \dfrac{4}{x+3} = \dfrac{4}{(x+3)^2} + \dfrac{4}{x+3}$

$$= \frac{4+4(x+3)}{(x+3)^2} = \frac{4+4x+12}{(x+3)^2} = \frac{4x+16}{(x+3)^2},$$
$$x \neq -3$$

51. $\dfrac{3x}{x^2+3x-10} - \dfrac{2x}{x^2+x-6}$

$$= \frac{3x}{(x+5)(x-2)} - \frac{2x}{(x+3)(x-2)}$$
$$= \frac{3x(x+3)-2x(x+5)}{(x+5)(x-2)(x+3)}$$
$$= \frac{3x^2+9x-2x^2-10x}{(x+5)(x-2)(x+3)}$$
$$= \frac{x^2-x}{(x+5)(x-2)(x+3)}, \ x \neq -5, 2, -3$$

61. $\dfrac{x - \frac{x}{x+3}}{x+2} = \dfrac{(x+3)\left[x - \frac{x}{x+3}\right]}{(x+3)(x+2)} = \dfrac{x(x+3) - x}{(x+3)(x+2)}$

$= \dfrac{x^2 + 3x - x}{(x+3)(x+2)} = \dfrac{x^2 + 2x}{(x+3)(x+2)}$

$= \dfrac{x(x+2)}{(x+3)(x+2)} = \dfrac{x}{x+3},\ x \neq -2, -3$

53. $\dfrac{4x^2 + x - 6}{x^2 + 3x + 2} - \dfrac{3x}{x+1} + \dfrac{5}{x+2}$

$= \dfrac{4x^2 + x - 6}{(x+1)(x+2)} + \dfrac{-3x}{x+1} + \dfrac{5}{x+2}$

$= \dfrac{4x^2 + x - 5}{(x+1)(x+2)} + \dfrac{-3x(x+2)}{(x+1)(x+2)} + \dfrac{5(x+1)}{(x+1)(x+2)}$

$= \dfrac{4x^2 + x - 6 - 3x^2 - 6x + 5x + 5}{(x+1)(x+2)}$

$= \dfrac{x^2 - 1}{(x+1)(x+2)}$

$= \dfrac{(x-1)(x+1)}{(x+1)(x+2)}$

$= \dfrac{x-1}{x+2}; x \neq -2, -1$

63. $\dfrac{\frac{3}{x-2} - \frac{4}{x+2}}{\frac{7}{x^2-4}} = \dfrac{\frac{3}{x-2} - \frac{4}{x+2}}{\frac{7}{(x-2)(x+2)}}$

$= \dfrac{\left[\frac{3}{x-2} - \frac{4}{x+2}\right](x-2)(x+2)}{\left[\frac{7}{(x-2)(x+2)}\right](x-2)(x+2)}$

$= \dfrac{3(x+2) - 4(x-2)}{7}$

$= \dfrac{3x + 6 - 4x + 8}{7} = \dfrac{-x + 14}{7}$

$= -\dfrac{x-14}{7}\ \ x \neq -2, 2$

55. $\dfrac{\frac{x}{3} - 1}{x-3} = \dfrac{3\left[\frac{x}{3} - 1\right]}{3[x-3]} = \dfrac{x-3}{3(x-3)} = \dfrac{1}{3},\ \ x \neq 3$

57. $\dfrac{1 + \frac{1}{x}}{3 - \frac{1}{x}} = \dfrac{x\left[1 + \frac{1}{x}\right]}{x\left[3 - \frac{1}{x}\right]} = \dfrac{x+1}{3x-1},\ \ x \neq 0,\ \dfrac{1}{3}$

59. $\dfrac{\frac{1}{x} + \frac{1}{y}}{x + y} = \dfrac{xy\left[\frac{1}{x} + \frac{1}{y}\right]}{xy[x+y]} = \dfrac{y + x}{xy(x+y)} = \dfrac{1}{xy},$

$x \neq 0,\ y \neq 0,\ x \neq -y$

65. a. $\dfrac{130x}{100-x}$ is equal to

   1. $\dfrac{130\cdot 40}{100-40}=\dfrac{130\cdot 40}{60}=86.67$,

      when $x=40$

   2. $\dfrac{130\cdot 80}{100-80}=\dfrac{130\cdot 80}{20}=520$,

      when $x=80$

   3. $\dfrac{130\cdot 90}{100-90}=\dfrac{130\cdot 90}{10}=1170$,

      when $x=90$

   It costs \$86,670,000 to inoculate 40%
   of the population against this strain of
   flu, and \$520,000,000 to inoculate 80%
   of the population, and \$1,170,000,000
   to inoculate 90% of the population.

b.   For $x=100$, the function is not defined.

c.   As x approaches close to 100, the value
   of the function increases rapidly. So it
   costs an astronomical amount of money
   to inoculate almost all of the people,
   and it is impossible to inoculate 100%
   of the population.

67. a.

$$\frac{L+60W}{L}-\frac{L-40W}{L}=\frac{L+60W-L+40W}{l}$$
$$=\frac{100W}{L}$$

b. $(100-5)/6=83.3$ Round skull

69.

$$\frac{2d}{\dfrac{d}{r_1}+\dfrac{d}{r_2}}=\frac{2d}{\dfrac{d}{r_1}+\dfrac{d}{r_2}}\cdot\frac{r_1r_2}{r_1r_2}$$
$$=\frac{2dr_1r_2}{dr_2+dr_1}$$
$$=\frac{d(2r_1r_2)}{d(r_2+r_1)}$$
$$=\frac{2r_1r_2}{r_1+r_2},$$

Let $r_1=30$ and $r_2=20$. The average speed

is $\dfrac{2(30)(20)}{30+20}=\dfrac{1200}{50}=24$ miles per hour.

The reason that the average speed is not

$\dfrac{30+20}{2}=25$ is that the average of speeds is

defined by $\dfrac{\text{total distance travelled}}{\text{total time}}$, not by

$\dfrac{\text{sum of every speed}}{\text{number of the speeds being added}}$.

71.–77.   Answers may vary.

79. $\dfrac{1}{a}+\dfrac{1}{b}=\dfrac{b}{ab}+\dfrac{a}{ab}=\dfrac{b+a}{ab}$

81. $\dfrac{a}{x}+\dfrac{a}{b}=\dfrac{ab}{xb}+\dfrac{ax}{xb}=\dfrac{ab+ax}{xb}$

83. a. $A=\dfrac{Pi}{1-\dfrac{1}{(1+i)^n}}$

$$=\frac{Pi(1+i)^n}{\left[1-\dfrac{1}{(1+i)^n}\right](1+i)^n}$$

$$=\frac{Pi(1+i)^n}{(1+i)^n-1}$$

b. $A = \dfrac{20000(.01)(1.01)^{48}}{1.01^{48} - 1}$

$= \$527$

85.

$$\dfrac{3x}{x-5} + \dfrac{\boxed{}}{5-x} = \dfrac{7x+1}{x-5}$$

$$\dfrac{3x}{x-5} + \dfrac{\boxed{}}{-1(x-5)} = \dfrac{7x+1}{x-5}$$

$$\dfrac{3x - \boxed{}}{x-5} = \dfrac{7x+1}{x-5}$$

$$3x - \boxed{} = 7x+1$$

$$\boxed{} = -4x - 1$$

87. It cubes x, $x \neq 0$.

Review Exercises

1. a. $\sqrt{81}$

b. $0,\ \sqrt{81}$

c. $-17,\ 0,\ \sqrt{81}$

d. $-17,\ -\dfrac{9}{13},\ 0,\ 0.75,\ \sqrt{81}$

e. $\sqrt{2},\ \pi$

2. $|-103| = 103$

3. $\left|\sqrt{2} - 1\right| = \sqrt{2} - 1$

4. $\left|3 - \sqrt{17}\right| = \sqrt{17} - 3$ since $\sqrt{17}$ is greater than 3.

5. $|4 - (-17)| = |4 + 17| = |21| = 21$

6. $\dfrac{5}{9}(F - 32) = \dfrac{5}{9}(68 - 32) = \dfrac{5}{9}(36) = 20$

7. $\dfrac{8(x+5)}{3x+8} = \dfrac{8(2+5)}{3 \cdot 2 + 8} = \dfrac{8 \cdot 7}{6+8} = \dfrac{56}{14} = 4$

8. $3 + 17 = 17 + 3$;
commutative property of addition.

9. $(6 \cdot 3) \cdot 9 = 6 \cdot (3 \cdot 9)$;
associative property of multiplication.

10. $\sqrt{3}(\sqrt{5} + \sqrt{3}) = \sqrt{15} + 3$;
distributive property of multiplication over addition.

11. $(6 \cdot 9) \cdot 2 = 2 \cdot (6 \cdot 9)$;
commutative property of multiplication.

12. $\sqrt{3}(\sqrt{5} + \sqrt{3}) = (\sqrt{5} + \sqrt{3})\sqrt{3}$;
commutative property of multiplication.

13. $(3 \cdot 7) + (4 \cdot 7) = (4 \cdot 7) + (3 \cdot 7)$;
commutative property of addition.

14. $3(7x - 5y) - 2(4y - x + 1)$
$= 21x - 15y - 8y + 2x - 2$
$= (21x + 2x) + (-15y - 8y) - 2$
$= 23x - 23y - 2$

15. $\dfrac{1}{5}(5x) + [(3y) + (-3y)] - (-x) = x + x = 2x$

16. $(-3)^3(-2)^2 = (-27) \cdot (4) = -108$

17.

$$2^{-4} + 4^{-1} = \frac{1}{2^4} + \frac{1}{4}$$
$$= \frac{1}{16} + \frac{1}{4}$$
$$= \frac{1}{16} + \frac{4}{16}$$
$$= \frac{5}{16}$$

18. $5^{-3} \cdot 5 = 5^{-3}5^1 = 5^{-3+1} = 5^{-2} = \frac{1}{5^2} = \frac{1}{25}$

19. $\dfrac{3^3}{3^6} = 3^{3-6} = 3^{-3} = \dfrac{1}{3^3} = \dfrac{1}{27}$

20. $(-2x^4 y^3)^3 = (-2)^3 (x^4)^3 (y^3)^3$
$$= (-2)^3 x^{4\cdot3} y^{3\cdot3}$$
$$= -8x^{12} y^9$$

21.

$$(-5x^3 y^2)(-2x^{-11} y^{-2})$$
$$= (-5)(-2)x^3 x^{-11} y^2 y^{-2}$$
$$= 10 \cdot x^{3-11} y^{2-2}$$
$$= 10x^{-8} y^0$$
$$= \frac{10}{x^8}$$

22. $(2x^3)^{-4} = (2)^{-4}(x^3)^{-4}$
$$= 2^{-4} x^{-12}$$
$$= \frac{1}{2^4 x^{12}}$$
$$= \frac{1}{16x^{12}}$$

23. $\dfrac{7x^5 y^6}{28x^{15} y^{-2}} = \left(\dfrac{7}{28}\right)(x^{5-15})(y^{6-(-2)})$
$$= \frac{1}{4} x^{-10} y^8$$
$$= \frac{y^8}{4x^{10}}$$

24. $3.74 \times 10^4 = 37,400$

25. $7.45 \times 10^{-5} = 0.0000745$

26. $3,590,000 = 3.59 \times 10^6$

27. $0.00725 = 7.25 \times 10^{-3}$

28. $(3 \times 10^3)(1.3 \times 10^2) = (3 \times 1.3) \times (10^3 \times 10^2)$
$$= 3.9 \times 10^5$$

29. $\dfrac{6.9 \times 10^3}{3 \times 10^5} = \left(\dfrac{6.9}{3}\right) \times 10^{3-5}$
$$= 2.3 \times 10^{-2}$$

30. $\dfrac{10^9}{10^6} = 10^{9-6} = 10^3$

It would take 10^3 or 1000 years to accumulate \$1 billion.

31. $(2.8 \times 10^8) \times 150$
$$= (2.8 \times 10^8) \times (1.5 \times 10^2)$$
$$= (2.8 \times 1.5) \times (10^8 \times 10^2)$$
$$= 4.2 \times 10^{10}$$
The total annual spending on movies is \$4.2 \times 10^{10}$.

32. $\sqrt{300} = \sqrt{100 \cdot 3} = \sqrt{100} \cdot \sqrt{3} = 10\sqrt{3}$

33. $\sqrt{12x^2} = \sqrt{4x^2 \cdot 3} = \sqrt{4x^2} \cdot \sqrt{3} = 2|x|\sqrt{3}$

34. $\sqrt{10x} \cdot \sqrt{2x} = \sqrt{20x^2}$
$$= \sqrt{4x^2} \cdot \sqrt{5}$$
$$= 2x\sqrt{5}$$

35. $\sqrt{r^3} = \sqrt{r^2} \cdot \sqrt{r} = r\sqrt{r}$

36. $\sqrt{\dfrac{121}{4}} = \dfrac{\sqrt{121}}{\sqrt{4}} = \dfrac{11}{2}$

37. $\dfrac{\sqrt{96x^3}}{\sqrt{2x}} = \sqrt{\dfrac{96x^3}{2x}}$
$$= \sqrt{48x^2}$$
$$= \sqrt{16x^2} \cdot \sqrt{3}$$
$$= 4x\sqrt{3}$$

38. $7\sqrt{5} + 13\sqrt{5} = (7+13)\sqrt{5} = 20\sqrt{5}$

39. $2\sqrt{50} + 3\sqrt{8} = 2\sqrt{25 \cdot 2} + 3\sqrt{4 \cdot 2}$
$$= 2 \cdot 5\sqrt{2} + 3 \cdot 2\sqrt{2}$$
$$= 10\sqrt{2} + 6\sqrt{2}$$
$$= 16\sqrt{2}$$

40. $4\sqrt{72} - 2\sqrt{48} = 4\sqrt{36 \cdot 2} - 2\sqrt{16 \cdot 3}$
$$= 4 \cdot 6\sqrt{2} - 2 \cdot 4\sqrt{3}$$
$$= 24\sqrt{2} - 8\sqrt{3}$$

41. $\dfrac{30}{\sqrt{5}} = \dfrac{30}{\sqrt{5}} \cdot \dfrac{\sqrt{5}}{\sqrt{5}} = \dfrac{30\sqrt{5}}{5} = 6\sqrt{5}$

42. $\dfrac{\sqrt{2}}{\sqrt{3}} = \dfrac{\sqrt{2}}{\sqrt{3}} \cdot \dfrac{\sqrt{3}}{\sqrt{3}} = \dfrac{\sqrt{6}}{3}$

43. $\dfrac{5}{6+\sqrt{3}} = \dfrac{5}{6+\sqrt{3}} \cdot \dfrac{6-\sqrt{3}}{6-\sqrt{3}}$
$$= \dfrac{5(6-\sqrt{3})}{36-3}$$
$$= \dfrac{5(6-\sqrt{3})}{33}$$

44.
$$\dfrac{14}{\sqrt{7}-\sqrt{5}} = \dfrac{14}{\sqrt{7}-\sqrt{5}} \cdot \dfrac{\sqrt{7}+\sqrt{5}}{\sqrt{7}+\sqrt{5}}$$
$$= \dfrac{14(\sqrt{7}+\sqrt{5})}{7-5}$$
$$= \dfrac{14(\sqrt{7}+\sqrt{5})}{2}$$
$$= 7(\sqrt{7}+\sqrt{5})$$

45. $\sqrt[3]{125} = 5$

46. $\sqrt[5]{-32} = -2$

47. $\sqrt[4]{-125}$ is not a real number.

48. $\sqrt[4]{(-5)^4} = \sqrt[4]{625} = \sqrt[4]{5^4} = 5$

49. $\sqrt[3]{81} = \sqrt[3]{27 \cdot 3} = \sqrt[3]{27} \cdot \sqrt[3]{3} = 3\sqrt[3]{3}$

50. $\sqrt[3]{y^5} = \sqrt[3]{y^3 y^2} = y\sqrt[3]{y^2}$

51. $\sqrt[4]{8} \cdot \sqrt[4]{10} = \sqrt[4]{80} = \sqrt[4]{16 \cdot 5} = \sqrt[4]{16} \cdot \sqrt[4]{5} = 2\sqrt[4]{5}$

52. $4\sqrt[3]{16} + 5\sqrt[3]{2} = 4\sqrt[3]{8 \cdot 2} + 5\sqrt[3]{2}$
$$= 4 \cdot 2\sqrt[3]{2} + 5\sqrt[3]{2}$$
$$= 8\sqrt[3]{2} + 5\sqrt[3]{2}$$
$$= 13\sqrt[3]{2}$$

53. $\dfrac{\sqrt[4]{32x^5}}{\sqrt[4]{16x}} = \sqrt[4]{\dfrac{32x^5}{16x}} = \sqrt[4]{2x^4} = |x|\sqrt[4]{2}$

54. $16^{1/2} = \sqrt{16} = 4$

55. $25^{-1/2} = \dfrac{1}{25^{1/2}} = \dfrac{1}{\sqrt{25}} = \dfrac{1}{5}$

56. $125^{1/3} = \sqrt[3]{125} = 5$

57. $27^{-1/3} = \dfrac{1}{27^{1/3}} = \dfrac{1}{\sqrt[3]{27}} = \dfrac{1}{3}$

58. $64^{2/3} = (\sqrt[3]{64})^2 = 4^2 = 16$

59. $27^{-4/3} = \dfrac{1}{27^{4/3}} = \dfrac{1}{(\sqrt[3]{27})^4} = \dfrac{1}{3^4} = \dfrac{1}{81}$

60. $(5x^{2/3})(4x^{1/4}) = 5 \cdot 4x^{2/3+1/4} = 20x^{11/12}$

61. $\dfrac{15x^{3/4}}{5x^{1/2}} = \left(\dfrac{15}{5}\right)x^{3/4-1/2} = 3x^{1/4}$

62. $(125 \cdot x^6)^{2/3} = (\sqrt[3]{125x^6})^2$
$\qquad\qquad\quad = (5x^2)^2$
$\qquad\qquad\quad = 25x^4$

63. $\sqrt[6]{y^3} = (y^3)^{1/6} = y^{3 \cdot 1/6} = y^{1/2}$

64. $(-6x^3 + 7x^2 - 9x + 3) + (14x^3 + 3x^2 - 11x - 7) = (-6x^3 + 14x^3) + (7x^2 + 3x^2) + (-9x - 11x) + (3 - 7)$
$$= 8x^3 + 10x^2 - 20x - 4$$
The degree is 3.

65. $(13x^4 - 8x^3 + 2x^2) - (5x^4 - 3x^3 + 2x^2 - 6) = (13x^4 - 8x^3 + 2x^2) + (-5x^4 + 3x^3 - 2x^2 + 6)$
$$= (13x^4 - 5x^4) + (-8x^3 + 3x^3) + (2x^2 - 2x^2) + 6$$
$$= 8x^4 - 5x^3 + 6$$
The degree is 4.

66. $(3x - 2)(4x^2 + 3x - 5) = (3x)(4x^2) + (3x)(3x) + (3x)(-5) + (-2)(4x^2) + (-2)(3x) + (-2)(-5)$
$$= 12x^3 + 9x^2 - 15x - 8x^2 - 6x + 10$$
$$= 12x^3 + x^2 - 21x + 10$$

67. $(3x - 5)(2x + 1) = (3x)(2x) + (3x)(1) + (-5)(2x) + (-5)(1)$
$$= 6x^2 + 3x - 10x - 5$$
$$= 6x^2 - 7x - 5$$

68. $(4x + 5)(4x - 5) = (4x^2) - 5^2 = 16x^2 - 25$

69. $(2x + 5)^2 = (2x)^2 + 2(2x) \cdot 5 + 5^2 = 4x^2 + 20x + 25$

70. $(3x - 4)^2 = (3x)^2 - 2(3x) \cdot 4 + (-4)^2 = 9x^2 - 24x + 16$

71. $(2x + 1)^3 = (2x)^3 + 3(2x)^2(1) + 3(2x)(1)^2 + 1^3 = 8x^3 + 12x^2 + 6x + 1$

72. $(5x - 2)^3 = (5x)^3 - 3(5x)^2(2) + 3(5x)(2)^2 - 2^3 = 125x^3 - 150x^2 + 60x - 8$

73. $(7x^2 - 8xy + y^2) + (-8x^2 - 9xy - 4y^2) = (7x^2 - 8x^2) + (-8xy - 9xy) + (y^2 - 4y^2)$
$$= -x^2 - 17xy - 3y^2$$
The degree is 2.

74. $(13x^3y^2 - 5x^2y - 9x^2) - (-11x^3y^2 - 6x^2y + 3x^2 - 4)$
$$= (13x^3y^2 - 5x^2y - 9x^2) + (11x^3y^2 + 6x^2y - 3x^2 + 4)$$
$$= (13x^3y^2 + 11x^3y^2) + (-5x^2y + 6x^2y) + (-9x^2 - 3x^2) + 4$$
$$= 24x^3y^2 + x^2y - 12x^2 + 4$$
The degree is 5.

75. $(x + 7y)(3x - 5y) = x(3x) + (x)(-5y) + (7y)(3x) + (7y)(-5y)$
$$= 3x^2 - 5xy + 21xy - 35y^2$$
$$= 3x^2 + 16xy - 35y^2$$

76. $(3x-5y)^2 = (3x)^2 - 2(3x)(5y) + (-5y)^2$
$= 9x^2 - 30xy + 25y^2$

77. $(3x^2+2y)^2 = (3x^2)^2 + 2(3x^2)(2y) + (2y)^2$
$= 9x^4 + 12x^2y + 4y^2$

78. $(7x+4y)(7x-4y) = (7x)^2 - (4y)^2$
$= 49x^2 - 16y^2$

79. $(a-b)(a^2+ab+b^2)$
$= a(a^2) + a(ab) + a(b^2) + (-b)(a^2)$
$+ (-b)(ab) + (-b)(b^2)$
$= a^3 + a^2b + ab^2 - a^2b - ab^2 - b^3$
$= a^3 - b^3$

80. $15x^3 + 3x^2 = 3x^2 \cdot 5x + 3x^2 \cdot 1$
$= 3x^2(5x+1)$

81. $x^2 - 11x + 28 = (x-4)(x-7)$

82. $15x^2 - x - 2 = (3x+1)(5x-2)$

83. $64 - x^2 = 8^2 - x^2 = (8-x)(8+x)$

84. $x^2 + 16$ is prime.

85. $3x^4 - 9x^3 - 30x^2 = 3x^2(x^2 - 3x - 10)$
$= 3x^2(x-5)(x+2)$

86. $20x^7 - 36x^3 = 4x^3(5x^4 - 9)$

87. $x^3 - 3x^2 - 9x + 27 = x^2(x-3) - 9(x-3)$
$= (x^2 - 9)(x-3)$
$= (x+3)(x-3)(x-3)$
$= (x+3)(x-3)^2$

88. $16x^2 - 40x + 25 = (4x-5)(4x-5)$
$= (4x-5)^2$

89. $x^4 - 16 = (x^2)^2 - 4^2$
$= (x^2+4)(x^2-4)$
$= (x^2+4)(x+2)(x-2)$

90. $y^3 - 8 = y^3 - 2^3 = (y-2)(y^2+2y+4)$

91. $x^3 + 64 = x^3 + 4^3 = (x+4)(x^2-4x+16)$

92. $3x^4 - 12x^2 = 3x^2(x^2-4)$
$= 3x^2(x-2)(x+2)$

93. $27x^3 - 125 = (3x)^3 - 5^3$
$= (3x-5)[(3x)^2 + (3x)(5) + 5^2]$
$= (3x-5)(9x^2+15x+25)$

94. $x^5 - x = x(x^4-1)$
$= x(x^2-1)(x^2+1)$
$= x(x-1)(x+1)(x^2+1)$

95. $x^3 + 5x^2 - 2x - 10 = x^2(x+5) - 2(x+5)$
$= (x^2-2)(x+5)$

96. $x^2 + 18x + 81 - y^2 = \left(x^2 + 18x + 81\right) - y^2$
$= \left(x+9\right)^2 - y^2$
$= \left(x+9-y\right)\left(x+9+y\right)$

97. $16x^{-\frac{3}{4}} + 32x^{\frac{1}{4}} = 16x^{-\frac{3}{4}}\left(1 + 2x^{\frac{1}{4}-\left(-\frac{3}{4}\right)}\right)$
$= 16x^{-\frac{3}{4}}\left(1+2x\right)$

98.

$$\left(x^2 - 4\right)\left(x^2 + 3\right)^{\frac{1}{2}} - \left(x^2 - 4\right)^2\left(x^2 + 3\right)^{\frac{3}{2}}$$

$$= \left(x^2 - 4\right)\left(x^2 + 3\right)^{\frac{1}{2}}\left[1 - \left(x^2 - 4\right)\left(x^2 + 3\right)\right]$$

$$= \left(x - 2\right)\left(x + 2\right)\left(x^2 + 3\right)^{\frac{1}{2}}\left[1 - \left(x - 2\right)\left(x + 2\right)\left(x^2 + 3\right)\right]$$

$$= (x - 2)(x + 2)(x^2 + 3)^{\frac{1}{2}}(-x^4 + x^2 + 13)$$

99. $12x^{-\frac{1}{2}} + 6x^{-\frac{3}{2}} = 6x^{-\frac{3}{2}}\left(2x + 1\right) = \dfrac{6(2x + 1)}{x^{\frac{3}{2}}}$

100. $\dfrac{x^3 + 2x^2}{x + 2} = \dfrac{x^2(x + 2)}{x + 2} = x^2,\ x \ne -2$

101. $\dfrac{x^2 + 3x - 18}{x^2 - 36} = \dfrac{(x + 6)(x - 3)}{(x + 6)(x - 6)} = \dfrac{x - 3}{x - 6},$
$x \ne -6, 6$

102. $\dfrac{x^2 + 2x}{x^2 + 4x + 4} = \dfrac{x(x + 2)}{(x + 2)^2} = \dfrac{x}{x + 2},$
$x \ne -2$

103. $\dfrac{x^2 + 6x + 9}{x^2 - 4} \cdot \dfrac{x + 3}{x - 2} = \dfrac{(x + 3)^2}{(x - 2)(x + 2)} \cdot \dfrac{x + 3}{x - 2}$

$$= \dfrac{(x + 3)^3}{(x - 2)^2(x + 2)},$$

$x \ne 2, -2$

104.

$$\dfrac{6x + 2}{x^2 - 1} \div \dfrac{3x^2 + x}{x - 1}$$

$$= \dfrac{2(3x + 1)}{(x - 1)(x + 1)} \div \dfrac{x(3x + 1)}{x - 1}$$

$$= \dfrac{2(3x + 1)}{(x - 1)(x + 1)} \cdot \dfrac{x - 1}{x(3x + 1)}$$

$$= \dfrac{2}{x(x + 1)},$$

$x \ne 0,\ 1,\ -1,\ -\dfrac{1}{3}$

105.

$$\dfrac{x^2 - 5x - 24}{x^2 - x - 12} \div \dfrac{x^2 - 10x + 16}{x^2 + x - 6}$$

$$= \dfrac{(x - 8)(x + 3)}{(x - 4)(x + 3)} \div \dfrac{(x - 2)(x - 8)}{(x + 3)(x - 2)}$$

$$= \dfrac{x - 8}{x - 4} \cdot \dfrac{x + 3}{x - 8}$$

$$= \dfrac{x + 3}{x - 4},$$

$x \ne -3, 4, 2, 8$

106. $\dfrac{2x - 7}{x^2 - 9} - \dfrac{x - 10}{x^2 - 9} = \dfrac{2x - 7 - (x - 10)}{x^2 - 9}$

$$= \dfrac{x + 3}{(x + 3)(x - 3)}$$

$$= \dfrac{1}{x - 3},$$

$x \ne 3, -3$

107.

$$\frac{3x}{x+2}+\frac{x}{x-2}=\frac{3x}{x+2}\cdot\frac{x-2}{x-2}+\frac{x}{x-2}\cdot\frac{x+2}{x+2}$$

$$=\frac{3x^2-6x+x^2+2x}{(x+2)(x-2)}$$

$$=\frac{4x^2-4x}{(x+2)(x-2)}$$

$$=\frac{4x(x-1)}{(x+2)(x-2)},$$

$$x\neq 2,-2$$

108.

$$\frac{x}{x^2-9}+\frac{x}{x^2-5x+6}$$

$$=\frac{x}{(x-3)(x+3)}+\frac{x}{(x-2)(x-3)}$$

$$=\frac{x}{(x-3)(x+3)}\cdot\frac{x-2}{x-2}$$

$$+\frac{x}{(x-2)(x-3)}\cdot\frac{x+3}{x+3}$$

$$=\frac{x(x-2)+x(x+3)}{(x-3)(x+3)(x-2)}$$

$$=\frac{2x^2+x}{(x-3)(x+3)(x-2)}$$

$$=\frac{x(2x+1)}{(x-3)(x+3)(x-2)}$$

$$x\neq 3,-3,2$$

109.

$$\frac{4x-1}{2x^2+5x-3}-\frac{x+3}{6x^2+x-2}$$

$$=\frac{4x-1}{(2x-1)(x+3)}-\frac{x+3}{(2x-1)(3x+2)}$$

$$=\frac{4x-1}{(2x-1)(x+3)}\cdot\frac{3x+2}{3x+2}$$

$$-\frac{x+3}{(2x-1)(3x+2)}\cdot\frac{x+3}{x+3}$$

$$=\frac{12x^2+8x-3x-2-x^2-6x-9}{(2x-1)(x+3)(3x+2)}$$

$$=\frac{11x^2-x-11}{(2x-1)(x+3)(3x+2)},$$

$$x\neq\frac{1}{2},-3,-\frac{2}{3}$$

110.

$$\frac{\frac{1}{x}-\frac{1}{2}}{\frac{1}{3}-\frac{x}{6}}=\frac{\frac{1}{x}-\frac{1}{2}}{\frac{1}{3}-\frac{x}{6}}\cdot\frac{6x}{6x}$$

$$=\frac{6-3x}{2x-x^2}$$

$$=\frac{-3(x-2)}{-x(x-2)}$$

$$=\frac{3}{x},$$

$$x\neq 0,2$$

111.

$$\frac{3+\frac{12}{x}}{1-\frac{16}{x^2}}=\frac{3+\frac{12}{x}}{1-\frac{16}{x^2}}\cdot\frac{x^2}{x^2}$$

$$=\frac{3x^2+12x}{x^2-16}$$

$$=\frac{3x(x+4)}{(x+4)(x-4)}$$

$$=\frac{3x}{x-4},$$

$$x\neq 0,4,-4$$

112.

$$\frac{3-\frac{1}{x+3}}{3+\frac{1}{x+3}} = \frac{3-\frac{1}{x+3}}{3+\frac{1}{x+3}} \cdot \frac{x+3}{x+3}$$

$$= \frac{3(x+3)-1}{3(x+3)+1}$$

$$= \frac{3x+9-1}{3x+9+1}$$

$$= \frac{3x+8}{3x+10},$$

$$x \neq -3,\ -\frac{10}{3}$$

Chapter P Test

1. $-7,\ -\dfrac{4}{5},\ 0,\ 0.25,\ \sqrt{4},\ \dfrac{22}{7}$ are rational numbers.

2. $3(2+5) = 3(5+2)$;
commutative property of addition

3. $6(7+4) = 6 \cdot 7 + 6 \cdot 4$
distributive property of multiplication over addition

4. $0.00076 = 7.6 \times 10^{-4}$

5. $9(10x-2y) - 5(x-4y+3)$
$= 90x - 18y - 5x + 20y - 15$
$= 85x + 2y - 15$

6. $\dfrac{30x^3 y^4}{6x^9 y^{-4}} = 5x^{3-9} y^{4-(-4)} = 5x^{-6} y^8 = \dfrac{5y^8}{x^6}$

7. $\sqrt{6r} \cdot \sqrt{3r} = \sqrt{18r^2} = \sqrt{9r^2} \cdot \sqrt{2} = 3r\sqrt{2}$

8. $4\sqrt{50} - 3\sqrt{18} = 4\sqrt{25 \cdot 2} - 3\sqrt{9 \cdot 2}$
$= 4 \cdot 5\sqrt{2} - 3 \cdot 3\sqrt{2}$
$= 20\sqrt{2} - 9\sqrt{2}$
$= 11\sqrt{2}$

9. $\dfrac{3}{5+\sqrt{2}} = \dfrac{3}{5+\sqrt{2}} \cdot \dfrac{5-\sqrt{2}}{5-\sqrt{2}}$
$= \dfrac{3(5-\sqrt{2})}{25-2}$
$= \dfrac{3(5-\sqrt{2})}{23}$

10. $\sqrt[3]{16x^4} = \sqrt[3]{8x^3 \cdot 2x}$
$= \sqrt[3]{8x^3} \cdot \sqrt[3]{2x}$
$= 2x\sqrt[3]{2x}$

11. $\dfrac{x^2+2x-3}{x^2-3x+2} = \dfrac{(x+3)(x-1)}{(x-2)(x-1)} = \dfrac{x+3}{x-2},$
$x \neq 2,\ 1$

12. $27^{-5/3} = \dfrac{1}{27^{5/3}} = \dfrac{1}{\left(\sqrt[3]{27}\right)^5} = \dfrac{1}{3^5} = \dfrac{1}{243}$

13. $(2x-5)(x^2-4x+3)$
$= 2x^3 - 8x^2 + 6x - 5x^2 + 20x - 15$
$= 2x^3 - 13x^2 + 26x - 15$

14. $(5x+3y)^2 = (5x)^2 + 2(5x)(3y) + (3y)^2$
$= 25x^2 + 30xy + 9y^2$

15. $x^2 - 9x + 18 = (x-3)(x-6)$

16. $x^3 + 2x^2 + 3x + 6 = x^2(x+2) + 3(x+2)$
$= (x^2+3)(x+2)$

17. $25x^2 - 9 = (5x)^2 - 3^2 = (5x-3)(5x+3)$

18. $36x^2 - 84x + 49 = (6x)^2 - 2(6x) \cdot 7 + 7^2$

$\qquad\qquad\qquad\quad = (6x - 7)^2$

19. $y^3 - 125 = y^3 - 5^3 = (y - 5)(y^2 + 5y + 25)$

20. $(x^2 + 10x + 25) - 9y^2$

$= (x + 5)^2 - 9y^2$

$= (x + 5 - 3y)((x + 5 + 3y)$

21. $x(x + 3)^{-\frac{3}{5}} + (x + 3)^{\frac{2}{5}}$

$= (x + 3)^{-\frac{3}{5}}\left[x + (x + 3)\right]$

$= (x + 3)^{-\frac{3}{5}}(2x + 3) = \dfrac{2x + 3}{(x + 3)^{\frac{3}{5}}}$

22.

$\dfrac{2x + 8}{x - 3} \div \dfrac{x^2 + 5x + 4}{x^2 - 9}$

$= \dfrac{2(x + 4)}{x - 3} \div \dfrac{(x + 1)(x + 4)}{(x - 3)(x + 3)}$

$= \dfrac{2(x + 4)}{x - 3} \cdot \dfrac{(x - 3)(x + 3)}{(x + 1)(x + 4)}$

$= \dfrac{2(x + 3)}{x + 1},$

$x \neq 3, -1, -4, -3$

23.

$\dfrac{x}{x + 3} + \dfrac{5}{x - 3}$

$= \dfrac{x}{x + 3} \cdot \dfrac{x - 3}{x - 3} + \dfrac{5}{x - 3} \cdot \dfrac{x + 3}{x + 3}$

$= \dfrac{x(x - 3) + 5(x + 3)}{(x + 3)(x - 3)}$

$= \dfrac{x^2 - 3x + 5x + 15}{(x + 3)(x - 3)}$

$= \dfrac{x^2 + 2x + 15}{(x + 3)(x - 3)}, \quad x \neq 3, -3$

24.

$\dfrac{2x + 3}{x^2 - 7x + 12} - \dfrac{2}{x - 3}$

$= \dfrac{2x + 3}{(x - 3)(x - 4)} - \dfrac{2}{x - 3}$

$= \dfrac{2x + 3}{(x - 3)(x - 4)} - \dfrac{2}{x - 3} \cdot \dfrac{x - 4}{x - 4}$

$= \dfrac{2x + 3 - 2(x - 4)}{(x - 3)(x - 4)}$

$= \dfrac{2x + 3 - 2(x - 4)}{(x - 3)(x - 4)}$

$= \dfrac{2x + 3 - 2x + 8}{(x - 3)(x - 4)}$

$= \dfrac{11}{(x - 3)(x - 4)},$

$x \neq 3, 4$

25. $\dfrac{\frac{1}{x} - \frac{1}{3}}{\frac{1}{x}} = \dfrac{\frac{1}{x} - \frac{1}{3}}{\frac{1}{x}} \cdot \dfrac{3x}{3x} = \dfrac{3 - x}{3},$

$x \neq 0$

Chapter 1

Check Point Exercises

1.

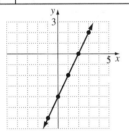

2.

x	$y = 2x - 4$	Ordered Pair
-1	$y = 2(-1) - 4 = -2 - 4 = -6$	$(-1, -6)$
0	$y = 2(0) - 4 = 0 - 4 = -4$	$(0, -4)$
1	$y = 2(1) - 4 = 2 - 4 = -2$	$(1, -2)$
2	$y = 2(2) - 4 = 4 - 4 = 0$	$(2, 0)$
3	$y = 2(3) - 4 = 6 - 4 = 2$	$(3, 2)$

3. The minimum x-value is -100 and the maximum x-value is 100. The distance between consecutive tick marks is 50. The minimum y-value is -80 and the maximum y-value is 80. The distance between consecutive tick marks is 10.

4. Maximum age corresponds to the highest point on the graph between 1900 and 1950. The coordinates of this point are approximately (1900, 21.5). This means that in 1900 the average age of a woman's first marriage reached a maximum for 1900 to 1950. The age for 1900 was approximately 21.5.

Exercise Set 1.1

1.

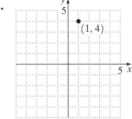

3.

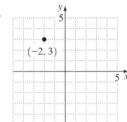

5.

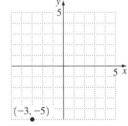

46

7.

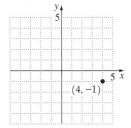

9.

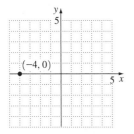

11.

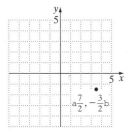

13.

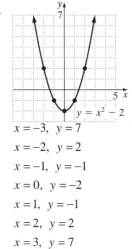

$x = -3, \ y = 7$

$x = -2, \ y = 2$

$x = -1, \ y = -1$

$x = 0, \ y = -2$

$x = 1, \ y = -1$

$x = 2, \ y = 2$

$x = 3, \ y = 7$

15.

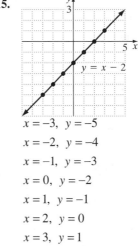

$x = -3, \ y = -5$

$x = -2, \ y = -4$

$x = -1, \ y = -3$

$x = 0, \ y = -2$

$x = 1, \ y = -1$

$x = 2, \ y = 0$

$x = 3, \ y = 1$

17.

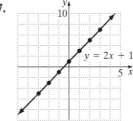

$x = -3, \ y = -5$

$x = -2, \ y = -3$

$x = -1, \ y = -1$

$x = 0, \ y = 1$

$x = 1, \ y = 3$

$x = 2, \ y = 5$

$x = 3, \ y = 7$

19.

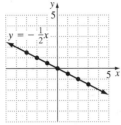

$x = -3, \quad y = \dfrac{3}{2}$

$x = -2, \quad y = 1$

$x = -1, \quad y = \dfrac{1}{2}$

$x = 0, \quad y = 0$

$x = 1, \quad y = -\dfrac{1}{2}$

$x = 2, \quad y = -1$

$x = 3, \quad y = -\dfrac{3}{2}$

21.

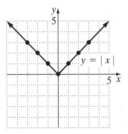

$x = -3, y = 3$

$x = -2, y = 2$

$x = -1, y = 1$

$x = 0, y = 0$

$x = 1, y = 1$

$x = 2, y = 2$

$x = 3, y = 3$

23.

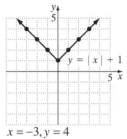

$x = -3, y = 4$

$x = -2, y = 3$

$x = -1, y = 2$

$x = 0, y = 1$

$x = 1, y = 2$

$x = 2, y = 3$

$x = 3, y = 4$

25.

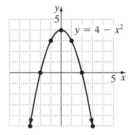

$x = -3, y = -5$

$x = -2, y = 0$

$x = -1, y = 3$

$x = 0, y = 4$

$x = 1, y = 3$

$x = 2, y = 0$

$x = 3, y = -5$

27.

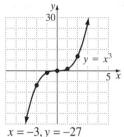

$x = -3, y = -27$

$x = -2, y = -8$

$x = -1, y = 1$

$x = 0, y = 0$

$x = 1, y = 1$

$x = 2, y = 8$

$x = 3, y = 27$

29. (c) *x*-axis tick marks –5, –4, –3, –2, –1, 0, 1, 2, 3, 4, 5; *y*-axis tick marks are the same.

31. (b); *x*-axis tick marks –20, –10, 0, 10, 20, 30, 40, 50, 60, 70, 80; *y*-axis tick marks –30, –20, –10, 0, 10, 20, 30, 40, 50, 60, 70

33. a. 2; The graph intersects the *x*-axis at (2, 0).

    b. –4; The graph intersects the *y*-axis at (0,–4).

35. a. 1, –2; The graph intersects the *x*-axis at (1, 0) and (–2, 0).

    b. 2; The graph intersects the *y*-axis at (0, 2).

37. a. –1; The graph intersects the *x*-axis at (–1, 0).

    b. None; The graph does not intersect the *y*-axis.

39. A (2, 7) When the football is 2 yards from the quarterback, it is 7 feet high.

41. C (6, 9.2)

43. Maximum height is 12 feet when the ball is 15 yards from the quarterback.

45. During 0 – 4 years of marriage the chance of divorce is increasing.

47. During the 4th year of marriage the chance of divorce us the highest at 8.2%.

49.–51. Answers may vary.

53. On the *x*-axis, the lowest point is -20, the highest point is 2, and each mark represents 1 space. On the *y*-axis, the lowest point is -4, the highest point is 4, and each mark represents one half of a space.

55. Exercises 13–27

Use your graphing calculator

57. $y = x^2 + 10$

    a.

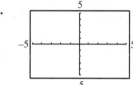

    b.

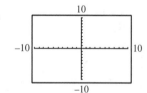

    c.

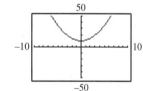

(c) gives a complete graph.

59. $y = x^3 - 30x + 20$

  a.

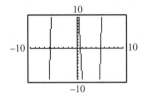

  b.

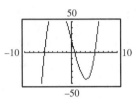

  c.

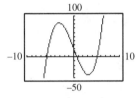

(c) gives a complete graph.

61. a

63. b

Section 1.2

Check Point Exercises

  1.
$$5x - 8 = 72$$
$$5x - 8 + 8 = 72 + 8$$
$$5x = 80$$
$$\frac{5x}{5} = \frac{80}{5}$$
$$x = 16$$

Check:
$$5x - 8 = 72$$
$$5(16) - 8 \,?\, 72$$
$$80 - 8 \,?\, 72$$
$$72 = 72$$
The solution set is $\{16\}$.

  2.
$$4(2x + 1) - 29 = 3(2x - 5)$$
$$8x + 4 - 29 = 6x - 15$$
$$8x - 25 = 6x - 15$$
$$8x - 25 - 6x = 6x - 15 - 6x$$
$$2x - 25 = -15$$
$$2x - 25 + 25 = -15 + 25$$
$$2x = 10$$
$$\frac{2x}{2} = \frac{10}{2}$$
$$x = 5$$

Check:
$$4(2x + 1) - 29 = 3(2x - 5)$$
$$4[2(5) + 1] - 29 \,?\, 3[2(5) - 5]$$
$$4[10 + 1] - 29 \,?\, 3[10 - 5]$$
$$4[11] - 29 \,?\, 3[]$$
$$44 - 29 \,?\, 15$$
$$15 = 15$$
The solution set is $\{5\}$.

  3.
$$\frac{x}{4} = \frac{2x}{3} + \frac{5}{6}$$
$$12 \cdot \frac{x}{4} = 12\left(\frac{2x}{3} + \frac{5}{6}\right)$$
$$12 \cdot \frac{x}{4} = 12 \cdot \frac{2x}{3} + 12 \cdot \frac{5}{6}$$
$$3x = 8x + 10$$
$$3x - 8x = 8x + 10 - 8x$$
$$-5x = 10$$
$$\frac{-5x}{-5} = \frac{10}{-5}$$
$$x = -2$$

Check:

$$\frac{x}{4} = \frac{2x}{3} + \frac{5}{6}$$

$$\frac{-2}{4} = \frac{2(-2)}{3} + \frac{5}{6}$$

$$-\frac{1}{2} = -\frac{4}{3} + \frac{5}{6}$$

$$-\frac{1}{2} = -\frac{1}{2}$$

The solution set is $\{-2\}$.

4. $\dfrac{5}{2x} = \dfrac{17}{18} - \dfrac{1}{3x}, \; x \neq 0$

$$18x \cdot \frac{5}{2x} = 18x\left(\frac{17}{18} - \frac{1}{3x}\right)$$

$$18 \cdot \frac{5}{2x} = 18x \cdot \frac{17}{18} - 18x \cdot \frac{1}{3x}$$

$$45 = 17x - 6$$

$$45 + 6 = 17x - 6 + 6$$

$$51 = 17x$$

$$\frac{51}{17} = \frac{17x}{17}$$

$$3 = x$$

The solution set is $\{3\}$.

5.

$$\frac{x}{x-2} = \frac{2}{x-2} - \frac{2}{3}, x \neq 2$$

$$3(x-2) \cdot \frac{x}{x-2} = 3(x-2)\left[\frac{2}{x-2} - \frac{2}{3}\right]$$

$$3(x-2) \cdot \frac{x}{x-2} = (3x-2) \cdot \frac{2}{x-2} - 3(x-2) \cdot \frac{2}{3}$$

$$3x = 6 - (x-2) \cdot 2$$

$$3x = 6 - 2(x-2)$$

$$3x = 6 - 2x + 4$$

$$3x = 10 - 2x$$

$$3x + 2x = 10 - 2x + 2x$$

$$5x = 10$$

$$\frac{5x}{5} = \frac{10}{5}$$

$$x = 2$$

The solution set is the empty set, $\varnothing$.

6. $2(x+1) = 2x + 2$

$$2x + 2 = 2x + 2$$

The given equation is an identity.

Exercise Set 1.2

1. $7x - 5 = 72$

$$7x = 77$$

$$x = 11$$

Check:

$$7x - 5 = 72$$

$$7(11) - 5 = 72$$

$$77 - 5 = 72$$

$$72 = 72$$

The solution set is $\{11\}$.

3. $11x - (6x - 5) = 40$

$$11x - 6x + 5 = 40$$

$$5x + 5 = 40$$

$$5x = 35$$

$$x = 7$$

The solution set is $\{7\}$.

Check:

$$11x - (6x - 5) = 40$$

$$11(7) - [6(7) - 5] = 40$$

$$77 - (42 - 5) = 40$$

$$77 - (37) = 40$$

$$40 = 40$$

5. $2x - 7 = 6 + x$

$$x - 7 = 6$$

$$x = 13$$
The solution set is {13}.

Check:
$$2(13) - 7 = 6 + 13$$
$$26 - 7 = 19$$
$$19 = 19$$

7. $7x + 4 = x + 16$
$$6x + 4 = 16$$
$$6x = 12$$
$$x = 2$$
The solution set is {2}.

Check:
$$7(2) + 4 = 2 + 16$$
$$14 + 4 = 18$$
$$18 = 18$$

9. $3(x - 2) + 7 = 2(x + 5)$
$$3x - 6 + 7 = 2x + 10$$
$$3x + 1 = 2x + 10$$
$$x + 1 = 10$$

13. $16 = 3(x - 1) - (x - 7)$
$$16 = 3x - 3 - x + 7$$
$$16 = 2x + 4$$
$$12 = 2x$$
$$6 = x$$
The solution set is {6}.
Check:
$$16 = 3(6 - 1) - (6 - 7)$$
$$16 = 3(5) - (-1)$$
$$16 = 15 + 1$$
$$16 = 16$$

15. $25 - [2 + 5y - 3(y + 2)] = -3(2y - 5) - [5(y - 1) - 3y + 3]$
$$25 - [2 + 5y - 3y - 6] = -6y + 15 - [5y - 5 - 3y + 3]$$
$$25 - [2y - 4] = -6y + 15 - [2y - 2]$$
$$25 - 2y + 4 = -6y + 15 - 2y + 2$$
$$-2y + 29 = -8y + 17$$
$$6y = -12$$
$$y = -2$$
The solution set is {-2}.

$$x = 9$$
The solution set is {9}.

Check:
$$3(9 - 2) + 7 = 2(9 + 5)$$
$$3(7) + 7 = 2(14)$$
$$21 + 7 = 28$$
$$28 = 28$$

11. $3(x - 4) - 4(x - 3) = x + 3 - (x - 2)$
$$3x - 12 - 4x + 12 = x + 3 - x + 2$$
$$-x = 5$$
$$x = -5$$
The solution set is {-5}.

Check:
$$3(-5 - 4) - 4(-5 - 3) = -5 + 3 - (-5 - 2)$$
$$3(-9) - 4(-8) = -2 - (-7)$$
$$-27 + 32 = -2 + 7$$
$$5 = 5$$

Check:
$$25 - [2 + 5y - 3(y + 2)] = -3(2y - 5) - [5(y - 1) - 3y + 3]$$
$$25 - [2 + 5(-2) - 3(-2 + 2)] = -3[2(-2) - 5] - [5(-2 - 1) - 3(-2) + 3]$$
$$25 - [2 - 10 - 3(0)] = -3[-4 - 5] - [5(-3) + 6 + 3]$$
$$25 - [-8] = -3(-9) - [-15 + 9]$$
$$25 + 8 = 27 - (-6)$$
$$33 = 27 + 6$$
$$33 = 33$$

17. $\dfrac{x}{3} = \dfrac{x}{2} - 2$

$$6\left[\dfrac{x}{3} = \dfrac{x}{2} - 2\right]$$
$$2x = 3x - 12$$
$$12 = 3x - 2x$$
$$x = 12$$

The solution set is $\{12\}$.

19.

$$20 - \frac{x}{3} = \frac{x}{2}$$

$$6\left[20 - \frac{x}{3} = \frac{x}{2}\right]$$

$$120 - 2x = 3x$$

$$120 = 3x + 2x$$

$$120 = 5x$$

$$x = \frac{120}{5}$$

$$x = 24$$

The solution set is {24}.

21.

$$\frac{3x}{5} = \frac{2x}{3} + 1$$

$$15\left[\frac{3x}{5} = \frac{2x}{3} + 1\right]$$

$$9x = 10x + 15$$

$$9x - 10x = 15$$

$$-x = 15$$

$$x = -15$$

The solution set is {−15}.

23.

$$\frac{3x}{5} - x = \frac{x}{10} - \frac{5}{2}$$

$$10\left[\frac{3x}{5} - x = \frac{x}{10} - \frac{5}{2}\right]$$

$$6x - 10x = x - 25$$

$$-4x - x = -25$$

$$-5x = -25$$

$$x = 5$$

The solution set is {5}.

25.

$$\frac{x+3}{6} = \frac{3}{8} + \frac{x-5}{4}$$

$$24\left[\frac{x+3}{6} = \frac{3}{8} + \frac{x-5}{4}\right]$$

$$4x + 12 = 9 + 6x - 30$$

$$4x - 6x = -21 - 12$$

$$-2x = -33$$

$$x = \frac{33}{2}$$

The solution set is $\left\{\frac{33}{2}\right\}$.

27.

$$\frac{x}{4} = 2 + \frac{x-3}{3}$$

$$12\left[\frac{x}{4} = 2 + \frac{x-3}{3}\right]$$

$$3x = 24 + 4x - 12$$

$$3x - 4x = 12$$

$$-x = 12$$

$$x = -12$$

The solution set is {−12}.

29.

$$\frac{x+1}{3} = 5 - \frac{x+2}{7}$$

$$21\left[\frac{x+1}{3} = 5 - \frac{x+2}{7}\right]$$

$$7x + 7 = 105 - 3x - 6$$

$$7x + 3x = 99 - 7$$

$$10x = 92$$

$$x = \frac{92}{10}$$

$$x = \frac{46}{5}$$

The solution set is $\left\{\frac{46}{5}\right\}$.

31. a. $$\frac{4}{x} = \frac{5}{2x} + 3 \ (x \neq 0)$$

b. $\dfrac{4}{x} = \dfrac{5}{2x} + 3$

$8 = 5 + 6x$

$3 = 6x$

$\dfrac{1}{2} = x$

The solution set is $\left\{ \dfrac{1}{2} \right\}$.

33. a. $\dfrac{2}{x} + 3 = \dfrac{5}{2x} + \dfrac{13}{4} \; (x \neq 0)$

b. $\dfrac{2}{x} + 3 = \dfrac{5}{2x} + \dfrac{13}{4}$

$8 + 12x = 10 + 13x$

$-x = 2$

$x = -2$

The solution set is $\{-2\}$.

35. a. $\dfrac{2}{3x} + \dfrac{1}{4} = \dfrac{11}{6x} - \dfrac{1}{3} \; (x \neq 0)$

b. $\dfrac{2}{3x} + \dfrac{1}{4} = \dfrac{11}{6x} - \dfrac{1}{3}$

$8 + 3x = 22 - 4x$

$7x = 14$

$x = 2$

The solution set is $\{2\}$.

37. a. $\dfrac{x-2}{2x} + 1 = \dfrac{x+1}{x} \quad (x \neq 0)$

b. $\dfrac{x-2}{2x} + 1 = \dfrac{x+1}{x}$

$x - 2 + 2x = 2x + 2$

$x - 2 = 2$

$x = 4$

The solution set is $\{4\}$.

39. a. $\dfrac{1}{x-1} + 5 = \dfrac{11}{x-1} \; (x \neq 1)$

b. $\dfrac{1}{x-1} + 5 = \dfrac{11}{x-1}$

$1 + 5(x-1) = 11$

$1 + 5x - 5 = 11$

$5x - 4 = 11$

$5x = 15$

$x = 3$

The solution set is $\{3\}$.

41. a. $\dfrac{8x}{x+1} = 4 - \dfrac{8}{x+1} \; (x \neq -1)$

b. $\dfrac{8x}{x+1} = 4 - \dfrac{8}{x+1}$

$8x = 4(x+1) - 8$

$8x = 4x + 4 - 8$

$4x = -4$

$x = -1 \Rightarrow$ no solution

The solution set is the empty set, $\varnothing$.

43. a. $\dfrac{3}{2x-2} + \dfrac{1}{2} = \dfrac{2}{x-1} \; (x \neq 1)$

b. $\dfrac{3}{2x-2} + \dfrac{1}{2} = \dfrac{2}{x-1}$

$\dfrac{3}{2(x-1)} + \dfrac{1}{2} = \dfrac{2}{x-1}$

$3 + 1(x-1) = 4$

$3 + x - 1 = 4$

$x = 2$

The solution set is $\{2\}$.

45. a. $\dfrac{3}{x+2} + \dfrac{2}{x-2} = \dfrac{8}{(x+2)(x-2)} ; (x \neq -2, 2)$

b.

$$\frac{3}{x+2} + \frac{2}{x-2} = \frac{8}{(x+2)(x-2)}$$

$$(x \neq 2, \ x \neq -2)$$

$$3(x-2) + 2(x+2) = 8$$

$$3x - 6 + 2x + 4 = 8$$

$$5x = 10$$

$$x = 2 \Rightarrow \text{ no solution}$$

The solution set is the empty set, $\varnothing$.

47. a. $\frac{2}{x+1} - \frac{1}{x-1} = \frac{2x}{x^2 - 1} \ (x \neq 1, \ x \neq -1)$

b.

$$\frac{2}{x+1} - \frac{1}{x-1} = \frac{2x}{x^2 - 1}$$

$$\frac{2}{x+1} - \frac{1}{x-1} = \frac{2x}{(x+1)(x-1)}$$

$$2(x-1) - 1(x+1) = 2x$$

$$2x - 2 - x - 1 = 2x$$

$$-x = 3$$

$$x = -3$$

The solution set is $\{-3\}$.

49. a. $\frac{1}{x-4} - \frac{5}{x+2} = \frac{6}{(x-4)(x+2)}; (x \neq -2, 4)$

b.

$$\frac{1}{x-4} - \frac{5}{x+2} = \frac{6}{x^2 - 2x - 8}$$

$$\frac{1}{x-4} - \frac{5}{x+2} = \frac{6}{(x-4)(x+2)}$$

$$(x \neq 4, \ x \neq -2)$$

$$1(x+2) - 5(x-4) = 6$$

$$x + 2 - 5x + 20 = 6$$

$$-4x = -16$$

$$x = 4 \Rightarrow \text{ no solution}$$

The solution set is the empty set, $\varnothing$.

51. $4(x-7) = 4x - 28$

$4x - 28 = 4x - 28$

The given equation is an identity.

53. $2x + 3 = 2x - 3$

$3 = -3$

The given equation is an inconsistent equation.

55. $4x + 5x = 8x$

$9x = 8x$

$x = 0$

The given equation is a conditional equation.

57. $\frac{2x}{x-3} = \frac{6}{x-3} + 4$

$$2x = 6 + 4(x-3)$$

$$2x = 6 + 4x - 12$$

$$-2x = -6$$

$$x = 3 \Rightarrow \text{ no solution}$$

The given equation is an inconsistent equation.

59. $\frac{x+5}{2} - 4 = \frac{2x-1}{3}$

$$3(x+5) - 24 = 2(2x-1)$$

$$3x + 15 - 24 = 4x - 2$$

$$-x = 7$$

$$x = -7$$

The solution set is $\{-7\}$.

61. $\frac{2}{x-2} = 3 + \frac{x}{x-2}$

$$2 = 3(x-2) + x$$

$$2 = 3x - 6 + x$$

$$-4x = -8$$

$$x = 2 \Rightarrow \text{ no solution}$$

The solution set is the empty set, $\varnothing$.

63. $8x - (3x + 2) + 10 = 3x$

$$8x - 3x - 2 + 10 = 3x$$

$$2x = -8$$

$$x = -4$$

The solution set is $\{-4\}$.

65. $\dfrac{2}{x}+\dfrac{1}{2}=\dfrac{3}{4}$

$8+2x=3x$

$-x=-8$

$x=8$

The solution set is $\{8\}$.

67. $\dfrac{4}{x-2}+\dfrac{3}{x+5}=\dfrac{7}{(x+5)(x-2)}$

$4(x+5)+3(x-2)=7$

$4x+20+3x-6=7$

$7x=-7$

$x=-1$

The solution set is $\{-1\}$.

69. $\dfrac{4x}{x+3}-\dfrac{12}{x-3}=\dfrac{4x^2+36}{x^2-9};x\neq 3,-3$

$4x(x-3)-12(x+3)=4x^2+36$

$4x^2-12x-12x-36=4x^2+36$

$4x^2-24x-36=4x^2+36$

$-24x-36=36$

$-24x=72$

$x=-3 \quad$ No solution

The solution set is $\{\ \}$.

71. a. Let $d=725{,}000$.

$d=5000c-525{,}000$

$725{,}000=5000c-525{,}000$

$1{,}250{,}000=5000c$

$250=c$

In 2000, the average cholesterol level was 250 milligrams per deciliter.

b. Let $c=180$.

$d=5000c-525{,}000$

$d=5000(180)-525{,}000$

$d=375{,}000$ annual deaths

$725{,}000-375{,}000=350{,}000$

$350{,}000$ lives could be saved.

73.

$p=15+\dfrac{15d}{33}$

$201=15+\dfrac{15d}{33}$

$186=\dfrac{15d}{33}$

$15d=6138$

$d=409\dfrac{1}{5}$ feet

Ferreras descended to $409\dfrac{1}{5}$ feet.

75.–85. Answers may vary.

87. Graph $y_1=9x+3-3x$

$\qquad y_2=2(3x+1)$

The given equation is an inconsistent equation.

89. Graph $y_1=\dfrac{2x-1}{3}-\dfrac{x-5}{6}$

$\qquad y_2=\dfrac{x-3}{4}$

The given equation is a conditional equation.

The solution set is $\{-5\}$.

91. $ax + b = c$

$$ax = c - b$$

$$x = \frac{c-b}{a}$$

93. Answers may vary.

95. $\dfrac{4x - b}{x - 5} = 3$

$4x - b = 3(x - 5)$

The solution set will be $\varnothing$ if x = 5.

$4(5) - b = 3(5 - 5)$

$$20 - b = 0$$

$$20 = b$$

$$b = 20$$

Section 1.3

Check Point Exercises

1. $W = 0.3x + 46.6$

$$55 = 0.3x + 46.6$$

$$8.4 = 0.3x$$

$$28 = x$$

$1980 + 28 = 2008$

In 2008, the average number of hours worked per week will be 55.

2. Let x = the number (in millions) of copies of the Bee Gees album sold. Let $x + 5$ = the number (in millions) of copies the Morissette album sold.

Then $x + x + 5 = 27$

$$2x + 5 = 27$$

$$2x + 5 - 5 = 27 - 5$$

$$2x = 22$$

$$\frac{2x}{2} = \frac{22}{2}$$

$$x = 11$$

There were 11 million copies of the Bee Gees album sold, and 11 + 5 = 16 million copies of the Morisette album sold.

3. Let x = the number of hours of use.

$15 + .08x = 3 + .12x$

$$12 = .04x$$

$$300 = x$$

The plans cost the same with 300 minutes of use.

4. Let x = the amount invested at 9%.

Let $25,000 - x$ = the amount invested at 12%.

Then $0.09x + 0.12(25,000 - x) = 2550$.

$$0.09x + 3000 - 0.12x = 2550$$

$$-0.03x + 3000 - 3000 = 2550 - 3000$$

$$-0.03x = -450$$

$$\frac{-0.03x}{-0.03} = \frac{-450}{-0.03}$$

$$x = 15,000$$

$15,000 should be invested at 9% and $10,000 at 12%.

5. Let x = the width of the basketball court. Let $x + 44$ = the length of the basketball court.

$2x + 2(x + 44) = 288$

$$2x + 2x + 88 = 288$$

$$4x = 200$$

$$x = 50$$

$$x + 44 = 94$$

The length of the pool is 94 feet; its width is 50 feet.

6. $y = mx + b$

$$y - b = mx + b - b$$

$$y - b = mx$$

$$\frac{y-b}{x} = \frac{mx}{x}$$

$$\frac{y-b}{x} = m$$

$$m = \frac{y-b}{x}$$

7.
$$P = C + MC$$
$$P = C(1 + M)$$
$$\frac{P}{1+M} = C$$

Exercise Set 1.3

1. $x + 9$

3. $20 - x$

5. $8 - 5x$

7. $15 \div x$

9. $2x + 20$

11. $7x - 30$

13. $4(x + 12)$

15. $x + 40 = 450$
    $x = 410$
    The solution set is {410}.

17. $5x - 7 = 123$
    $5x = 130$
    $x = 26$
    The solution set is {26}.

19. $9x = 3x + 30$
    $6x = 30$
    $x = 5$
    The solution set is {5}.

21. $R = 143 - 0.65A$
      $117 = 143 - 0.65A$
    $-0.65A = -26$
      $A = 40$
    She is 40 years old. Find 117 on the vertical axis and follow it over to the Female graph.

23. $.5 = -0.22t + 9.6$
      $.22t = 9.1$
      $t = 41.4$
    $1960 + 41 = 2001$

The salmon population will be .5 million in 2001.

25.
$$\frac{W}{2} - 3H = 53$$
$$\frac{W}{2} - 3(15) = 53$$
$$\frac{W}{2} - 45 = 53$$
$$\frac{W}{2} = 98$$
$$W = 196$$
The recommended weight is 196 pounds.

27. Let x = cost to make *Waterworld*
    $x + 40$ = cost to make *Titanic*
    $x + x + 40 = 360$
        $2x = 320$
        $x = 160$
    $x + 40 = 200$
    $160 million to make *Waterworld* and $200 million to make *Titanic*.

29. Let x = Miami
    $2x - 32$ = Los Angeles
    $x + 2x - 32 = 139$
        $3x - 32 = 139$
        $3x = 171$
        $x = 57$
    The average person in Miami wastes 57 hours per year. The average person in Los Angeles wastes 82 hours per year.

31. Let x = number of miles
    $200 + 0.15x = 320$
        $0.15x = 120$
        $x = 800$
    You can travel 800 miles.

33. $28 + .6x = 37$
        $.6x = 9$
        $x = 15$
    $1990 + 15 = 2005$

In 2005, 37% of the babies will be born out of wedlock.

35. a. with book: $21 + 0.5x$
without book: $1.25x$

b. $21 + 0.5x = 1.25x$
$21 = 0.75x$
$x = 28$
If the bus is used 28 times, the costs are the same.

37. $100 + .8x = 40 + .9x$
$60 = .1x$
$600 = x$
For $600 worth of merchandise, your cost is $580.

39. Let x = amount invested at 15%
$50000 - x$ = amount invested at 7%
$.15x + .07(50000 - x) = 6000$
$.15x + 3500 - .07x = 6000$
$.08x = 2500$
$x = 31250$
$50000 - 31250 = 18750$
$31,250 at 15\%, \$18750 at 7\%$

41. Let x = amount invested at 12%
$8000 - x$ = amount invested at 5% loss
$.12x - .05(8000 - x) = 620$
$.12x - 400 + .05x = 620$
$.17x = 1020$
$x = 6000$
$8000 - x = 2000$
$6000 at 12\%, \$2000 at 5\% loss$

43. Let x = width
$2x + 6$ = length
$2x + 2(2x + 6) = 228$
$2x + 4x + 12 = 228$
$6x + 12 = 228$
$6x = 216$
$x = 36$

$2(36) + 6 = 78$
The dimensions are 78 feet by 36 feet

45. Let x = length
$x + 3$ = height
$4x + 2(x + 3) = 18$
$4x + 2x + 6 = 18$
$6x = 12$
$x = 2$
$x + 3 = 5$
Length is 2 feet, height is 5 feet.

47. Let x = number of hours
$35x$ = labor cost
$35x + 63 = 448$
$35x = 385$
$x = 11$
It took 11 hours.

49. Let x = salary with associate's degree
$x + .35x = 41851$
$1.35x = 41851$
$x = 31000$
$31000 is the average annual salary with an associate's degree.

51. Let x = the weight of unpeeled bananas.
$\dfrac{7}{8}x$ = weight of peeled bananas
$x = \dfrac{7}{8}x + \dfrac{7}{8}$
$\dfrac{1}{8}x = \dfrac{7}{8}$
$x = 7$
The banana with peel weighs 7 ounces.

53. Let x = the original cost
$x - .12x = 17600$
$.88x = 17600$
$x = 20000$
The original cost of the car was $20000.

55. Let x = inches over 5 feet
$100 + 5x = 135$
$5x = 35$

$$x = 7$$
A height of 5 feet 7 inches corresponds to 135 pounds.

57. $A = lw$

$$w = \frac{A}{l};$$

area of rectangle

59. $A = \frac{1}{2}bh$

$$2A = bh$$

$$b = \frac{2A}{h};$$

area of triangle

61. $I = Prt$

$$P = \frac{I}{rt};$$

interest

63. $E = mc^2$

$$m = \frac{E}{c^2};$$

energy

65. $T = D + pm$

$$T - D = pm$$

$$p = \frac{(T - D)}{m}$$

67. $A = \frac{1}{2}h(a + b)$

$$2A = h(a + b)$$

$$\frac{2A}{h} = a + b$$

$$\frac{2A}{h} - b = a;$$

area of trapezoid

69. $S = P + Prt$

$$S - P = Prt$$

$$\frac{S - P}{Pt} = r;$$

interest

71. $B = \dfrac{F}{S - V}$

$$B(S - V) = F$$

$$S - V = \frac{F}{B}$$

$$S = \frac{F}{B} + V$$

73. $IR + Ir = E$

$$I(R + r) = E$$

$$I = \frac{E}{R + r}$$

75. $\dfrac{1}{p} + \dfrac{1}{q} = \dfrac{1}{f}$

$$qf + pf = pq$$

$$f(q + p) = pq$$

$$f = \frac{pq}{q + p}$$

77.–79. Answers may vary.

81.

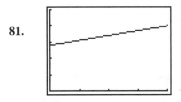

$x = 15$ when $y = 37$, 2005
$x = 20$ when $y = 40$, 2010

83. $.1x + .9(1000 - x) = 420$

$\quad\quad .1 + 900 - .9x = 420$

$\quad\quad\quad\quad -.8x = -480$

$\quad\quad\quad\quad\quad\quad x = 600$

600 students at the north campus,
400 students at south campus.

85. Let x = woman's age

$3x$ = Coburn's age

$3x + 20 = 2(x + 20)$

$3x + 20 = 2x + 40$

$\quad x + 20 = 40$

$\quad\quad\quad x = 20$

Coburn is 60 years old the woman is
20 years old.

87. Let x = mother's amount

$2x$ = boy's amount

$\dfrac{x}{2}$ = girl's amount

$x + 2x + \dfrac{x}{2} = 14,000$

$\dfrac{7}{2}x = 14,000$

$\quad x = \$4,000$

The mother got $4000, the boy got $8000, and
the girl got $2000.

Section 1.4

Check Point Exercises

1. a. $(5 - 2i) + (3 + 3i)$

$\quad = 5 - 2i + 3 + 3i$

$\quad = (5 + 3) + (-2 + 3)i$

$\quad = 8 + i$

b. $(2 + 6i) - (12 - 4i)$

$\quad = 2 + 6i - 12 + 4i$

$\quad = (2 - 12) + (6 + 4)i$

$\quad = -10 + 10i$

2. a. $7i(2 - 9i) = 7i(2) - 7i(9i)$

$\quad\quad = 14i - 63i^2$

$\quad\quad = 14i - 63(-1)$

$\quad\quad = 63 + 14i$

b. $(5 + 4i)(6 - 7i) = 30 - 35i + 24i - 28i^2$

$\quad\quad = 30 - 35i + 24i - 28(-1)$

$\quad\quad = 30 + 28 - 35i + 24i$

$\quad\quad = 58 - 11i$

3. The complex conjugate of the denominator,
$4 - 2i$, is $4 + 2i$, so multiply the numerator and
denominator by $4 + 2i$.

$\dfrac{5 + 4i}{4 - 2i} = \dfrac{(5 + 4i)}{(4 - 2i)} \cdot \dfrac{(4 + 2i)}{(4 + 2i)}$

$\quad = \dfrac{20 + 10i + 16i + 8i^2}{4^2 + 2^2}$

$\quad = \dfrac{20 + 26i + 8(-1)}{20}$

$\quad = \dfrac{12 + 26i}{20}$

$\quad = \dfrac{12}{20} + \dfrac{26}{20}i$

$\quad = \dfrac{3}{5} + \dfrac{13}{10}i$

4. a. $\sqrt{-27} + \sqrt{-48} = i\sqrt{27} + i\sqrt{48}$

$\quad\quad = i\sqrt{9 \cdot 3} + i\sqrt{16 \cdot 3}$

$\quad\quad = 3i\sqrt{3} + 4i\sqrt{3}$

$\quad\quad = 7i\sqrt{3}$

b. $(-2 + \sqrt{-3})^2 = (-2 + i\sqrt{3})^2$

$\quad\quad = (-2)^2 + 2(-2)(i\sqrt{3}) + (i\sqrt{3})^2$

$\quad\quad = 4 - 4i\sqrt{3} + 3i^2$

$\quad\quad = 4 - 4i\sqrt{3} + 3(-1)$

$\quad\quad = 1 - 4i\sqrt{3}$

c.

$$\frac{-14+\sqrt{-12}}{2} = \frac{-14+i\sqrt{12}}{2}$$

$$= \frac{-14+2i\sqrt{3}}{2}$$

$$= \frac{-14}{2} + \frac{2i\sqrt{3}}{2}$$

$$= -7+i\sqrt{3}$$

Exercise Set 1.4

1. $(7+2i)+(1-4i) = 7+2i+1-4i$
$= 7+1+2i-4i$
$= 8-2i$

3. $(3+2i)-(5-7i) = 3-5+2i+7i$
$= 3+2i-5+7i$
$= -2+9i$

5. $6-(-5+4i)-(-13-11i)$
$= 6+5-4i+13+11i$
$= 24+7i$

7. $8i-(14-9i) = 8i-14+9i$
$= -14+8i+9i$
$= -14+17i$

9. $-3i(7i-5) = -21i^2+15i$
$= -21(-1)+15i$
$= 21+15i$

11. $(-5+4i)(3+7i) = -15-35i+12i+28i^2$
$= -15-35i+12i+28(-1)$
$= -43-23i$

13. $(7-5i)(-2-3i) = -14-21i+10i+15i^2$
$= -14-15-11i$
$= -29-11i$

15. $(3+5i)(3-5i) = 9-25i^2 = 9+25 = 34$

17. $(-5+3i)(-5-3i) = 25-9i^2 = 25+9 = 34$

19. $(2+3i)^2 = 4+12i+9i^2$
$= 4+12i-9$
$= -5+12i$

21.

$$\frac{2}{3-i} = \frac{2}{3-i} \cdot \frac{3+i}{3+i}$$

$$= \frac{2(3+i)}{9+1}$$

$$= \frac{2(3+i)}{10}$$

$$= \frac{3+i}{5}$$

$$= \frac{3}{5} + \frac{1}{5}i$$

23. $\dfrac{2i}{1+i} = \dfrac{2i}{1+i} \cdot \dfrac{1-i}{1-i} = \dfrac{2i-2i^2}{1+1} = \dfrac{2+2i}{2} = 1+i$

25.

$$\frac{8i}{4-3i} = \frac{8i}{4-3i} \cdot \frac{4+3i}{4+3i}$$

$$= \frac{32i+24i^2}{16+9}$$

$$= \frac{-24+32i}{25}$$

$$= -\frac{24}{25} + \frac{32}{25}i$$

27.

$$\frac{2+3i}{2+i} = \frac{2+3i}{2+i} \cdot \frac{2-i}{2-i}$$

$$= \frac{4+4i-3i^2}{4+1}$$

$$= \frac{7+4i}{5}$$

$$= \frac{7}{5} + \frac{4}{5}i$$

29. $\sqrt{-64} - \sqrt{-25} = i\sqrt{64} - i\sqrt{25}$
$$= 8i - 5i = 3i$$

31. $5\sqrt{-16} + 3\sqrt{-81} = 5(4i) + 3(9i)$
$$= 20i + 27i = 47i$$

33. $\left(-2 + \sqrt{-4}\right)^2 = \left(-2 + 2i\right)^2$
$$= 4 - 8i + 4i^2$$
$$= 4 - 8i - 4$$
$$= -8i$$

35. $\left(-3 - \sqrt{-7}\right)^2 = \left(-3 - i\sqrt{7}\right)^2$
$$= 9 + 6i\sqrt{7} + i^2(7)$$
$$= 9 - 7 + 6i\sqrt{7}$$
$$= 2 + 6i\sqrt{7}$$

37.
$$\frac{-8 + \sqrt{-32}}{24} = \frac{-8 + i\sqrt{32}}{24}$$
$$= \frac{-8 + i\sqrt{16 \cdot 2}}{24}$$
$$= \frac{-8 + 4i\sqrt{2}}{24}$$
$$= -\frac{1}{3} + \frac{\sqrt{2}}{6}i$$

39.
$$\frac{-6 - \sqrt{-12}}{48} = \frac{-6 - i\sqrt{12}}{48}$$
$$= \frac{-6 - i\sqrt{4 \cdot 3}}{48}$$
$$= \frac{-6 - 2i\sqrt{3}}{48}$$
$$= -\frac{1}{8} - \frac{\sqrt{3}}{24}i$$

41. $\sqrt{-8}\left(\sqrt{-3} - \sqrt{5}\right) = i\sqrt{8}(i\sqrt{3} - \sqrt{5})$
$$= 2i\sqrt{2}\left(i\sqrt{3} - \sqrt{5}\right)$$
$$= -2\sqrt{6} - 2i\sqrt{10}$$

43. $\left(3\sqrt{-5}\right)\left(-4\sqrt{-12}\right) = \left(3i\sqrt{5}\right)\left(-8i\sqrt{3}\right)$
$$= -24i^2\sqrt{15}$$
$$= 24\sqrt{15}$$

45.–51. Answers may vary.

53. a. False; all irrational numbers are complex numbers.

   b. False; $(3 + 7i)(3 - 7i) = 9 + 49 = 58$ is a real number.

   c. False; $\dfrac{7 + 3i}{5 + 3i} = \dfrac{7 + 3i}{5 + 3i} \cdot \dfrac{5 - 3i}{5 - 3i}$
$$= \frac{44 - 6i}{34} = \frac{22}{17} - \frac{3}{17}i$$

   d. True; $\left(x + yi\right)\left(x - yi\right) = x^2 - \left(yi\right)^2 = x^2 + y^2$

   (d) is true.

55.

$$\frac{4}{(2+i)(3-i)} = \frac{4}{6+i-i^2}$$

$$= \frac{4}{6+i+1}$$

$$= \frac{4}{7+i}$$

$$= \frac{4}{7+i} \cdot \frac{7-i}{7-i}$$

$$= \frac{4(7-i)}{49+1}$$

$$= \frac{28-4i}{50}$$

$$= \frac{28}{50} - \frac{4}{50}i$$

$$= \frac{14}{25} - \frac{2}{25}i$$

57. $x^2 - 2x + 2$ for $x = 1+i$

$$x^2 - 2x + 2 = (1+i)^2 - 2(1+i) + 2$$

$$= 1 + 2i - 1 - 2 - 2i + 2$$

$$= 0$$

Section 1.5

Check Point Exercises

1. a. $3x^2 - 9x = 0$

$3x(x-3) = 0$

$3x = 0$ or $x - 3 = 0$

$x = 0$ $x = 3$

The solution set is {0, 3}.

b. $2x^2 + x = 1$

$2x^2 + x - 1 = 0$

$(2x - 1)(x + 1) = 0$

$2x - 1 = 0$ or $x + 1 = 0$

$2x = 1$ $x = -1$

$x = \frac{1}{2}$

The solution set is $\left\{-1, \frac{1}{2}\right\}$.

2. a. $3x^2 = 21$

$$\frac{3x^2}{3} = \frac{21}{3}$$

$$x^2 = 7$$

$$x = \pm\sqrt{7}$$

The solution set is $\left\{-\sqrt{7}, \sqrt{7}\right\}$.

b. $(x+5)^2 = 11$

$$x + 5 = \pm\sqrt{11}$$

$$x = -5 \pm \sqrt{11}$$

The solution set is $\left\{-5 + \sqrt{11}, -5 - \sqrt{11}\right\}$.

3. Add $\left(\frac{14}{2}\right)^2 = 49$.

$$x^2 - 14x + 7^2 = x^2 - 14x + 49 = (x-7)^2$$

4.

$$x^2 - 2x - 2 = 0$$

$$x^2 - 2x - 2 + 2 = 0 + 2$$

$$x^2 - 2x = 2$$

$$x^2 - 2x + 1 = 2 + 1$$

$$(x-1)^2 = 3$$

$$x - 1 = \pm\sqrt{3}$$

$$x = 1 \pm \sqrt{3}$$

The solution set is $\left\{1 + \sqrt{3}, 1 - \sqrt{3}\right\}$.

5. $2x^2 + 2x - 1 = 0$

$a = 2, \ b = 2, \ c = -1$

$x = \dfrac{-b \pm \sqrt{b^2 - 4ac}}{2a}$

$= \dfrac{-2 \pm \sqrt{2^2 - 4(2)(-1)}}{2(2)}$

$= \dfrac{-2 \pm \sqrt{4 + 8}}{4}$

$= \dfrac{-2 \pm \sqrt{12}}{4}$

$= \dfrac{-2 \pm 2\sqrt{3}}{4}$

$= \dfrac{2(-1 \pm \sqrt{3})}{4}$

$= \dfrac{-1 \pm \sqrt{3}}{2}$

The solution set is $\left\{ \dfrac{-1 + \sqrt{3}}{2}, \ \dfrac{-1 - \sqrt{3}}{2} \right\}$.

6. $x^2 - 2x + 2 = 0$

$a = 1, \ b = -2, \ c = 2$

$x = \dfrac{-b \pm \sqrt{b^2 - 4ac}}{2a}$

$x = \dfrac{-(-2) \pm \sqrt{(-2)^2 - 4(1)(2)}}{2(1)}$

$x = \dfrac{2 \pm \sqrt{4 - 8}}{2}$

$x = \dfrac{2 \pm \sqrt{-4}}{2}$

$x = \dfrac{2 \pm 2i}{2}$

$x = 1 \pm i$

The solution set is $\{1 + i, \ 1 - i\}$.

7. $3x^2 - 2x + 5 = 0$

$a = 3, \ b = -2, \ c = 5$

$b^2 - 4ac = (-2)^2 - 4 \cdot 3 \cdot 5 = 4 - 60 = -56$

The discriminant is –56. The equation has two complex imaginary solutions.

8. $250 = 23.4x^2 - 259.1x + 815.8$

$0 = 23.4x^2 - 259.1x + 565.8$

$x = \dfrac{-(-259.1) \pm \sqrt{(2259.1)^2 - 4(23.4)(565.8)}}{2(23.4)}$

$x = \dfrac{259.1 \pm \sqrt{67132.81 - 52{,}958.88}}{46.8}$　　　19

$x = \dfrac{259.1 \pm \sqrt{14{,}173.93}}{46.8}$

$x = \dfrac{259.1 \pm 119.1}{468.8}$

$x \approx 8.1, 2.99$

$90 + 3 = 1993$

$1990 + 8 = 1998$ is closer to the graph.

In 1998, 250 police officers were convicted of felonies.

9. $w^2 + 9^2 = 15^2$

$w^2 + 81 = 225$

$w^2 = 144$

$w = \pm\sqrt{144}$

$w = \pm 12$

The width of the television is 12 inches.

Exercise Set 1.5

1. $x^2 - 3x - 10 = 0$

$(x + 2)(x - 5) = 0$

$x + 2 = 0 \quad \text{or} \quad x - 5 = 0$

$x = -2 \quad \text{or} \quad x = 5$

The solution set is $\{-2, 5\}$.

3. $x^2 = 8x - 15$

$x^2 - 8x + 15 = 0$

$(x - 3)(x - 5) = 0$

$x - 3 = 0$ or $x - 5 = 0$
$x = 3$ or $x = 5$
The solution set is $\{3, 5\}$.

5. $6x^2 + 11x - 10 = 0$
$(2x + 5)(3x - 2) = 0$
$2x + 5 = 0$ or $3x - 2 = 0$
$2x = -5$ $3x = 2$
$x = -\dfrac{5}{2}$ or $x = \dfrac{2}{3}$
The solution set is $\left\{ -\dfrac{5}{2}, \dfrac{2}{3} \right\}$.

7. $3x^2 - 2x = 8$
$3x^2 - 2x - 8 = 0$
$(3x + 4)(x - 2) = 0$
$3x + 4 = 0$ or $x - 2 = 0$
$3x = -4$
$x = -\dfrac{4}{3}$ or $x = 2$
The solution set is $\left\{ -\dfrac{4}{3}, 2 \right\}$.

9. $3x^2 + 12x = 0$
$3x(x + 4) = 0$
$3x = 0$ or $x + 4 = 0$
$x = 0$ or $x = -4$
The solution set is $\{-4, 0\}$.

11. $2x(x - 3) = 5x^2 - 7x$
$2x^2 - 6x - 5x^2 + 7x = 0$
$-3x^2 + x = 0$
$x(-3x + 1) = 0$
$x = 0$ or $-3x + 1 = 0$
           $-3x = -1$
             $x = \dfrac{1}{3}$
The solution set is $\left\{ 0, \dfrac{1}{3} \right\}$.

13. $7 - 7x = (3x + 2)(x - 1)$
$7 - 7x = 3x^2 - x - 2$
$7 - 7x - 3x^2 + x + 2 = 0$
$-3x^2 - 6x + 9 = 0$
$-3(x + 3)(x - 1) = 0$
$x + 3 = 0$ or $x - 1 = 0$
$x = -3$ or $x = 1$
The solution set is $\{-3, 1\}$.

15. $3x^2 = 27$
$x^2 = 9$
$x = \pm\sqrt{9} = \pm 3$
The solution set is $\{-3, 3\}$.

17. $5x^2 + 1 = 51$
$5x^2 = 50$
$x^2 = 10$
$x = \pm\sqrt{10}$
The solution set is $\left\{ -\sqrt{10}, \sqrt{10} \right\}$.

19. $(x + 2)^2 = 25$
$x + 2 = \pm\sqrt{25} = \pm 5$
$x = -2 \pm 5$
The solution set is $\{-7, 3\}$.

21. $(3x + 2)^2 = 9$
$3x + 2 = \pm\sqrt{9} = \pm 3$
$3x + 2 = -3$ or $3x + 2 = 3$
$3x = -5$ $3x = 1$
$x = -\dfrac{5}{3}$ or $x = \dfrac{1}{3}$
The solution set is $\left\{ -\dfrac{5}{3}, \dfrac{1}{3} \right\}$.

23. $(5x - 1)^2 = 7$
$5x - 1 = \pm\sqrt{7}$
$5x = 1 \pm \sqrt{7}$

$$x = \frac{1 \pm \sqrt{7}}{5}$$

The solution set is $\left\{ \frac{1 - \sqrt{7}}{5}, \frac{1 + \sqrt{7}}{5} \right\}$.

25. $(3x - 4)^2 = 8$

$3x - 4 = \pm\sqrt{8} = \pm 2\sqrt{2}$

$3x = 4 \pm 2\sqrt{2}$

$x = \frac{4 \pm 2\sqrt{2}}{3}$

The solution set is $\left\{ \frac{4 - 2\sqrt{2}}{3}, \frac{4 + 2\sqrt{2}}{3} \right\}$.

27. $x^2 + 12x$

$\left(\frac{12}{2} \right)^2 = 6^2 = 36$

$x^2 + 12x + 36 = (x + 6)^2$

29. $x^2 - 10x$

$\left(\frac{10}{2} \right)^2 = 5^2 = 25$

$x^2 - 10x + 25 = (x - 5)^2$

31. $x^2 + 3x$

$\left(\frac{3}{2} \right)^2 = \frac{9}{4}$

$x^2 + 3x + \frac{9}{4} = \left(x + \frac{3}{2} \right)^2$

33. $x^2 - 7x$

$\left(\frac{7}{2} \right)^2 = \frac{49}{4}$

$x^2 - 7x + \frac{49}{4} = \left(x - \frac{7}{2} \right)^2$

35. $x^2 - \frac{2}{3}x$

$\left(\frac{\frac{2}{3}}{2} \right)^2 = \left(\frac{1}{3} \right)^2 = \frac{1}{9}$

$x^2 - \frac{2}{3}x + \frac{1}{9} = \left(x - \frac{1}{3} \right)^2$

37. $x^2 - \frac{1}{3}x$

$\left(\frac{\frac{1}{3}}{2} \right)^2 = \left(\frac{1}{6} \right)^2 = \frac{1}{36}$

$x^2 - \frac{1}{3}x + \frac{1}{36} = \left(x - \frac{1}{6} \right)^2$

39. $x^2 + 6x = 7$

$x^2 + 6x + 9 = 7 + 9$

$(x + 3)^2 = 16$

$x + 3 = \pm 4$

$x = -3 \pm 4$

The solution set is $\{-7, 1\}$.

41. $x^2 - 2x = 2$

$x^2 - 2x + 1 = 2 + 1$

$(x - 1)^2 = 3$

$x - 1 = \pm\sqrt{3}$

$x = 1 \pm \sqrt{3}$

The solution set is $\left\{ 1 + \sqrt{3}, \ 1 - \sqrt{3} \right\}$.

43.

$$x^2 - 6x - 11 = 0$$
$$x^2 - 6x = 11$$
$$x^2 - 6x + 9 = 11 + 9$$
$$(x - 3)^2 = 20$$
$$x - 3 = \pm\sqrt{20}$$
$$x = 3 \pm 2\sqrt{5}$$

The solution set is $\left\{3 + 2\sqrt{5}, \ 3 - 2\sqrt{5}\right\}$.

45.

$$x^2 + 4x + 1 = 0$$
$$x^2 + 4x = -1$$
$$x^2 + 4x + 4 = -1 + 4$$
$$(x + 2)^2 = 3$$
$$x + 2 = \pm\sqrt{3}$$
$$x = -2 \pm \sqrt{3}$$

The solution set is $\left\{-2 + \sqrt{3}, \ -2 - \sqrt{3}\right\}$.

47. $x^2 + 3x - 1 = 0$

$$x^2 + 3x = 1$$
$$x^2 + 3x + \frac{9}{4} = 1 + \frac{9}{4}$$
$$\left(x + \frac{3}{2}\right)^2 = \frac{13}{4}$$
$$x + \frac{3}{2} = \pm\frac{\sqrt{13}}{2}$$
$$x = \frac{-3 \pm \sqrt{13}}{2}$$

The solution set is $\left\{\dfrac{-3 + \sqrt{13}}{2}, \ \dfrac{-3 - \sqrt{13}}{2}\right\}$.

49. $2x^2 - 7x + 3 = 0$

$$x^2 - \frac{7}{2}x + \frac{3}{2} = 0$$
$$x^2 - \frac{7}{2}x = \frac{-3}{2}$$
$$x^2 - \frac{7}{2}x + \frac{49}{16} = -\frac{3}{2} + \frac{49}{16}$$
$$\left(x - \frac{7}{4}\right)^2 = \frac{25}{16}$$
$$x - \frac{7}{4} = \pm\frac{5}{4}$$
$$x = \frac{7}{4} \pm \frac{5}{4}$$

The solution set is $\left\{\dfrac{1}{2}, \ 3\right\}$.

51. $4x^2 - 4x - 1 = 0$

$$4x^2 - 4x - 1 = 0$$
$$x^2 - x - \frac{1}{4} = 0$$
$$x^2 - x = \frac{1}{4}$$
$$x^2 - x + \frac{1}{4} = \frac{1}{4} + \frac{1}{4}$$
$$\left(x - \frac{1}{2}\right)^2 = \frac{2}{4}$$
$$x - \frac{1}{2} = \frac{\pm\sqrt{2}}{2}$$
$$x = \frac{1 \pm \sqrt{2}}{2}$$

The solution set is $\left\{\dfrac{1 + \sqrt{2}}{2}, \ \dfrac{1 - \sqrt{2}}{2}\right\}$.

53. $3x^2 - 2x - 2 = 0$

$$x^2 - \frac{2}{3}x - \frac{2}{3} = 0$$

$$x^2 - \frac{2}{3}x = \frac{2}{3}$$

$$x^2 - \frac{2}{3}x + \frac{1}{9} = \frac{2}{3} + \frac{1}{9}$$

$$\left(x - \frac{1}{3}\right)^2 = \frac{7}{9}$$

$$x - \frac{1}{3} = \frac{\pm\sqrt{7}}{3}$$

$$x = \frac{1 \pm \sqrt{7}}{3}$$

The solution set is $\left\{ \dfrac{1+\sqrt{7}}{3},\ \dfrac{1-\sqrt{7}}{3} \right\}$.

55. $x^2 + 8x + 15 = 0$

$$x = \frac{-8 \pm \sqrt{8^2 - 4(1)(15)}}{2(1)}$$

$$x = \frac{-8 \pm \sqrt{64 - 60}}{2}$$

$$x = \frac{-8 \pm \sqrt{4}}{2}$$

$$x = \frac{-8 \pm 2}{2}$$

The solution set is $\{-5,\ -3\}$.

57.

$$x^2 + 5x + 3 = 0$$

$$x = \frac{-5 \pm \sqrt{5^2 - 4(1)(3)}}{2(1)}$$

$$x = \frac{-5 \pm \sqrt{25 - 12}}{2}$$

$$x = \frac{-5 \pm \sqrt{13}}{2}$$

The solution set is $\left\{ \dfrac{-5+\sqrt{13}}{2},\ \dfrac{-5-\sqrt{13}}{2} \right\}$.

59.

$$3x^2 - 3x - 4 = 0$$

$$x = \frac{3 \pm \sqrt{(-3)^2 - 4(3)(-4)}}{2(3)}$$

$$x = \frac{3 \pm \sqrt{9 + 48}}{6}$$

$$x = \frac{3 \pm \sqrt{57}}{6}$$

The solution set is $\left\{ \dfrac{3+\sqrt{57}}{6},\ \dfrac{3-\sqrt{57}}{6} \right\}$

61.

$$4x^2 = 2x + 7$$

$$4x^2 - 2x - 7 = 0$$

$$x = \frac{2 \pm \sqrt{(-2)^2 - 4(4)(-7)}}{2(4)}$$

$$x = \frac{2 \pm \sqrt{4 + 112}}{8}$$

$$x = \frac{2 \pm \sqrt{116}}{8}$$

$$x = \frac{2 \pm 2\sqrt{29}}{8}$$

$$x = \frac{1 \pm \sqrt{29}}{4}$$

The solution set is $\left\{ \dfrac{1+\sqrt{29}}{4}, \dfrac{1-\sqrt{29}}{4} \right\}$.

63. $x^2 - 6x + 10 = 0$

$$x = \frac{6 \pm \sqrt{(-6)^2 - 4(1)(10)}}{2(1)}$$

$$x = \frac{6 \pm \sqrt{36 - 40}}{2}$$

$$x = \frac{6 \pm \sqrt{-4}}{2}$$

$$x = \frac{6 \pm 2i}{2}$$

$$x = 3 \pm i$$

The solution set is $\left\{ 3+i,\ 3-i \right\}$.

65. $x^2 - 4x - 5 = 0$

$(-4)^2 - 4(1)(-5)$

$= 16 + 20$

$= 36$; 2 unequal real solutions

67. $2x^2 - 11x + 3 = 0$

$(-11)^2 - 4(2)(3)$

$= 121 - 24$

$= 97$; 2 unequal real solutions

69. $x^2 - 2x + 1 = 0$

$(-2)^2 - 4(1)(1)$

$= 4 - 4$

$= 0$; 1 real solution

71. $x^2 - 3x - 7 = 0$

$(-3)^2 - 4(1)(-7)$

$= 9 + 28$

$= 37$; 2 unequal real solutions

73.

$$2x^2 - x = 1$$

$$2x^2 - x - 1 = 0$$

$$(2x + 1)(x - 1) = 0$$

$$2x + 1 = 0 \text{ or } x - 1 = 0$$

$$2x = -1$$

$$x = -\frac{1}{2} \text{ or } x = 1$$

The solution set is $\left\{ -\dfrac{1}{2},\ 1 \right\}$.

75.

$$5x^2 + 2 = 11x$$

$$5x^2 - 11x + 2 = 0$$

$$(5x - 1)(x - 2) = 0$$

$$5x - 1 = 0 \text{ or } x - 2 = 0$$

$$5x = 1$$

$$x = \frac{1}{5} \text{ or } x = 2$$

The solution set is $\left\{ \dfrac{1}{5},\ 2 \right\}$.

77. $3x^2 = 60$

$$x^2 = 20$$

$$x = \pm\sqrt{20}$$

$$x = \pm 2\sqrt{5}$$

The solution set is $\left\{ -2\sqrt{5},\ 2\sqrt{5} \right\}$.

79. $x^2 - 2x = 1$

$$x^2 - 2x + 1 = 1 + 1$$

$$(x - 1)^2 = 2$$

$$x - 1 = \pm\sqrt{2}$$

$$x = 1 \pm \sqrt{2}$$

The solution set is $\left\{ 1+\sqrt{2},\ 1-\sqrt{2} \right\}$.

81. $(2x+3)(x+4)=1$

$$2x^2+8x+3x+12=1$$

$$2x^2+11x+11=0$$

$$x=\frac{-11\pm\sqrt{11^2-4(2)(11)}}{2(2)}$$

$$x=\frac{-11\pm\sqrt{121-88}}{4}$$

$$x=\frac{-11\pm\sqrt{33}}{4}$$

The solution set is $\left\{\dfrac{-11+\sqrt{33}}{4},\ \dfrac{-11-\sqrt{33}}{4}\right\}$.

83. $(3x-4)^2=16$

$$3x-4=\pm\sqrt{16}$$

$$3x-4=\pm4$$

$$3x=4\pm4$$

$$3x=8 \text{ or } 3x=0$$

$$x=\frac{8}{3} \text{ or } x=0$$

The solution set is $\left\{0,\ \dfrac{8}{3}\right\}$.

85. $3x^2-12x+12=0$

$$x^2-4x+4=0$$

$$(x-2)(x-2)=0$$

$$x-2=0$$

$$x=2$$

The solution set is $\{2\}$.

87. $4x^2-16=0$

$$4x^2=16$$

$$x^2=4$$

$$x=\pm2$$

The solution set is $\left\{-2,\ 2\right\}$.

89. $x^2-6x+13=0$

$$x^2-6x=-13$$

$$x^2-6x+9=-13+9$$

$$(x-3)^2=-4$$

$$x-3=\pm2i$$

$$x=3\pm2i$$

The solution set is $\left\{3+2i,\ 3-2i\right\}$.

91.

$$x^2=4x-7$$

$$x^2-4x=-7$$

$$x^2-4x+4=-7+4$$

$$(x-2)^2=-3$$

$$x-2=\pm i\sqrt{3}$$

$$x=2\pm i\sqrt{3}$$

The solution set is $\left\{2+i\sqrt{3},\ 2-i\sqrt{3}\right\}$.

93. $2x^2-7x=0$

$$x(2x-7)=0$$

$$x=0 \text{ or } 2x-7=0$$

$$2x=7$$

$$x=0 \text{ or } x=\frac{7}{2}$$

The solution set is $\left\{0,\ \dfrac{7}{2}\right\}$.

95.

$$\frac{1}{x}+\frac{1}{x+2}=\frac{1}{3};x\neq 0,-2$$

$$3x+6+3x=x^2+2x$$

$$0=x^2-4x-6$$

$$x=\frac{-(-4)\pm\sqrt{(-4)^2-4(1)(-6)}}{2(1)}$$

$$x=\frac{4\pm\sqrt{16+24}}{2}$$

$$x=\frac{4\pm\sqrt{40}}{2}$$

$$x=\frac{4\pm2\sqrt{10}}{2}$$

$$x=2\pm\sqrt{10}$$

The solution set is $\{2+\sqrt{10},\ 2-\sqrt{10}\}$.

97.

$$\frac{2x}{x-3}+\frac{6}{x+3}=\frac{28}{x^2-9};x\neq 3,-3$$

$$2x(x+3)+6(x-3)=28$$

$$2x^2+6x+6x-18=28$$

$$2x^2+12x-46=0$$

$$x^2+6x-23=0$$

$$x=\frac{-(6)\pm\sqrt{(6)^2-4(1)(-23)}}{2(1)}$$

$$x=\frac{-6\pm\sqrt{36+92}}{2}$$

$$x=\frac{-6\pm\sqrt{128}}{2}$$

$$x=\frac{-6\pm8\sqrt{2}}{2}$$

$$x=-3\pm4\sqrt{2}$$

The solution set is $\{-3+4\sqrt{2},\ -3-4\sqrt{2}\}$.

99.

$$10=0.013x^2-1.19x+28.24$$

$$0=0.013x^2-1.19x+18.24$$

$$x=\frac{-(-1.19)\pm\sqrt{(-1.19)^2-4(.013)(18.24)}}{2(.013)}$$

$$x=\frac{1.19\pm\sqrt{.46762}}{.026}$$

$$x=\frac{1.19\pm.6838}{.026}$$

$$x=\frac{1.19+.6838}{.026}\qquad x=\frac{1.19-.6838}{.026}$$

$$x=72\qquad\qquad x=19$$

19 and 72 year olds are expected to be involved in 10 fatal crashes per 100 million miles driven.

101.

$$27=-\frac{1}{2}x^2+4x+19$$

$$54=-x^2+8x+38$$

$$x^2-8x-16=0$$

$$(x-4)(x-4)=0$$

$$x=4$$

$$1990+4=1994$$

In 1994, 27 million people received food stamps.

103. $(4, 27)$ is the graph's highest point. The greatest number of participants was 27 million in 1994.

105.

$$740=2x^2+22x+320$$

$$0=2x^2+22x-420$$

$$0=x^2+11x-210$$

$$0=(x+21)(x-10)$$

$$x=-21\qquad x=10$$

$1980+10=1990$ In 1990, there were 740 thousand inmates in U.S. federal and state prisons.

107.
$$90^2 + 90^2 = x^2$$
$$8100 + 8100 = x^2$$
$$16200 = x^2$$
$$x \approx \pm 127.28$$
The distance is 127.28 feet.

109.
$$15^2 + 8^2 = x^2$$
$$225 + 64 = x^2$$
$$289 = x^2$$
$$x = \pm 17$$
$$17 \times 2 = 34$$
The total length is 34 feet.

111. Let x = width
$$x + 5 = \text{length}$$
$$x(x + 5) = 300$$
$$x^2 + 5x = 300$$
$$x^2 + 5x - 300 = 0$$
$$(x + 20)(x - 15) = 0$$
$$x + 20 = 0 \quad x - 15 = 0$$
$$x = -20 \quad\quad x = 15$$
The width is 15 feet, the length is 20 feet.

113.
$$x(x)(2) = 200$$
$$2x^2 = 200$$
$$x^2 = 100$$
$$x = \pm 10$$
The length and width are 10 inches.

129. a. False;
$$(2x - 3)^2 = 25$$
$$2x - 3 = \pm 5$$

b. False;
Consider $x^2 = 0$, then $x = 0$ is the only distinct solution.

c. True

115.
$$x(20 - 2x) = 13$$
$$20x - 2x^2 = 13$$
$$0 = 2x^2 - 20x + 13$$
$$x = \frac{-(-20) \pm \sqrt{(-20)^2 - 4(2)(13)}}{2(2)}$$
$$x = \frac{20 \pm \sqrt{296}}{4}$$
$$x = \frac{10 \pm 17.2}{4}$$
$$x = 9.3, 0.7$$
9.3 in and 0.7 in

117.
$$(10 + 2x)(16 + 2x) = 280$$
$$160 + 52x + 4x^2 = 280$$
$$4x^2 + 52x - 120 = 0$$
$$x^2 + 13x - 30 = 0$$
$$(x + 15)(x - 2) = 0$$
$$x = -154 \quad\quad x = 2$$
2 inches

119.–127. Answers may vary.

d. False;

$$ax^2 + c = 0$$

$$x = \frac{0 \pm \sqrt{0 - 4ac}}{2a} = \frac{2i\sqrt{ac}}{2a} = \frac{i\sqrt{ac}}{a}$$

(c) is true.

131. $(x + 3)(x - 5) = 0$

$$x^2 - 5x + 3x - 15 = 0$$

$$x^2 - 2x - 15 = 0$$

133. $\left(12 + 2x\right)\left(8 + 2x\right) - 96 = 120$

$$96 + 40x + 4x^2 - 96 = 120$$

$$4x^2 + 40x - 120 = 0$$

$$x^2 + 10x - 30 = 0$$

$$x = \frac{-10 \pm \sqrt{(-10)^2 - 4(1)(-30)}}{2(1)}$$

$$x = \frac{-10 \pm \sqrt{220}}{2}$$

$$x = \frac{-10 \pm 14.8}{2}$$

$$x = 2.4 \qquad x = -12.4$$

The pool can be made with 2.4 in border.

Section 1.6

Check Point Exercises

1. $$4x^4 = 12x^2$$
    $$4x^4 - 12x^2 = 0$$
    $$4x^2(x^2 - 3) = 0$$
    $$4x^2 = 0 \quad \text{or} \quad x^2 - 3 = 0$$
    $$x^2 = 0 \qquad\qquad x^2 = 3$$
    $$x = \pm\sqrt{0} \qquad\quad x = \pm\sqrt{3}$$
    $$x = 0 \qquad\qquad x = \pm\sqrt{3}$$
    The solution set is $\left\{-\sqrt{3},\ 0,\ \sqrt{3}\right\}$.

2. $$2x^3 + 3x^2 = 8x + 12$$
    $$x^2(2x + 3) - 4(2x + 3) = 10$$
    $$(2x + 3)(x^2 - 4) = 0$$
    $$2x + 3 = 0 \quad \text{or} \quad x^2 - 4 = 0$$
    $$2x = -3 \qquad\qquad x^2 = 4$$
    $$x = -\frac{3}{2} \qquad\qquad x = \pm 2$$
    The solution set is $\left\{-2,\ -\dfrac{3}{2},\ 2\right\}$.

3. $$\sqrt{6x + 7} - x = 2$$
    $$\sqrt{6x + 7} = x + 2$$
    $$6x + 7 = (x + 2)^2$$
    $$6x + 7 = x^2 + 4x + 4$$
    $$0 = x^2 - 2x - 3$$
    $$0 = (x - 3)(x + 1)$$
    $$x - 3 = 0 \quad \text{or} \quad x + 1 = 0$$
    $$x = 3 \qquad\qquad x = -1$$

Check 3:
$$\sqrt{6(3) + 7} - 3 = 2$$
$$\sqrt{18 + 7} - 3 = 2$$
$$\sqrt{25} - 3 = 2$$
$$5 - 3 = 2$$
$$2 = 2$$

Check 1:
$$\sqrt{6(-1) + 7} - (-1) = 2$$
$$\sqrt{-6 + 7} + 1 = 2$$
$$\sqrt{1} + 1 = 2$$
$$1 + 1 = 2$$
$$2 = 2$$
The solution set is $\{-1,\ 3\}$.

4.

$$\sqrt{x + 5} - \sqrt{x - 3} = 2$$
$$\sqrt{x + 5} = \sqrt{x - 3} + 2$$
$$x + 5 = \left(\sqrt{x - 3} + 2\right)^2$$
$$x + 5 = x - 3 + 4\sqrt{x - 3} + 4$$
$$x + 5 = x + 1 + 4\sqrt{x - 3}$$
$$4 = 4\sqrt{x - 3}$$
$$1 = \sqrt{x - 3}$$
$$1 = x - 3$$
$$4 = x$$

Check:
$$\sqrt{4 + 5} - \sqrt{4 - 3} = 2$$
$$\sqrt{9} - \sqrt{1} = 2$$
$$3 - 1 = 2$$
$$2 = 2$$
The solution set is $\{4\}$.

5. a. $5x^{3/2} - 25 = 0$

$$5x^{3/2} = 25$$
$$x^{3/2} = 5$$
$$x = 5^{2/3}$$

Check:

$$5\left(5^{2/3}\right)^{3/2} - 25 = 0$$
$$5(5) - 25 = 0$$
$$25 - 25 = 0$$
$$0 = 0$$

The solution set is $\left\{5^{2/3}\right\}$.

b.
$$x^{\frac{2}{3}} - 8 = -4$$
$$x^{2/3} = 4$$
$$\left(x^{2/3}\right)^{3/2} = 4^{3/2} \quad \text{or}$$
$$x = \left(2^2\right)^{3/2}$$
$$x = 2^3 \qquad x = (-2)^3$$
$$x = 8 \qquad x = -8$$

The solution set is $\{-8, 8\}$.

6. $x^4 - 5x^2 + 6 = 0$

$$\left(x^2\right)^2 - 5x^2 + 6 = 0$$

Let $t = x^2$.

$$t^2 - 5t + 6 = 0$$
$$(t - 3)(t - 2) = 0$$
$$t - 3 = 0 \qquad \text{or} \quad t - 2 = 0$$
$$t = 3 \qquad \text{or} \qquad t = 2$$
$$x^2 = 3 \qquad \text{or} \qquad x^2 = 2$$
$$x = \pm\sqrt{3} \quad \text{or} \qquad x = \pm\sqrt{2}$$

The solution set is $\left\{-\sqrt{3}, \ \sqrt{3}, \ -\sqrt{2}, \ \sqrt{2}\right\}$.

7. $3x^{2/3} - 11x^{1/3} - 4 = 0$

Let $t = x^{1/3}$.

$$3t^2 - 11t - 4 = 0$$
$$(3t + 1)(t - 4) = 0$$
$$3t + 1 = 0 \quad \text{or} \quad t - 4 = 0$$
$$3t = -1$$
$$t = -\frac{1}{3} \qquad\qquad t = 4$$
$$x^{1/3} = -\frac{1}{3} \qquad\qquad x^{1/3} = 4$$
$$x = \left(-\frac{1}{3}\right)^3 \qquad\qquad x = 4^3$$
$$x = -\frac{1}{27} \qquad\qquad x = 64$$

The solution set is $\left\{-\dfrac{1}{27}, \ 64\right\}$.

8. $|2x - 1| = 5$

$$2x - 1 = 5 \quad \text{or} \quad 2x - 1 = -5$$
$$2x = 6 \qquad\qquad 2x = -4$$
$$x = 3 \qquad\qquad x = -2$$

The solution set is $\{-2, 3\}$.

Exercise Set 1.6

1.
$$3x^4 - 48x^2 = 0$$
$$3x^2(x^2 - 16) = 0$$
$$3x^2(x + 4)(x - 4) = 0$$
$$3x^2 = 0 \quad x + 4 = 0 \quad x - 4 = 0$$
$$x^2 = 0 \qquad x = -4 \qquad x = 4$$
$$x = 0$$

The solution set is $\{0, -4, 4\}$.

3.
$$3x^3 + 2x^2 = 12x + 8$$
$$3x^3 + 2x^2 - 12x - 8 = 0$$
$$x^2(3x + 2) - 4(3x + 2) = 0$$
$$(3x + 2)(x^2 - 4) = 0$$
$$3x + 2 = 0 \qquad x^2 - 4 = 0$$
$$3x = -2 \qquad x^2 = 4$$
$$x = -\frac{2}{3} \qquad x = \pm 2$$
The solution set is $\left\{ -\frac{2}{3}, 2, -2 \right\}$.

5.
$$2x - 3 = 8x^3 - 12x^2$$
$$8x^3 - 12x^2 - 2x + 3 = 0$$
$$4x^2(2x - 3) - (2x - 3) = 0$$
$$(2x - 3)(4x^2 - 1) = 0$$
$$2x - 3 = 0 \qquad 4x^2 - 1 = 0$$
$$2x = 3 \qquad 4x^2 = 1$$
$$x^2 = \frac{1}{4}$$
$$x = \frac{3}{2} \qquad x = \pm\frac{1}{2}$$
The solution set is $\left\{ \frac{3}{2}, \frac{1}{2}, -\frac{1}{2} \right\}$.

7.
$$4y^3 - 2 = y - 8y^2$$
$$4y^3 + 8y^2 - y - 2 = 0$$
$$4y^2(y + 2) - (y + 2) = 0$$
$$(y + 2)(4y^2 - 1) = 0$$
$$y + 2 = 0 \qquad 4y^2 - 1 = 0$$
$$4y^2 = 1$$
$$y^2 = \frac{1}{4}$$
$$y = -2 \qquad y = \pm\frac{1}{2}$$
The solution set is $\left\{ -2, \frac{1}{2}, -\frac{1}{2} \right\}$.

9.
$$2x^4 = 16x$$
$$2x^4 - 16x = 0$$
$$2x\left(x^3 - 8\right) = 0$$
$$2x = 0 \qquad\qquad x^3 - 8 = 0$$
$$x = 0 \qquad (x - 2)(x^2 + 2x + 2) = 0$$
$$x - 2 = 0 \qquad x^2 + 2x + 4 = 0$$
$$x = 2 \qquad x = \frac{-2 \pm \sqrt{2^2 - 4(1)(4)}}{2(1)}$$
$$x = \frac{-2 \pm \sqrt{-12}}{2}$$
$$x = \frac{-2 \pm 2i\sqrt{3}}{2}$$
$$x = -1 \pm i\sqrt{3}$$
The solution set is $\left\{ 0, 2, -1 \pm i\sqrt{3} \right\}$..

11.
$$\sqrt{3x + 18} = x$$
$$3x + 18 = x^2$$
$$x^2 - 3x - 18 = 0$$
$$(x + 3)(x - 6) = 0$$
$$x + 3 = 0 \qquad x - 6 = 0$$
$$x = -3 \qquad x = 6$$
$$\sqrt{3(-3) + 18} = -3 \qquad \sqrt{3(6) + 18} = 6$$
$$\sqrt{-9 + 18} = -3 \qquad \sqrt{18 + 18} = 6$$
$$\sqrt{9} = -3 \text{ False} \qquad \sqrt{36} = 6$$
The solution set is $\{6\}$.

13.
$$\sqrt{x + 3} = x - 3$$
$$x + 3 = x^2 - 6x + 9$$
$$x^2 - 7x + 6 = 0$$
$$(x - 1)(x - 6) = 0$$
$$x - 1 = 0 \qquad x - 6 = 0$$
$$x = 1 \qquad x = 6$$

$$\sqrt{1+3} = 1-3 \qquad \sqrt{6+3} = 6-3$$
$$\sqrt{4} = -2 \qquad \text{False} \quad \sqrt{9} = 3$$

The solution set is {6}.

15.

$$\sqrt{2x+13} = x+7$$
$$2x+13 = (x+7)^2$$
$$2x+13 = x^2 + 14x + 49$$
$$x^2 + 12x + 36 = 0$$
$$(x+6)^2 = 0$$
$$x+6 = 0$$
$$x = -6$$
$$\sqrt{2(-6)+13} = -6+7$$
$$\sqrt{-12+13} = 1$$
$$\sqrt{1} = 1$$

The solution set is {–6}.

17.

$$x - \sqrt{2x+5} = 5$$
$$x - 5 = \sqrt{2x+5}$$
$$(x-5)^2 = 2x+5$$
$$x^2 - 10x + 25 = 2x + 5$$
$$x^2 - 12x + 20 = 0$$
$$(x-2)(x-10) = 0$$
$$x-2 = 0 \quad x-10 = 0$$
$$x = 2 \qquad x = 10$$
$$2 - \sqrt{2(2)+5} = 5 \quad 10 - \sqrt{2(10)+5} = 5$$
$$2 - \sqrt{9} = 5 \qquad 10 - \sqrt{25} = 5$$
$$2 - 3 = 5 \quad \text{False} \quad 10 - 5 = 5$$

The solution set is {10}.

19.

$$\sqrt{3x} + 10 = x + 4$$
$$\sqrt{3x} = x - 6$$
$$3x = (x-6)^2$$
$$3x = x^2 - 12x + 36$$
$$x^2 - 15x + 36 = 0$$
$$(x-12)(x-3) = 0$$
$$x - 12 = 0 \quad x - 3 = 0$$
$$x = 12 \qquad x = 3$$
$$\sqrt{3(12)} + 10 = 12 + 4$$
$$\sqrt{36} + 10 = 16$$
$$6 + 10 = 16$$
$$\sqrt{3(3)} + 10 = 3 + 4$$
$$\sqrt{9} + 10 = 7$$
$$3 + 10 = 7 \quad \text{False}$$

The solution set is {12}.

21. $\sqrt{x+8} - \sqrt{x-4} = 2$

$$\sqrt{x+8} = \sqrt{x-4} + 2$$
$$x + 8 = (\sqrt{x-4} + 2)^2$$
$$x + 8 = x - 4 + 4\sqrt{x-4} + 4$$
$$x + 8 = x + 4\sqrt{x-4}$$
$$8 = 4\sqrt{x-4}$$
$$2 = \sqrt{x-4}$$
$$4 = x - 4$$
$$x = 8$$
$$\sqrt{8+8} - \sqrt{8-4} = 2$$
$$\sqrt{16} - \sqrt{4} = 2$$
$$4 - 2 = 2$$

The solution set is {8}.

23.

$$\sqrt{x-5} - \sqrt{x-8} = 3$$
$$\sqrt{x-5} = \sqrt{x-8} + 3$$
$$x-5 = (\sqrt{x-8} + 3)^2$$
$$x-5 = x-8 + 6\sqrt{x-8} + 9$$
$$x-5 = x+1 + 6\sqrt{x-8}$$
$$-6 = 6\sqrt{x-8}$$
$$-1 = \sqrt{x-8}$$
$$1 = x-8$$
$$x = 9$$
$$\sqrt{9-5} - \sqrt{9-8} = 3$$
$$\sqrt{4} - \sqrt{1} = 3$$
$$2 - 1 = 3 \text{ False}$$

The solution set is the empty set, $\varnothing$.

25. $\sqrt{2x+3} + \sqrt{x-2} = 2$
$$\sqrt{2x+3} = 2 - \sqrt{x-2}$$
$$2x+3 = (2 - \sqrt{x-2})^2$$
$$2x+3 = 4 - 4\sqrt{x-2} + x-2$$
$$x+1 = -4\sqrt{x-2}$$
$$(x+1)^2 = 16(x-2)$$
$$x^2 + 2x+1 = 16x - 32$$
$$x^2 - 14x + 33 = 0$$
$$(x-11)(x-3) = 0$$
$$x-11 = 0 \quad x-3 = 0$$
$$x = 11 \qquad x = 3$$

$$\sqrt{2(11)+3} + \sqrt{11-2} = 2$$
$$\sqrt{22+3} + \sqrt{9} = 2$$
$$5 + 3 = 2 \text{ False}$$
$$\sqrt{2(3)+3} + \sqrt{3-2} = 2$$
$$\sqrt{6+3} + \sqrt{1} = 2$$
$$3 + 1 = 2 \text{ False}$$

The solution set is the empty set, $\varnothing$.

27.

$$\sqrt{3\sqrt{x+1}} = \sqrt{3x-5}$$
$$3\sqrt{x+1} = 3x-5$$
$$9(x+1) = 9x^2 - 30x + 25$$
$$9x^2 - 39x + 16 = 0$$
$$x = \frac{39 \pm \sqrt{945}}{18} = \frac{13 \pm \sqrt{105}}{6}$$

Check proposed solutions.

The solution set is $\left\{ \dfrac{13 + \sqrt{105}}{6} \right\}$.

29. $x^{3/2} = 8$
$$(x^{3/2})^{2/3} = 8^{2/3}$$
$$x = \sqrt[3]{8}^2$$
$$x = 2^2$$
$$x = 4$$
$$4^{3/2} = 8$$
$$\sqrt{4}^3 = 8$$
$$2^3 = 8$$

The solution set is {4}.

31.

$$(x-4)^{3/2} = 27$$

$$((x-4)^{3/2})^{2/3} = 27^{2/3}$$

$$x-4 = \sqrt[3]{27}^{\,2}$$

$$x-4 = 3^2$$

$$x-4 = 9$$

$$x = 13$$

$$(13-4)^{3/2} = 27$$

$$9^{3/2} = 27$$

$$\sqrt{9}^{\,3} = 27$$

$$3^3 = 27$$

The solution set is $\{13\}$.

33.

$$6x^{5/2} - 12 = 0$$

$$6x^{5/2} = 12$$

$$x^{5/2} = 2$$

$$(x^{5/2})^{2/5} = 2^{2/5}$$

$$x = \sqrt[5]{2^2}$$

$$x = \sqrt[5]{4}$$

$$6(\sqrt[5]{4})^{5/2} - 12 = 0$$

$$6(4^{1/5})^{5/2} - 12 = 0$$

$$6(4^{1/2}) - 12 = 0$$

$$6(2) - 12 = 0$$

The solution set is $\left\{\sqrt[5]{4}\right\}$.

35.

$$\left(x-4\right)^{2/3} = 16$$

$$\left[\left(x-4\right)^{2/3}\right]^{3/2} = \left(16\right)^{3/2}$$

$$x-4 = \left(2^4\right)^{3/2}$$

$$x-4 = 4^3 \qquad x-4 = (-4)^3$$

$$x-4 = 64 \qquad x-4 = -64$$

$$x = 68 \qquad x = -60$$

The solution set is $\{-60, 68\}$.

37.

$$(x^2 - x - 4)^{3/4} - 2 = 6$$

$$(x^2 - x - 4)^{3/4} = 8$$

$$((x^2 - x - 4)^{3/4})^{4/3} = 8^{4/3}$$

$$x^2 - x - 4 = \sqrt[3]{8}^{\,4}$$

$$x^2 - x - 4 = 2^4$$

$$x^2 - x - 4 = 16$$

$$x^2 - x - 20 = 0$$

$$(x-5)(x+4) = 0$$

$$x - 5 = 0 \quad x + 4 = 0$$

$$x = 5 \qquad x = -4$$

$$(5^2 - 5 - 4)^{3/4} - 2 = 6$$

$$(25 - 9)^{3/4} - 2 = 6$$

$$16^{3/4} - 2 = 6$$

$$\sqrt[4]{16}^{\,3} - 2 = 6$$

$$2^3 - 2 = 6$$

$$8 - 2 = 6$$

$$((-4)^2 - (-4) - 4)^{3/4} - 2 = 6$$

$$(16 + 4 - 4)^{3/4} - 2 = 6$$

$$16^{3/4} - 2 = 6$$

$$\sqrt[4]{16}^{\,3} - 2 = 6$$

$$2^3 - 2 = 6$$

$$8 - 2 = 6$$

The solution set is $\{5, -4\}$.

39. $x^4 - 5x^2 + 4 = 0$ let $t = x^2$

$$t^2 - 5t + 4 = 0$$

$$(t-1)(t-4) = 0$$

$$t - 1 = 0 \quad t - 4 = 0$$

$$t = 1 \qquad t = 4$$

$$x^2 = 1 \qquad x^2 = 4$$

$$x = \pm 1 \qquad x = \pm 2$$

The solution set is $\{1, -1, 2, -2\}$

41. $9x^4 = 25x^2 - 16$

$9x^4 - 25x^2 + 16 = 0$ let $t = x^2$

$9t^2 - 25t + 16 = 0$

$(9t - 16)(t - 1) = 0$

$9t - 16 = 0 \qquad t - 1 = 0$

$9t = 16 \qquad t = 1$

$t = \dfrac{16}{9} \qquad x^2 = 1$

$\qquad\qquad x = \pm 1$

$x^2 = \dfrac{16}{9}$

$x = \pm\dfrac{4}{3}$

The solution set is $\left\{1, -1, \dfrac{4}{3}, -\dfrac{4}{3}\right\}$.

43. $x - 13\sqrt{x} + 40 = 0$ \quad Let $t = \sqrt{x}$.

$t^2 - 13t + 40 = 0$

$(t - 8)(t - 5) = 0$

$t - 8 = 0 \qquad t - 5 = 0$

$t = 8 \qquad t = 5$

$\sqrt{x} = 8 \qquad \sqrt{x} = 5$

$x = 64 \qquad x = 25$

The solution set is $\{25, 64\}$.

45. $x^{-2} - x^{-1} - 20 = 0$ \quad Let $t = x^{-1}$

$t^2 - t - 20 = 0$

$(t - 5)(t + 4) = 0$

$t - 5 = 0 \quad t + 4 = 0$

$t = 5 \qquad t = -4$

$x^{-1} = 5 \quad x^{-1} = -4$

$\dfrac{1}{x} = 5 \qquad \dfrac{1}{x} = -4$

$1 = 5x \qquad 1 = -4x$

$\dfrac{1}{5} = x \qquad -\dfrac{1}{4} = x$

The solution set is $\left\{-\dfrac{1}{4}, \dfrac{1}{5}\right\}$.

47. $x^{2/3} - x^{1/3} - 6 = 0$ let $t = x^{1/3}$

$t^2 - t - 6 = 0$

$(t - 3)(t + 2) = 0$

$t - 3 = 0 \qquad t + 2 = 0$

$t = 3 \qquad t = -2$

$x^{1/3} = 3 \qquad x^{1/3} = -2$

$x = 3^3 \qquad x = (-2)^3$

$x = 27 \qquad x = -8$

The solution set is $\{27, -8\}$.

49. $x^{3/2} - 2x^{3/4} + 1 = 0$ let $t = x^{3/4}$

$t^2 - 2t + 1 = 0$

$(t - 1)(t - 1) = 0$

$t - 1 = 0$

$t = 1$

$x^{3/4} = 1$

$x = 1^{4/3}$

$x = 1$

The solution set is $\{1\}$.

51. $2x - 3x^{1/2} + 1 = 0$ let $t = x^{1/2}$

$2t^2 - 3t + 1 = 0$

$(2t - 1)(t - 1) = 0$

$2t - 1 = 0 \qquad t - 1 = 0$

$2t = 1$

$t = \dfrac{1}{2} \qquad t = 1$

$x^{1/2} = \dfrac{1}{2} \qquad x^{1/2} = 1$

$x = \left(\dfrac{1}{2}\right)^2 \qquad x = 1^2$

$x = \dfrac{1}{4} \qquad x = 1$

The solution set is $\left\{\dfrac{1}{4}, 1\right\}$.

53. $(x-5)^2 - 4(x-5) - 21 = 0$ let $t = x - 5$

$$t^2 - 4t - 21 = 0$$
$$(t+3)(t-7) = 0$$

$t + 3 = 0 \quad\quad t - 7 = 0$

$t = -3 \quad\quad\quad t = 7$

$x - 5 = -3 \quad x - 5 = 7$

$x = 2 \quad\quad\quad x = 12$

The solution set is $\{2, 12\}$.

55. $\left(x^2 - x\right)^2 - 14\left(x^2 - x\right) + 24 = 0$

Let $t = x^2 - x$.

$$t^2 - 14t + 24 = 0$$
$$(t-2)(t-12) = 0$$

$t = 2$ or $t = 12$

$x^2 - x = 2 \quad\quad$ or $\quad x^2 - x = 12$

$x^2 - x - 2 = 0 \quad\quad\quad x^2 - x - 12 = 0$

$(x-2)(x+1) = 0 \quad\quad (x-4)(x+3) = 0$

The solution set is $\{-3, -1, 2, 4\}$.

57. $\left(y - \dfrac{8}{y}\right)^2 + 5\left(y - \dfrac{8}{y}\right) - 14 = 0$

Let $t = y - \dfrac{8}{y}$.

$$t^2 + 5t - 14 = 0$$
$$(t+7)(t-2) = 0$$

$t = -7$ or $t = 2$

$y - \dfrac{8}{y} = -7 \quad\quad$ or $\quad y - \dfrac{8}{y} = 2$

$y^2 + 7y - 8 = 0 \quad\quad\quad y^2 - 2y - 8 = 0$

$(y+8)(y-1) = 0 \quad\quad (y-4)(y+2) = 0$

The solution set is $\{-8, -2, 1, 4\}$.

59. $|x| = 8$

$x = 8, x = -8$

The solution set is $\{8, -8\}$.

61. $|x-2| = 7$

$x - 2 = 7 \quad x - 2 = -7$

$x = 9 \quad\quad x = -5$

The solution set is $\{9, -5\}$.

63. $|2x - 1| = 5$

$2x - 1 = 5 \quad 2x - 1 = -5$

$2x = 6 \quad\quad 2x = -4$

$x = 3 \quad\quad\quad x = -2$

The solution set is $\{3, -2\}$.

65. $2|3x - 2| = 14$

$|3x - 2| = 7$

$3x - 2 = 7 \quad\quad 3x - 2 = -7$

$3x = 9 \quad\quad\quad 3x = -5$

$x = 3 \quad\quad\quad x = -5/3$

The solution set is $\{3, -5/3\}$

67. $7|5x| + 2 = 16$

$7|5x| = 14$

$|5x| = 2$

$5x = 2 \quad\quad\quad 5x = -2$

$x = 2/5 \quad\quad\quad x = -2/5$

The solution set is $\left\{\dfrac{2}{5}, -\dfrac{2}{5}\right\}$.

69. $|x + 1| + 5 = 3$

$|x + 1| = \_2$

No solution

The solution set is $\{\ \}$.

71. $|2x - 1| + 3 = 3$

$|2x - 1| = 0$

$2x - 1 = 0$

$2x = 1$

$x = 1/2$

The solution set is $\{1/2\}$.

73. $|3x - 1| = |x + 5|$

$3x - 1 = x + 5 \quad\quad 3x - 1 = \_x - 5$

$2x - 1 = 5 \quad\quad\quad 4x - 1 = \_5$

$2x = 6 \quad\quad\quad\quad 4x = \_4$

$x = 3 \quad\quad\quad\quad\quad x = \_1$

The solution set is $\{3, \_1\}$.

75. $x + 2\sqrt{x} - 3 = 0$ let $t = \sqrt{x}$

$t^2 + 2t - 3 = 0$

$(t-1)(t+3) = 0$

$t - 1 = 0 \quad t + 3 = 0$

$t = 1 \qquad t = -3$

$\sqrt{x} = 1 \quad \sqrt{x} = -3$

$x = 1 \qquad x = 9$

The solution set is $\{1\}$.

77.

$(x+4)^{3/2} = 8$

$x + 4 = 8^{2/3}$

$x + 4 = \sqrt[3]{8}^{\,2}$

$x + 4 = 2^2$

$x + 4 = 4$

$x = 0$

The solution set is $\{0\}$.

79. $\sqrt{4x + 15} - 2x = 0$

$\sqrt{4x + 15} = 2x$

$4x + 15 = 4x^2$

$4x^2 - 4x - 15 = 0$

$(2x - 5)(2x + 3) = 0$

$2x - 5 = 0 \quad 2x + 3 = 0$

$2x = 5 \qquad 2x = -3$

$x = \dfrac{5}{2} \qquad x = \dfrac{-3}{2}$

The solution set is $\left\{ \dfrac{5}{2} \right\}$.

81. $\left| x^2 + 2x - 36 \right| = 12$

$x^2 + 2x - 36 = 12 \quad x^2 + 2x - 36 = -12$

$x^2 + 2x - 48 = 0 \quad x^2 + 2x - 24 = 0$

$(x-6)(x+8) = 0 \quad (x+6)(x-4) = 0$

$x - 6 = 0 \quad x + 8 = 0 \quad x + 6 = 0 \quad x - 4 = 0$

$x = 6 \qquad x = -8 \qquad x = -6 \qquad x = 4$

The solution set is $\{6, -8, -6, 4\}$.

83. $x^3 - 2x^2 = x - 2$

$x^3 - 2x^2 - x + 2 = 0$

$x^2(x - 2) - (x - 2) = 0$

$(x - 2)(x^2 - 1) = 0$

$x - 2 = 0 \quad x^2 - 1 = 0$

$x = 2 \qquad x^2 = 1$

$x = \pm 1$

The solution set is $\{1, -1, 2\}$

85. $304 = 4\sqrt{x} + 280$

$24 = 4\sqrt{x}$

$6 = \sqrt{x}$

$(6)^2 = \left(\sqrt{x} \right)^2$

$36 = x$

$1982 + 36 = 2018$

The average science test score will be 304 in 2018.

87. $40000 = 5000\sqrt{100 - x}$

$8 = \sqrt{100 - x}$

$64 = 100 - x$

$x = 36$

$(36, 40000)$

40,000 people in the group will live to age 36.

89.

$365 = 0.2 x^{\frac{3}{2}}$

$1825 = x^{\frac{3}{2}}$

$(1825)^{\frac{2}{3}} = \left(x^{\frac{3}{2}} \right)^{\frac{2}{3}}$

$149 \approx x$

The earth is an average of 149 km from the sun.

91. $\sqrt{6^2 + x^2} + \sqrt{8^2 + (10 - x)^2} = 18$

$\sqrt{36 + x^2} = 18 - \sqrt{64 + 100 - 20x + x^2}$

$36 + x^2 = 324 - 36\sqrt{x^2 - 20x + 164} + x^2 - 20x + 164$

$36\sqrt{x^2 - 20x + 164} = -20x + 452$

$9\sqrt{x^2 - 20x + 164} = -5x + 113$

$81(x^2 - 20x + 164) = 25x^2 - 1130x + 12769$

$81x^2 - 1620x + 13284 = 25x^2 - 1130x + 12769$

$56x^2 - 490x + 515 = 0$

$x = \dfrac{490 \pm \sqrt{(-490)^2 - 4(56)(515)}}{2(56)}$

$x = \dfrac{490 \pm 353.19}{112}$

$x \approx 1.2 \qquad x \approx 7.5$

The point should be located approximately either 1.2 feet or 7.5 feet from the base of the 6-foot pole.

93.–99. Answers may vary.

101. $x^3 + 3x^2 - x - 3 = 0$

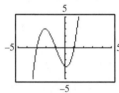

$x = -3, -1, 1$

$(-3)^3 + 3(-3)^2 - (-3) - 3 = 0$

$-27 + 27 + 3 - 3 = 0$

$(-1)^3 + 3(-1)^2 - (-1) - 3 = 0$

$-1 + 3 + 1 - 3 = 0$

$1^3 + 3(1)^2 - (1) - 3 = 0$

$1 + 3 - 1 - 3 = 0$

The solution set is $\{-3, -1, 1\}$.

103. $\sqrt{2x + 13} - x - 5 = 0$

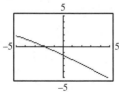

$x = -2$

$\sqrt{2(-2)+13} - (-2) - 5 = 0$

$\sqrt{-4+13} + 2 - 5 = 0$

$\sqrt{9} - 3 = 0$

$3 - 3 = 0$

The solution set is $\{-2\}$.

105. a. False;

$$\left(\sqrt{y+4} + \sqrt{y-1}\right)^2 \neq y + 4 + y - 1$$

   b. False; if $t = (x^2 - 2x)^3$, the original equation can be written as $t^3 - 5t + 6 = 0$, not a quadratic form.

   c. False; the other value may be a solution.

   d. True

   (d) is true

107. $5 - \dfrac{2}{x} = \sqrt{5 - \dfrac{2}{x}}$

   or

   $5 - \dfrac{2}{x} = 0$ $\qquad 5 - \dfrac{2}{x} = 1$

   $\qquad 5 = \dfrac{2}{x}$ $\qquad -\dfrac{2}{x} = -4$

   $\qquad 5x = 2$ $\qquad -4x = -2$

   $\qquad x = \dfrac{2}{5}$ $\qquad x = \dfrac{1}{2}$

   The solution set is $\left\{\dfrac{2}{5}, \dfrac{15}{2}\right\}$.

109. $x^{5/6} + x^{2/3} - 2x^{1/2} = 0$

   $x^{1/2}(x^{2/6} + x^{1/6} - 2) = 0$ let $t = x^{1/6}$

   $x^{1/2}(t^2 + t - 2) = 0$

   $x^{1/2} = 0 \quad t^2 + t - 2 = 0$

   $\qquad\qquad (t-1)(t+2) = 0$

   $t - 1 = 0 \quad t + 2 = 0$

   $\qquad t = 1 \qquad t = -2$

   $\qquad x^{1/6} = 1 \qquad x^{1/6} = -2$

   $\qquad x = 1^6 \qquad x = (-2)^6$

   $x = 0 \quad x = 1 \qquad x = 64$

   The solution set is $\{0, 1, 64\}$.

Section 1.7

Check Point Exercises

1. a. 

     b.

     c.

2. a. $[-2,\ 5) = \left\{x\middle|-2 \le x < 5\right\}$

     b. $[1,\ 3.5] = \left\{x\middle|1 \le x \le 3.5\right\}$

     c. $[-\infty,\ -1) = \left\{x\middle|x < -1\right\}$

3. $2 - 3x \le 5$

     $-3x \le 3$

     $x \ge -1$

     The solution set is $\left\{x\middle|x \ge -1\right\}$ or $[-1,\ \infty)$.

4. $6 - 3x \le 5x - 2$

     $8 - 3x \le 5x$

     $8 \le 8x$

     $1 \le x$

     $x \ge 1$

     The solution set is $\left\{x\middle|x \ge 1\right\}$ or $[1,\ \infty)$.

5. $1 \le 2x + 3 < 11$

     $-2 \le 2x < 8$

     $-1 \le x < 4$

     The solution set is

$\left\{x\middle|-1 \le x < 4\right\}$ or $[-1,\ 4)$.

6. $|x - 2| < 5$

     $-5 < x - 2 < 5$

     $-3 < x < 7$

     The solution set is

$\left\{x\middle|-3 < x < 7\right\}$ or $(-3,\ 7)$.

7. $|2x - 5| \ge 3$

     $2x - 5 \le -3$ or $2x - 5 \ge 3$

     $2x \le 2$ or $2x \ge 8$

     $x \le 1$ or $x \ge 4$

     The solution set is $\left\{x\middle|x \le 1 \text{ or } x \ge 4\right\}$, that

     is, all x in $(-\infty,\ 1]$ or $[4,\ \infty)$.

8. Let $x =$ the number of miles driven in a
     week.

     $260 < 80 + 0.25x$

     $180 < 0.25x$

     $720 < x$

     Driving more than 720 miles in a week
     makes Basic the better deal.

Exercise Set 1.7

1.

3.

5.

7.

9.

11.

$$-1 \qquad 4$$

13. $1 < x \le 6$

$$1 \qquad 6$$

15. $-5 \le x < 2$

$$-5 \qquad 2$$

17. $-3 \le x \le 1$

$$-3 \qquad 1$$

19. $x > 2$

$$2$$

21. $x \ge -3$

$$-3$$

23. $x < 3$

$$3$$

25. $x < 5.5$

$$5.5$$

27. $5x + 11 < 26$

$5x < 15$

$x < 3$

The solution set is $\left\{x \middle| x < 3\right\}$, or $(-\infty, 3)$.

$$3$$

29. $3x - 7 \ge 13$

$3x \ge 20$

$x \ge \dfrac{20}{3}$

The solution set is $\left\{x \middle| x > \dfrac{20}{3}\right\}$, or

$\left[\dfrac{20}{3}, \infty\right)$.

$$\frac{20}{3}$$

31. $-9x \ge 36$

$x \le -4$

The solution set is $\left\{x \middle| x \le -4\right\}$, or $\left(-\infty, -4\right]$.

$$-4$$

33. $8x - 11 \le 3x - 13$

$8x - 3x \le -13 + 11$

$5x \le -2$

$x \le -\dfrac{2}{5}$

The solution set is $\left\{x \middle| x \le -\dfrac{2}{5}\right\}$, or

$\left(-\infty, -\dfrac{2}{5}\right]$.

$$-\frac{2}{5}$$

35. $4(x + 1) + 2 \ge 3x + 6$

$4x + 4 + 2 \ge 3x + 6$

$4x + 6 \ge 3x + 6$

$4x - 3x \ge 6 - 6$

$x \ge 0$

The solution set is $\left\{x \middle| x > 0\right\}$, or $[0, \infty)$.

$$0$$

37. $2x - 11 < -3(x + 2)$

$2x - 11 < -3x - 6$

$5x < 5$

$x < 1$

The solution set is $\left\{x \middle| x < 1\right\}$, or $(-\infty, 1)$.

$$1$$

39. $1 - (x + 3) \ge 4 - 2x$

$1 - x - 3 \ge 4 - 2x$

$-x - 2 \ge 4 - 2x$

$x \geq 6$

The solution set is $\left\{x \mid x \geq 6\right\}$, or $[6, \infty)$.

41. $\dfrac{x}{4} - \dfrac{3}{5} \leq \dfrac{x}{2} + 1$

$-\dfrac{8}{5} \leq \dfrac{x}{4}$

$x \geq -\dfrac{32}{5}$

The solution set is $\left\{x \mid x \geq -\dfrac{32}{5}\right\}$, or

$\left[-\dfrac{32}{5}, \infty\right)$.

43. $1 - \dfrac{x}{2} > 4$

$-\dfrac{x}{2} > 3$

$x < -6$

The solution set is $\left\{x \mid x, -6\right\}$, or $\left(-\infty, -6\right)$.

45. $\dfrac{x-4}{6} \geq \dfrac{x-2}{9} + \dfrac{5}{18}$

$3(x-4) \geq 2(x-2) + 5$

$3x - 12 \geq 2x - 4 + 5$

$x \geq 13$

The solution set is $\left\{x \mid x \geq 13\right\}$, or $\left(13, \infty\right)$.

47. $4(3x - 2) - 3x < 3(1 + 3x) - 7$

$12x - 8 - 3x < 3 + 9x - 7$

$9x - 8 < -4 + 9x$

$-8 < -4$

True for all x

The solution set is

$\left\{x \mid x \text{ is any real number}\right\}$, or $\left(-\infty, \infty\right)$.

49. $6 < x + 3 < 8$

$6 - 3 < x + 3 - 3 < 8 - 3$

$3 < x < 5$

The solution set is $\left\{x \mid 3 < x < 5\right\}$, or $(3, 5)$.

51. $-3 \leq x - 2 < 1$

$-1 \leq x < 3$

The solution set is $\left\{x \mid -1 \leq x < 3\right\}$, or

$[-1, 3)$.

53. $-11 < 2x - 1 \leq -5$

$-10 < 2x \leq -4$

$-5 < x \leq -2$

The solution set is $\left\{x \mid -5 < x \leq -2\right\}$, or

$(-5, -2]$.

55. $-3 \leq \dfrac{2}{3}x - 5 < -1$

$2 \leq \dfrac{2}{3}x < 4$

$3 \leq x < 6$

The solution set is $\left\{x \mid 3 \leq x < 6\right\}$, or $[3, 6)$.

57. $|x| < 3$

$-3 < x < 3$

The solution set is $\left\{x \mid -3 < x < 3\right\}$, or

$(-3, 3)$.

59. $|x - 1| \le 2$

$-2 \le x - 1 \le 2$

$-1 \le x \le 3$

The solution set is $\{x \mid -1 \le x \le 3\}$, or

$[-1, 3]$.

61. $|2x - 6| < 8$

$-8 < 2x - 6 < 8$

$-2 < 2x < 14$

$-1 < x < 7$

The solution set is $\{x \mid -1 < x < 7\}$, or

$(-1, 7)$.

63. $|2(x - 1) + 4| \le 8$

$-8 \le 2(x - 1) + 4 \le 8$

$-8 \le 2x - 2 + 4 \le 8$

$-8 \le 2x + 2 \le 8$

$-10 \le 2x \le 6$

$-5 \le x \le 3$

The solution set is $\{x \mid -5 \le x \le 3\}$, or

$[-5, 3]$.

65. $\left| \dfrac{2y + 6}{3} \right| < 2$

$-2 < \dfrac{2y + 6}{3} < 2$

$-6 < 2y + 6 < 6$

$-12 < 2y < 0$

$-6 < y < 0$

The solution set is $\{x \mid -6 < y < 0\}$, or

$(-6, 0)$.

67. $|x| > 3$

$x > 3 \text{ or } x < -3$

The solution set is $\{x \mid x > 3 \text{ or } x < -3\}$, that

is, $(-\infty, -3) \text{ or } (3, \infty)$.

69. $|x - 1| \ge 2$

$x - 1 \ge 2 \quad \text{or} \quad x - 1 \le -2$

$x \ge 3 \qquad\qquad x \le -1$

The solution set is $\{x \mid x \le -1 \text{ or } x \ge 3\}$, that

is, $(-\infty, -1] \text{ or } [3, \infty)$.

71. $|3x - 8| > 7$

$3x - 8 > 7 \quad \text{or} \quad 3x - 8 < -7$

$3x > 15 \qquad\qquad 3x < 1$

$x > 5 \qquad\qquad x < \dfrac{1}{3}$

The solution set is $\left\{ x \mid x < \dfrac{1}{3} \text{ or } x > 5 \right\}$, that

is, $\left(-\infty, \dfrac{1}{3} \right) \text{ or } (5, \infty)$.

73. $\left| \dfrac{2x + 2}{4} \right| \ge 2$

$\dfrac{2x + 2}{4} \ge 2 \quad \text{or} \quad \dfrac{2x + 2}{4} \le -2$

$2x + 2 \ge 8 \qquad\qquad 2x + 2 \le -8$

$2x \ge 6 \qquad\qquad 2x \le -10$

$x \ge 3 \qquad\qquad x \le -5$

The solution set is $\{x \mid x \le -5 \text{ or } x \ge 3\}$, that

is, $(-\infty, -5] \text{ or } [3, \infty)$.

75. $\left|3 - \dfrac{2}{3}x\right| > 5$

$3 - \dfrac{2}{3}x > 5$ or $3 - \dfrac{2}{3}x < -5$

$-\dfrac{2}{3}x > 2$ $-\dfrac{2}{3}x < -8$

$x < -3$ $x > 12$

The solution set is $\left\{x \mid x < -3 \text{ or } x > 12\right\}$,

that is, $\left(-\infty, -3\right)$ or $\left(12, \infty\right)$.

77. $3|x - 1| + 2 \geq 8$

$3|x - 1| \geq 6$

$|x - 1| \geq 2$

$x - 1 \geq 2$ or $x - 1 \leq -2$

$x \geq 3$ $x \leq -1$

The solution set is $\left\{x \mid x \leq 1 \text{ or } x \geq 3\right\}$, that

is, $\left(-\infty, -1\right]$ or $\left[3, \infty\right)$.

79. $3 < |2x - 1|$

$2x - 1 > 3$ or $2x - 1 < -3$

$2x > 4$ $2x < -2$

$x > 2$ $x < -1$

The solution set is $\left\{x \mid x < -1 \text{ or } x > 2\right\}$, that

is, $\left(-\infty, -1\right)$ or $\left(2, \infty\right)$.

81. $12 < \left|-2x + \dfrac{6}{7}\right| + \dfrac{3}{7}$

$\dfrac{81}{7} < \left|-2x + \dfrac{6}{7}\right|$

$-2x + \dfrac{6}{7} > \dfrac{81}{7}$ or $-2x + \dfrac{6}{7} < -\dfrac{81}{7}$

$-2x > \dfrac{75}{7}$ $-2x < -\dfrac{87}{7}$

$x < -\dfrac{75}{14}$ $x > \dfrac{87}{14}$

The solution set is $\left\{x \mid x < -\dfrac{75}{14} \text{ or } x > \dfrac{87}{14}\right\}$,

that is, $\left(-\infty, -\dfrac{75}{14}\right)$ or $\left(\dfrac{87}{14}, \infty\right)$.

83. $4 + \left|3 - \dfrac{x}{3}\right| \geq 9$

$\left|3 - \dfrac{x}{3}\right| \geq 5$

$3 - \dfrac{x}{3} \geq 5$ or $3 - \dfrac{x}{3} \leq -5$

$-\dfrac{x}{3} \geq 2$ $-\dfrac{x}{3} \leq -8$

$x \leq -6$ $x \geq 24$

The solution set is $\left\{x \mid x \leq -6 \text{ or } x \geq 24\right\}$,

that is, $\left(-\infty, -6\right]$ or $\left[24, \infty\right)$.

85. Playing Sports, Sports Events

87. Amusement Parks, Gardening, Movies, Exercise

89. Movies, Gardening

91. Home Improvement, Amusement Parks, Gardening

93. $550 - 9x < 370$

$-9x < -180$

$x > 20$

$1988 + 20 = 2008$, All years after 2008.

95.
$$15 \le \frac{5}{9}(F - 32) \le 35$$
$$15 \le \frac{5}{9}F - \frac{160}{9} \le 35$$
$$135 \le 5F - 160 \le 315$$
$$295 \le 5F \le 475$$
$$59 \le F \le 95$$
$[59° \text{ F}, 95° \text{ F}]$

97. $|x - 60.2| \le 1.6$
$$-1.6 \le x - 60.2 \le 1.6$$
$$58.6 \le x \le 61.8$$
The actual percent viewing "M*A*S*H"
was between 58.6% and 61.8%.

99. $\left| \dfrac{h - 50}{5} \right| \ge 1.645$

$\dfrac{h - 50}{5} \ge 1.645$ or $\dfrac{h - 50}{5} \le -1.645$

$h - 50 \ge 8.225$ $h - 50 \le -8.225$

$h \ge 58.225$ $h \le 41.775$

The number of outcomes would be 59 or
more, or 41 or less.

101. $50 + .2x < 20 + .5x$
$$30 < .3x$$
$$100 < x$$
Basic Rental is a better deal when driving
more than 100 miles per day.

103. $1800 + .03x < 200 + .08x$
$$1600 < .05x$$
$$32000 < x$$
A home assessment of greater than \$32000
would make the first bill a better deal.

105. $10000 + .4x < 2x$
$$10000 < 1.6x$$
$$6250 < x$$
More than 6250 tapes need to be sold a
week to make a profit.

107. $265 + 65x \le 2800$
$$65x \le 2535$$
$$x \le 39$$
39 bags or fewer can be lifted safely.

109. a. $\dfrac{86 + 88 + x}{3} \ge 90$

$\dfrac{174 + x}{3} \ge 90$

$174 + x \ge 270$

$x \ge 96$

You must get at least a 96.

b. $\dfrac{86 + 88 + x}{3} < 80$

$\dfrac{174 + x}{3} < 80$

$174 + x < 240$

$x < 66$

This will happen if you get a grade less
than 66.

111.–119. Answers may vary.

121.

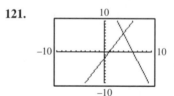

The solution set is $\{x \mid x < 4\}$ or $(-\infty, 4)$.

123.

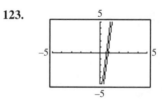

The graph of the left side of the inequality is
never greater than the graph of the right
side, therefore there is no solution.

$12x - 10 > 2(x - 4) + 10x$

$12x - 10 > 2x - 8 + 10x$

$12x - 10 > 12x - 8$

$\qquad 0 > 2$

You get a false statement with no variable.

125 a. The cost of Plan A is $4 + 0.10x$; The cost of Plan B is $2 + 0.15x$.

b.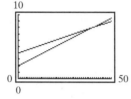

c. 41 or more checks makes Plan A better.

d. $\quad 4 + 0.10x < 2 + 0.15x$

$\qquad 2 < 0.05x$

$\qquad x \not> 40$

The solution set is

$\left\{ x \middle| x > 40 \right\}$ or $(40, \infty)$.

127. Because $x > y$, $y - x$ represents a negative number. When both sides are multiplied by $(y - x)$ the sense of the inequality must be reversed.

129. $|p - 0.3| \le 0.2$

$-0.2 \le p - 0.3 \le 0.2$

$0.1 \le p \le 0.5$

$\$5(100,000)(0.001) \le \text{Cost}$

$\le \$5(100,000)(0.005)$

$\$500 \le \text{Cost} \le \$2500$

The cost for refunds would be at least $500, but no more than $2500.

Section 1.8

Check Point Exercises

1. $x^2 + 2x - 3 < 0$

Solve $\quad x^2 + 2x - 3 = 0$.

$\qquad (x - 1)(x + 3) = 0$

$\quad x - 1 = 0 \quad \text{or} \quad x + 3 = 0$

$\qquad x = 1 \quad \text{or} \qquad x = -3$

The boundary points are 1 and –3.

The test intervals are

$(-\infty, -3)$, $(-3, 1)$, and $(1, \infty)$.

Test –5: $(-5)^2 + 2(-5) - 3 < 0$

$\qquad\qquad 25 - 10 - 3 < 0$

$\qquad\qquad\qquad 12 < 0 \text{ False}$

Test 0: $0^2 + 2(0) - 3 < 0$

$\qquad\qquad\qquad -3 = 0 \text{ True}$

Test 2: $2^2 + 2(2) - 3 < 0$

$\qquad\qquad 4 + 4 - 3 < 0$

$\qquad\qquad\qquad 5 < 0 \text{ False}$

The solution set is (–3, 1).

$$\xleftarrow{\quad\overset{(\qquad\qquad)}{\underset{-3 \qquad\qquad 1}{\rule{4cm}{0pt}}}\quad}\rightarrow$$

2. $\qquad x^2 - x \ge 20$

$x^2 - x - 20 \ge 0$

Solve $\quad x^2 - x - 20 = 0$.

$\qquad (x - 5)(x + 4) = 0$

$\quad x - 5 = 0 \quad \text{or} \quad x + 4 = 0$

$\qquad x = 5 \quad \text{or} \qquad 4 = -4$

The boundary points are –4 and 5.

The test intervals are

$(-\infty, -4]$, $[-4, 5]$, and $[5, \infty)$.

Test –5: $(-5)^2 - (5) \ge 20$

$\qquad\qquad 25 + 5 \ge 20$

$\qquad\qquad\qquad 30 \ge 20 \text{ True}$

Test 0: $0^2 - 0 \geq 20$

$\qquad 0 \geq 20$ False

Test 6: $6^2 - 6 \geq 20$

$\qquad 36 - 6 \geq 20$

$\qquad 30 \geq 20$ True

The solution set is $(-\infty, -4]$ or $[5, \infty)$.

$\qquad -4 \qquad\qquad 5$

3. $\dfrac{x-5}{x+2} > 0$

$x - 5 = 0 \quad x + 2 = 0$

$\quad x = 5 \qquad x = -2$

The boundary points are –2 and 5.

The test intervals are

$(-\infty, -2), \ (-2, \ 5), \text{ and } (5, \ \infty).$

Test –3: $\dfrac{-3-5}{-3+2} > 0$

$\qquad\quad \dfrac{-8}{-1} > 0$ True

Test 0: $\dfrac{0-5}{0+2} > 0$

$\qquad\quad \dfrac{-5}{2} > 0$ False

Test 6: $\dfrac{6-5}{6+2} > 0$

$\qquad\quad \dfrac{1}{8} > 0$ True

The solution set is $(-\infty, -2)$ or $(5, \infty)$.

$\qquad -2 \qquad\qquad 5$

4.

$\dfrac{2x}{x+1} \leq 1$

$\dfrac{2x}{x+1} - 1 \leq 0$

$\dfrac{2x - x - 1}{x+1} \leq 0$

$\dfrac{x-1}{x+1} \leq 0$

$x - 1 = 0 \quad x + 1 = 0$

$\quad x = 1 \qquad x = -1$

The boundary points are –1 and 1.

The test intervals are

$(-\infty, \ -1), \ (-1, \ 1], \text{ and } [1, \ \infty).$

Test –2: $\dfrac{2(2)}{-2+1} \leq 1$

$\qquad\quad \dfrac{-4}{-1} \leq 1$

$\qquad\qquad 4 \leq 1$ False

Test 0: $\dfrac{2(0)}{0+1} \leq 1$

$\qquad\qquad 0 \leq 1$ True

Test 2: $\dfrac{2(2)}{2+1} \leq 1$

$\qquad\quad \dfrac{4}{3} \leq 1$ False

The solution set is $(-1, 1]$.

$\qquad -1 \qquad\qquad 1$

5. $\qquad -16t^2 + 80t > 64$

$\qquad -16t^2 + 80t - 64 > 0$

$\qquad\qquad t^2 - 5t + 4 < 0$

Solve $\quad t^2 - 5t + 4 = 0$

$\qquad\qquad (t-4)(t-1) = 0$

$t - 4 = 0 \quad \text{or} \quad t - 1 = 0$

$\qquad t = 4 \quad \text{or} \qquad t = 1$

The boundary points are 1 and 4.

Note that the object is at ground level when $s = 0$.

$0 = 16t^2 + 80t$

$0 = -16t(t - 5)$

$t = 0$ or $t = 5$

The test intervals are (0, 1), (1, 4), and (4, 5).

Test $\dfrac{1}{2}$: $-16\left(\dfrac{1}{2}\right)^2 + 80\left(\dfrac{1}{2}\right) > 64$

$-4 + 40 > 64$

$36 > 64$ False

Test 2: $-16(2)^2 + 80(2) > 64$

$-64 + 160 > 64$

$96 > 64$ True

Test $\dfrac{9}{2}$: $-16\left(\dfrac{9}{2}\right)^2 + 80\left(\dfrac{9}{2}\right) > 64$

$-324 + 360 > 64$

$36 > 64$ False

The object will be more than 64 feet above the ground between 1 and 4 seconds, excluding $t = 1$ and $t = 4$.

Exercise Set 1.8

1. $(x - 4)(x + 2) > 0$

$x = 4$ or $x = -2$

T	F	T
−2		4

Test −3: $(-3 - 4)(-3 + 2) > 0$

$7 > 0$ True

Test 0: $(0 - 4)(0 + 2) > 0$

$-8 > 0$ False

Test 5: $(5 - 4)(5 + 2) > 0$

$7 > 0$ True

$(-\infty, -2)$ or $(4, \infty)$

3. $(x - 7)(x + 3) \le 0$

$x = 7$ or $x = -3$

F	T	F
−3		7

Test −4: $(-4 - 7)(-4 + 3) \le 0$

$11 \le 0$ False

Test 0: $(0 - 7)(0 + 3) \le 0$

$-21 \le 0$ True

Test 8: $(8 - 7)(8 + 3) \le 0$

$11 \le 0$ False

The solution set is $[-3, 7]$.

5. $x^2 - 5x + 4 > 0$

$(x - 4)(x - 1) > 0$

$x = 4$ or $x = 1$

T	F	T
1		4

Test 0: $0^2 - 5(0) + 4 > 0$

$4 > 0$ True

Test 2: $2^2 - 5(2) + 4 > 0$

$-2 > 0$ False

Test 5: $5^2 - 5(5) + 4 > 0$

$4 > 0$ True

The solution set is $(-\infty, 1)$ or $(4, \infty)$.

7. $x^2 + 5x + 4 > 0$

$(x + 1)(x + 4) > 0$

$x = -1$ or $x = -4$

T	F	T
−4		−1

Test −5: $(-5)^2 + 5(-5) + 4 > 0$

$4 > 0$ True

Test −3: $(-3)^2 + 5(-3) + 4 > 0$

$-2 > 0$ False

Test 0: $0^2 + 5(0) + 4 > 0$

$4 > 0$ True

The solution set is $(-\infty, -4)$ or $(-1, \infty)$.

9. $x^2 - 6x + 9 < 0$

$(x-3)(x-3) < 0$

$x = 3$

F		F
	3	

Test 0: $0^2 - 6(0) + 9 < 0$

$9 < 0$ False

Test 4: $4^2 - 6(4) + 9 < 0$

$1 < 0$ False

The solution set is the empty set, $\varnothing$.

11. $x^2 - 6x + 8 \le 0$

$(x-4)(x-2) \le 0$

$x = 4$ or $x = 2$

F		T		F
	2		4	

Test 0: $0^2 - 6(0) + 8 \le 0$

$8 \le 0$ False

Test 3: $3^2 - 6(3) + 8 \le 0$

$-1 \le 0$ True

Test 5: $5^2 - 6(5) + 8 \le 0$

$3 \le 0$ False

The solution set is $[2, 4]$.

13. $3x^2 + 10x - 8 \le 0$

$(3x-2)(x+4) \le 0$

$x = \dfrac{2}{3}$ or $x = -4$

F		T		F
	-4		$\frac{2}{3}$	

Test -5: $3(-5)^2 + 10(-5) - 8 \le 0$

$17 \le 0$ False

Test 0: $3(0)^2 + 10(0) - 8 \le 0$

$8 \le 0$ True

Test 1: $3(1)^2 + 10(1) - 8 \le 0$

$5 \le 0$ False

The solution set is $\left[-4, \dfrac{2}{3} \right]$.

15. $2x^2 + x < 15$

$2x^2 + x - 15 < 0$

$(2x-5)(x+3) < 0$

$2x - 5 = 0$ or $x + 3 = 0$

$2x = 5$

$x = \dfrac{5}{2}$ or $x = -3$

F		T		F
	-3		$\frac{5}{2}$	

Test -4: $2(-4)^2 + (-4) < 15$

$28 < 15$ False

Test 0: $2(0)^2 + 0 < 15$

$0 < 15$ True

Test 3: $2(3)^2 + 3 < 15$

$21 < 15$ False

The solution set is $\left(-3, \dfrac{5}{2} \right)$.

17. $4x^2 + 7x < -3$

$4x^2 + 7x + 3 < 0$

$(4x + 3)(x + 1) < 0$

$4x + 3 = 0$ or $x + 1 = 0$

$4x - 3 = 0$

$x = -\dfrac{3}{4}$ or $x = -1$

F		T		F
	-1		$-\frac{3}{4}$	

Test -2: $4(-2)^2 + 7(-2) < -3$

$2 < -3$ False

Test $-\dfrac{7}{8}$: $4\left(-\dfrac{7}{8}\right)^2 + 7\left(-\dfrac{7}{8}\right) < -3$

$\dfrac{49}{16} - \dfrac{49}{8} < -3$

$-\dfrac{49}{16} < -3$ True

Test 0: $4(0)^2 + 7(0) < -3$

$0 < -3$ False

The solution set is $\left(-1, \ -\dfrac{3}{4}\right)$.

19. $5x \le 2 - 3x^2$

$3x^2 + 5x - 2 \le 0$

$(3x - 1)(x + 2) \le 0$

$3x - 1 = 0$ or $x + 2 = 0$

$3x = 1$

$3x - 1 = 0$ or $x + 2 = 0$

$3x = 1$

$x = \dfrac{1}{3}$ or $x = -2$

F		T		F

-2 $\dfrac{1}{3}$

Test -3: $5(-3) \le 2 - 3(-3)^2$

$-15 \le -25$ False

Test 0: $5(0) \le 2 - 3(0)^2$

$0 \le 2$ True

Test 1: $5(1) \le 2 - 3(1)^2$

$5 \le -1$ False

Ths solution set is $\left[-2, \dfrac{1}{3}\right]$.

21. $x^2 - 4x \geq 0$

$x(x-4) \geq 0$

$x = 0$ or $x - 4 = 0$

$\qquad\qquad x = 4$

T	F	T
0	4	

Test -1: $(-1)^2 - 4(-1) \geq 0$

$\qquad\qquad 5 \geq 0$ True

Test 1: $(1)^2 - 4(1) \geq 0$

$\qquad\qquad -3 \geq 0$ False

$\qquad 0 \leq 2$ True

Test 5: $5^2 - 4(5) \geq 0$

$\qquad\qquad 5 \geq 0$ True

The solution set is $(-\infty, \ 0]$ or $[4, \ \infty)$.

23. $2x^2 + 3x > 0$

$x(2x + 3) > 0$

$x = 0$ or $x = -\dfrac{3}{2}$

T	F	T
$-\frac{3}{2}$	0	

Test -2: $2(-2)^2 + 3(-2) > 0$

$\qquad\qquad 2 > 0$ True

Test -1: $2(-1)^2 + 3(-1) > 0$

$\qquad\qquad -1 > 0$ False

Test 1: $2(1)^2 + 3(1) > 0$

$\qquad\qquad 5 > 0$ True

The solution set is $\left(-\infty, \ -\dfrac{3}{2}\right)$ or $(0, \ \infty)$.

25. $-x^2 + x \geq 0$

$x^2 - x \leq 0$

$x(x-1) \leq 0$

$x = 0$ or $x = 1$

F	T	F
0	1	

Test -1: $-(-1)^2 + (-1) \geq 0$

$\qquad\qquad -2 \geq 0$ False

Test $\dfrac{1}{2}$: $-\left(\dfrac{1}{2}\right)^2 + \left(\dfrac{1}{2}\right) \geq 0$

$\qquad\qquad \dfrac{1}{4} \geq 0$ True

Test 2: $-(2)^2 + 2 \geq 0$

$\qquad\qquad -2 \geq 0$ False

The solution set is $[0, 1]$.

27. $\left|x^2 + 2x - 36\right| > 12$

$x^2 + 2x - 36 > 12$

$x^2 - 2x - 48 > 0$

$(x + 8)(x - 6) > 0$

$x + 8 = 0 \qquad x - 6 = 0$

$x = -8 \qquad\quad x = 6$

T	F	T
-8	6	

Test -7: $(-9)^2 - 2(-9) - 36 > 12$

$\qquad\qquad 27 > 12$ True

Test 0: $0^2 + 2(0) - 36 > 12$

$\qquad\qquad -36 > 12$ False

Test 10: $(10)^2 + 2(10) - 36 > 12$

$\qquad\qquad 84 > 12$ True

$$x^2 + 2x - 36 < -12$$

$$x^2 + 2x - 24 < 0$$

OR $(x+6)(x-4) < 0$

$$x + 6 = 0 \qquad x - 4 = 0$$

$$x = -6 \qquad\quad x = 4$$

	F		T		F
		_6		4	

Test _5: $(-7)^2 + 2(-7) - 24 < 0$

$$11 < \_12 \quad \text{False}$$

Test 0: $(0)^2 + 2(0) - 24 < 0$

$$-24 < 0 \quad \text{True}$$

Test 7: $7^2 + 2(7) - 24 < 0$

$$39 < 0 \quad \text{False}$$

The solution set is $(\_\infty, \_8)$ or $(\_6, 4)$ or $(6, \infty)$

29. $\dfrac{x-4}{x+3} > 0$

$$x - 4 = 0 \quad x + 3 = 0$$

$$x = 4 \qquad x = -3$$

T		F		T
	-3		4	

Test -4: $\dfrac{-4-4}{-4+3} > 0$

$$\dfrac{-8}{-1} > 0$$

$$8 > 0 \quad \text{True}$$

Test 0: $\dfrac{0-4}{0+3} > 0$

$$-\dfrac{4}{3} > 0 \quad \text{False}$$

Test 5: $\dfrac{5-4}{5+3} > 0$

$$\dfrac{1}{8} > 0 \quad \text{True}$$

The solution set is $\left(-\infty, -3\right)$ or $(4, \infty)$.

31. $\dfrac{x+3}{x+4} < 0$

$$x = -3 \quad \text{or} \quad x = -4$$

	F		T		F
		-4		-3	

Test -5: $\dfrac{-5+3}{-5+4} < 0$

$$2 < 0 \quad \text{False}$$

Test $-\dfrac{7}{2}$: $\dfrac{-\frac{7}{2}+3}{-\frac{7}{2}+4} < 0$

$$-1 < 0 \quad \text{True}$$

Test 0: $\dfrac{0+3}{0+4} < 0$

$$\dfrac{3}{4} < 0 \quad \text{False}$$

The solution set is $(-4, -3)$.

33. $\dfrac{-x+2}{x-4} \geq 0$

$$x = 2 \text{ or } x = 4$$

	F		T		F
		2		4	

Test 0: $\dfrac{0+2}{0-4} \geq 0$

$$-\dfrac{1}{2} \geq 0 \quad \text{False}$$

Test 3: $\dfrac{-3+2}{3-4} \geq 0$

$$1 \geq 0 \quad \text{True}$$

Test 5: $\dfrac{-5+2}{5-4} \geq 0$

$$-3 \geq 0 \quad \text{False}$$

The solution set is $[2, 4)$.

35. $\dfrac{4-2x}{3x+4} \le 0$

$x = 2$ or $x = -\dfrac{4}{3}$

T	F	T

$-\dfrac{4}{3}$ 2

Test -2: $\dfrac{4-2(-2)}{3(-2)+4} \le 0$

$\qquad\qquad -4 \le 0$ True

Test 0: $\dfrac{4-2(0)}{3(0)+4} \le 0$

$\qquad\qquad 1 \le 0$ False

Test 3: $\dfrac{4-2(3)}{3(3)+4} \le 0$

$\qquad\qquad \dfrac{-2}{13} \le 0$ True

The solution set is $\left(-\infty,\ \dfrac{-4}{3}\right)$ or $[2,\ \infty)$.

$-\dfrac{4}{3} \qquad 2$

37. $\dfrac{x}{x-3} > 0$

$x = 0$ or $x = 3$

T	F	T

0 3

Test -1: $\dfrac{-1}{-1-3} > 0$

$\qquad\qquad \dfrac{1}{4} > 0$ True

Test 2: $\dfrac{2}{2-3} > 0$

$\qquad\qquad -2 > 0$ False

Test 4: $\dfrac{4}{4-3} > 0$

$\qquad\qquad 4 > 0$ True

The solution set is $(-\infty,\ 0)$ or $(3,\ \infty)$.

$0 \qquad 3$

39.

$\dfrac{x+1}{x+3} < 0$

$\dfrac{x+1}{x+3} - 2 < 0$

$\dfrac{x+1-2(x+3)}{x+3} < 0$

$\dfrac{x+1-2x-6}{x+3} < 0$

$\dfrac{-x-5}{x+3} < 0$

$x = -5$ or $x = -3$

T	F	T

-5 -3

Test -6: $\dfrac{-6+1}{-6+3} < 2$

$\qquad\qquad \dfrac{5}{3} < 2$ True

Test -4: $\dfrac{-4+1}{-4+3} < 2$

$\qquad\qquad 3 < 2$ False

Test 0: $\dfrac{0+1}{0+3} < 2$

$\qquad\qquad \dfrac{1}{3} < 2$ True

The solution set is $(-\infty,\ -5)$ or $(-3,\ \infty)$.

$-5 \qquad -3$

41.

$$\frac{x+4}{2x-1} \leq 3$$

$$\frac{x+4}{2x-1} - 3 \leq 0$$

$$\frac{x+4-3(2x-1)}{2x-1} \leq 0$$

$$\frac{x+4-6x+3}{2x-1} \leq 0$$

$$\frac{-5x+7}{2x-1} \leq 0$$

$$x = \frac{7}{5} \quad \text{or} \quad x = \frac{1}{2}$$

$$\begin{array}{ccc} T & F & T \\ \hline & \frac{1}{2} & \frac{7}{5} \end{array}$$

Test 0: $\dfrac{0+4}{2(0)-1} \leq 3$

$\qquad -4 \leq 3$ True

Test 1: $\dfrac{1+4}{2(1)-1} \leq 3$

$\qquad 5 \leq 3$ False

Test 2: $\dfrac{2+4}{2(2)-1} \leq 3$

$\qquad 2 \leq 3$ True

The solution set is $\left(-\infty, \dfrac{1}{2}\right)$ or $\left[\dfrac{7}{5}, \infty\right)$.

43.

$$\frac{x-2}{x+2} \leq 2$$

$$\frac{x-2}{x+2} - 2 \leq 0$$

$$\frac{x-2-2(x+2)}{x+2} \leq 0$$

$$\frac{x-2-2x-4}{x+2} \leq 0$$

$$\frac{-x-6}{x+2} \leq 0$$

$$x = -6 \quad \text{or} \quad x = -2$$

$$\begin{array}{ccc} T & F & T \\ \hline -6 & & -2 \end{array}$$

Test -7: $\dfrac{-7-2}{-7+2} \leq 2$

$\qquad \dfrac{9}{5} \leq 2$ True

Test -3: $\dfrac{-3-2}{-3+2} \leq 2$

$\qquad 5 \leq 2$ False

Test 0: $\dfrac{0-2}{0+2} \leq 2$

$\qquad -1 \leq 2$ True

The solution set is $(-\infty, -6]$ or $(-2, \infty)$.

45.

$$\frac{3}{x+3} > \frac{3}{x-2}$$

$$\frac{3}{x+3} - \frac{3}{x-2} > 0$$

$$\frac{3(x-2)}{(x+3)(x-2)} - \frac{3(x+3)}{(x+3)(x-2)} > 0$$

$$\frac{3x-6-3x-9}{(x+3)(x-2)} > 0$$

$$\frac{-15}{(x+3)(x-2)} > 0$$

$$x+3 = 0 \qquad x-2 = 0$$
$$x = -3 \qquad x = 2$$

F		T		F
	-3		2	

Test -4:
$$\frac{3}{-4+3} > \frac{3}{-4-2}$$

$$-3 > \frac{-1}{2} \quad \text{False}$$

Test 0:
$$\frac{3}{0+3} > \frac{3}{0-2}$$

$$1 > \text{-3/2} \quad \text{True}$$

$$\frac{3}{3+3} > \frac{3}{3-2}$$

Test 3: $\dfrac{3}{6} > \dfrac{3}{1}$

$$\frac{1}{2} > 3 \quad \text{False}$$

The solution set is (_3, 2).

47.

$$\frac{x^2-x-2}{x^2-4x+3} > 0$$

$$\frac{(x-2)(x+1)}{(x-3)(x-1)} > 0$$

$$x-2 = 0 \quad x+1 = 0 \quad x-3 = 0 \quad x-1 = 0$$
$$x = 2 \quad x = -1 \quad x = 3 \quad x = 1$$

T		F		T		F		T
	-1		1		2		3	

Test _2: $$\frac{(-2)^2-(-2)-2}{(-2)^2-4(-2)+3} > 0$$

$$\frac{4}{15} > 0 \quad \text{True}$$

The solution set is (_∞, _1) or (1, 2) or (3, ∞).

49.
$$S = -16t^2 + v_0t + s_0$$
$$96 < -16t^2 + 80t + 0$$
$$0 < -16t^2 + 80t - 96$$
$$0 < -16\left(t^2 - 5t + 6\right)$$
$$0 < -16(t-3)(t-2)$$

F		T		F
	2		3	

$2 < t < 3$

The projectile's height will exceed 96 feet between 2 and 3 seconds exclusive.

51.
$$S = -16t^2 + v_0t + s_0$$
$$96 < -16t^2 + 64t + 80$$
$$0 < -16t^2 + 64t - 16$$
$$0 < -16\left(t^2 - 4t + 1\right)$$

$$t = \frac{4 \pm \sqrt{(-4)^2 - 4(1)(1)}}{2}$$

$$t = \frac{4 \pm 2\sqrt{3}}{2}$$

$$t = 2 \pm \sqrt{3}$$

F	T	F

$$2 - \sqrt{3} \qquad 2 + \sqrt{3}$$

$$2 + \sqrt{3} - \left(2 - \sqrt{3}\right) = 2\sqrt{3} \approx 3.46$$

The ball is higher than 96 feet for about 3.46 seconds.

53. $H = \frac{15}{8}x^2 - 30x + 200$

a. $H = \frac{15}{8}(0)^2 - 30(0) + 200$

$H = 200$ beats per minute

b. $110 < \frac{15}{8}x^2 - 30x + 200$

$880 < 15x^2 - 240x + 1600$

$0 < x^2 - 16x + 48$

$0 < (x - 12)(x - 4)$

$x = 12$ or $x = 4$

T	F	T

$$4 \qquad\qquad 12$$

Test 0: $110 < \frac{15}{8}(0)^2 - 30(0) + 200$

$110 < 200$ True

Test 8: $110 < \frac{15}{8}(8)^2 - 30(8) + 200$

$110 < 80$ False

Test 16: $110 < \frac{15}{8}(16)^2 - 30(16) + 200$

$110 < 200$ True

Heart rate exceeds 110 beats per minute up to 4 minutes after work-out.

55. $1.2x^2 + 15.2x + 181.4 > 536.6$

$1.2x^2 + 15.2 + -355.2 > 0$

$$x = \frac{-15.2 \pm \sqrt{(1.5.)^2 - 4(1.2)(-355.2)}}{2(1.2)}$$

$$x = \frac{-15.2 \pm \sqrt{1936}}{2.4}$$

$$x = \frac{-15.2 \pm 44}{2.4}$$

$$x = 12 \qquad x = -25$$

T	F	T

$$-25 \qquad\qquad 12$$

Test 0: $181.4 > 536.6$ False

$1995 + 12 = 2207$, after 2007

57.
$$\frac{500000 + 400x}{x} \leq 425$$

$$\frac{500000 + 400x}{x} - 425 \leq 0$$

$$\frac{500000 + 400x - 425x}{x} \leq 0$$

$$\frac{500000 - 25x}{x} \leq 0$$

$$500000 - 25x = 0 \qquad x = 0$$

$$20000 = x$$

T	F	T

$$0 \qquad\qquad 20000$$

Test 10,000:

$$\frac{500000 + 400(10000)}{10000} \leq 425$$

$$450 \leq 425 \quad \text{False}$$

The solution set is $[20,000, \infty)$.

The company must make at least 20,000 wheelchairs.

59. – 61. Answers may vary.

63. Graph $y_1 = 2x^2 + 5x - 3$ in a standard window. The graph is below or equal to the x-axis for

$$-3 \le x \le \frac{1}{2}.$$

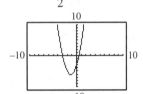

The solution set is

$$\left\{ x \middle| -3 \le x \le \frac{1}{2} \right\} \text{ or } \left[-3, \frac{1}{2} \right].$$

65. Graph $y_1 = \dfrac{x-4}{x-1}$ in a standard viewing window. The graph is below the x-axis for $1 < x \le 4$.

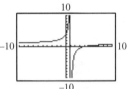

The solution set is $\{1, 4\}$.

67. Answers may vary.

69. Because any non-zero number squared is positive, the solution is all real numbers except 2.

71. Because any number squared is positive, the solution is the empty set, $\varnothing$.

73. $x^3 + x^2 - 4x - 4 > 0$

$\qquad x^2(x+1) - 4(x+1) > 0$

$\qquad\quad (x^2 - 4)(x+1) > 0$

$\quad (x-2)(x+2)(x+1) > 0$

$\quad x - 2 = 0 \qquad x + 2 = 0 \qquad x + 1 = 0$

$\qquad x = 2 \qquad\quad x = -2 \qquad\quad x = -1$

F	T	F	T

$\qquad\quad -2 \qquad\qquad -1 \qquad\qquad 2$

Test 0: $0^3 + 0^2 - 4(0) - 4 > 0$

$\qquad\qquad\qquad\qquad\qquad -4 > 0 \quad$ False

The solution set is $(-2, -1)$ and $(2, \infty)$.

75. a. The solution set is all real numbers.

     b. The solution set is the empty set, $\varnothing$.

     c. $4x^2 - 8x + 7 > 0$

$$x = \frac{8 \pm \sqrt{(-8)^2 - 4(4)(7)}}{2(4)}$$

$$x = \frac{8 \pm \sqrt{64 - 112}}{8}$$

$$x = \frac{8 \pm \sqrt{-48}}{8} \Rightarrow \text{imaginary}$$

no critical values

Test 0: $4(0)^2 - 8(0) + 7 > 0$

$\qquad\qquad\qquad\qquad\quad 7 > 0 \text{ True}$

The inequality is true for all numbers.

Chapter 1 Review Exercises

1. $y = 2x - 2$

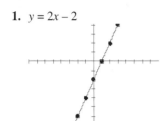

$x = -3, y = -8$
$x = -2, y = -6$
$x = -1, y = -4$
$x = 0, y = -2$
$x = 1, y = 0$
$x = 2, y = 2$
$x = 3, y = 4$

2. $y = x^2 - 3$

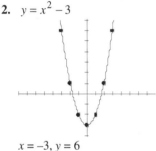

$x = -3, y = 6$
$x = -2, y = 1$
$x = -1, y = -2$
$x = 0, y = -3$
$x = 1, y = -2$
$x = 2, y = 1$
$x = 3, y = 6$

3. $y = x$

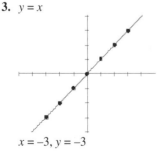

$x = -3, y = -3$

$x = -2, y = -2$
$x = -1, y = -1$
$x = 0, y = 0$
$x = 1, y = 1$
$x = 2, y = 2$
$x = 3, y = 3$

4. $y = |x| - 2$

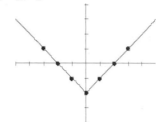

$x = -3, y = 1$
$x = -2, y = 0$
$x = -1, y = -1$
$x = 0, y = -2$
$x = 1, y = -1$
$x = 2, y = 0$
$x = 3, y = 1$

5. A portion of Cartesian coordinate plane with minimum *x*-value equal to –20, maximum *x*-value equal to 40, *x*-scale equal to 10 and with minimum *y*-value equal to –5, maximum *y*-value equal to 5, and *y*-scale equal to 1.

6. *x*-intercept: –2; The graph intersects the *x*-axis at (–2, 0).
y-intercept: 2; The graph intersects the *y*-axis at (0, 2).

7. *x*-intercepts: 2, –2; The graph intersects the *x*-axis at (–2, 0) and (2, 0).
y-intercept: –4; The graph intercepts the *y*-axis at (0, –4).

8. *x*-intercept: 5; The graph intersects the *x*-axis at (5, 0).
y-intercept: None; The graph does not intersect the *y*-axis.

9. 20%

10. 85 years old.

11. Low occurrence of Alzheimer's until 55
years old, then the percent increases rapidly.

12. $2x - 5 = 7$
$2x = 12$
$x = 6$
$2(6) - 5 = 7$
$12 - 5 = 7$
The solution set is $\{6\}$.

13. $5x + 20 = 3x$
$2x = -20$
$x = -10$
$5(-10) + 20 = 3(-10)$
$-50 + 20 = -30$
The solution set is $\{-10\}$.

14. $7(x - 4) = x + 2$
$7x - 28 = x + 2$
$6x = 30$
$x = 5$
$7(5 - 4) = 5 + 2$
$7(1) = 7$
The solution set is $\{5\}$.

15. $1 - 2(6 - x) = 3x + 2$
$1 - 12 + 2x = 3x + 2$
$-11 - x = 2$
$-x = 13$
$x = -13$
$1 - 2[6 - (-13)] = 3(-13) + 2$
$1 - 2(19) = -39 + 2$
$1 - 38 = -37$
The solution set is $\{-13\}$.

16. $2(x - 4) + 3(x + 5) = 2x - 2$
$2x - 8 + 3x + 15 = 2x - 2$
$5x + 7 = 2x - 2$
$3x = -9$
$x = -3$
$2(-3 - 4) + 3(-3 + 5) = 2(-3) - 2$

$2(-7) + 3(2) = -6 - 2$
$-14 + 6 = -8$
The solution set is $\{-3\}$.

17. $2x - 4(5x + 1) = 3x + 17$
$2x - 20x - 4 = 3x + 17$
$-18x - 4 = 3x + 17$
$-21x = 21$
$x = -1$
$2(-1) - 4(5(-1) + 1) = 3(-1) + 17$
$-2 - 4(-4) = -3 + 17$
$-2 + 16 = 14$
The solution set is $\{-1\}$.

18. $\dfrac{2x}{3} = \dfrac{x}{6} + 1$
$2(2x) = x + 6$
$4x = x + 6$
$3x = 6$
$x = 2$
$\dfrac{2(2)}{3} = \dfrac{2}{6} + 1$
$\dfrac{4}{3} = \dfrac{1}{3} + \dfrac{3}{3}$
$\dfrac{4}{3} = \dfrac{4}{3}$
The solution set is $\{2\}$.

19. $\dfrac{x}{2} - \dfrac{1}{10} = \dfrac{x}{5} + \dfrac{1}{2}$
$5x - 1 = 2x + 5$
$3x = 6$
$x = 2$
$\dfrac{2}{2} - \dfrac{1}{10} = \dfrac{2}{5} + \dfrac{1}{2}$
$1 - \dfrac{1}{10} = \dfrac{4}{10} + \dfrac{5}{10}$
$\dfrac{9}{10} = \dfrac{9}{10}$
The solution set is $\{2\}$.

20. $\dfrac{2x}{3} = 6 - \dfrac{x}{4}$

$4(2x) = 12(6) - 3x$

$8x = 72 - 3x$

$11x = 72$

$x = \dfrac{72}{11}$

$\dfrac{2\left(\frac{72}{11}\right)}{3} = 6 - \dfrac{\frac{72}{11}}{4}$

$\dfrac{\frac{144}{11}}{3} = 6 - \dfrac{72}{11} \cdot \dfrac{1}{4}$

$\dfrac{144}{11} \cdot \dfrac{1}{3} = 6 - \dfrac{18}{11}$

$\dfrac{48}{11} = \dfrac{66}{11} - \dfrac{18}{11}$

$\dfrac{48}{11} = \dfrac{48}{11}$

The solution set is $\left\{\dfrac{72}{11}\right\}$.

21. $\dfrac{x}{4} = 2 + \dfrac{x-3}{3}$

$3x = 12(2) + 4(x-3)$

$3x = 24 + 4x - 12$

$-x = 12$

$x = -12$

$\dfrac{-12}{4} = 2 + \dfrac{-12-3}{3}$

$-3 = 2 + \dfrac{-15}{3}$

$-3 = 2 - 5$

The solution set is $\{-12\}$.

22. $\dfrac{3x+1}{3} - \dfrac{13}{2} = \dfrac{1-x}{4}$

$4(3x+1) - 6(13) = 3(1-x)$

$12x + 4 - 78 = 3 - 3x$

$12x - 74 = 3 - 3x$

$15x = 77$

$x = \dfrac{77}{15}$

$\dfrac{3\left(\frac{77}{15}\right)+1}{3} - \dfrac{13}{2} = \dfrac{1-\frac{77}{15}}{4}$

$\dfrac{\frac{77}{5}+1}{3} - \dfrac{13}{2} = \dfrac{\frac{-62}{15}}{4}$

$\dfrac{82}{5} \cdot \dfrac{1}{3} - \dfrac{13}{2} = \dfrac{-62}{15} \cdot \dfrac{1}{4}$

$\dfrac{82}{15} - \dfrac{13}{2} = \dfrac{-31}{30}$

$\dfrac{164}{30} - \dfrac{195}{30} = \dfrac{-31}{30}$

The solution set is $\left\{\dfrac{77}{15}\right\}$.

23. a. $x \neq 0$

b. $\dfrac{9}{4} - \dfrac{1}{2x} = \dfrac{4}{x}$

$9x - 2 = 16$

$9x = 18$

$x = 2$

The solution set is $\{2\}$.

24. a. $x \neq 5$

b.

$\dfrac{7}{x-5} + 2 = \dfrac{x+2}{x-5}$

$7 + 2(x-5) = x+2$

$7 + 2x - 10 = x + 2$

$2x - 3 = x + 2$

$x = 5$

The solution set is the empty set, $\varnothing$.

25. a. $x \neq 1, x \neq -1$

b.

$$\frac{1}{x-1} - \frac{1}{x+1} = \frac{2}{x^2-1}$$

$$\frac{1}{x-1} - \frac{1}{x+1} = \frac{2}{(x+1)(x-1)}$$

$$x+1 - (x-1) = 2$$

$$x+1 - x + 1 = 2$$

$$2 = 2$$

The solution set is all real numbers except 1 and –1.

26. a. $x \neq -2, x \neq 4$

b.

$$\frac{4}{x+2} + \frac{2}{x-4} = \frac{30}{(x+2)(x-4)}$$

$$4(x-4) + 2(x+2) = 30$$

$$4x - 16 + 2x + 4 = 30$$

$$6x - 12 = 30$$

$$6x = 42$$

$$x = 7$$

The solution set is {7}.

27. $\dfrac{1}{x+5} = 0$

$$1 = 0$$

The given equation is an inconsistent equation.

28. $7x + 13 = 4x - 10 + 3x + 23$

$$7x + 13 = 7x + 13$$

$$13 = 13$$

The given equation is an identity.

29. $7x + 13 = 3x - 10 + 2x + 23$

$$7x + 13 = 5x + 13$$

$$2x = 0$$

$$x = 0$$

The given equation is a conditional equation.

30. $P = -.7x + 80$

$$52 = -.7x + 80$$

$$-28 = -.7x$$

$$40 = x$$

$$1965 + 40 = 2005$$

31. $47{,}587 = 1321.7(x - 1980) + 21{,}153$

$$26{,}434 = 1321.7(x - 1980)$$

$$20 = x - 1980$$

$$x = 2000$$

The median income was \$47,587 in 2000.

32.
$$x = \text{cost to low - income}$$
$$x + 63 = \text{cost to middle - income}$$
$$2x - 3 = \text{cost to high - income}$$
$$x + x + 63 + 2x - 3 = 756$$
$$4x + 60 = 756$$
$$4x = 696$$
$$x = 174$$
$$x + 63 = 237$$
$$2x - 3 = 345$$

\$174 thousand for low-income families
\$237 thousand for middle-income families
\$345 thousand for high-income families

33. $567 + 15x = 702$

$$15x = 135$$

$$x = 9$$

$$2009$$

34. $15 + .05x = 5 + .07x$

$$10 = .02x$$

$$500 = x$$

$$500 \text{ min.}$$

35. Let $x = $ amount at 8%

$$10{,}000 - x = \text{amount at } 12\%$$

$$0.08x + 0.12(10{,}000 - x) = 950$$

$$0.08x + 1200 - 0.12x = 950$$

$$-0.04x = -250$$

$$x = \$6250$$

Invest \$6250 at 8%, \$3750 at 12%.

36. Let $x = $ width of field

$$2x + 14 = \text{length of field}$$

$$2x + 2(2x + 14) = 346$$

$$2x + 4x + 28 = 346$$

$$6x = 318$$

$$x = 53$$

$$2(53) + 14 = 120$$

The width is 53 meters, the length is
120 meters.

37. Let x = number of times bus is used
$1.50x$ = fare without coupon book
$25 + .0.25x$ = fare with coupon book
$1.50x = 25 + 0.25x$
$1.25x = 25$
$\qquad x = 20$
The bus must be used 20 times.

38. Let x = amount sold
$300 + 0.05x = 800$
$\qquad 0.05x = 500$
$\qquad\qquad x = 10,000$
$10,000 in sales must be sold.

39. Let x = number of concerts over 50
$2627 = 2987 - 8x$
$\quad 8x = 360$
$\quad\ x = 45$
$50 + 45 = 95$
95 concerts should be given.

40. $V = \dfrac{1}{3}Bh$
$3V = Bh$
$h = \dfrac{3V}{B}$

41. $F = f(1 - M)$
$\quad F = f - fM$
$F - f = -fM$
$\quad M = \dfrac{F - f}{-f}$
$\quad M = \dfrac{f - F}{f}$

42.
$T = g(r + vt)$
$\dfrac{T}{r + vt} = g$

43. $(8 - 3i) - (17 - 7i) = 8 - 3i - 17 + 7i$
$\qquad\qquad\qquad\qquad = -9 + 4i$

44. $4i(3i - 2) = (4i)(3i) + (4i)(-2)$
$\qquad\qquad\quad = 12i^2 - 8i$
$\qquad\qquad\quad = -12 - 8i$

45. $(7 - 5i)(2 + 3i)$
$= 7 \cdot 2 + 7(3i) + (-5i)(2) + (-5i)(3i)$
$= 14 + 21i - 10i + 15$
$= 29 + 11i$

46. $(3 - 4i)^2 = 3^2 + 2 \cdot 3(-4i) + (-4i)^2$
$\qquad\qquad = 9 - 24i - 16$
$\qquad\qquad = -7 - 24i$

47. $(7 + 8i)(7 - 8i) = 7^2 + 8^2 = 49 + 64 = 113$

48.
$\dfrac{6}{5 + i} = \dfrac{6}{5 + i} \cdot \dfrac{5 - i}{5 - i}$
$\qquad = \dfrac{6(5 - i)}{25 + 1}$
$\qquad = \dfrac{6(5 - i)}{26}$
$\qquad = \dfrac{3(5 - i)}{13} = \dfrac{15}{13} - \dfrac{3}{13}i$

49.
$\dfrac{3 + 4i}{4 - 2i} = \dfrac{3 + 4i}{4 - 2i} \cdot \dfrac{4 + 2i}{4 + 2i}$
$\qquad = \dfrac{12 + 6i + 16i + 8i^2}{4^2 + 2^2}$
$\qquad = \dfrac{12 + 22i - 8}{16 + 4}$
$\qquad = \dfrac{4 + 22i}{20}$
$\qquad = \dfrac{1}{5} + \dfrac{11}{10}i$

50. $\sqrt{-32} - \sqrt{-18} = i\sqrt{32} - i\sqrt{18}$
$\qquad\qquad\qquad = i\sqrt{16 \cdot 2} - i\sqrt{9 \cdot 2}$
$\qquad\qquad\qquad = 4i\sqrt{2} - 3i\sqrt{2}$
$\qquad\qquad\qquad = (4i - 3i)\sqrt{2}$
$\qquad\qquad\qquad = i\sqrt{2}$

51. $(-2 + \sqrt{-100})^2 = (-2 + i\sqrt{100})^2$
$\qquad\qquad\qquad = (-2 + 10i)^2$
$\qquad\qquad\qquad = 4 - 40i + (10i)^2$
$\qquad\qquad\qquad = 4 - 40i - 100$
$\qquad\qquad\qquad = -96 - 40i$

52. $\dfrac{4+\sqrt{-8}}{2} = \dfrac{4+i\sqrt{8}}{2} = \dfrac{4+2i\sqrt{2}}{2} = 2+i\sqrt{2}$

53.
$$2x^2 + 15x = 8$$
$$2x^2 + 15x - 8 = 0$$
$$(2x-1)(x+8) = 0$$
$$2x - 1 = 0 \quad x + 8 = 0$$
$$x = \dfrac{1}{2} \text{ or } x = -8$$
The solution set is $\left\{\dfrac{1}{2}, -8\right\}$.

54.
$$5x^2 + 20x = 0$$
$$5x(x+4) = 0$$
$$5x = 0 \quad x + 4 = 0$$
$$x = 0 \text{ or } x = -4$$
The solution set is $\{0, -4\}$.

55.
$$2x^2 - 3 = 125$$
$$2x^2 = 128$$
$$x^2 = 64$$
$$x = \pm 8$$
The solution set is $\{8, -8\}$.

56.
$$(3x-4)^2 = 18$$
$$3x - 4 = \pm\sqrt{18}$$
$$3x = 4 \pm 3\sqrt{2}$$
$$x = \dfrac{4 \pm 3\sqrt{2}}{3}$$
The solution set is $\left\{\dfrac{4+3\sqrt{2}}{3}, \dfrac{4-3\sqrt{2}}{3}\right\}$.

57. $x^2 + 20x$
$$\left(\dfrac{20}{2}\right)^2 = 10^2 = 100$$
$$x^2 + 20x + 100 = (x+10)^2$$

58. $x^2 - 3x$
$$\left(\dfrac{3}{2}\right)^2 = \dfrac{9}{4}$$
$$x^2 - 3x + \dfrac{9}{4} = \left(x - \dfrac{3}{2}\right)^2$$

59.
$$x^2 - 12x = -27$$
$$x^2 - 12x + 36 = -27 + 36$$
$$(x-6)^2 = 9$$
$$x - 6 = \pm 3$$
$$x = 6 \pm 3$$
$$x = 9, \ 3$$
The solution set is $\{9, 3\}$.

60.
$$3x^2 - 12x + 11 = 0$$
$$x^2 - 4x = -\dfrac{11}{3}$$
$$x^2 - 4x + 4 = -\dfrac{11}{3} + 4$$
$$(x-2)^2 = \dfrac{1}{3}$$
$$x - 2 = \pm\sqrt{\dfrac{1}{3}}$$
$$x = 2 \pm \dfrac{\sqrt{3}}{3}$$
The solution set is $\left\{2 + \dfrac{\sqrt{3}}{3}, 2 - \dfrac{\sqrt{3}}{3}\right\}$.

61.
$$x^2 = 2x + 4$$
$$x^2 - 2x - 4 = 0$$
$$x = \dfrac{2 \pm \sqrt{(-2)^2 - 4(1)(-4)}}{2(1)}$$
$$x = \dfrac{2 \pm \sqrt{4 + 16}}{2}$$
$$x = \dfrac{2 \pm \sqrt{20}}{2}$$
$$x = \dfrac{2 \pm 2\sqrt{5}}{2}$$
$$x = 1 \pm \sqrt{5}$$
The solution set is $\left\{1 + \sqrt{5}, 1 - \sqrt{5}\right\}$.

62. $x^2 - 2x + 19 = 0$

$$x = \frac{2 \pm \sqrt{(-2)^2 - 4(1)(19)}}{2(1)}$$

$$x = \frac{2 \pm \sqrt{4 - 76}}{2}$$

$$x = \frac{2 \pm \sqrt{-72}}{2}$$

$$x = \frac{2 \pm 6i\sqrt{2}}{2}$$

$$x = 1 \pm 3i\sqrt{2}$$

The solution set is $\left\{1 + 3i\sqrt{2}, 1 - 3i\sqrt{2}\right\}$.

63. $2x^2 = 3 - 4x$

$2x^2 + 4x - 3 = 0$

$$x = \frac{-4 \pm \sqrt{4^2 - 4(2)(-3)}}{2(2)}$$

$$x = \frac{-4 \pm \sqrt{16 + 24}}{4}$$

$$x = \frac{-4 \pm \sqrt{40}}{4}$$

$$x = \frac{-4 \pm 2\sqrt{10}}{4}$$

$$x = \frac{-2 \pm \sqrt{10}}{2}$$

The solution set is $\left\{\dfrac{-2 + \sqrt{10}}{2}, \dfrac{-2 - \sqrt{10}}{2}\right\}$.

64. $x^2 - 4x + 13 = 0$

$(-4)^2 - 4(1)(13)$

$= 16 - 52$

$= -36$; 2 complex imaginary solutions

65. $9x^2 = 2 - 3x$

$9x^2 + 3x - 2 = 0$

$3^2 - 4(9)(-2)$

$= 9 + 72$

$= 81$; 2 unequal real solutions

66. $2x^2 - 11x + 5 = 0$

$(2x - 1)(x - 5) = 0$

$2x - 1 = 0 \quad x - 5 = 0$

$x = \dfrac{1}{2}$ or $x = 5$

The solution set is $\left\{5, \dfrac{1}{2}\right\}$.

67. $(3x + 5)(x - 3) = 5$

$3x^2 + 5x - 9x - 15 = 5$

$3x^2 - 4x - 20 = 0$

$$x = \frac{4 \pm \sqrt{(-4)^2 - 4(3)(-20)}}{2(3)}$$

$$x = \frac{4 \pm \sqrt{16 + 240}}{6}$$

$$x = \frac{4 \pm \sqrt{256}}{6}$$

$$x = \frac{4 \pm 16}{6}$$

$$x = \frac{20}{6}, \ \frac{-12}{6}$$

$$x = \frac{10}{3}, \ -2$$

The solution set is $\left\{-2, \dfrac{10}{3}\right\}$.

68. $3x^2 - 7x + 1 = 0$

$$x = \frac{7 \pm \sqrt{(-7)^2 - 4(3)(1)}}{2(3)}$$

$$x = \frac{7 \pm \sqrt{49 - 12}}{6}$$

$$x = \frac{7 \pm \sqrt{37}}{6}$$

The solution set is $\left\{\dfrac{7 + \sqrt{37}}{6}, \dfrac{7 - \sqrt{37}}{6}\right\}$.

69. $x^2 - 9 = 0$

$x^2 = 9$

$x = \pm 3$

The solution set is $\{-3, 3\}$.

70. $(x-3)^2 - 25 = 0$

$$(x-3)^2 = 25$$
$$x - 3 = \pm 5$$
$$x = 3 \pm 5$$
$$x = 8, -2$$

The solution set is $\{8, -2\}$.

71. $3x^2 - x + 2 = 0$

$$x = \frac{1 \pm \sqrt{(-1)^2 - 4(3)(2)}}{2(3)}$$

$$x = \frac{1 \pm \sqrt{1 - 24}}{6}$$

$$x = \frac{1 \pm \sqrt{-23}}{6}$$

$$x = \frac{1 \pm i\sqrt{23}}{6}$$

The solution set is $\left\{\dfrac{1 + i\sqrt{23}}{6}, \dfrac{1 - i\sqrt{23}}{6}\right\}$.

72. $W = 3t^2$

$$1200 = 3t^2$$
$$400 = t^2$$
$$t = \pm 20$$

Discard negative time; it will weigh 1200 grams in 20 weeks.

73.

$$-10x^2 + 475x + 3500 = 7250$$
$$-10x^2 + 475x - 3750 = 0$$
$$10x^2 - 475x + 3750 = 0$$
$$x = \frac{475 \pm \sqrt{475^2 - 4(10)(-3750)}}{2(10)}$$
$$x = \frac{475 \pm \sqrt{75625}}{20}$$
$$x = \frac{475 \pm 275}{20}$$
$$x = 20, \ x = 37.5$$

After 10 years.

74. $(10, 7250)$

75. $5 = 2(2l - 7) + 2l$

$$5 = 4l - 14 + 2l$$
$$19 = 6l$$
$$4.8 = l$$
$$2l - 7 = 2.6$$

The length is 4.8 yards, the width is 2.6 yards.

76. Let x = height of building

$2x$ = shadow height

$$x^2 + (2x)^2 = 300^2$$
$$x^2 + 4x^2 = 90,000$$
$$5x^2 = 90,000$$
$$x^2 = 18,000$$
$$x \approx \pm 134.164$$

Discard negative height.

The building is approximately 134 meters high.

77. $2x^4 = 50x^2$

$$2x^4 - 50x^2 = 0$$
$$2x^2(x^2 - 25) = 0$$
$$x = 0$$
$$x = \pm 5$$

The solution set is $\{-5, 0, 5\}$.

78. $2x^3 - x^2 - 18x + 9 = 0$

$$x^2(2x - 1) - 9(2x - 1) = 0$$
$$(x^2 - 9)(2x - 1) = 0$$
$$x = \pm 3, \ x = \frac{1}{2}$$

The solution set is $\left\{-3, \dfrac{1}{2}, 3\right\}$.

79. $\sqrt{2x-3}+x=3$

$\sqrt{2x-3}=3-x$

$2x-3=9-6x+x^2$

$x^2-8x+12=0$

$x^2-8x=-12$

$x^2-8x+16=-12+16$

$(x-4)^2=4$

$x-4=\pm2$

$x=4+2$

$x=6,2$

The solution set is $\{2\}$.

80. $\sqrt{x-4}+\sqrt{x+1}=5$

$\sqrt{x-4}=5-\sqrt{x+1}$

$x-4=25-10\sqrt{x+1}+(x+1)$

$x-4=26+x-10\sqrt{x+1}$

$-30=-10\sqrt{x+1}$

$3=\sqrt{x+1}$

$9=x+1$

$x=8$

The solution set is $\{8\}$.

81. $3x^{3/4}-24=0$

$3x^{3/4}=24$

$x^{3/4}=8$

$x=8^{4/3}$

$x=16$

The solution set is $\{16\}$.

82. $(x-7)^{\frac{2}{3}}=25$

$\left[(x-7)^{\frac{2}{3}}\right]^{\frac{3}{2}}=25^{\frac{3}{2}}$

$x-7=\left(5^2\right)^{\frac{3}{2}}$

$x-7=5^3$

$x-7=125$

$x=132$

The solution set is $\{132\}$.

83. $x^4-5x^2+4=0$

Let $t=x^2$

$t^2-5t+4=0$

$(t-4)(t-1)=0$

$t=4$ or $t=1$

$x^2=4$ $x^2=1$

$x=\pm2$ $x=\pm1$

The solution set is $\{-2,-1,1,2\}$.

84. $x^{1/2}+3x^{1/4}-10=0$

Let $t=x^{1/4}$

$t^2+3t-10=0$

$(t+5)(t-2)=0$

$t=-5$ or $t=2$

$x^{1/4}=-5$ or $x^{1/4}=2$

$x=625$ $x=16$

The solution set is $\{16\}$.

85. $|2x+1|=7$

$2x+1=7$ or $2x+1=-7$

$2x=6$ $2x=-8$

$x=3$ or $x=-4$

The solution set is $\{-4,3\}$.

86. $2|x-3|-6=10$

$2|x-3|=16$

$|x-3|=8$

$x-3=8$ or $x-3=-8$

$x=11$ $x=-5$

The solution set is $\{-5,11\}$.

87. $3x^{4/3}-5x^{2/3}+2=0$

Let $t=x^{2/3}$.

$3t^2-5t+2=0$

$(3t-2)(t-1)=0$

$t=\dfrac{2}{3}$ or $t=1$

$x^{2/3}=\dfrac{2}{3}$ $x^{2/3}=1$

$x=\pm\left(\dfrac{2}{3}\right)^{3/2}$ $x=\pm1^{3/2}$

$x=\pm\dfrac{2\sqrt{6}}{9}$ $x=\pm1$

The solution set is $\left\{-1,-\dfrac{2\sqrt{6}}{9},\dfrac{2\sqrt{6}}{9},1\right\}$.

88. $2\sqrt{x-1} = x$

$4(x-1) = x^2$

$4x - 4 = x^2$

$x^2 - 4x + 4 = 0$

$(x-2)^2 = 0$

$x = 2$

The solution set is $\{2\}$.

89. $|2x-5| - 3 = 0$

$|2x-5| = 3$

$2x - 5 = 3$ or $2x - 5 = -3$

$2x = 8 \qquad 2x = 2$

$x = 4 \qquad x = 1$

The solution set is $\{4, 1\}$.

90. $x^3 + 2x^2 - 9x - 18 = 0$

$x^2(x+2) - 9(x+2) = 0$

$(x^2 - 9)(x+2) = 0$

$x + 2 = 0 \quad$ or $\quad x^2 - 9 = 0$

$x = -2 \qquad\qquad x = -3, 3$

The solution set is $\{-3, -2, 3\}$.

91. $D = \sqrt{2H}$

$50 = \sqrt{2H}$

$2500 = 2H$

$H = 1250$

The mountain is 1250 feet high.

92.

93.

94.

95. $-2 < x \le 3$

96. $-1.5 \le x \le 2$

97. $x > -1$

98. $-6x + 3 \le 15$

$-6x \le 12$

$x \ge 2$

The solution set is $[-2, \infty)$.

99. $6x - 9 \ge -4x - 3$

$10x \ge 6$

$x \ge \dfrac{3}{5}$

The solution set is $\left[\dfrac{3}{5}, \infty\right)$.

100. $\dfrac{x}{3} - \dfrac{3}{4} - 1 > \dfrac{x}{2}$

$12\left(\dfrac{x}{3} - \dfrac{3}{4} - 1\right) > 12\left(\dfrac{x}{2}\right)$

$4x - 9 - 12 > 6x$

$-21 > 2x$

$-\dfrac{21}{2} > x$

The solution set is $\left(-\infty, -\dfrac{21}{2}\right)$.

101. $6x + 5 > -2(x-3) - 25$

$6x + 5 > -2x + 6 - 25$

$8x + 5 > -19$

$8x > -24$

$x > -3$

The solution set is $(-3, \infty)$.

102. $3(2x-1) - 2(x-4) \ge 7 + 2(3 + 4x)$

$6x - 3 - 2x + 8 \ge 7 + 6 + 8x$

$4x + 5 \ge 8x + 13$

$$-4x \geq 8$$
$$x \leq -2$$

The solution set is $[-\infty, -2)$.

103. $7 < 2x + 3 \leq 9$
$4 < 2x \leq 6$
$2 < x \leq 3$
$(2, 3]$

The solution set is $[2, 3)$.

104. $|2x + 3| \leq 15$
$-15 \leq 2x + 3 \leq 15$
$-18 \leq 2x \leq 12$
$-9 \leq x \leq 6$

The solution set is $[-9, 6]$.

105. $\left| \dfrac{2x+6}{3} \right| > 2$

$\dfrac{2x+6}{3} > 2 \qquad \dfrac{2x+6}{3} < -2$

$2x + 6 > 6 \qquad 2x + 6 < -6$

$2x > 0 \qquad\quad 2x < -12$

$x > 0 \qquad\quad x < -6$

The solution set is $(-\infty, -6)$ or $(0, \infty)$.

106. $|2x + 5| - 7 \geq -6$

$|2x + 5| \geq 1$

$2x + 5 \geq 1 \text{ or } 2x + 5 \leq -1$

$2x \geq -4 \qquad\quad 2x \leq -6$

$x \geq -2 \quad \text{or} \quad x \leq -3$

The solution set is $(-\infty, -3]$ or $[-2, \infty)$.

107. $|h - 6.5| \leq 1$

$-1 \leq h - 6.5 \leq 1$

$5.5 \leq h \leq 7.5$
Most people sleep between 5.5 and 7.5 hours.

108. $10 \leq \dfrac{5}{9}(F - 32) \leq 25$

$\dfrac{9}{5} \cdot 10 \leq F - 32 \leq \dfrac{9}{5} \cdot 25$

$\quad 18 \leq F - 32 \leq 45$

$\quad 50 \leq F \leq 77$

The range is between 50° and 77°, inclusively.

109. Option 1: $11 + 0.06x$
Option 2: $4 + 0.20x$
$11 + 0.06x < 4 + 0.20x$
$-0.14x < -7$
$x > 50$
More than 50 checks should be written.

110.

$\dfrac{76 + 80 + 72 + x}{4} \geq 80$

$228 + x \geq 32$

$x > 92$

111. $2x^2 + 7x \leq 4$
$2x^2 + 7x - 4 \leq 0$
$(2x - 1)(x + 4) \leq 0$
$x = -4 \text{ or } x = \dfrac{1}{2}$

$2(-5)^2 + 7(-5) \leq 4$
Test -5: $\qquad 50 - 35 \leq 4$
$\qquad\qquad\qquad 15 \leq 4 \text{ False}$

Test 0: $2(0)^2 + 7(0) \leq 4$
$\qquad\qquad\qquad 0 \leq 4 \text{ True}$

$2(1)^2 + 7(1) \leq 4$
Test 1: $\qquad 2 + 7 \leq 4$
$\qquad\qquad\qquad 9 \leq 4 \text{ False}$

The solution set is $\left[-4, \dfrac{1}{2}\right]$.

-4　　$\dfrac{1}{2}$

112. $2x^2 > 6x - 3$

$2x^2 - 6x + 3 > 0$

$x = \dfrac{6 \pm \sqrt{(-6)^2 - 4(2)(3)}}{2(2)}$

$x = \dfrac{6 \pm 2\sqrt{3}}{4}$

$x = \dfrac{3 \pm \sqrt{3}}{2}$

T	F	T
$\dfrac{3-\sqrt{3}}{2}$	$\dfrac{3+\sqrt{3}}{2}$	

Test 0: $2(0)^2 > 6(0) - 4$　　Test 1: $2(1)^2 > 6(1) - 3$
　　　　$0 > -3$ True　　　　　　　　$2 > 3$ True

Test 3: $2(3)^2 > 6(3) - 3$
　　　　$18 > 15$ True

The solution set is $\left(-\infty, \dfrac{3-\sqrt{3}}{2}\right)$ or

$\left(\dfrac{3+\sqrt{3}}{2}, \infty\right)$.

$\dfrac{3-\sqrt{3}}{2}$　　$\dfrac{3+\sqrt{3}}{2}$

113. $\dfrac{x-6}{x+2} > 0$

$x - 6 = 0$ or $x + 2 = 0$

$x = 6$ or $x = -2$

T	F	T
-2	6	

Test -3: $\dfrac{-3-6}{-3+2} > 0$

　　　　$9 > 0$ True

Test 0: $\dfrac{0-6}{0+2} > 0$

　　　　$-3 > 0$ False

Test 7: $\dfrac{7-6}{7+2} > 0$

　　　$\dfrac{1}{9} > 0$ True

The solution set is $(-\infty, -2)$ or $(6, \infty)$.

-2　　6

114. $\dfrac{x+3}{x-4} \le 5$

$\dfrac{x+3-5(x-4)}{x-4} \le 0$

$\dfrac{x+3-5x+20}{x-4} \le 0$

$\dfrac{23-4x}{x-4} \le 0$

$x = 4$ or $x = \dfrac{23}{4}$

T	F	T
4	$\dfrac{23}{4}$	

Test 0: $\dfrac{0+3}{0-4} \le 5$

　　　　$-\dfrac{3}{4} \le 5$ True

Test 5: $\dfrac{5+3}{5-4} \le 5$

　　　　$8 \le 5$ False

Test 6: $\dfrac{6+3}{6-4} \le 5$

　　　　$\dfrac{9}{2} \le 5$ True

The solution set is $(-\infty, 4)$ or $\left[\dfrac{23}{4}, \infty\right)$.

4　　$\dfrac{23}{4}$

115. $s = -16t^2 + v_0 t + s_0$

$32 < -16t^2 + 48t + 0$

$0 < -16t^2 + 48t - 32$

$0 < -16\left(t^2 - 3t + 2\right)$

$0 < -16(t-2)(t-1)$

The projectile's height exceeds 32 feet
during the time period from 1 to 2 seconds.

Chapter 1 Test

1.

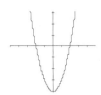

2. *x*-intercept $(2, 0)$　*y*-intercept $(0, 3)$

3. 1992, 7.8%

4. $7(x - 2) = 4(x + 1) - 21$
$7x - 14 = 4x + 4 - 21$
$7x - 14 = 4x - 17$
$3x = -3$
$x = -1$
The solution set is $\{-1\}$.

5. $\dfrac{2x - 3}{4} = \dfrac{x - 4}{2} - \dfrac{x + 1}{4}$
$2x - 3 = 2(x - 4) - (x + 1)$
$2x - 3 = 2x - 8 - x - 1$
$2x - 3 = x - 9$
$\quad x = -6$
The solution set is $\{-6\}$.

6. $\dfrac{2}{x - 3} - \dfrac{4}{x + 3} = \dfrac{8}{(x - 3)(x + 3)}$
$2(x + 3) - 4(x - 3) = 8$
$2x + 6 - 4x + 12 = 8$
$-2x + 18 = 8$
$-2x = -10$
$x = 5$
The solution set is $\{5\}$.

7. $2x^2 - 3x - 2 = 0$
$(2x + 1)(x - 2) = 0$

$2x + 1 = 0$　or　$x - 2 = 0$
$x = -\dfrac{1}{2}$　or　$x = 2$
The solution set is $\left\{-\dfrac{1}{2}, 2\right\}$.

8. $(3x - 1)^2 = 75$
$3x - 1 = \pm\sqrt{75}$
$3x = 1 \pm 5\sqrt{3}$
$x = \dfrac{1 \pm 5\sqrt{3}}{3}$
The solution set is $\left\{\dfrac{1 - 5\sqrt{3}}{3}, \dfrac{1 + 5\sqrt{3}}{3}\right\}$.

9. $x(x - 2) = 4$
$x^2 - 2x - 4 = 0$
$x = \dfrac{2 \pm \sqrt{(-2)^2 - 4(1)(-4)}}{2}$
$x = \dfrac{2 \pm 2\sqrt{5}}{2}$
$x = 1 \pm \sqrt{5}$
The solution set is $\left\{1 - \sqrt{5}, 1 + \sqrt{5}\right\}$.

10. $4x^2 = 8x - 5$
$4x^2 - 8x + 5 = 0$
$x = \dfrac{8 \pm \sqrt{(-8)^2 - 4(4)(5)}}{2(4)}$
$x = \dfrac{8 \pm \sqrt{-16}}{8}$
$x = \dfrac{8 \pm 4i}{8}$
$x = \dfrac{2 \pm i}{2}$
The solution set is $\left\{\dfrac{2 - i}{2}, \dfrac{2 + i}{2}\right\}$.

11. $x^3 - 4x^2 - x + 4 = 0$
$x^2(x - 4) - 1(x - 4) = 0$
$\left(x^2 - 1\right)(x - 4) = 0$
$(x - 1)(x + 1)(x - 4) = 0$
$x = 1$ or $x = -1$ or $x = 4$
The solution set is $\{-1, 1, 4\}$.

12.
$$\sqrt{x-3}+5=x$$
$$\sqrt{x-3}=x-5$$
$$x-3=x^2-10x+25$$
$$x^2-11x+28=0$$
$$x=\frac{11\pm\sqrt{11^2-4(1)(28)}}{2(1)}$$
$$x=\frac{11\pm\sqrt{121-112}}{2}$$
$$x=\frac{11\pm\sqrt{9}}{2}$$
$$x=\frac{11\pm3}{2}$$
$$x=7 \text{ or } x=4$$
The solution set is $\{7\}$.

13. $\sqrt{x+4}+\sqrt{x-1}=5$
$$\sqrt{x+4}=5-\sqrt{x-1}$$
$$x+4=25-10\sqrt{x-1}+(x-1)$$
$$x+4=25-10\sqrt{x-1}+x-1$$
$$-20=-10\sqrt{x-1}$$
$$2=\sqrt{x-1}$$
$$4=x-1$$
$$x=5$$
The solution set is $\{5\}$.

14. $5x^{3/2}-10=0$
$$5x^{3/2}=10$$
$$x^{3/2}=2$$
$$x=2^{2/3}$$
$$x=\sqrt[3]{4}$$
The solution set is $\left\{\sqrt[3]{4}\right\}$.

15. $x^{2/3}-9x^{1/3}+8=0$ let $t=x^{1/3}$
$$t^2-9t+8=0$$
$$(t-1)(t-8)=0$$
$$t=1 \qquad t=8$$
$$x^{1/3}=1 \quad x^{1/3}=8$$
$$x=1 \qquad x=512$$
The solution set is $\{1,512\}$.

16. $\left|\frac{2}{3}x-6\right|=2$
$$\frac{2}{3}x-6=2 \qquad \frac{2}{3}x-6=-2$$
$$\frac{2}{3}x=8 \qquad \frac{2}{3}x=4$$
$$x=12 \qquad x=6$$
The solution set is $\{6, 12\}$.

17. $3(x+4)\geq 5x-12$
$$3x+12\geq 5x-12$$
$$-2x\geq -24$$
$$x\leq 12$$
The solution set is $(-\infty,\ 12]$.

12

18. $\frac{x}{6}+\frac{1}{8}\leq\frac{x}{2}-\frac{3}{4}$
$$4x+3\leq 12x-18$$
$$-8x\leq -21$$
$$x\geq\frac{21}{8}$$
The solution set is $\left[\frac{21}{8},\infty\right)$.

$\frac{21}{8}$

19. $-3\leq\frac{2x+5}{3}<6$
$$-9\leq 2x+5<18$$
$$-14\leq 2x<13$$
$$-7\leq x<\frac{13}{2}$$
The solution set is $\left[-7,\frac{13}{2}\right)$.

$-7 \qquad \frac{13}{2}$

20. $|3x+2|\geq 3$
$$3x+2\geq 3 \quad \text{or} \quad 3x+2\leq -3$$
$$3x\geq 1 \qquad\qquad 3x\leq -5$$
$$x\geq\frac{1}{3} \qquad\qquad x\leq-\frac{5}{3}$$

The solution set is $\left(-\infty, -\dfrac{5}{3}\right]$ or $\left[\dfrac{1}{3}, \infty\right)$.

$$-\dfrac{5}{3} \qquad \dfrac{1}{3}$$

21. $x^2 < x + 12$

$x^2 - x - 12 < 0$

$(x-4)(x+3) < 0$

$x = 4$ or $x = -3$

F		T		F

$$-3 \qquad 4$$

Test -4: $(-4)^2 < -4 + 12$
$\qquad\qquad 16 < 8$ False

Test 0: $0^2 < 0 + 12$
$\qquad\qquad 0 < 12$ True

Test 5: $5^2 < 5 + 12$
$\qquad\qquad 25 < 17$ False

The solution set is $(-3, 4)$.

$$3 \qquad 10$$

22. $\dfrac{2x+1}{x-3} > 3$

$\dfrac{2x+1-3(x-3)}{x-3} > 0$

$\dfrac{2x+1-3x+9}{x-3} > 0$

$\dfrac{10-x}{x-3} > 0$

$x = 3$ or $x = 10$

F		T		F

$$3 \qquad 10$$

Test 0: $\dfrac{2(0)+1}{0-3} > 3$
$\qquad\qquad -\dfrac{1}{3} > 3$ False

Test 4: $\dfrac{2(4)+1}{4-3} > 3$
$\qquad\qquad 9 > 3$ True

Test 11: $\dfrac{2(11)+1}{11-3} \ge 3$

$\dfrac{23}{8} > 3$ False

The solution set is $(3, 10)$.

$$3 \qquad 10$$

23. $(6-7i)(2+5i) = 12 + 30i - 14i - 35i^2$
$\qquad\qquad = 12 + 16i + 35$
$\qquad\qquad = 47 + 16i$

24. $\dfrac{5}{2-i} = \dfrac{5}{2-i} \cdot \dfrac{2+i}{2+i}$

$\qquad = \dfrac{5(2+i)}{4+1}$

$\qquad = \dfrac{5(2+i)}{5}$

$\qquad = 2 + i$

25. $2\sqrt{-49} + 3\sqrt{-64} = 2(7i) + 3(8i)$
$\qquad\qquad\qquad = 14i + 24i$
$\qquad\qquad\qquad = 38i$

26. $V = \dfrac{1}{3}lwh$

$3V = lwh$

$\dfrac{3V}{lw} = h$

27. $y - y_1 = m(x - x_1)$

$\qquad y - y_1 = mx - mx_1$

$\qquad y - y_1 + mx_1 = mx$

$\qquad \dfrac{y - y_1 + mx_1}{m} = x$

$\qquad \dfrac{y - y_1}{m} + x_1 = x$

28. $4.1 = 0.01x + 3.9$

$0.2 = 0.01x$

$20 = x$

$1984 + 20 = 2004$

29.
$$4.1 + .07x = 5.71$$
$$.07x = 1.61$$
$$x = 23$$
$$1984 + 23 = 2007$$

30. Let x = days for New York
$3x + 48$ = days for Los Angeles
$$x + 3x + 48 = 268$$
$$4x = 220$$
$$x = 55$$
$$3x + 48 = 213$$
55 unhealthy days for New York, 213 for Los Angeles.

31.
$$29700 + 150x = 5000 + 1100x$$
$$24700 = 950x$$
$$26 = x$$

In 26 years, the cost will be $33,600.

32. Let x = amount invested at 8%
$10000 - x$ = amount invested at 10%
$$.08x + .1(10000 - x) = 940$$
$$.08x + 1000 - .1x = 940$$
$$-.02x = -60$$
$$x = 3000$$
$$10000 - x = 7000$$

$3000 at 8%, $7000 at 10%

33.
$$l = 2w + 4$$
$$A = lw$$
$$48 = (2w + 4)w$$
$$48 = 2w^2 + 4w$$
$$0 = 2w^2 + 4w - 48$$
$$0 = w^2 + 2w - 24$$
$$0 = (w + 6)(w - 4)$$

$$w + 6 = 0 \qquad w - 4 = 0$$
$$w = -6 \qquad w = 4$$
$$2w + 4 = 2(4) + 4 = 12$$

width is 4 feet, length is 12 feet

34.
$$24^2 + x^2 = 26^2$$
$$576 + x^2 = 676$$
$$x^2 = 100$$
$$x = \pm 10$$
The wire should be attached 10 feet up the pole.

35.
$$600 + 0.04x > 2500$$
$$0.04x > 1900$$
$$x > 47500$$

You need to sell more than $47,500 in supplies.

Chapter 2

Section 2.1

Check Point Exercises

1. a. $m = \dfrac{-2-4}{-4-(-3)} = \dfrac{-6}{-1} = 6$

b. $m = \dfrac{5-(-2)}{-1-4} = \dfrac{7}{-5} = -\dfrac{7}{5}$

2. $y - y_1 = m(x - x_1)$
$y - (-5) = 6(x - 2)$
$y + 5 = 6x - 12$
$y = 6x - 17$

3. $m = \dfrac{-6-(-1)}{-1-(-2)} = \dfrac{-5}{1} = -5$,

so the slope is –5. Using the point (–2, –1), we get the point slope equation:
$y - y_1 = m(x - x_1)$
$y - (-1) = -5[x - (-2)]$
$y + 1 = -5(x + 2)$. Solve the equation for y:
$y + 1 = -5x - 10$
$y = -5x - 11$.

4. The slope m is $\frac{3}{5}$ and the y-intercept is 1, so one point on the line is (1, 0). We can find a second point on the line by using the slope $m = \frac{3}{5} = \frac{\text{Rise}}{\text{Run}}$: starting at the point (0, 1), move 3 units up and 5 units to the right, to obtain the point (5, 4).

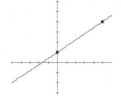

5. $y = 3$, horizontal line through (0, 3).

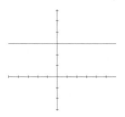

6. $x = \_1$, vertical line through (_1, 0).

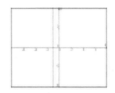

7. $3x + 6y - 12 = 0$
$6y = -3x + 12$
$y = \dfrac{-3}{6}x + \dfrac{12}{6}$
$y = -\dfrac{1}{2}x + 2$

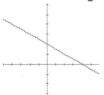

The slope is $-\dfrac{1}{2}$ and the y-intercept is 2.

8. Since the line is to pass through the point (_2, 5), in the point-slope formula we have $x_1 = -2$ and $y_1 = 5$. Also since the line is to be parallel to the line $y = 3x + 1$, the two lines must have the same slope $m = 3$.
point-slope form: $y - 5 = 3(x + 2)$
slope-intercept form:
$y - 5 = 3x + 6$, $y = 3x + 11$

9. $x + 3y - 12 = 0$
$$3y = -x + 12$$
$$y = -\frac{1}{3}x + 4$$

The given line has slope $m = -\frac{1}{3}$, so any line perpendicular to it has a slope that is the negative reciprocal of $-\frac{1}{3}$, or 3.

10. (1995, 10)   (2010, 12)
$$m = \frac{12 - 10}{2010 - 1995} = \frac{2}{15} = 0.13$$

The number of men living alone is increasing 0.13 million per year.

11. Using the points (10, 203.3) and (20, 226.5), we obtain a slope of

$$m = \frac{\text{change in } y}{\text{change in } x}$$
$$= \frac{226.5 - 203.3}{20 - 10} = \frac{23.2}{10} = 2.32.$$

Using the point (10, 203.3), the point slope equation of the line is given by:
$$y - y_1 = m(x - x_1)$$
$$y - 203.3 = 2.32(x - 10)$$
$$y - 203.3 = 2.32x - 23.2$$
$$y = 2.32x + 180.1.$$

The linear equation that models U.S. population, y, in millions, x years after 1960 is $y = 2.32x + 180.1$. To estimate the U.S. population in 2020, note that 2020 is $x = 60$ years after 1960, so substitute 60 for x and compute y. $y = 2.32(60) + 180.1 = 319.3$ Our equation predicts that the U.S. population in the year 2020 will be 319.3 million.

Exercise Set 2.1

1. $m = \dfrac{10 - 7}{8 - 4} = \dfrac{3}{4}$; rises

3. $m = \dfrac{2 - 1}{2 - (-2)} = \dfrac{1}{4}$; rises

5. $m = \dfrac{2 - (-2)}{3 - 4} = \dfrac{0}{-1} = 0$; horizontal

7. $m = \dfrac{-1 - 4}{-1 - (-2)} = \dfrac{-5}{1} = -5$; falls

9. $m = \dfrac{-2 - 3}{5 - 5} = \dfrac{-5}{0}$ undefined; vertical

11. $m = 2$, $x_1 = 3$, $y_1 = 5$;
point-slope form: $y - 5 = 2(x - 3)$;
slope-intercept form: $y - 5 = 2x - 6$
$$y = 2x - 1$$

13. $m = 6$, $x_1 = -2$, $y_1 = 5$;
point-slope form: $y - 5 = 6(x + 2)$;
slope-intercept form: $y - 5 = 6x + 12$
$$y = 6x + 17$$

15. $m = -3$, $x_1 = -2$, $y_1 = -3$;
point-slope form: $y + 3 = -3(x + 2)$;
slope-intereept form: $y + 3 = -3x - 6$
$$y = -3x - 9$$

17. $m = -4$, $x_1 = -4$, $y_1 = 0$;
point-slope form: $y - 0 = -4(x + 4)$;
slope-intercept form: $y = -4(x + 4)$
$$y = -4x - 16$$

19. $m = -1$, $x_1 = \dfrac{-1}{2}$, $y_1 = -2$;
point-slope form: $y + 2 = -1\left(x + \dfrac{1}{2}\right)$;
slope-intercept form: $y + 2 = -x - \dfrac{1}{2}$
$$y = -x - \dfrac{5}{2}$$

21. $m = \dfrac{1}{2}$, $x_1 = 0$, $y_1 = 0$;
point-slope form: $y - 0 = \dfrac{1}{2}(x - 0)$;
slope-intercept form: $y = \dfrac{1}{2}x$

23. $m = -\dfrac{2}{3},\ x_1 = 6,\ y_1 = -2;$

point-slope form: $y + 2 = -\dfrac{2}{3}(x - 6);$

slope-intercept form: $y + 2 = -\dfrac{2}{3}x + 4$

$$y = -\dfrac{2}{3}x + 2$$

25. $m = \dfrac{10 - 2}{5 - 1} = \dfrac{8}{4} = 2;$

point-slope form: $y - 2 = 2(x - 1)$ using
$(x_1,\ y_1) = (1,\ 2),$ or $y - 10 = 2(x - 5)$ using
$(x_1,\ y_1) = (5,\ 10);$ slope-intercept form:
$y - 2 = 2x - 2$ or
$y - 10 = 2x - 10,$
$$y = 2x$$

27. $m = \dfrac{3 - 0}{0 - (-3)} = \dfrac{3}{3} = 1;$

point-slope form: $y - 0 = 1(x + 3)$ using
$(x_1,\ y_1) = (-3,\ 0),$ or $y - 3 = 1(x - 0)$ using
$(x_1,\ y_1) = (0,\ 3);$ slope-intercept form:
$y = x + 3$

29. $m = \dfrac{4 - (-1)}{2 - (-3)} = \dfrac{5}{5} = 1;$

point-slope form: $y + 1 = 1(x + 3)$ using
$(x_1,\ y_1) = (-3,\ -1),$ or $y - 4 = 1(x - 2)$ using
$(x_1,\ y_1) = (2,\ 4);$ slope-intercept form:
$y + 1 = x + 3$ or
$y - 4 = x - 2$
$$y = x + 2$$

31. $m = \dfrac{6 - (-2)}{3 - (-3)} = \dfrac{8}{6} = \dfrac{4}{3};$

point-slope form: $y + 2 = \dfrac{4}{3}(x + 3)$ using

$(x_1,\ y_1) = (-3,\ -2),$ or $y - 6 = \dfrac{4}{3}(x - 3)$

using $(x_1,\ y_1) = (3,\ 6);$ slope-intercept form:

$y + 2 = \dfrac{4}{3x} + 4$ or

$y - 6 = \dfrac{4}{3}x - 4,$

$$y = \dfrac{4}{3}x + 2$$

33. $m = \dfrac{-1 - (-1)}{4 - (-3)} = \dfrac{0}{7} = 0;$

point-slope form: $y + 1 = 0(x + 3)$ using
$(x_1,\ y_1) = (-3,\ -1),$ or $y + 1 = 0(x - 4)$ using
$(x_1,\ y_1) = (4,\ -1);$ slope-intercept form:
$y + 1 = 0,$ so
$y = -1$

35. $m = \dfrac{0 - 4}{-2 - 2} = \dfrac{-4}{-4} = 1;$

point-slope form: $y - 4 = 1(x - 2)$ using
$(x_1,\ y_1) = (2,\ 4),$ or $y - 0 = 1(x + 2)$ using
$(x_1,\ y_1) = (-2,\ 0);$ slope-intercept form:
$y - 9 = x - 2,$ or
$y = x + 2$

37. $m = \dfrac{4 - 0}{0 - \left(-\frac{1}{2}\right)} = \dfrac{4}{\frac{1}{2}} = 8;$

point-slope form: $y - 4 = 8(x - 0)$ using
$(x_1,\ y_1) = (0,\ 4),$ or $y - 0 = 8\left(x + \frac{1}{2}\right)$ using
$(x_1,\ y_1) = \left(-\frac{1}{2},\ 0\right);$ or $y - 0 = 8\left(x + \frac{1}{2}\right)$
slope-intercept form: $y - 4 = 8x$ or
$$y = 8x + 4$$

39. $m = 2;\ b = 1$

41. $m = -2; b = 1$

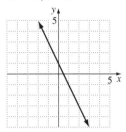

43. $m = \dfrac{3}{4}; \ b = -2$

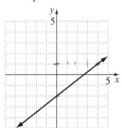

45. $m = -\dfrac{3}{5}; \ b = 7$

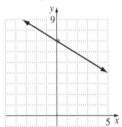

47.

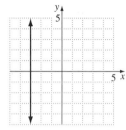

49.

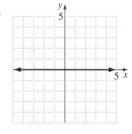

51.

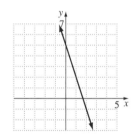

53. a. $3x + y - 5 = 0$
$$y - 5 = -3x$$
$$y = -3x + 5$$

  b. $m = -3; b = 5$

  c.

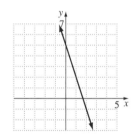

55. a. $2x + 3y - 18 = 0$
$$2x - 18 = -3y$$
$$-3y = 2x - 18$$
$$y = \frac{2}{-3}x - \frac{18}{-3}$$
$$y = -\frac{2}{3}x + 6$$

  b. $m = -\dfrac{2}{3}; \ b = 6$

c.

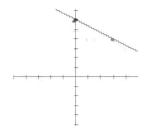

57. a. $8x - 4y - 12 = 0$
$$8x - 12 = 4y$$
$$4y = 8x - 12$$
$$y = \frac{8}{4}x - \frac{12}{4}$$
$$y = 2x - 3$$

b. $m = 2; b = -3$

c.

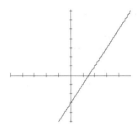

59. a. $3x - 9 = 0$
$$3x = 9$$
$$x = 3$$

b. m is undefined since the line is vertical; no y-intercept since all x values are 3.

c.

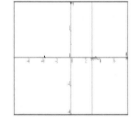

61. $m = -4$ since the line is parallel to
$y = -4x + 3; x_1 = -8, y_1 = -10;$
point-slope form: $y + 10 = -4(x + 8)$

slope-intercept form: $y + 10 = -4x - 32$
$$y = -4x - 42$$

63. $m = -5$ since the line is perpendicular to
$y = \frac{1}{5}x + 6; x_1 = 2, y_1 = -3;$
point-slope form: $y + 3 = -5(x - 2)$
slope-intercept form: $y + 3 = -5x + 10$
$$y = -5x + 7$$

65. $2x - 3y - 7 = 0$
$$-3y = -2x + 7$$
$$y = \frac{2}{3}x - \frac{7}{3}$$
The slope of the given line is $\frac{2}{3}$, so $m = \frac{2}{3}$
since the lines are parallel.
point-slope form: $y - 2 = \frac{2}{3}(x + 2)$
slope-intercept form: $y = \frac{2}{3}x + \frac{10}{3}$

67. $x - 2y - 3 = 0$
$$-2y = -x + 3$$
$$y = \frac{1}{2}x - \frac{3}{2}$$
The slope of the given line is $\frac{1}{2}$, so
$m = -2$ since the lines are perpendicular.
point-slope form: $y + 7 = -2(x - 4)$
slope-intercept form: $y + 7 = -2x + 8$
$$y = -2x + 1$$

69. Answers may vary. The equation $y = 15$ is a reasonable approximation to model the data, since the data are almost constant.

71. $m = \dfrac{1200 - 200}{2010 - 2001} = \dfrac{1000}{9} = 11$

From 2001 to 2010, the budget surplus will increase $111 trillion a year.

73. a. $b = 16$ In 1950, there were 16 workers for each beneficiary.

b. $m = \dfrac{4-16}{50-0} = \dfrac{-12}{50} = -0.24$

The number of workers for each beneficiary is decreasing 0.24 each year.

c. $y = \_0.24x + 16$

d. $2010 - 1950 = 60$

$y = \_0.24(60)+16 = 1.6$ In 2010, there will be 1.6 workers for each beneficiary.

$\dfrac{1.6\,\text{workers}}{1\,\text{beneficiary}} = \dfrac{8\,\text{workers}}{x\,\text{beneficiaries}}$

$1.6x = 8$

$x = \dfrac{8}{1.6}$

$x = 5$

For every 8 workers, there will be 5 beneficiaries.

75. a. $m = \dfrac{38-30}{4-2} = \dfrac{8}{2} = 4$

$y - 30 = 4(x - 2)$

b. $y - 30 = 4x - 8$

$y = 4x + 22$

c. $2008 - 1995 = 13$

$y = 4(13) + 22 = 74$

74 thousand screens in 2008.

77. $(10, 230)$　$(60, 110)$ Points will vary.

$m = \dfrac{110-230}{60-10} = -\dfrac{120}{50} = -2.4$

$y - 230 = -2.4(x - 10)$

$y - 230 = -2.4x + 24$

$y = -2.4x + 254$

Answers will vary for predictions.

79. $y = -0.7x + 60$

81. $m = \dfrac{2000-20000}{55-19} = \dfrac{-18000}{36} = -500$

$y - 20000 = -500(x - 19)$

$y - 20000 = -500x + 9500$

$y = -500x + 29500$

$y = -500(50) + 29500$

$y = 4500$

4500 shirts will be sold at \$50 each.

83.–91. Answers may vary.

93. Two points are $(0, 6)$ and $(10, -24)$.

$m = \dfrac{-24-6}{10-0} = \dfrac{-30}{10} = -3.$

Check: $y = mx + b$: $y = -3x + 6$.

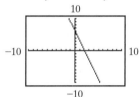

95. Two points are $(0, -2)$ and $(10, 5.5)$.

$m = \dfrac{5.5 - (-2)}{10 - 0} = \dfrac{7.5}{10} = 0.75$ or $\dfrac{3}{4}$.

Check: $y = mx + b$: $y = \dfrac{3}{4}x - 2$.

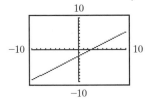

97. a. False; if $m = 0$, the graph does not rise.

b. False; the product of their slopes is -16.

c. True; the point $(6, 0)$ satisfies the equation. Write the equation in slope-intercept form,

$y = -\dfrac{5}{6} + 5$, so the slope $m = -\dfrac{5}{6}$.

d. False; the graph of $y = 7$ is a horizontal line through $(0, 7)$.

(c) is true

99. a. m_1, m_3, m_2, m_4

b. b_2, b_1, b_4, b_3

Section 2.2

Check Point Exercises

1. $(2, -2)$ $(5, 2)$

$d = \sqrt{(5-2)^2 + [2-(-2)]^2}$
$d = \sqrt{3^2 + 4^2}$
$d = \sqrt{9 + 16}$
$d = \sqrt{25}$
$d = 5$

2. $\left(\dfrac{1+7}{2}, \dfrac{2+(-3)}{2} \right) = \left(\dfrac{8}{2}, \dfrac{-1}{2} \right) = \left(4, -\dfrac{1}{2} \right)$

3. $h = 0$, $k = 0$, $r = 4$;
$(x - 0)^2 + (y - 0)^2 = 4^2$
$x^2 + y^2 = 16$

4. $h = 5$, $k = -6$, $r = 10$;
$(x - 5)^2 + [y - (-6)]^2 = 10^2$
$(x - 5)^2 + (y + 6)^2 = 100$

5. $(x + 3)^2 + (y - 1)^2 = 4$
$[x - (-3)]^2 + (y - 1)^2 = 2^2$
So in the standard form of the circle's equation $(x - h)^2 + (y - k)^2 = r^2$,
we have $h = -3$, $k = 1$, $r = 2$.
center: $(h, k) = (-3, 1)$
radius: $r = 2$

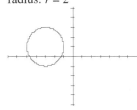

6. $x^2 + y^2 + 4x - 4y - 1 = 0$
$\left(x^2 + 4x \right) + \left(y^2 - 4y \right) = 0$
$\left(x^2 + 4x + 4 \right) + \left(y^2 + 4y + 4 \right) = 1 + 4 + 4$
$(x + 2)^2 + (y - 2)^2 = 9$
$[x - (-x)]^2 + (y - 2)^2 = 3^2$

So in the standard form of the circle's equation $(x - h)^2 + (y - k)^2 = r^2$, we have

$h = -2$, $k = 2$, $r = 3$.

Exercise Set 2.2

1.
$$d = \sqrt{(14-2)^2 + (8-3)^2}$$
$$d = \sqrt{12^2 + 5^2}$$
$$d = \sqrt{144 + 25}$$
$$d = \sqrt{169}$$
$$d = 13$$

3.
$$d = \sqrt{(6-4)^2 + (3-1)^2}$$
$$d = \sqrt{2^2 + 2^2}$$
$$d = \sqrt{4+4}$$
$$d = \sqrt{8}$$
$$d = 2\sqrt{2}$$
$$d \approx 2.83$$

5.
$$d = \sqrt{(-3-0)^2 + (4-0)^2}$$
$$d = \sqrt{3^2 + 4^2}$$
$$d = \sqrt{9+16}$$
$$d = \sqrt{25}$$
$$d = 5$$

7.
$$d = \sqrt{3-(-2]^2 + [-4-(-6)]^2}$$
$$d = \sqrt{5^2 + 2^2}$$
$$d = \sqrt{25+4}$$
$$d = \sqrt{29}$$
$$d \approx 5.39$$

9.
$$d = \sqrt{(4-0)^2 + [1-(-3)]^2}$$
$$d = \sqrt{4^2 + 4^2}$$
$$d = \sqrt{6+16}$$
$$d = \sqrt{32}$$
$$d = 4\sqrt{2}$$
$$d \approx 5.66$$

11.
$$d = \sqrt{(-.5-3.5)^2 + (6.2-8.2)^2}$$
$$d = \sqrt{(-4)^2 + (-2)^2}$$
$$d = \sqrt{6+4}$$
$$d = \sqrt{20}$$
$$d = 2\sqrt{5}$$
$$d \approx 4.47$$

13.
$$d = \sqrt{(\sqrt{5}-0)^2 + [0-(-\sqrt{3})]^2}$$
$$d = \sqrt{(\sqrt{5})^2 + (\sqrt{3})^2}$$
$$d = \sqrt{5+3}$$
$$d = \sqrt{8}$$
$$d = 2\sqrt{2}$$
$$d \approx 2.83$$

15.
$$d = \sqrt{(-\sqrt{5}-3\sqrt{5})^2 + (4\sqrt{5}-\sqrt{5})^2}$$
$$d = \sqrt{(-4\sqrt{5})^2 + (3\sqrt{5})^2}$$
$$d = \sqrt{6(3)+9(5)}$$
$$d = \sqrt{48+45}$$
$$d = \sqrt{93}$$
$$d \approx 9.64$$

17.
$$d = \sqrt{\left(\frac{1}{3} - \frac{7}{3}\right)^2 + \left(\frac{6}{5} - \frac{1}{5}\right)^2}$$
$$d = \sqrt{(-2)^2 + 1^2}$$
$$d = \sqrt{4+1}$$
$$d = \sqrt{5}$$
$$d = \approx 2.24$$

19. $\left(\dfrac{6+2}{2}, \dfrac{8+4}{2}\right) = \left(\dfrac{8}{2}, \dfrac{12}{2}\right) = (4,6)$

21.
$$\left(\frac{-2+(-6)}{2}, \frac{-8+(-2)}{2}\right)$$
$$= \left(\frac{-8}{2}, \frac{-10}{2}\right) = (-4,-5)$$

23.
$$\left(\frac{-3+6}{2}, \frac{-4+(-8)}{2}\right)$$
$$= \left(\frac{3}{2}, \frac{-12}{2}\right) = \left(\frac{3}{2}, -6\right)$$

25.
$$\left(\frac{-\frac{7}{2}+\left(-\frac{5}{2}\right)}{2}, \frac{\frac{3}{2}+\left(-\frac{11}{2}\right)}{2}\right)$$
$$= \left(\frac{\frac{-12}{2}}{2}, \frac{\frac{-8}{2}}{2}\right) = \left(-\frac{6}{2}, \frac{-4}{2}\right) = (-3,-2)$$

27.
$$\left(\frac{8+(-6)}{2}, \frac{3\sqrt{5}+7\sqrt{5}}{2}\right)$$
$$= \left(\frac{2}{2}, \frac{10\sqrt{5}}{2}\right) = \left(1, 5\sqrt{5}\right)$$

29.
$$\left(\frac{\sqrt{8}+\sqrt{2}}{2}, \frac{-4+4}{2}\right)$$
$$= \left(\frac{3\sqrt{2}+\sqrt{2}}{2}, \frac{0}{2}\right) = \left(\frac{4\sqrt{2}}{2}, 0\right) = (2\sqrt{2}, 0)$$

31. $(x-0)^2 + (y-0)^2 = 7^2$
$$x^2 + y^2 = 49$$

33. $(x-3)^2 + (y-2)^2 = 5^2$
$$(x-3)^2 + (y-2)^2 = 25$$

35. $[x-(-1)]^2 + (y-4)^2 = 2^2$
$$(x+1)^2 + (y-4)^2 = 4$$

37. $[x-(-3)]^2 + [y-(-1)]^2 = \left(\sqrt{3}\right)^2$
$$(x+3)^2 + (y+1)^2 = 3$$

39. $[x-(-4)]^2 + (y-0)^2 = 10^2$
$$(x+4)^2 + (y-0)^2 = 100$$

41.
$$x^2 + y^2 = 16$$
$$(x-0)^2 + (y-0)^2 = y^2$$
$$h = 0, \ k = 0, \ r = 4;$$
center = (0, 0)
radius = 4

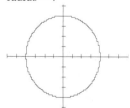

43. $(x-3)^2 + (y-1)^2 = 36$
$$(x-3)^2 + (y-1)^2 = 6^2$$
$$h = 3, \ k = 1, \ r = 6;$$
center = (3, 1)

radius = 6

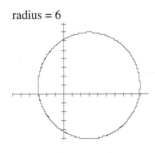

45. $(x+3)^2 + (y-2)^2 = 4$

$[x-(-3)]^2 + (y-2)^2 = 2^2$

$h = -3$, $k = 2$, $r = 2$

center = $(-3, 2)$

radius = 2

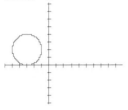

47. $(x+2)^2 + (y+2)^2 = 4$

$[x-(-2)]^2 + [y-(-2)]^2 = 2^2$

$h = -2$, $k = -2$, $r = 2$

center = $(-2, -2)$

radius = 2

49. $x^2 + y^2 + 6x + 2y + 6 = 0$

$(x^2 + 6x) + (y^2 + 2y) = -6$

$(x^2 + 6x + 9) + (y^2 + 2y + 1) = 9 + 1 - 6$

$(x+3)^2 + (y+1)^2 = 4$

$[x-(-3)]^2 + [9-(-1)]^2 = 2^2$

center = $(-3, -1)$

radius = 2

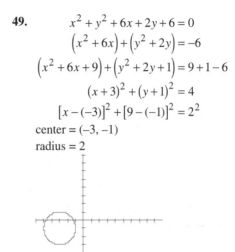

51. $x^2 + y^2 - 10x - 6y - 30 = 0$

$(x^2 - 10x) + (y^2 - 6y) = 30$

$(x^2 - 10x + 25) + (y^2 - 6y + 9) = 25 + 9 + 30$

$(x-5)^2 + (y-3)^2 = 64$

$(x-5)^2 + (y-3)^2 = 8^2$

center = $(5, 3)$

radius = 8

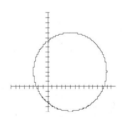

53. $x^2 + y^2 + 8x - 2y - 8 = 0$

$(x^2 + 8x) + (y^2 - 2y) = 8$

$(x^2 + 8x + 16) + (y^2 - 2y + 1) = 16 + 1 + 8$

$(x+4)^2 + (y-1)^2 = 25$

$[x-(-4)]^2 + (y-1)^2 = 5^2$

center = $(-4, 1)$

radius = 5

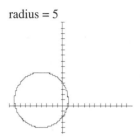

55.
$$x^2 - 2x + y^2 - 15 = 0$$
$$\left(x^2 - 2x\right) + y^2 = 15$$
$$\left(x^2 - 2x + 1\right) + (y - 0)^2 = 1 + 0 + 15$$
$$(x - 1)^2 + (y - 0)^2 = 16$$
$$(x - 1)^2 + (y - 0)^2 = 4^2$$

center = (1, 0)
radius = 4

57.
$$d = \sqrt{65 - (-115)]^2 + (70 - 170)^2}$$
$$d = \sqrt{(65 + 115)^2 + \left(-100\right)^2}$$
$$d = \sqrt{180^2 + 10000}$$
$$d = \sqrt{32400 + 10000}$$
$$d = \sqrt{42400}$$
$$d = 205.9 \text{ miles}$$
$$\frac{205.9 \text{ miles}}{400} = 0.5 \text{ hours or } 30 \text{ minutes}$$

59. $C(0, 68 + 14) = (0, 82)$
$$(x - 0)^2 + (y - 82)^2 = 68^2$$
$$x^2 + (y - 82)^2 = 4624$$

61.–67. Answers may vary.

69.

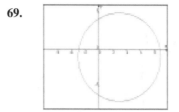

71. a. False; the equation should be
$$x^2 + y^2 = 256.$$

b. False; the center is at (3, –5).

c. False; this is not an equation for a circle.

d. True

(d) is true.

73. a.

d_1 is distance from (x_1, x_2) to midpoint

$$d_1 = \sqrt{\left(\frac{x_1 + x_2}{2} - x_1\right)^2 + \left(\frac{y_1 + y_2}{2} - y_1\right)^2}$$

$$d_1 = \sqrt{\left(\frac{x_1 + x_2 - 2x_1}{2}\right)^2 + \left(\frac{y_1 + y_2 - 2y_1}{2}\right)^2}$$

$$d_1 = \sqrt{\left(\frac{x_2 - x_1}{2}\right)^2 + \left(\frac{y_2 - y_1}{2}\right)^2}$$

$$d_1 = \sqrt{\frac{x_2^2 - 2x_1 x_2 + x_1^2}{4} + \frac{y_2^2 - 2y_2 y_1 + y_1^2}{4}}$$

$$d_1 = \sqrt{\frac{1}{4}\left(x_2^2 - 2x_1 x_2 + x_1^2 + y_2^2 - 2y_2 y_1 + y_1^2\right)}$$

$$d_1 = \frac{1}{2}\sqrt{x_2^2 - 2x_1 x_2 + x_1^2 + y_2^2 - 2y_2 y_1 + y_1^2}$$

d_2 is distance from midpoint to (x_2, y_2)

$$d_2 = \sqrt{\left(\frac{x_1 + x_2}{2} - x_2\right)^2 + \left(\frac{y_1 + y_2}{2} - y_2\right)^2}$$

$$d_2 = \sqrt{\left(\frac{x_1 + x_2 - 2x_2}{2}\right)^2 + \left(\frac{y_1 + y_2 - 2y_2}{2}\right)^2}$$

$$d_2 = \sqrt{\left(\frac{x_1 - x_2}{2}\right)^2 + \left(\frac{y_1 - y_2}{2}\right)^2}$$

$$d_2 = \sqrt{\frac{x_1^2 - 2x_1 x_2 + x_2^2}{4} + \frac{y_1^2 - 2y_2 y_1 + y_2^2}{4}}$$

$$d_2 = \sqrt{\frac{1}{4}\left(x_1^2 - 2x_1 x_2 + x_2^2 + y_1^2 - 2y_2 y_1 + y_2^2\right)}$$

$$d_2 = \frac{1}{2}\sqrt{x_1^2 - 2x_1 x_2 + x_2^2 + y_1^2 - 2y_2 y_1 + y_2^2}$$

$$d_1 = d_2$$

b.

d_3 is the distance from (x_1, y_1) to (x_2, y_2)

$$d_3 = \sqrt{(x_2 - x_1)^2 + (y_2 - y_1)^2}$$

$$d_3 = \sqrt{x_2^2 - 2x_1 x_2 + x_1^2 + y_2^2 - 2y_2 y_1 + y_1^2}$$

$d_1 + d_2 = d_3$ because $\frac{1}{2}\sqrt{a} + \frac{1}{2}\sqrt{a} = \sqrt{a}$

75. Since $(-7, 2)$ and $(1, 2)$ lie on a line that passes through the center, they are endpoints of a diameter. Find the length of the diameter using the distance formula:

$$d = \sqrt{(2-2)^2 + (1+7)^2}$$

$$d = \sqrt{0^2 + 8^2} = 8$$

The radius of the circle is 4. The center of the circle is located at the midpoint of the diameter.

Use the midpoint formula:

$$M = \left(-\frac{7+1}{2}, \frac{2+2}{2}\right)$$
$$= \left(-\frac{6}{2}, \frac{4}{2}\right)$$
$$= (-3, 2).$$

The center is at $(-3, 2)$. The equation of the circle is: $[x - (-3)]^2 + (y - 2)^2 = 4^2$, or

$$(x + 3)^2 + (y - 2)^2 = 16.$$

The general form of the equation is

$$x^2 + y^2 + 6x - 4y - 3 = 0.$$

77. The circle is centered at $(0,0)$. The slope of the radius with endpoints $(0,0)$ and $(3,-4)$ is $m = -\frac{-4-0}{3-0} = -\frac{4}{3}$. The line perpendicular to the radius has slope $\frac{3}{4}$. The tangent line has slope $\frac{3}{4}$ and passes through $(3,-4)$, so its equation is:

$$y + 4 = \frac{3}{4}(x - 3).$$

Section 2.3

Check Point Exercises

1. The domain is the set of all first components: $\{5, 10, 15, 20, 25\}$. The range is the set of all second components: $\{12.8, 16.2, 18.9, 20.7, 21.8\}$.

2. **a.** The relation is not a function since the two ordered pairs $(5, 6)$ and $(5, 8)$ have the same first component but different second components.

   b. The relation is a function since no two ordered pairs have the same first component and different second components.

3. **a.** $2x + y = 6$
   $$y = -2x + 6$$
   For each value of x, there is one and only one value for y, so the equation defines y as a function of x.

   b. $x^2 + y^2 = 1$
   $$y^2 = 1 - x^2$$
   $$y = \pm\sqrt{1 - x^2}$$
   Since there are values of x (all values between -1 and 1 exclusive) that give more than one value for y (for example, if $x = 0$, then $y = \pm\sqrt{1 - 0^2} = \pm 1$), the equation does not define y as a function of x.

4. **a.** $f(-5) = (-5)^2 - 2(-5) + 7$
   $$= 25 - (-10) + 7$$
   $$= 42$$

   b. $f(x + 4) = (x + 4)^2 - 2(x + 4) + 7$
   $$= x^2 + 8x + 16 - 2x - 8 + 7$$
   $$= x^2 + 6x + 15$$

   c. $f(-x) = (-x)^2 - 2(-x) + 7$
   $$= x^2 - (-2x) + 7$$
   $$= x^2 + 2x + 7$$

5. $f(x + h) = (x + h)^2 - 7(x + h) + 3$
   $$= x^2 + 2xh + h^2 - 7x - 7h + 3$$

   a.

   b. $\dfrac{f(x + h) - f(x)}{h}$
   $$= \frac{x^2 + 2xh + h^2 - 7x - 7h + 3 - (x^2 - 7x + 3)}{h}$$
   $$= \frac{x^2 + 2xh + h^2 - 7x - 7h + 3 - x^2 + 7x - 3}{h}$$
   $$= \frac{2xh + h^2 - 7h}{h}$$
   $$= \frac{h(2x + h - 7)}{h}$$
   $$= 2x + h - 7$$

6. **a.** Since $-5 < 0$, we use the first line of the piece wise function:
   $$f(-5) = (-5)^2 + 3 = 25 + 3 = 28.$$

   b. Since $6 > 0$, we use the second line of the piece wise function:
   $$f(6) = 5(6) + 3 = 30 + 3 = 33.$$

7. **a.** The function $f(x) = x^2 + 3x - 17$ contains neither division nor an even root. The domain of f is the set of all real numbers.

   b. The denominator equals zero when $x = 7$ or $x = -7$, so we must exclude these values. Thus, the domain of g is $\{x \mid x \neq -7, x \neq 7\}$.

   c. Since $h(x) = \sqrt{9x - 27}$ contains an even root, the quantity under the radical must be greater than or equal to 0.

$$9x - 27 \geq 0$$
$$9x \geq 27$$
$$x \geq 3$$

Thus, the domain of h is $\{x | x \geq 3\}$, or the interval $[3, \infty)$.

Exercise Set 2.3

1. The relation is a function since no two ordered pairs have the same first component and different second components. The domain is $\{1, 3, 5\}$ and the range is $\{2, 4, 5\}$.

3. The relation is not a function since the two ordered pairs $(3, 4)$ and $(3, 5)$ have the same first component but different second components (the same could be said for the ordered pairs $(4, 4)$ and $(4, 5)$). The domain is $\{3, 4\}$ and the range is $\{4, 5\}$.

5. The relation is a function since there are no same first components with different second components. The domain is $\{-3, -2, -1, 0\}$ and the range is $\{-3, -2, -1, 0\}$.

7. The relation is not a function since there are ordered pairs with the same first component and different second components. The domain is $\{1\}$ and the range is $\{4, 5, 6\}$.

9. $x + y = 16$
$$y = 16 - x$$
Since only one value of y can be obtained for each value of x, y is a function of x.

11. $x^2 + y = 16$
$$y = 16 - x^2$$
Since only one value of y can be obtained for each value of x, y is a function of x.

13. $x^2 + y^2 = 16$
$$y^2 = 16 - x^2$$
$$y = \pm\sqrt{16 - x^2}$$
If $x = 0$, $y = \pm 4$.
Since two values, $y = 4$ and $y = -4$, can be obtained for one value of x, y is not a function of x.

15. $x = y^2$
$$y = \pm\sqrt{x}$$
If $x = 1$, $y = \pm 1$.
Since two values, $y = 1$ and $y = -1$, can be obtained for $x = 1$, y is not a function of x.

17. $y = \sqrt{x + 4}$
Since only one value of y can be obtained for each value of x, y is a function of x.

19. $x + y^3 = 8$
$$y^3 = 8 - x$$
$$y = \sqrt[3]{8 - x}$$
Since only one value of y can be obtained for each value of x, y is a function of x.

21. **a.** $f(6) = 4(6) + 5 = 29$

   b. $f(x + 1) = 4(x + 1) + 5 = 4x + 9$

   c. $f(-x) = 4(-x) + 5 = -4x + 5$

23. **a.** $g(-1) = (-1)^2 + 2(-1) + 3$
$$= 1 - 2 + 3$$
$$= 2$$

   b. $g(x + 5) = (x + 5)^2 + 2(x + 5) + 3$
$$= x^2 + 10x + 25 + 2x + 10 + 3$$
$$= x^2 + 12x + 38$$

   c. $g(-x) = (-x)^2 + 2(-x) + 3$
$$= x^2 - 2x + 3$$

25. a.
$$h(2) = 2^4 - 2^2 + 1$$
$$= 16 - 4 + 1$$
$$= 13$$

b.
$$h(-1) = (-1)^4 - (-1)^2 + 1$$
$$= 1 - 1 + 1$$
$$= 1$$

c. $h(-x) = (-x)^4 - (-x)^2 + 1 = x^4 - x^2 + 1$

d.
$$h(3a) = (3a)^4 - (3a)^2 + 1$$
$$= 81a^4 - 9a^2 + 1$$

27. a. $f(-6) = \sqrt{-6+6} + 3 = \sqrt{0} + 3 = 3$

b.
$$f(10) = \sqrt{10+6} + 3$$
$$= \sqrt{16} + 3$$
$$= 4 + 3$$
$$= 7$$

c. $f(x-6) = \sqrt{x-6+6} + 3 = \sqrt{x} + 3$

29. a. $f(2) = \dfrac{4(2)^2 - 1}{2^2} = \dfrac{15}{4}$

b. $f(-2) = \dfrac{4(-2)^2 - 1}{(-2)^2} = \dfrac{15}{4}$

c. $f(-x) = \dfrac{4(-x)^2 - 1}{(-x)^2} = \dfrac{4x^2 - 1}{x^2}$

31. a. $f(6) = \dfrac{6}{|6|} = 1$

b. $f(-6) = \dfrac{-6}{|-6|} = \dfrac{-6}{6} = -1$

c. $f(r^2) = \dfrac{r^2}{|r^2|} = \dfrac{r^2}{r^2} = 1$

33.
$$\dfrac{4(x+h) - 4x}{h}$$
$$= \dfrac{4x + 4h - 4x}{h}$$
$$= \dfrac{4h}{h}$$
$$= 4$$

35.
$$\dfrac{3(x+h) + 7 - (3x + 7)}{h}$$
$$= \dfrac{3x + 3h + 7 - 3x - 7}{h}$$
$$= \dfrac{3h}{h}$$
$$= 3$$

37.
$$\dfrac{(x+h)^2 - x^2}{h}$$
$$= \dfrac{x^2 + 2xh + h^2 - x^2}{h}$$
$$= \dfrac{2xh + h^2}{h}$$
$$= \dfrac{h(2x + h)}{h}$$
$$= 2x + h$$

39.
$$\dfrac{(x+h)^2 - 4(x+h) + 3 - (x^2 - 4x + 3)}{h}$$
$$= \dfrac{x^2 + 2xh + h^2 - 4x - 4h + 3 - x^2 + 4x - 3}{h}$$
$$= \dfrac{2xh + h^2 - 4h}{h}$$
$$= \dfrac{h(2x + h - 4)}{h}$$
$$= 2x + h - 4$$

41. $\dfrac{6 - 6}{h} = \dfrac{0}{h} = 0$

43.

$$\frac{\dfrac{1}{x+h}-\dfrac{1}{x}}{h}$$

$$=\frac{\dfrac{x}{x(x+h)}+\dfrac{-(x+h)}{x(x+h)}}{h}$$

$$=\frac{\dfrac{x-x-h}{x(x+h)}}{h}$$

$$=\frac{\dfrac{-h}{x(x+h)}}{h}$$

$$=\frac{-h}{x(x+h)}\cdot\frac{1}{h}$$

$$=\frac{-1}{x(x+h)}$$

45. a. $f(-2)=3(-2)+5=-1$

    b. $f(0)=4(0)+7=7$

    c. $f(3)=4(3)+7=19$

47. a. $g(0)=0+3=3$

    b. $g(-6)=-(-6+3)=-(-3)=3$

    c. $g(-3)=-3+3=0$

49. a. $h(5)=\dfrac{5^2-9}{5-3}=\dfrac{25-9}{2}=\dfrac{16}{2}=8$

    b. $h(0)=\dfrac{0^2-9}{0-3}=\dfrac{-9}{-3}=3$

    c. $h(3)=6$

51. Since the function is defined and equal to a real number for all real numbers, the domain is $(-\infty,\infty)$.

53. The denominator equals zero when $x=4$. The domain is $\{x|x\neq 4\}$.

55. Factor the denominator:
$$h(x)=\frac{7x}{(x-4)(x+4)}$$
The denominator equals zero when $x=4$ or $x=-4$. The domain is $\{x|x\neq -4 \text{ and } x\neq 4\}$.

57. The denominator is zero when $x=-3$ or $x=7$. The domain is 3 $\{x|x\neq -3 \text{ and } x\neq 7\}$.

59. Factor the denominator.
$$H(r)=\frac{4}{(r+8)(r+3)}$$
The denominator equals zero when $r=-8$ or $r=-3$. The domain is $\{x|x\neq -8 \text{ and } x\neq -3\}$.

61. The denominator is never equal to zero. Since the function is defined and equal to a real number for all real numbers, the domain is $(-\infty,\infty)$.

63. We want $\sqrt{x-3}$ to equal a real number.
$$x-3\geq 0$$
$$x\geq 3$$
The domain is $[3,\infty)$.

65. We want $\sqrt{x-3}$ to equal a positive real number.
$$x-3>0$$
$$x>3$$
The domain is $(3,\infty)$.

67. We want $\sqrt{5x+35}$ to equal a real number.
$$5x+35\geq 0$$
$$5x\geq -35$$
$$x\geq -7$$
The domain is $[-7,\infty)$.

69. We want $\sqrt{24-2x}$ to equal a real number.
$$24-2x\geq 0$$
$$-2x\geq -24$$

$x \le 12$

The domain is $(-\infty, \ 12]$.

71. We want $\sqrt{x^2 - 5x - 14}$ to equal a real number.

$x^2 - 5x - 14 \ge 0$

Solve $\quad x^2 - 5x - 14 = 0$

$\qquad\qquad (x + 2)(x - 7) = 0$

$\qquad\qquad x = -2 \text{ or } x = 7$

The test intervals are
$(-\infty, \ -2), \ (-2, \ 7), \ (7, \ \infty)$. Using a representative number from each test interval, the solution is $(-\infty, \ -2] \text{ or } [7, \ \infty)$.

73. $\quad x - 2 \ge 0 \qquad x - 5 \ne 0$

$\qquad\quad x \ge 2 \qquad\quad\ x \ne 5$

The domain is $[2, 5) \text{ or } (5, \infty)$.

75. $\{(1, 31), (2, 53), (3, 70), (4, 86), (5, 86)\}$
Domain: $\{1, 2, 3, 4, 5,\}$
Range: $(31, 53, 70, 86\}$ The relation is a function. Each member of the domain has only one member of the range.

77. No, season 33 has 2 members in the range, "Walt Disney" and "60 Minutes."

79. $P(30) = 0.72(30)^2 + 9.4(30) + 783 = 1713$
In 1990, there were 1713 gray wolves.

81. $P(0) = 19$ In 1997, 19% of U.S. households were online.

83. $P(3) - P(1) = 6.85\sqrt{3} + 19 - \left(6.85\sqrt{1} + 19\right) = 5$
From 1998 to 1999, there was a 5% increase of households online.

85. $f(0) = 6.5(0) + 200 = 200$ In 1955, there were 200 thousand lawyers.

87. $f(50) = 26.2(50) - 252 = 1058$ In 2001, there were 1058 thousand lawyers.

89. $T(40000) = 0.28(40,000 - 17900) + 2685 = 8873$ A married person who files separately who earns $40,000 will owe $8873 in taxes.

91. $C(90) = 100(90) + 100000 = 109000$
It will cost $109,000 to produce 90 bicycles.

93.

$$T(30) = \frac{40}{30} + \frac{40}{30 + 30}$$
$$= \frac{80}{60} + \frac{40}{60}$$
$$= \frac{120}{60}$$
$$= 2$$

If you travel 30 mph going and 60 mph returning, your total trip will take 2 hours.

95 - 101. Answers may vary.

103.

The domain is $.1, \infty)$.

Algebraically, $\sqrt{x - 1}$ must equal a real number.

$x - 1 \ge 0$

$\quad x \ge 1$

105.

The domain is $(-\infty, 5]$.

Algebraically, $\sqrt{5 - 3x}$ must equal a real number.
$$15 - 3x \geq 0$$
$$-3x \geq -15$$
$$x \leq 5$$

107. Answers may vary.

109. $f(r_1) = 0$; r_1 is a solution to the equation $ax^2 + bx + c = 0$ by the quadratic formula

Section 2.4

Check Point Exercises

1.

x	$f(x) = x^2 - 2$	(x, y) or $(x, f(x))$
–3	$f(-3) = (-3)^2 - 2 = 7$	(–3, 7)
–2	$f(-2) = (-2)^2 - 2 = 2$	(–2, 2)
–1	$f(-1) = (-1)^2 - 2 = -1$	(–1, –1)
0	$f(0) = 0^2 - 2 = -2$	(0, – 2)
1	$f(1) = 1^2 - 2 = -1$	(1, –1)
2	$f(2) = 2^2 - 2 = 2$	(2, 2)
3	$f(3) = 3^2 - 2 = 7$	(3, 7)

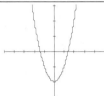

2. $f(4) = 1$
domain: [0, 6)
range: (–2, 2]

3. y is a function of x for the graphs in (a) and (b).

4. a. $f(10) \approx 16$ **b.** $x \approx 8$

5. The function is increasing on the interval $(-\infty, -1)$, decreasing on the interval $(-1, 1)$, and increasing on the interval $(1, \infty)$.

6. a. $\dfrac{1^3 - 0^3}{1 - 0} = 1$

  b. $\dfrac{2^3 - 1^3}{2 - 1} = \dfrac{8 - 1}{1} = 7$

  c. $\dfrac{0^3 - (-2)^3}{0 - (-2)} = \dfrac{8}{2} = 4$

7. a. $f(-x) = (-x)^2 + 6 = x^2 + 6 = f(x)$
The function is even.

  b. $g(-x) = 7(-x)^3 - (-x) = -7x^3 + x = -f(x)$
The function is odd.

  c. $h(-x) = (-x)^5 + 1 = -x^5 + 1$
The function is neither even nor odd.

Exercise Set 2.4

1. (–3, 11), (–2, 6), (–1, 3), (0, 2), (1, 3), (2, 6), (3, 11)

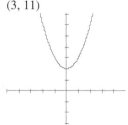

domain: $(-\infty, \infty)$
range: $[2, \infty)$

3. (0, –1), (1, 0), (4, 1), (9, 2)

domain: $[0, \infty)$
range: $[-1, \infty)$

5. (1, 0), (2, 1), (5, 2), (10, 3)

domain: [1, ∞)
range: [0, ∞)

7. (–3, 2), (–2, 1), (–1, 0), (0, –1), (1, 0), (2, 1), (3, 2)

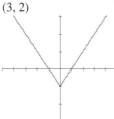

domain: (–∞, ∞)
range: [–1, ∞)

9. (–3, 4), (–2, 3), (–1, 2), (0, 1), (1, 0), (2, 1), (3, 2)

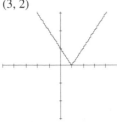

domain: (–∞, ∞)
range: [0, ∞)

11. (–3, 5), (–2, 5), (–1, 5), (0, 5), (1, 5), (2, 5), (3, 5)

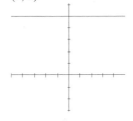

domain: (–∞, ∞)
range: {5}

13. (–2, –10), (–1, –3), (0, –2), (1, –1), (2, 6)

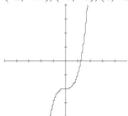

domain: (–∞, ∞)
range: (–∞, ∞)

15. a. domain: (–∞, ∞)

   b. range: [–4, ∞)

   c. *x*-intercepts: –3 and 1

   d. *y*-intercept: –3

17. a. domain: (–∞, ∞)

   b. range: [1, ∞)

   c. *x*-intercept: none

   d. *y*-intercept: 1

   e. $f(-1) = 2$ and $f(3) = 4$

19. a. domain: [0, 5)

   b. range: [–1, 5)

   c. *x*-intercept: 2

   d. *y*-intercept: –1

   e. $f(3) = 1$

21. a. domain: [0, ∞)

   b. range: [1, ∞)

   c. *x*-intercept: none

    d. y-intercept: 1

    e. $f(4) = 3$

23. **a.**   domain: $[-2, 6]$

    b.   range: $[-2, 6]$

    c. x-intercept: 4

    d. y-intercept: 4

    e. $f(-1) = 5$

25. **a.**   domain: $(-\infty, \infty)$

    b.   range: $(-\infty, -2]$

    c. x-intercept: none

    d. y-intercept: -2

    e. $f(-4) = -5$ and $f(4) = -2$

27. **a.**   domain: $(-\infty, \infty)$

    b.   range: $(0, \infty)$

    c. x-intercept: none

    d. y-intercept: 1

29. **a.**   domain: $\{-5, -2, 0, 1, 3\}$

    b.   range: $\{2\}$

    c. x-intercept: none

    d. y-intercept: 2

31. function

33. function

35. not a function

37. function

39. **a.**   increasing: $(-1, \infty)$

    b.   decreasing: $(-\infty, -1)$

    c.   constant: none

41. **a.**   increasing: $(0, \infty)$

    b.   decreasing: none

    c.   constant: none

43. **a.**   increasing: none

    b.   decreasing: $(-2, 6)$

    c.   constant: none

45. **a.**   increasing: $(-\infty, -1)$

    b.   decreasing: none

    c.   constant: $(-1, \infty)$

47. **a.**   increasing: $(-\infty, 0)$ or $(1.5, 3)$

    b.   decreasing: $(0, 1.5)$ or $(3, \infty)$

    c.   constant: none

49. **a.**   increasing: $(-2, 4)$

    b.   decreasing: none

    c.   constant: $(-\infty, -2)$ or $(4, \infty)$

51. **a.** $x = 0$, relative maximum $= 4$

    b. $x = \_3, 3$, relative minimum $= 0$

53. **a.** $x = \_2$, relative maximum $= 21$

    b. $x = 1$, relative mimimum $= \_6$

55. $\dfrac{15-0}{5-0} = \dfrac{15}{5} = 3$

57. $\dfrac{5^2 + 2 \cdot 5 - (3^2 + 2 \cdot 3)}{5 - 3}$

$= \dfrac{25 + 10 - (9 + 6)}{2}$

$= \dfrac{20}{2}$

$= 10$

59. $\dfrac{\sqrt{9} - \sqrt{4}}{9 - 4} = \dfrac{3 - 2}{5} = \dfrac{1}{5}$

61. $f(x) = x^3 + x$

$f(-x) = (-x)^3 + (-x)$

$f(-x) = -x^3 - x = -(x^3 + x)$

$f(-x) = -f(x)$, odd function

63. $g(x) = x^2 + x$

$g(-x) = (-x)^2 + (-x)$

$g(-x) = x^2 - x$, neither

65. $h(x) = x^2 - x^4$

$h(-x) = (-x)^2 - (-x)^4$

$h(-x) = x^2 - x^4$

$h(-x) = h(x)$, even function

67. $f(x) = x^2 - x^4 + 1$

$f(-x) = (-x)^2 - (-x)^4 + 1$

$f(-x) = x^2 - x^4 + 1$

$f(-x) = f(x)$, even function

69. $f(x) = \dfrac{1}{5}x^6 - 3x^2$

$f(-x) = \dfrac{1}{5}(-x)^6 - 3(-x)^2$

$f(-x) = \dfrac{1}{5}x^6 - 3x^2$

$f(-x) = f(x)$, even function

71. $f(x) = x\sqrt{1 - x^2}$

$f(-x) = -x\sqrt{1 - (-x)^2}$

$f(-x) = -x\sqrt{1 - x^2}$

$\quad\quad = -\left(x\sqrt{1 - x^2}\right)$

$f(-x) = -f(x)$, odd function

73. The graph is symmetric with respect to the *y*-axis. The function is even.

75. The graph is symmetric with respect to the origin. The function is odd.

77. $f(1.06) = 1$

79. $f\left(\dfrac{1}{3}\right) = 0$

81. $f(-2.3) = -3$

83. $f(60) \text{ k} \approx 3.1$

In 1960, about 3.1% of the population were Jewish-Americans.

85. $x \approx 19$ and 64

In 1919 and 1964, about 3% of the population were Jewish-Americans.

87. In 1940, the maximum of 3.7% of the population were Jewish-American.

89. Each year corresponds to only 1 percentage.

91. Increasing: (45, 74)

Decreasing: (16, 45)

The number of accidents occurring per 50 million miles driven increases with age starting at age 45, while it decreases with age starting at age 16.

93. Answers will vary. An example is 16 and 74 year olds will have 526.4 accidents per million miles.

95.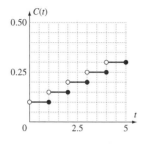

97.–107. Answers may vary.

109.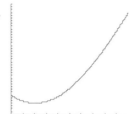

b. The number of doctor visits decreases during childhood and then increases as you get older.

c. The minimum is (20.29, 3.99), which means that the minimum number of doctor visits, about 4, occurs at around age 20.

111.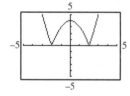

Increasing: (–2, 0) or (2, ∞)
Decreasing: (–∞, –2) or (0, 2)

113.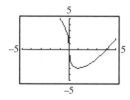

Increasing: (1, ∞)
Decreasing: (–∞, 1)

115.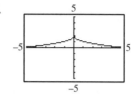

Increasing: (–∞, 0)
Decreasing: (0, ∞)

117. **a.** False; the domain of *f* is [–4, 4].

b. False; the range of *f* is [–2, 2).

c. True; $f(-1) - f(4) = 1 - (-1) = 2$.

d. False; $f(0) < 1$.

(c) is true.

119. Answers may vary.

121.

Weight at least	Cost
0 oz.	$0.33
1	0.55
2	0.77
3	0.99
4	1.21

Section 2.5

Check Point Exercises

1. Shift up vertically 3 units.

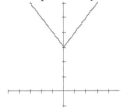

2. Shift horizontally to the right 4 units.

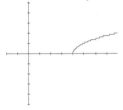

3. Shift horizontally to the right 1 unit and vertically down 2 units.

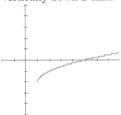

4. Reflect about the *x*-axis.

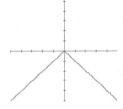

5. Reflect about the *y*-axis.

6. Vertically stretch the graph.

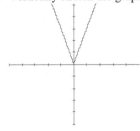

7. Vertically shrink the graph.

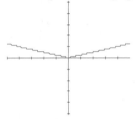

8. Shift horizontally to the right 2 units, reflect across the *x*-axis, and shift vertically up 3 units.

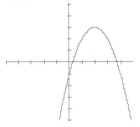

Exercise Set 2.5

1.

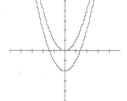

3.

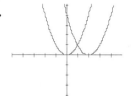

5.

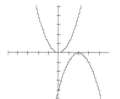

7.

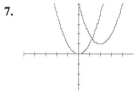

9.

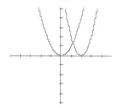

11.

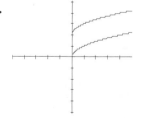

13.

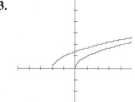

15.

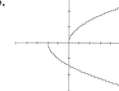

17.

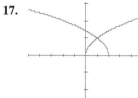

19.

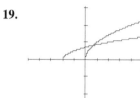

21.

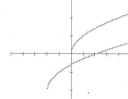

23.

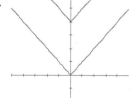

25.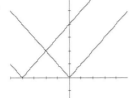

27.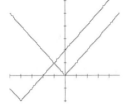

29.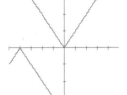

31.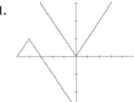

33.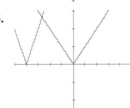

35.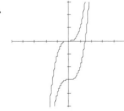

37.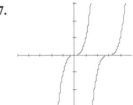

39.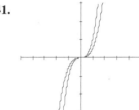

41.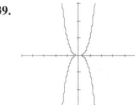

43.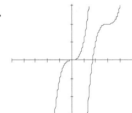

45. Move the graph up one space.

47. Move the graph to the left one space.

49. Rotate the graph about the x – axis.

51. Move the graph to the left one space and vertically stretch.

53. $y = \sqrt{x-4}$

55. $y = (x+1)^2 - 4$

57. a. Move the graph up 20.1 spaces and multiply each y – coordinate by 2.9 to vertically stretch the graph.

    b. $f(48) = 2.9\sqrt{48} + 20.1 = 40.2$

      The median height for boy 48 months old is 40.2 inches.

    c. $\dfrac{2.9\sqrt{10}+20.1-\left(2.9\sqrt{5}+20.1\right)}{10-0}$

$$=\frac{9.17}{10}$$
$$= 0.9$$

    d. $\dfrac{2.9\sqrt{60}+20.1-\left(2.9\sqrt{50}+20.1\right)}{60-50}$

$$=\frac{1.96}{10}$$
$$= 0.2$$

      The rate of change is decreasing. The graph is not rising as fast.

59.–63. Answers may vary.

65. a.

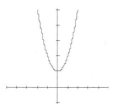

    b.

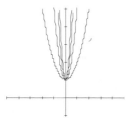

    c.   Answers may vary.

    d.   Answers may vary.

    e.   Answers may vary.

67. $g(x) = -(x+4)^2$

69. $g(x) = -\sqrt{x-2} + 2$

71. $(-a, b)$

73. $(a + 3, b)$

Section 2.6

Check Point Exercises

1. a. $(f + g)(x) = f(x) + g(x)$
$$= 3x^2 + 4x - 1 + 2x + 7$$
$$(f + g)(x) = 3x^2 + 6x + 6$$

    b. $(f + g)(4) = 3(4)^2 + 6(4) + 6 = 78$

2. a. $(f + g)(x) = f(x) + g(x)$
$$= \sqrt{x-3} + \sqrt{x+1}$$

    b.   Domain of f:
$$x - 3 \geq 0$$
$$x \geq 3$$
$$[3, \infty)$$
      Domain of g:
$$x + 1 \geq 0$$
$$x \geq -1$$
$$[-1, \infty)$$
      The domain of $f + g$ is the set of all real numbers that are common to the domain of f and the domain of g. Thus, the domain of $f + g$ is $[3, \infty)$.

3. a. $(f - g)(x) = f(x) - g(x)$
$$= x - 5 - \left(x^2 - 1\right)$$
$$= x - 5 - x^2 - 1$$
$$= -x^2 + x - 4$$

    b. $(fg)(x) = (x - 5)\left(x^2 - 1\right)$
$$= x\left(x^2 - 1\right) - 5\left(x^2 - 1\right)$$
$$= x^3 - x - 5x^2 + 5$$
$$= x^3 - 5x^2 - x + 5$$

c. $\left(\dfrac{f}{g}\right)(x) = \dfrac{f(x)}{g(x)}$

$\qquad = \dfrac{x-5}{x^2-1},\ x \neq \pm 1$

4. a. $(f \circ g)(x) = f(g(x)) = 5g(x) + 6$

$\qquad = 5\left(x^2 - 1\right) + 6$

$\qquad = 5x^2 - 5 + 6$

$\qquad = 5x^2 + 1$

b. $(g \circ f)(x) = g(f(x)) = \left(f(x)\right)^2 - 1$

$\qquad = (5x + 6)^2 - 1$

$\qquad = 25x^2 + 60x + 36 - 1$

$\qquad = 25x^2 + 60x + 35$

5. a. $f \circ g(x) = \dfrac{4}{\dfrac{1}{x} + 2} = \dfrac{4x}{1 + 2x}$

b. $x \neq 0, -\dfrac{1}{2}$

6. $h(x) = f \circ g$ where $f(x) = \sqrt{x}$; $g(x) = x^2 + 5$

Exercise Set 2.6

1. a. $(f + g)(x) = 2x^2 + 3x + 2$

b. $(f + g)(4) = 2(4)^2 + 3(4) + 2$

$\qquad = 32 + 12 + 2$

$\qquad = 46$

3. a. $(f + g)(x) = \sqrt{x - 6} + \sqrt{x + 2}$

b. Domain: $[6, \infty)$.

5. $(f + g)(x) = 3x + 2$

Domain: $(-\infty, \infty)$

$(f - g)(x) = f(x) - g(x)$

$\qquad = (2x + 3) - (x - 1)$

$\qquad = x + 4$

Domain: $(-\infty, \infty)$

$(fg)(x) = f(x) \cdot g(x)$

$\qquad = (2x + 3) \cdot (x - 1)$

$\qquad = 2x^2 + x - 3$

Domain: $(-\infty, \infty)$

$\left(\dfrac{f}{g}\right)(x) = \dfrac{f(x)}{g(x)} = \dfrac{2x + 3}{x - 1}$

Domain: $\{x | x \neq 1\}$

7. $(f + g)(x) = 3x^2 + x - 5$

Domain: $(-\infty, \infty)$

$(f - g)(x) = -3x^2 + x - 5$

Domain: $(-\infty, \infty)$

$(fg)(x) = (x - 5)(3x^2) = 3x^3 - 15x^2$

Domain: $(-\infty, \infty)$

$\left(\dfrac{f}{g}\right)(x) = \dfrac{x - 5}{3x^2}$

Domain: $\{x | x \neq 0\}$

9. $(f + g)(x) = 2x^2 - 2$

Domain: $(-\infty, \infty)$

$(f - g)(x) = 2x^2 - 2x - 4$

Domain: $(-\infty, \infty)$

$(fg)(x) = (2x^2 - x - 3)(x + 1)$

$\qquad = 2x^3 + x^2 - 4x - 3$

Domain: $(-\infty, \infty)$

$\left(\dfrac{f}{g}\right)(x) = \dfrac{2x^2 - x - 3}{x + 1}$

$\qquad = \dfrac{(2x - 3)(x + 1)}{(x + 1)} = 2x - 3$

Domain: $\{x | x \neq -1\}$

11. $(f + g)(x) = \sqrt{x} + x - 4$

Domain: $[0, \infty)$

$(f - g)(x) = \sqrt{x} - x + 4$

Domain: $[0, \infty)$

$(fg)(x) = \sqrt{x}(x - 4)$

Domain: $[0, \infty)$

$\left(\dfrac{f}{g}\right)(x) = \dfrac{\sqrt{x}}{x - 4}$

Domain: $\{x | x \geq 0 \text{ and } x \neq 4\}$

13. $(f+g)(x) = 2 + \dfrac{1}{x} + \dfrac{1}{x} = 2 + \dfrac{2}{x} = \dfrac{2x+2}{x}$

Domain: $\{x|x \neq 0\}$

$(f-g)(x) = 2 + \dfrac{1}{x} - \dfrac{1}{x} = 2$

Domain: $\{x|x \neq 0\}$

$(fg)(x) = \left(2 + \dfrac{1}{x}\right) \cdot \dfrac{1}{x} = \dfrac{2}{x} + \dfrac{1}{x^2} = \dfrac{2x+1}{x^2}$

Domain: $\{x|x \neq 0\}$

$\left(\dfrac{f}{g}\right)(x) = \dfrac{2 + \frac{1}{x}}{\frac{1}{x}} = \left(2 + \dfrac{1}{x}\right) \cdot x = 2x+1$

Domain: $\{x|x \neq 0\}$

15. $(f+g)(x) = \sqrt{x+4} + \sqrt{x-1}$

Domain: $[1, \infty)$

$(f-g)(x) = \sqrt{x+4} - \sqrt{x-1}$

Domain: $[1, \infty)$

$(fg)(x) = \sqrt{x+4} \cdot \sqrt{x-1} = \sqrt{x^2+3x-4}$

Domain: $[1, \infty)$

$\left(\dfrac{f}{g}\right)(x) = \dfrac{\sqrt{x+4}}{\sqrt{x-1}}$

Domain: $(1, \infty)$

17. $f(x) = 2x; g(x) = x+7$

   a. $(f \circ g)(x) = 2(x+7) = 2x+14$

   b. $(g \circ f)(x) = 2x+7$

   c. $(f \circ g)(2) = 2(2)+14 = 18$

19. $f(x) = x+4; g(x) = 2x+1$

   a. $(f \circ g)(x) = (2x+1)+4 = 2x+5$

   b. $(g \circ f)(x) = 2(x+4)+1 = 2x+9$

   c. $(f \circ g)(2) = 2(2)+5 = 9$

21. $f(x) = 4x-3; g(x) = 5x^2-2$

   a. $(f \circ g)(x) = 4(5x^2-2)-3$
                   $= 20x^2-11$

   b. $(g \circ f)(x) = 5(4x-3)^2-2$
                   $= 5(16x^2-24x+9)-2$
                   $= 80x^2-120x+43$

   c. $(f \circ g)(2) = 20(2)^2-11 = 69$

23. $f(x) = x^2+2; \ g(x) = x^2-2$

   a. $(f \circ g)(x) = (x^2-2)^2+2$
                   $= x^4-4x^2+4+2$
                   $= x^4-4x^2+6$

   b. $(g \circ f)(x) = (x^2+2)^2-2$
                   $= x^4+4x^2+4-2$
                   $= x^4+4x^2+2$

   c. $(f \circ g)(2) = 2^4-4(2)^2+6 = 6$

25. $f(x) = \sqrt{x}; \ g(x) = x-1$

   a. $(f \circ g)(x) = \sqrt{x-1}$

   b. $(g \circ f)(x) = \sqrt{x}-1$

   c. $(f \circ g)(2) = \sqrt{2-1} = \sqrt{1} = 1$

27. $f(x) = 2x-3; \ g(x) = \dfrac{x+3}{2}$

   a. $(f \circ g)(x) = 2\left(\dfrac{x+3}{2}\right)-3$
                   $= x+3-3$
                   $= x$

   b. $(g \circ f)(x) = \dfrac{(2x-3)+3}{2} = \dfrac{2x}{2} = x$

   c. $(f \circ g)(2) = 2$

29. a.
$$(f \circ g)(x) = f\left(\frac{1}{x}\right) = \frac{2}{\frac{1}{x}+3}, x \neq 0$$

$$= \frac{2(x)}{\left(\frac{1}{x}+3\right)(x)}$$

$$= \frac{2x}{1+3x}, x \neq -\frac{1}{3}$$

b. Domain: $(\_\infty, \_1/3)$ and $(\_1/3, 0)$ and $(0, \infty)$.

31. a.
$$(f \circ g)(x) = f\left(\frac{4}{x}\right) = \frac{\frac{4}{x}}{\frac{4}{x}+1}, x \neq 0$$

$$= \frac{\left(\frac{4}{x}\right)(x)}{\left(\frac{4}{x}+1\right)(x)}$$

$$= \frac{4}{4+x}, x \neq -4$$

b. Domain: $(\_\infty, \_4)$ and $(\_4, 0)$ and $(0, \infty)$.

33. a. $(f \circ g)(x) = f(x+3) = \sqrt{x+3}, x \geq -3$

b. Domain: $[\_3, \infty)$.

35. a. $(f \circ g)(x) = f(\sqrt{1-x}) = \left(\sqrt{1-x}\right)^2 + 4, x \leq 1$
$$= 1 - x + 4 = 5 - x$$

b. Domain: $(\_\infty, 1]$.

37. a. $(f \circ g)(x) = f(\sqrt{x^2-4}) = 4 - \left(\sqrt{x^2-4}\right)^2$
$$= 4 - x^2 + 4 = 8 - x^2$$

b. Domain: $(\_\infty, \_2]$ and $[2, \infty)$.

$$x^2 - 4 \geq 0$$
$$(x-2)(x+2) = 0$$
$$x = 2 \quad x = -2$$

	T		F		T	

-2   2

Test 0: $)^2 - 4 \geq 0$ False
$$-4 \geq 0$$

39. $f(x) = x^4 \quad g(x) = 3x -$

41. $f(x) = \sqrt[3]{\quad} \quad g(x) = x^2 - 9$

43. $f(x) = |x| \quad g(x) = 2x - 5$

45. $f(x) = \frac{1}{x} \quad g(x) = 2x - 3$

47. $f + g)(-3) = f(-3) + g(-3) = -1 + (-1) = 0$

49. $f - g)(2) = f(2) - g(2) = 4 - (-6) = 10$

51. $\left(\frac{f}{g}\right)(-6) = \frac{f(-6)}{g(-6)} = \frac{4}{2} = 2$

53. $fg)(-4) = f(-4)g(-4) = 2(0) =$

55. $f \circ g)(2) = f(0) =$

57. $(g \circ f)(0) = g(2) = -6$

59. $(D + C)(2000) = D(2000) + C(2000)$
$$= 14 + 6 = 20$$
In 2000 veterinary bills for cats and dogs were about \$20 billion dollars.

61. $\{1983, 1987, 1991, 1996, 2000\}$

63. $f + g$ represents the total world population in year x.

150

65. $f(2000) \approx 1.5$ billion people

$g(2000) \approx 6$ billion people

$$(f + g)(2000) = f(2000) + g(2000)$$
$$\approx 1.5 + 6.0$$
$$= 7.5 \text{ billion people.}$$

67. $(R - C)(20,000)$
$$= 65(20,000) - (600,000 + 45(20,000))$$
$$= -200,000$$

The company lost $200,000 since costs exceeded revenues.

$(R - C)(30,000)$
$$= 65(30,000) - (600,000 + 45(30,000))$$
$$= 0$$

69. a. f gives the price of the computer after a $400 discount. g gives the price of the computer after a 25% discount.

b. $(f \circ g)(x) = 0.75x - 400$

This models the price of a computer after first a 25% discount and then a $400 discount.

c. $(g \circ f)(x) = 0.75(x - 400)$

This models the price of a computer after first a $400 discount and then a 25% discount.

d.   The function $f \circ g$ models the greater discount, since the 25% discount is taken on the regular price first.

e. $f(x) = x - 400$
$$y = x - 400$$
$$x = y - 400$$
$$y = x + 400$$
$$f^{-1}(x) = x + 400$$

If x is the discount price of the computer, then $f^{-1}(x)$ is the regular price.

71. – 75. Answers will vary.

77.

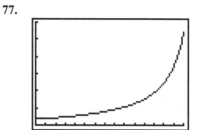

The per capita cost of Medicare is rising.

79.

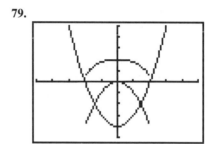

Domain of f °g: [-2, 2]
$$(f \circ g)(x) = \left(\sqrt{4 - x^2}\right)^2 - 4$$
$$= 4 - x^2 - 4 = -x$$

Domain of f °g is same as domain of g.

$-x^2 \geq 0$
$2 - x)(2 + x) = 0$
$= 2$ $x = -2$

F		T		F
	-2		2	

Test 0: $4 - 0 \geq 0$

$4 \geq 0$ True

Domain: [-2, 2]

81. $f \circ g)(x) = (f \circ g)(-x)$
$f(g(x)) = f(g(-x))$ since g is even
$f(g(x)) = f(g(x))$ so $f \circ g$ is even

Section 2.7

Check Point Exercises

1. $f(g(x)) = 7g(x) = 7\left(\dfrac{x}{7}\right) = x$

    $g(f(x)) = \dfrac{f(x)}{7} = \dfrac{7x}{7} = x$

    f and g are inverses.

2. $f(g(x)) = 4g(x) - 7$

    $\qquad = 4\left(\dfrac{x+7}{4}\right) - 7$

    $\qquad = x + 7 - 7$

    $\qquad = x$

    $g(f(x)) = \dfrac{f(x) + 7}{4}$

    $\qquad = \dfrac{4x - 7 + 7}{4}$

    $\qquad = \dfrac{4x}{4}$

    $\qquad = x$

    f and g are inverses.

3. $f(x) = 2x + 7$

    $y = 2x + 7$

    $x = 2y + 7$

    $x - 7 = 2y$

    $\dfrac{x-7}{2} = y$

    $f^{-1}(x) = \dfrac{x-7}{2}$

4. $f(x) = 4x^3 - 1$

    $y = 4x^3 - 1$

    $x = 4y^3 - 1$

    $x + 1 = 4y^3$

    $\dfrac{x+1}{4} = y^3$

    $\sqrt[3]{\frac{x+1}{4}} = y$

    $f^{-1}(x) = \sqrt[3]{\frac{x+1}{4}}$

5. **(b)** and **(c)** have inverse functions.

6.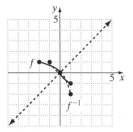

Exercise Set 2.7

1. $f(x) = 4x; \ g(x) = \dfrac{x}{4}$

    $f(g(x)) = 4\left(\dfrac{x}{4}\right) = x$

    $g(f(x)) = \dfrac{4x}{4} = x$

    f and g are inverses.

3. $f(x) = 3x + 8; \ g(x) = \dfrac{x-8}{3}$

    $f(g(x)) = 3\left(\dfrac{x-8}{3}\right) + 8 = x - 8 + 8 = x$

    $g(f(x)) = \dfrac{(3x+8) - 8}{3} = \dfrac{3x}{3} = x$

    f and g are inverses.

5. $f(x) = 5x - 9; \ g(x) = \dfrac{x+5}{9}$

    $f(g(x)) = 5\left(\dfrac{x+5}{9}\right) - 9$

    $\qquad = \dfrac{5x + 25}{9} - 9$

    $\qquad = \dfrac{5x - 56}{9}$

    $g(f(x)) = \dfrac{5x - 9 + 5}{9} = \dfrac{5x - 4}{9}$

    f and g are not inverses.

7. $f(x) = \dfrac{3}{x-4}; \; g(x) = \dfrac{3}{x} + 4$

$f(g(x)) = \dfrac{3}{\frac{3}{x} + 4 - 4} = \dfrac{3}{\frac{3}{x}} = x$

$g(f(x)) = \dfrac{3}{\frac{3}{x-4}} + 4$

$\qquad = 3 \cdot \left(\dfrac{x-4}{3} \right) + 4$

$\qquad = x - 4 + 4$

$\qquad = x$

f and g are inverses.

9. $f(x) = -x; g(x) = -x$

$f(g(x)) = -(-x) = x$

$g(f(x)) = -(-x) = x$

f and g are inverses.

11. a. $f(x) = x + 3$

$\qquad y = x + 3$

$\qquad x = y + 3$

$\qquad y = x - 3$

$\quad f^{-1}(x) = x - 3$

b. $f(f^{-1}(x)) = x - 3 + 3 = x$

$\quad f^{-1}(f(x)) = x + 3 - 3 = x$

13. a. $f(x) = 2x$

$\qquad y = 2x$

$\qquad x = 2y$

$\qquad y = \dfrac{x}{2}$

$\quad f^{-1}(x) = \dfrac{x}{2}$

b. $f(f^{-1}(x)) = 2\left(\dfrac{x}{2} \right) = x$

$\quad f^{-1}(f(x)) = \dfrac{2x}{2} = x$

15. a. $f(x) = 2x + 3$

$\qquad y = 2x + 3$

$\qquad x = 2y + 3$

$\quad x - 3 = 2y$

$\qquad y = \dfrac{x-3}{2}$

$\quad f^{-1}(x) = \dfrac{x-3}{2}$

b. $f(f^{-1}(x)) = 2\left(\dfrac{x-3}{2} \right) + 3$

$\qquad = x - 3 + 3$

$\qquad = x$

$f^{-1}(f(x)) = \dfrac{2x+3-3}{2} = \dfrac{2x}{2} = x$

17. a. $f(x) = x^3 + 2$

$\qquad y = x^3 + 2$

$\qquad x = y^3 + 2$

$\quad x - 2 = y^3$

$\qquad y = \sqrt[3]{x-2}$

$\quad f^{-1}(x) = \sqrt[3]{x-2}$

b. $f(f^{-1}(x)) = \left(\sqrt[3]{x-2} \right)^3 + 2$

$\qquad = x - 2 + 2$

$\qquad = x$

$f^{-1}(f(x)) = \sqrt[3]{x^3 + 2 - 2} = \sqrt[3]{x^3} = x$

19. a. $f(x) = (x+2)^3$

$\qquad y = (x+2)^3$

$\qquad x = (y+2)^3$

$\quad \sqrt[3]{x} = y + 2$

$\qquad y = \sqrt[3]{x} - 2$

$\quad f^{-1}(x) = \sqrt[3]{x} - 2$

b. $f(f^{-1}(x)) = \left(\sqrt[3]{x} - 2 + 2 \right)^3 = \left(\sqrt[3]{x} \right)^3 = x$

$f^{-1}(f(x)) = \sqrt[3]{(x+2)^3} - 2$

$\qquad = x + 2 - 2$

$\qquad = x$

21. a.
$$f(x) = \frac{1}{x}$$
$$y = \frac{1}{x}$$
$$x = \frac{1}{y}$$
$$xy = 1$$
$$y = \frac{1}{x}$$
$$f^{-1}(x) = \frac{1}{x}$$

b.
$$f(f^{-1}(x)) = \frac{1}{\frac{1}{x}} = x$$
$$f^{-1}(f(x)) = \frac{1}{\frac{1}{x}} = x$$

23. a.
$$f(x) = \sqrt{x}$$
$$y = \sqrt{x}$$
$$x = \sqrt{y}$$
$$y = x^2$$
$$f^{-1}(x) = x^2, \ x \ge 0$$

b.
$$f(f^{-1}(x)) = \sqrt{x^2} = |x| = x \text{ for } x \ge 0.$$
$$f^{-1}(f(x)) = (\sqrt{x})^2 = x$$

25. a.
$$f(x) = x^2 + 1, \text{ for } x \ge 0$$
$$y = x^2 + 1$$
$$x = y^2 + 1, \text{ for } y \ge 0$$
$$x - 1 = y^2$$
$$y = \sqrt{x-1} \text{ since } y \ge 0$$
$$f^{-1}(x) = \sqrt{x-1}$$

b.
$$f(f^{-1}(x)) = (\sqrt{x-1})^2 + 1$$
$$= x - 1 + 1$$
$$= x$$
$$f^{-1}(f(x)) = \sqrt{x^2 + 1 - 1} = \sqrt{x^2} = x$$
for $x \ge 0$.

27. a.
$$f(x) = \frac{2x+1}{x-3}$$
$$y = \frac{2x+1}{x-3}$$
$$x = \frac{2y+1}{y-3}$$
$$x(y-3) = 2y+1$$
$$xy - 3x = 2y + 1$$
$$xy - 2y = 3x + 1$$
$$y(x-2) = 3x + 1$$
$$y = \frac{3x+1}{x-2}$$
$$f^{-1}(x) = \frac{3x+1}{x-2}$$

b.
$$f(f^{-1}(x)) = \frac{2\left(\frac{3x+1}{x-2}\right)+1}{\frac{3x+1}{x-2}-3}$$
$$= \frac{2(3x+1)+x-2}{3x+1-3(x-2)} = \frac{6x+2+x-2}{3x+1-3x+6}$$
$$= \frac{7x}{7} = x$$
$$f^{-1}(f(x)) = \frac{3\left(\frac{2x+1}{x-3}\right)+1}{\frac{2x+1}{x-3}-2}$$
$$= \frac{3(2x+1)+x-3}{2x+1-2(x-3)}$$
$$= \frac{6x+3+x-3}{2x+1-2x+6} = \frac{7x}{7} = x$$

29. a.
$$f(x) = \sqrt[3]{x-4} + 3$$
$$y = \sqrt[3]{x-4} + 3$$
$$x = \sqrt[3]{y-4} + 3$$
$$x - 3 = \sqrt[3]{y-4}$$
$$(x-3)^3 = y - 4$$
$$y = (x-3)^3 + 4$$
$$f^{-1}(x) = (x-3)^3 + 4$$

b.
$$f(f^{-1}(x)) = \sqrt[3]{(x-3)^3 + 4 - 4} + 3$$
$$= \sqrt[3]{(x-3)^3} + 3$$
$$= x - 3 + 3 = x$$
$$f^{-1}(f(x)) = \left(\sqrt[3]{x-4} + 3 - 3\right)^3 + 4$$
$$= \left(\sqrt[3]{x-4}\right)^3 + 4 = x - 4 + 4 = x$$

31. The function is not one-to-one, so it does not have an inverse function.

33. The function is not one-to-one, so it does not have an inverse function.

35. The function is one-to-one, so it does have an inverse function.

37.

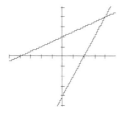

39.

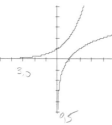

41. **a.** {(Zambia, _7.2), (Colombia, _4.5), (Poland, _2.9), (Italy, _2.9), (United States, _1.9)} This relation is not a function.

     b. {(_7.2, Zambia), (_4.5, Colombia), (_2.9, Poland), (_2.9, Italy), (_1.9, United States)}

43. **a.** It passes the horizontal line test and is one-to-one.

     b. $f^{-1}(0.25) = 15$ If there are 15 people in the room, the probability that 2 of them have the same birthday is .25.

       $f^{-1}(0.5) = 21$ If there are 21 people in the room, the probability that 2 of them have the same birthday is .5.

       $f^{-1}(0.7) = 30$ If there are 30 people in the room, the probability that 2 of them have the same birthday is .7.

45.

$$f(g(x)) = \frac{9}{5}\left[\frac{5}{9}(x - 32)\right] + 32$$
$$= x - 32 + 32$$
$$= x$$

f and *g* are inverses.

47. – 51. Answers will vary.

53.

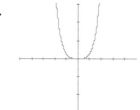

one-to-one

55.

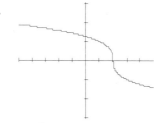

not one-to-one

57.

not one-to-one

59.

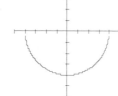

not one-to-one

61.

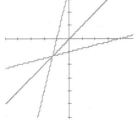

f and g are inverses

63.

f and g are inverses

65. $(f \circ g)(x) = 3(x + 5) = 3x + 15.$

$y = 3x + 15$

$x = 3y + 15$

$y = \dfrac{x - 15}{3}$

$(f \circ g)^{-1}(x) = \dfrac{x - 15}{3}$

$g(x) = x + 5$

$y = x + 5$

$x = y + 5$

$y = x - 5$

$g^{-1}(x) = x - 5$

$f(x) = 3x$

$y = 3x$

$x = 3y$

$y = \dfrac{x}{3}$

$f^{-1}(x) = \dfrac{x}{3}$

$\left(g^{-1} \circ f^{-1}\right)(x) = \dfrac{x}{3} - 5 = \dfrac{x - 15}{3}$

67. No, there will be 2 times when the spacecraft
is at the same height, when it is going up
and when it is coming down.

Chapter 3

Section 3.1

Check Point Exercises

1. $f(x) = -(x-1)^2 + 4$
   The vertex is (1, 4).
   $0 = -(x-1)^2 + 4$
   $(x-1)^2 = 4$
   $x - 1 = \pm 2$
   $x = 3$ or $x = -1$
   The x-intercepts are 3 and -1.
   $f(0) = -(0-1)^2 + 4 = 3$
   The y-intercept is 3.

2. $f(x) = (x-2)^2 + 1$
   The vertex is (2, 1).
   $0 = (x-2)^2 + 1$
   $(x-2)^2 = -1$
   No x-intercepts.
   $f(0) = (0-2)^2 + 1 = 5$
   The y-intercept is 5.

   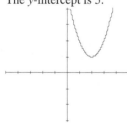

3. $f(x) = x^2 - 2x - 3$
   $x = -\dfrac{b}{2a} = -\dfrac{-2}{2} = 1$
   $f(1) = 1^2 - 2(1) - 3 = -4$
   $x^2 - 2x - 3 = 0$
   $(x-3)(x+1) = 0$
   $x = 3$ or $x = -1$
   The x-intercepts are 3 and -1.
   $f(0) = 0^2 - 2(0) - 3 = -3$
   The y-intercept is -3.

   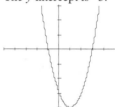

4. $x = -\dfrac{b}{2a} = -\dfrac{-36}{2(0.4)} = 45$
   $f(45) = 0.4(45)^2 - 36(45) + 1000 = 190$
   The age of a driver having the least number of accidents is 45. The minimum number of accidents is 190 per 50 million miles driven.

Exercise Set 3.1

1. vertex: (1, 1)
   $h(x) = (x-1)^2 + 1$

3. vertex: (1, −1)
   $j(x) = (x-1)^2 - 1$

5. The graph is $f(x) = x^2$ translated down one.
   $h(x) = x^2 - 1$

7. The point (1, 0) is on the graph and
   $g(1) = 0$. $g(x) = x^2 - 2x + 1$

157

9. $f(x) = 2(x-3)^2 + 1$

$h = 3,\ k = 1$

The vertex is at (3, 1).

11. $f(x) = -2(x+1)^2 + 5$

$h = -1,\ k = 5$

The vertex is at (-1, 5).

13. $f(x) = 2x^2 - 8x + 3$

$x = \dfrac{-b}{2a} = \dfrac{8}{4} = 2$

$f(2) = 2(2)^2 - 8(2) + 3$

$= 8 - 16 + 3 = -5$

The vertex is at (2, -5).

15. $f(x) = -x^2 - 2x + 8$

$x = \dfrac{-b}{2a} = \dfrac{2}{-2} = -1$

$f(-1) = -(-1)^2 - 2(-1) + 8$

$\qquad = -1 + 2 + 8 = 9$

The vertex is at (-1, 9).

17. $f(x) = (x-4)^2 - 1$

vertex: (4, -1)

x-intercepts:

$0 = (x-4)^2 - 1$

$1 = (x-4)^2$

$\pm 1 = x - 4$

$x = 3$ or $x = 5$

y-intercept:

$f(0) = (0-4)^2 - 1 = 15$

The axis of symmetry is $x = 4$.

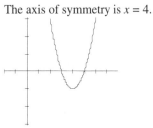

19. $f(x) = (x-1)^2 + 2$

vertex: (1, 2)

x-intercepts:

$0 = (x-1)^2 + 2$

$(x-1)^2 = -2$

$x - 1 = \pm\sqrt{-2}$

$x = 1 \pm i\sqrt{2}$

No x-intercepts.

y-intercept:

$f(0) = (0-1)^2 + 2 = 3$

The axis of symmetry is $x = 1$.

21. $y - 1 = (x-3)^2$

$y = (x-3)^2 + 1$

vertex: (3, 1)

x-intercepts:

$0 = (x-3)^2 + 1$

$(x-3)^2 = -1$

$x - 3 = \pm i$

$x = 3 \pm i$

No x-intercepts.

y-intercept: 10

$y = (0-3)^2 + 1 = 10$

The axis of symmetry is $x = 3$.

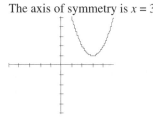

23. $y = 2(x+2)^2 - 1$

vertex: (-2, -1)

x-intercepts:

$0 = 2(x+2)^2 - 1$

$2(x+2)^2 = 1$

$(x+2)^2 = \dfrac{1}{2}$

$x + 2 = \pm \dfrac{1}{\sqrt{2}}$

$x = -2 \pm \dfrac{1}{\sqrt{2}} = -2 \pm \dfrac{\sqrt{2}}{2}$

y-intercept:

$y = 2(0+2)^2 - 1 = 7$

The axis of symmetry is $x = -2$.

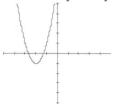

25. $f(x) = 4 - (x-1)^2$

$f(x) = -(x-1)^2 + 4$

vertex: $(1, 4)$

x-intercepts:

$0 = -(x-1)^2 + 4$

$(x-1)^2 = 4$

$x - 1 = \pm 2$

$x = -1$ or $x = 3$

y-intercept:

$f(x) = -(0-1)^2 + 4 = 3$

The axis of symmetry is $x = 1$.

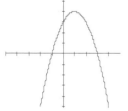

27. $f(x) = x^2 - 2x - 3$

$f(x) = \left(x^2 - 2x + 1\right) - 3 - 1$

$f(x) = (x-1)^2 - 4$

vertex: $(1, -4)$

x-intercepts:

$0 = (x-1)^2 - 4$

$(x-1)^2 = 4$

$x - 1 = \pm 2$

$x = -1$ or $x = 3$

y-intercept: -3

$f(0) = 0^2 - 2(0) - 3 = -3$

The axis of symmetry is $x = 1$.

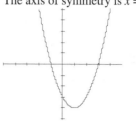

29. $f(x) = x^2 + 3x - 10$

$f(x) = \left(x^2 + 3x + \dfrac{9}{4}\right) - 10 - \dfrac{9}{4}$

$f(x) = \left(x + \dfrac{3}{2}\right)^2 - \dfrac{49}{4}$

vertex: $\left(-\dfrac{3}{2}, -\dfrac{49}{4}\right)$

x-intercepts:

$0 = \left(x + \dfrac{3}{2}\right)^2 - \dfrac{49}{4}$

$\left(x + \dfrac{3}{2}\right)^2 = \dfrac{49}{4}$

$x + \dfrac{3}{2} = \pm \dfrac{7}{2}$

$x = -\dfrac{3}{2} \pm \dfrac{7}{2}$

$x = 2$ or $x = -5$

y-intercept:

$f(x) = 0^2 + 3(0) - 10 = -10$

The axis of symmetry is $x = -\dfrac{3}{2}$.

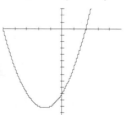

31. $y = 2x - x^2 + 3$

$y = -x^2 + 2x + 3$

$y = -\left(x^2 - 2x + 1\right) + 3 + 1$

$y = -(x-1)^2 + 4$

vertex: $(1, 4)$

x-intercepts:

$0 = -(x-1)^2 + 4$

$(x-1)^2 = 4$

$x - 1 = \pm 2$

$x = -1$ or $x = 3$

y-intercept:

$f(0) = 2(0) - (0)^2 + 3 = 3$

The axis of symmetry is $x = 1$.

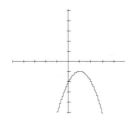

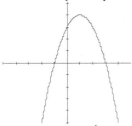

33. $y = 2x - x^2 - 2$

$y = -x^2 + 2x - 2$

$y = -\left(x^2 - 2x + 1\right) - 2 + 1$

$y = -(x-1)^2 - 1$

vertex: $(1, -1)$

x-intercepts:

$0 = -(x-1)^2 - 1$

$(x-1)^2 = -1$

$x - 1 = \pm i$

$x = 1 \pm i$

No x-intercepts.

y-intercept:

$y = 2(0) - (0)^2 - 2 = -2$

The axis of symmetry is $x = 1$.

35. $f(x) = 3x^2 - 12x - 1$

$a = 3$. The parabola opens upward and has a minimum value.

$x = \dfrac{-b}{2a} = \dfrac{12}{6} = 2$

$f(2) = 3(2)^2 - 12(2) - 1$

$= 12 - 24 - 1 = -13$

The minimum point is (2, –13).

37. $f(x) = -4x^2 + 8x - 3$

$a = -4$. The parabola opens downward and has a maximum value.

$x = \dfrac{-b}{2a} = \dfrac{-8}{-8} = 1$

$f(1) = -4(1)^2 + 8(1) - 3$

$= -4 + 8 - 3 = 1$

The maximum point is (1, 1).

39. $f(x) = 5x^2 - 5x$

$a = 5$. The parabola opens upward and has a minimum value.

$x = \dfrac{-b}{2a} = \dfrac{5}{10} = \dfrac{1}{2}$

$f\left(\dfrac{1}{2}\right) = 5\left(\dfrac{1}{2}\right)^2 - 5\left(\dfrac{1}{2}\right)$

$= \dfrac{5}{4} - \dfrac{5}{2} = \dfrac{5}{4} - \dfrac{10}{4} = \dfrac{-5}{4}$

The minimum point is $\left(\dfrac{1}{2}, \dfrac{-5}{4}\right)$.

41. $f(x) = -3.1x^2 + 51.4x + 4024.5$

$a = -3.1,\ b = 51.4$

$x = \dfrac{-51.4}{2(-3.1)} \approx 8.3$ years

$1960 + 8.3 = 1968.3 \approx 1968$

Year: 1968

$f(8.3) = -3.1(8.3)^2 + 51.4(8.3) + 40214.5$

≈ 4238

The consumption is 4238 cigarettes per person.

43. $s(t) = -16^2 + 200t + 4$

$a = -16,\ b = 200$

$t = \dfrac{-200}{2(-16)} = 6.25$

$s(6.25) = -16(6.25)^2 + 200(6.25) + 4$

$= 629$

The highest point, 629 feet, is reached after 6.25 seconds.

45. The graph has the shape of a parabola.

47. $A(x) = x(120 - 2x)$

$= 12x - 2x^2$

$a = -2,\ b = 120$

$x = \dfrac{-b}{2a} = \dfrac{-120}{-4} = 30$

length $= 120 - 2x = 120 - 2(30)$

$= 120 - 60 = 60$

width: 30 ft

length: 60 ft

$A(30) = 120(30) - 2(30)^2$

$= 1800$

The maximum area is 1800 ft².

49. $A = x(20 - 2x)$

$A = -2x^2 + 20x$

$a = -2,\ b = 20$

$x = \dfrac{-20}{2(-2)} = 5$

A depth of 5 inches will maximize the volume.

51.–57. Answers may vary.

59. $y = 2x^2 - 82x + 720$

a.

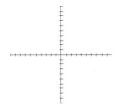

You can not see the parabola.

b. $a = 2; b = -82$

$$x = -\frac{b}{2a} = -\frac{-82}{4} = 20.5$$

$$y = 2(20.5)^2 - 82(20.5) + 720$$
$$= 840.5 - 1681 + 720$$
$$= -120.5$$
vertex: $(20.5, -120.5)$

c. Answers may vary.

d. Answers may vary.

61. $y = -4x^2 + 20x + 160$

$$x = \frac{-b}{2a} = \frac{-20}{-8} = 2.5$$

$$y = -4(2.5)^2 + 20(2.5) + 160$$
$$= -2.5 + 50 + 160 = 185$$
The vertex is at $(2.5, 185)$.

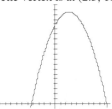

63. $y = 0.01x^2 + 0.6x + 100$

$$x = \frac{-b}{2a} = \frac{-0.6}{0.02} = -30$$

$$y = 0.01(-30)^2 + 0.6(-30) + 100$$
$$= 9 - 18 + 100 = 91$$

The vertex is at $(-30, 91)$.

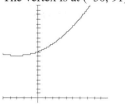

65. a.

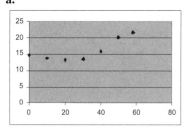

b. $y = 0.0055x^2 - 0.1918x + 14.929$

c.

$$x = \frac{-(-.1918)}{2(.0055)} = 17.4;\ 1970 + 17 = 1957$$

$$y = 0.0055(17.4)^2 - .1918(17.4) + 14.929$$
$$\approx 13.26$$

The worst gas mileage was 13.26 mpg in 1957.

d.

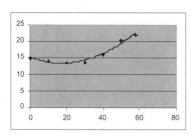

67. Answers may vary.

69. Vertex (3, 2) Axis: $x = 3$
second point (0, 11)

Section 3.2

Check Point Exercises

1. Since n is even and $a_n > 0$, the graph rises
to the left and to the right.

2. Since n is odd and the leading coefficient is
negative, the function falls to the right.
Since the ratio cannot be negative, the model
won't be appropriate.

3. The graph does not show the function's end
behavior. Since $a_n > 0$ and n is odd, the
graph should fall to the left.

4. $f(x) = x^3 + 2x^2 - 4x - 8$
$0 = x^2(x + 2) - 4(x + 2)$
$0 = (x + 2)(x^2 - 4)$
$0 = (x + 2)^2(x - 2)$
$x = 2$ or $x = -2$
The zeros are 2 and –2.

5. $f(x) = x^4 - 4x^2$
$x^4 - 4x^2 = 0$
$x^2(x^2 - 4) = 0$
$x^2(x + 2)(x - 2) = 0$
$x = 0$ or $x = -2$ or $x = 2$
The zeros are 0, –2, and 2.

6. $f(x) = x^3 - 3x^2$
Since $a_n > 0$ and n is odd, the graph falls to
the left and rises to the right.
$x^3 - 3x^2 = 0$
$x^2(x - 3) = 0$
$x = 0$ or $x = 3$
The x-intercepts are 0 and 3.
$f(0) = 0^3 - 3(0)^2 = 0$
The y-intercept is 0.
$f(-x) = (-x)^3 - 3(-x)^2 = -x^3 - 3x^2$
No symmetry.

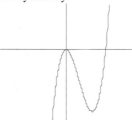

Exercise Set 3.2

1. polynomial function;
degree: 3

3. polynomial function;
degree: 5

5. not a polynomial function

7. not a polynomial function

9. not a polynomial function

11. polynomial function

13. Not a polynomial function because graph is
not continuous.

15. (c)

17. (b)

19. (a)

21. $f(x) = 5x^3 + 7x^2 - x + 9$

Since $a_n > 0$ and n is odd, the graph of $f(x)$ falls to the left and rises to the right.

23. $f(x) = 5x^4 + 7x^2 - x + 9$

Since $a_n > 0$ and n is even, the graph of $f(x)$ rises to the left and to the right.

25. $f(x) = -5x^4 + 7x^2 - x + 9$

Since $a_n < 0$ and n is even, the graph of $f(x)$ falls to the left and to the right.

27. $f(x) = 2(x - 5)(x + 4)^2$

$x = 5$ has multiplicity 1;
The graph crosses the x-axis.
$x = -4$ has multiplicity 2;
The graph touches the x-axis and turns around.

29. $f(x) = 4(x - 3)(x + 6)^3$

x = 3 has multiplicity 1;
The graph crosses the x-axis.
$x = -6$ has multiplicity 3;
The graph crosses the x-axis.

31. $f(x) = x^3 - 2x^2 + x$

$= x\left(x^2 - 2x + 1\right)$

$= x(x - 1)^2$

$x = 0$ has multiplicity 1;
The graph crosses the x-axis.
$x = 1$ has multiplicity 2;
The graph touches the x-axis and turns around.

33. $f(x) = x^3 + 7x^2 - 4x - 28$

$= x^2(x + 7) - 4(x + 7)$

$= \left(x^2 - 4\right)(x + 7)$

$= (x - 2)(x + 2)(x + 7)$

$x = 2, x = -2$ and $x = -7$ have multiplicity 1;
The graph crosses the x-axis.

35. $f(x) = x^3 + 2x^2 - x - 2$

a. Since $a_n > 0$ and n is odd, $f(x)$ rises to the right and falls to the left.

b. $x^3 + 2x^2 - x - 2 = 0$

$x^2(x + 2) - (x + 2) = 0$

$(x + 2)(x^2 - 1) = 0$

$(x + 2)(x - 1)(x + 1) = 0$

$x = -2, x = 1, x = -1$

The zeros at $-2, -1$, and 1 have odd multiplicity so $f(x)$ crosses the x-axis at these points.

c. $f(0) = (0)^3 + 2(0)^2 - 0 - 2$

$= -2$

The y-intercept is -2.

d. $f(-x) = (-x) + 2(-x)^2 - (-x) - 2$

$= -x^3 + 2x^2 + x - 2$

$-f(x) = -x^3 - 2x^2 + x + 2$

The graph has neither origin symmetry or y-axis symmetry.

e. The graph has 2 turning points and $2 \le 3 - 1$.

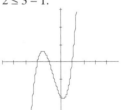

37. $f(x) = x^4 - 9x^2$

a. Since $a_n > 0$ and n is even, $f(x)$ rises to the left and the right.

b. $x^4 - 9x^2 = 0$

$x^2\left(x^2 - 9\right) = 0$

$x^2(x - 3)(x + 3) = 0$

$x = 0, x = 3, x = -3$

The zeros at -3 and 3 have odd multiplicity, so $f(x)$ crosses the x-axis at these points. The root at 0 has even multi-plicity, so $f(x)$ touches the x-axis at 0.

c. $f(0) = (0)^4 - 9(0)^2 = 0$
The y-intercept is 0.

d. $f(-x) = x^4 - 9x^2$
$f(-x) = f(x)$
The graph has y-axis symmetry.

e. The graph has 3 turning points and $3 \le 4 - 1$.

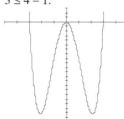

39. $f(x) = -x^4 + 16x^2$

a. Since $a_n < 0$ and n is even, $f(x)$ falls to the left and the right.

b. $-x^4 + 16x^2 = 0$
$x^2(-x^2 + 16) = 0$
$x^2(4 - x)(4 + x) = 0$
$x = 0, x = 4, x = -4$
The zeros at -4 and 4 have odd multi--plicity, so $f(x)$ crosses the x-axis at these points. The root at 0 has even multi-plicity, so $f(x)$ touches the x-axis at 0.

c. $f(0) = (0)^4 - 9(0)^2 = 0$
The y-intercept is 0.

d. $f(-x) = -x^4 + 16x^2$
$f(-x) = f(x)$
The graph has y-axis symmetry.

e. The graph has 3 turning points and $3 \le 4 - 1$.

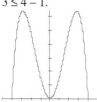

41. $f(x) = x^4 - 2x^3 + x^2$

a. Since $a_n > 0$ and n is even, $f(x)$ rises to the left and the right.

b. $x^4 - 2x^3 + x^2 = 0$
$x^2(x^2 - 2x + 1) = 0$
$x^2(x - 1)(x - 1) = 0$
$x = 0, x = 1$
The zeros at 1 and 0 have even multiplicity, so $f(x)$ touches the x-axis at 0 and 1.

c. $f(0) = (0)^4 - 2(0)^3 + (0)^2 = 0$
The y-intercept is 0.

d. $f(-x) = x^4 + 2x^3 + x^2$
The graph has neither y-axis nor origin symmetry.

e. The graph has 3 turning points and $3 \le 4 - 1$.

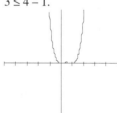

43. $f(x) = -2x^4 + 4x^3$

a. Since $a_n < 0$ and n is even, $f(x)$ falls to the left and the right.

b. $-2x^4 + 4x^3 = 0$

$x^3(-2x + 4) = 0$

$x = 0, x = 2$

The zeros at 0 and 1 have odd multiplicity, so $f(x)$ crosses the x-axis at these points. At 0 the multiplicity is greater than 1, so the function will also flatten out.

c. $f(0) = -2(0)^4 + 4(0)^3 = 0$

The y-intercept is 0.

d. $f(-x) = -2x^4 - 4x^3$

The graph has neither y-axis nor origin symmetry.

e.   The graph has 1 turning point and $1 \le 4 - 1$.

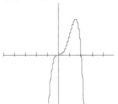

45. $f(x) = 6x^3 - 9x - x^5$

a.   Since $a_n < 0$ and n is odd, $f(x)$ rises to the left and falls to the right.

b. $-x^5 + 6x^3 - 9x = 0$

$-x(x^4 - 6x^2 + 9) = 0$

$-x(x^2 - 3)(x^2 - 3) = 0$

$x = 0, \ x = \pm\sqrt{3}$

The root at 0 has odd multiplicity so $f(x)$ crosses the x-axis at (0, 0). The zeros at $-\sqrt{3}$ and $\sqrt{3}$ have even multiplicity so $f(x)$ touches the x-axis at $\sqrt{3}$ and $-\sqrt{3}$.

c. $f(0) = -(0)^5 + 6(0)^3 - 9(0) = 0$

The y-intercept is 0.

d. $f(-x) = x^5 - 6x^3 + 9x$

$f(-x) = -f(x)$

The graph has origin symmetry.

e.   The graph has 4 turning point and $4 \le 5 - 1$.

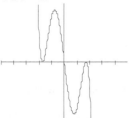

47. $f(x) = 3x^2 - x^3$

a.   Since $a_n < 0$ and n is odd, $f(x)$ rises to the left and falls to the right.

b. $-x^3 + 3x^2 = 0$

$-x^2(x - 3) = 0$

$x = 0, x = 3$

The zero at 3 has odd multiplicity so $f(x)$ crosses the x-axis at that point. The root at 0 has even multiplicity so $f(x)$ touches the axis at (0, 0).

c. $f(0) = -(0)^3 + 3(0)^2 = 0$

The y-intercept is 0.

d. $f(-x) = x^3 + 3x^2$

The graph has neither y-axis nor origin symmetry.

e.   The graph has 2 turning point and $2 \le 3 - 1$.

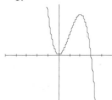

49. $f(x) = -3(x-1)^2(x^2-4)$

a. Since $a_n < 0$ and n is even, $f(x)$ falls to the left and the right.

b. $-3(x-1)^2(x^2-4) = 0$
$x = 1, x = -2, x = 2$
The zeros at -2 and 2 have odd multiplicity, so $f(x)$ crosses the x-axis at these points. The root at 1 has even multiplicity, so $f(x)$ touches the x-axis at $(1, 0)$.

c. $f(0) = -3(0-1)^2(0^2-4)^3$
$= -3(1)(-4) = 12$
The y-intercept is 12.

d. $f(-x) = -3(-x-1)^2(x^2-4)$
The graph has neither x-axis nor origin symmetry.

e. The graph has 3 turning point and $3 \le 4 - 1$.

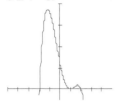

51. a. Leading coefficient test suggests the elk population will decline and eventually will die off.

b.
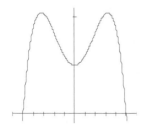

c.

The population reaches extinction at the end of 5 years.

53. $2005 - 1987 = 18$
$T(18) = -0.87(18)^3 + 0.35(18)^2$
$+ 81.62(18) + 7684.94$
≈ 4193.66

There will be 4994 thousand larceny thefts in 2005.
No. Since $a_n < 0$ and n is odd, the graph of $F(x)$ falls to the right. Eventually the function would predict a negative number of larceny thefts, which is impossible.

55. There are three turning points, so the degree of the polynomial is 4. Since the right end is rising, the leading coefficient will be positive.

57.–73. Answers may vary.

75.
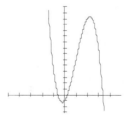

77.
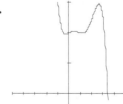

79.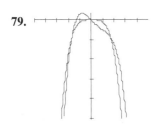

81. $f(x) = x^3 + x^2 - 12x$

Section 3.3

Check Point Exercises

1.
$$
\begin{array}{r}
x + 5 \\
x + 9 \overline{)\, x^2 + 14x + 45} \\
\underline{x^2 + 9x} \\
5x + 45 \\
\underline{5x + 45} \\
0
\end{array}
$$
The answer is $x + 5$.

2.
$$
\begin{array}{r}
2x^2 + 3x - 2 \\
x - 3 \overline{)\, 2x^3 - 3x^2 - 11x + 7} \\
\underline{2x^3 - 6x^2} \\
3x^2 - 11x \\
\underline{3x^2 - 9x} \\
-2x + 7 \\
\underline{-2x + 6} \\
1
\end{array}
$$
The answer is $2x^2 + 3x - 2 + \dfrac{1}{x-3}$.

3.
$$
\begin{array}{r}
2x^2 + 7x + 14 \\
x^2 - 2x \overline{)\, 2x^4 + 3x^3 + 0x^2 - 7x - 10} \\
\underline{2x^4 - 4x^3} \\
7x^3 + 0x^2 \\
\underline{7x^3 - 14x^2} \\
14x^2 - 7x \\
\underline{14x^2 - 28x} \\
21x - 10
\end{array}
$$

The answer is $2x^2 + 7x + 14 + \dfrac{21x - 10}{x^2 - 2x}$.

4.
$$
\begin{array}{r|rrrr}
-2 & 1 & 0 & -7 & -6 \\
   &   & -2 & 4 & 6 \\
\hline
   & 1 & -2 & -3 & 0
\end{array}
$$
The answer is $x^2 - 2x - 3$.

5.
$$
\begin{array}{r|rrrr}
-4 & 3 & 4 & -5 & 3 \\
   &   & -12 & 32 & -108 \\
\hline
   & 3 & -8 & 27 & -105
\end{array}
$$
$f(-4) = -105$

6.
$$
\begin{array}{r|rrrr}
-1 & 15 & 14 & -3 & -2 \\
   &   & -15 & 1 & 2 \\
\hline
   & 15 & -1 & -2 & 0
\end{array}
$$
$15x^2 - x - 2 = 0$
$(3x + 1)(5x - 2) = 0$
$x = -\dfrac{1}{3}$ or $x = \dfrac{2}{5}$
The solution set is $\left\{ -1, -\dfrac{1}{3}, \dfrac{2}{5} \right\}$.

Exercise Set 3.3

1.
$$
\begin{array}{r}
x + 3 \\
x + 5 \overline{)\, x^2 + 8x + 15} \\
\underline{x^2 + 5x} \\
3x + 15 \\
\underline{3x + 15} \\
0
\end{array}
$$
The answer is $x + 3$.

3.
$$
\begin{array}{r}
x^2 + 3x + 1 \\
x + 2 \overline{)\, x^3 + 5x^2 + 7x + 2} \\
\underline{x^3 + 2x^2} \\
3x^2 + 7x \\
\underline{3x^2 + 6x} \\
x + 2 \\
\underline{x + 2} \\
0
\end{array}
$$

The answer is $x^2 + 3x + 1$.

5.

$$
\begin{array}{r}
2x^2 + 3x + 5 \\
3x-1{\overline{\smash{\big)}\,6x^3 + 7x^2 + 12x - 5}} \\
\underline{6x^3 - 2x^2} \\
9x^2 + 12x \\
\underline{9x^2 - 3x} \\
15x - 5 \\
\underline{15x - 5} \\
0
\end{array}
$$

The answer is $2x^2 + 3x + 5$.

7.

$$
\begin{array}{r}
4x + 3 + \dfrac{2}{3x-2} \\
3x-2{\overline{\smash{\big)}\,12x^2 + x - 4}} \\
\underline{12x^2 - 8x} \\
9x - 4 \\
\underline{9x - 6} \\
2
\end{array}
$$

The answer is $4x + 3 + \dfrac{2}{3x-2}$.

9.

$$
\begin{array}{r}
2x^2 + x + 6 - \dfrac{38}{x+3} \\
x+3{\overline{\smash{\big)}\,2x^3 + 7x^2 + 9x - 20}} \\
\underline{2x^3 + 6x^2} \\
x^2 + 9x \\
\underline{x^2 + 3x} \\
6x - 20 \\
\underline{6x + 18} \\
-38
\end{array}
$$

The answer is $2x^2 + x + 6 - \dfrac{38}{x+3}$.

11.

$$
\begin{array}{r}
4x^3 + 16x^2 + 60x + 246 + \dfrac{984}{x-4} \\
x-4{\overline{\smash{\big)}\,4x^4 - 4x^2 + 6x}} \\
\underline{4x^4 - 16x^3} \\
16x^3 - 4x^2 \\
\underline{16x^3 - 64x^2} \\
60x^2 + 6x \\
\underline{60x^2 - 240x} \\
246x \\
\underline{246x - 984} \\
984
\end{array}
$$

The answer is

$$4x^3 + 16x^2 + 60x + 246 + \dfrac{984}{x-4}.$$

13.

$$
\begin{array}{r}
2x + 5 \\
3x^2-x-3{\overline{\smash{\big)}\,6x^3 + 13x^2 - 11x - 15}} \\
\underline{6x^3 - 2x^2 - 6x} \\
15x^2 - 5x - 15 \\
\underline{15x^2 - 5x - 15} \\
0
\end{array}
$$

The answer is $2x + 5$.

15.

$$
\begin{array}{r}
6x^2 + 3x - 1 \\
3x^2+1{\overline{\smash{\big)}\,18x^4 + 9x^3 + 3x^2}} \\
\underline{18x^4 + 6x^2} \\
9x^3 - 3x^2 \\
\underline{9x^3 + 3x} \\
-3x^2 - 3x \\
\underline{-3x^2 - 1} \\
-3x + 1
\end{array}
$$

The answer is $6x^2 + 3x - 1 - \dfrac{3x-1}{3x^2+1}$.

17. $\left(2x^2 + x - 10\right) \div (x - 2)$

$$
\begin{array}{r|rrr}
2 & 2 & 1 & -10 \\
  &   & 4 & 10 \\
\hline
  & 2 & 5 & 0
\end{array}
$$

The answer is $2x + 5$.

19. $\left(3x^2 + 7x - 20\right) \div (x + 5)$

$$
\begin{array}{r|rrr}
-5 & 3 & 7 & -20 \\
   &   & -15 & 40 \\
\hline
   & 3 & -8 & 20
\end{array}
$$

The answer is $3x - 8 + \dfrac{20}{x + 5}$.

21. $\left(4x^3 - 3x^2 + 3x - 1\right) \div (x - 1)$

$$
\begin{array}{r|rrrr}
1 & 4 & -3 & 3 & -1 \\
  &   & 4 & 1 & 4 \\
\hline
  & 4 & 1 & 4 & 3
\end{array}
$$

The answer is $4x^2 + x + 4 + \dfrac{3}{x - 1}$.

23. $\left(6x^5 - 2x^3 + 4x^2 - 3x + 1\right) \div (x - 2)$

$$
\begin{array}{r|rrrrrr}
2 & 6 & 0 & -2 & 4 & -3 & 1 \\
  &   & 12 & 24 & 44 & 96 & 186 \\
\hline
  & 6 & 12 & 22 & 48 & 93 & 187
\end{array}
$$

The answer is
$$6x^4 + 12x^3 + 22x^2 + 48x + 93 + \dfrac{187}{x - 2}.$$

25. $\left(x^2 - 5x - 5x^3 + x^4\right) \div (5 + x) \Rightarrow$
$\left(x^4 - 5x^3 + x^2 - 5x\right) \div (x + 5)$

$$
\begin{array}{r|rrrrr}
-5 & 1 & -5 & 1 & -5 & 0 \\
   &   & -5 & 50 & -255 & 1300 \\
\hline
   & 1 & -10 & 51 & -260 & 1300
\end{array}
$$

The answer is
$$x^3 - 10x^2 + 51x - 260 + \dfrac{1300}{x + 5}.$$

27. $\dfrac{x^5 + x^3 - 2}{x - 1}$

$$
\begin{array}{r|rrrrrr}
1 & 1 & 0 & 1 & 0 & 0 & -2 \\
  &   & 1 & 1 & 2 & 2 & 2 \\
\hline
  & 1 & 1 & 2 & 2 & 2 & 0
\end{array}
$$

The answer is $x^4 + x^3 + 2x^2 + 2x + 2$.

29. $\dfrac{x^4 - 256}{x - 4}$

$$
\begin{array}{r|rrrrr}
4 & 1 & 0 & 0 & 0 & -256 \\
  &   & 4 & 16 & 64 & 256 \\
\hline
  & 1 & 4 & 16 & 64 & 0
\end{array}
$$

The answer is $x^3 + 4x^2 + 16x + 64$.

31. $\dfrac{2x^5 - 3x^4 + x^3 - x^2 + 2x - 1}{x + 2}$

$$
\begin{array}{r|rrrrrr}
-2 & 2 & -3 & 1 & -1 & 2 & -1 \\
   &   & -4 & 14 & -30 & 62 & -128 \\
\hline
   & 2 & -7 & 15 & -31 & 64 & -129
\end{array}
$$

The answser is
$$2x^4 - 7x^3 + 15x^2 - 31x + 64 - \dfrac{129}{x + 2}.$$

33. $f(x) = 2x^3 - 11x^2 + 7x - 5$

$$
\begin{array}{r|rrrr}
4 & 2 & -11 & 7 & -5 \\
  &   & 8 & -12 & -20 \\
\hline
  & 2 & -3 & -5 & -25
\end{array}
$$

$f(4) = -25$

35. $f(x) = 7x^4 - 3x^3 + 6x + 9$

$$
\begin{array}{r|rrrrr}
-5 & 7 & -3 & 0 & 6 & 9 \\
   &   & -35 & 190 & -950 & 4720 \\
\hline
   & 7 & -38 & 190 & -944 & 4729
\end{array}
$$

$$f(-5) = 4729$$

37. Dividend: $x^3 - 4x^2 + x + 6$
Divisor: $x + 1$

$$
\begin{array}{r|rrrr}
-1 & 1 & -4 & 1 & 6 \\
   &   & -1 & 5 & -6 \\
\hline
   & 1 & -5 & 6 & 0
\end{array}
$$

The answer is $x^2 - 5x + 6$.
$(x+1)(x^2 - 5x + 6) = 0$
$(x + 1)(x - 2)(x - 3) = 0$
$x = -1, x = 2, x = 3$
The solution set is $\{-1, 2, 3\}$.

39. $2x^3 - 5x^2 + x + 2 = 0$

$$
\begin{array}{r|rrrr}
2 & 2 & -5 & 1 & 2 \\
  &   & 4 & -2 & -2 \\
\hline
  & 2 & -1 & -1 & 0
\end{array}
$$

$(x - 2)(2x^2 - x - 1) = 0$
$(x - 2)(2x + 1)(x - 1) = 0$
$x = 2, \ x = -\dfrac{1}{2}, x = 1$
The solution set is $\left\{-\dfrac{1}{2}, 1, 2\right\}$.

41. $12x^3 + 16x^2 - 5x - 3 = 0$

$$
\begin{array}{r|rrrr}
-\frac{3}{2} & 12 & 16 & -5 & -3 \\
             &   & -18 & 3 & 3 \\
\hline
             & 12 & -2 & -2 & 0
\end{array}
$$

$\left(x + \dfrac{3}{2}\right)(12x^2 - 2x - 2) = 0$
$\left(x + \dfrac{3}{2}\right)2\left(6x^2 - x - 1\right) = 0$
$\left(x + \dfrac{3}{2}\right)2(3x + 1)(2x - 1) = 0$

$x = -\dfrac{3}{2}, \ x = -\dfrac{1}{3}, \ x = \dfrac{1}{2}$
The solution set is $\left\{-\dfrac{3}{2}, -\dfrac{1}{3}, \dfrac{1}{2}\right\}$.

43.

$$
\require{enclose}
\begin{array}{r}
x^3 + 5x^2 - 9x - 45 \\[2pt]
2x+5 \enclose{longdiv}{2x^4 + 15x^3 + 7x^2 - 135x - 225} \\
\end{array}
$$

$$
\begin{array}{l}
\underline{2x^4 + 5x^3} \\
\quad 10x^3 + 7x^2 \\
\quad \underline{10x^3 + 25x^2} \\
\qquad\quad -18x^2 - 135x \\
\qquad\quad \underline{-18x^2 - 45x} \\
\qquad\qquad\quad -90x - 225 \\
\qquad\qquad\quad \underline{-90x - 225}
\end{array}
$$

Width: $x^3 + 5x^2 - 9x - 45$

45. a. $f(30) = \dfrac{80(30) - 8000}{30 - 110} = 70$

(30, 70) At a 30% tax rate, the government tax revenue will be $70 ten billion.

b.

$$
\begin{array}{r|rr}
110 & 80 & -8000 \\
    &   & 8800 \\
\hline
    & 80 & 800
\end{array}
$$

$f(x) = 80 + \dfrac{800}{x - 110}$

$f(30) = 80 + \dfrac{800}{80 - 110} = 70$

(30, 70) same answer as in **a.**

c. $f(x)$ is not a function. Its graph has a vertical asymptote at $x = 110$, so it is not a continuous curve.

47.–55. Answers may vary.

57.

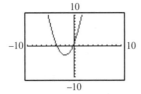

The division is correct.

59.

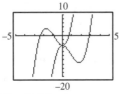

The division is not correct.

$$
\begin{array}{r|rrrrr}
-4 & 3 & 4 & -32 & -5 & -20 \\
  &   & -12 & 32 & 0 & 20 \\
\hline
  & 3 & -8 & 0 & -5 & 0
\end{array}
$$

Quotient: $3x^3 - 8x^2 - 5$

61.
$$
\begin{array}{r}
5x^2 + 2x - 4 \\
4x+3 \overline{\smash{\big)}\, 20x^3 + 23x^2 - 10x + k} \\
\underline{20x^3 + 15x^2} \\
8x^2 - 10 \\
\underline{8x^2 + 6x} \\
-16x + k \\
\underline{-16x - 12}
\end{array}
$$

To get a remainder of zero, k must equal -12.
$k = -12$

63.
$$
\begin{array}{r}
x^{2n} - x^n + 1 \\
x^n + 1 \overline{\smash{\big)}\, x^{3n} \qquad\qquad +1} \\
\underline{x^{3n} + x^{2n}} \\
-x^{2n} \\
\underline{-x^{2n} - x^n} \\
x^n + 1 \\
\underline{x^n + 1} \\
0
\end{array}
$$

Section 3.4

Check Point Exercises

1. p: ± 1, ± 2, ± 3, ± 6
   q: ± 1
   $\dfrac{p}{q}$: ± 1, ± 2, ± 3, ± 6
   are the possible rational zeros.

2. p: ± 1, ± 3
   q: ± 1, ± 2, ± 4
   $\dfrac{p}{q}$: ± 1, ± 3, $\pm\dfrac{1}{2}$, $\pm\dfrac{1}{4}$, $\pm\dfrac{3}{2}$, $\pm\dfrac{3}{4}$
   are the possible rational zeros.

3. ± 1, ± 2, ± 4, ± 5, ± 10, ± 20 are possible rational zeros

$$
\begin{array}{r|rrrr}
1 & 1 & 8 & 11 & -20 \\
  &   & 1 & 9 & 20 \\
\hline
  & 1 & 9 & 20 & 0
\end{array}
$$

1 is a zero.
$x^2 + 9x + 20 = 0$
$(x + 4)(x + 5) = 0$
$x = -4$ or $x = -5$
The solution set is $\{1, -4, -5\}$.

4. ± 1, ± 13 are possible rational zeros.

$$
\begin{array}{r|rrrrr}
1 & 1 & -6 & 22 & -30 & 13 \\
  &   & 1 & -5 & 17 & -13 \\
\hline
  & 1 & -5 & 17 & -13 & 0
\end{array}
$$

1 is a zero.

$$
\begin{array}{r|rrrr}
1 & 1 & 5 & 17 & -13 \\
  &   & 1 & -4 & 13 \\
\hline
  & 1 & -4 & 13 & 0
\end{array}
$$

1 is a double root.

$x^2 - 4x + 13 = 0$

$x = \dfrac{4 \pm \sqrt{16 - 52}}{2} = \dfrac{4 \pm \sqrt{-36}}{2} = 2 + 3i$

The solution set is $\{1,\ 2 + 3i,\ 2 - 3i\}$.

5. $f(x) = x^4 - 14x^3 + 71x^2 - 154x + 120$

$f(-x) = x^4 + 14x^3 + 71x^2 + 154x + 120$

Since $f(x)$ has 4 changes of sign, there are 4, 2, or 0 positive real zeros.

Since $f(-x)$ has no changes of sign, there are no negative real zeros.

Exercise Set 3.4

1. $f(x) = x^3 + x^2 - 4x - 4$

$p: \pm 1, \pm 2, \pm 4$

$q: \pm 1$

$\dfrac{p}{q}: \pm 1, \pm 2, \pm 4$

3. $f(x) = 3x^4 - 11x^3 - x^2 + 19x + 6$

$p: \pm 1, \pm 2, \pm 3, \pm 6$

$q: \pm 1, \pm 3$

$\dfrac{p}{q}: \pm 1, \pm 2, \pm 3, \pm 6, \pm \dfrac{1}{3}, \pm \dfrac{2}{3}$

5. $f(x) = 4x^4 - x^3 + 5x^2 - 2x - 6$

$p: \pm 1, \pm 2, \pm 3, \pm 6$

$q: \pm 1, \pm 2, \pm 4$

$\dfrac{p}{q}: \pm 1, \pm 2, \pm 3, \pm 6, \pm \dfrac{1}{2}, \pm \dfrac{1}{4}, \pm \dfrac{3}{2}, \pm \dfrac{3}{4}$

7. $f(x) = x^5 - x^4 - 7x^3 + 7x^2 - 12x - 12$

$p: \pm 1, \pm 2, \pm 3 \pm 4 \pm 6 \pm 12$

$q: \pm 1$

$\dfrac{p}{q}: \pm 1, \pm 2, \pm 3 \pm 4 \pm 6 \pm 12$

9. $f(x) = x^3 + x^2 - 4x - 4$

  a. $p: \pm 1, \pm 2, \pm 4$

  $q: \pm 1$

  $\dfrac{p}{q}: \pm 1, \pm 2, \pm 4$

  b.
$$
\begin{array}{r|rrrr}
2 & 1 & 1 & -4 & -4 \\
  &   & 2 & 6 & 4 \\
\hline
  & 1 & 3 & 2 & 0
\end{array}
$$

  2 is a zero.

  c. $x^3 + x^2 - 4x - 4 = 0$

  $(x - 2)(x^2 + 3x + 2) = 0$

  $(x - 2)(x + 2)(x + 1) = 0$

  $x - 2 = 0 \quad x + 2 = 0 \quad x + 1 = 0$

  $x = 2,\ x = -2,\ x = -1$

  The solution set is $\{2, -2, -1\}$.

11. $f(x) = 2x^3 - 3x^2 - 11x + 6$

  a. $p: \pm 1, \pm 2, \pm 3, \pm 6$

  $q: \pm 1, \pm 2$

  $\dfrac{p}{q}: \pm 1, \pm 2, \pm 3, \pm 6, \pm \dfrac{1}{2}, \pm \dfrac{3}{2}$

  b.
$$
\begin{array}{r|rrrr}
3 & 2 & -3 & -11 & 6 \\
  &   & 6 & 9 & -6 \\
\hline
  & 2 & 3 & -2 & 0
\end{array}
$$

  3 is a zero.

c. $2x^3 - 3x^2 - 11x + 6 = 0$
$(x-3)(2x^2 + 3x - 2) = 0$
$(x-3)(2x-1)(x+2) = 0$
$x = 3, \ x = \dfrac{1}{2}, \ x = -2$

The solution set is $\left\{3, \dfrac{1}{2}, -2\right\}$.

13. $f(x) = 3x^3 + 7x^2 - 22x - 8$

a. $p: \pm 1, \pm 2, \pm 4, \pm 8$
$q: \pm 1, \pm 3$
$\dfrac{p}{q}: \pm 1, \pm 2, \pm 4, \pm 8, \pm \dfrac{1}{3}, \pm \dfrac{2}{3}, \pm \dfrac{4}{3}, \pm \dfrac{8}{3}$

b.

4	3	7	−22	−8
		12	76	216
	3	19	54	208

4 is not a zero.

2	3	7	−22	−8
		6	26	8
	3	13	4	0

2 is a zero.

c. $3x^3 + 7x^2 - 22x - 8 = 0$
$(x-2)(3x^2 + 13x + 4) = 0$
$(x-2)(3x+1)(x+4) = 0$
$x = 2, \ x = -\dfrac{1}{3}, \ x = -4$

The solution set is $\left\{2, -\dfrac{1}{3}, -4\right\}$.

15. $x^3 - 2x^2 - 11x + 12 = 0$

a. $p: \pm 1, \pm 2, \pm 3, \pm 4, \pm 6, \pm 12$
$q: \pm 1$
$\dfrac{p}{q}: \pm 1, \pm 2, \pm 3, \pm 4, \pm 6, \pm 12$

b.

3	1	−2	−11	12
		3	3	−24

	1	1	−8	−12

3 is not a zero.

4	1	−2	−11	12
		4	8	−12
	1	2	−3	0

4 is a zero.

c. $x^3 - 2x^2 - 11x + 12$
$(x-4)(x^2 + 2x - 3) = 0$
$(x-4)(x+3)(x-1) = 0$
$x - 4 = 0 \quad x + 3 = 0 \quad x - 1 = 0$
$x = 4 \qquad x = -3 \qquad x = 1$
The solution set is $\{-3, 1, 4\}$.

17. $x^3 - 10x - 12 = 0$

a. $p: \pm 1, \pm 2, \pm 3, \pm 4, \pm 6, \pm 12$
$q: \pm 1$
$\dfrac{p}{q}: \pm 1, \pm 2, \pm 3, \pm 4, \pm 6, \pm 12$

b.

−2	1	0	−10	−12
		−2	4	12
	1	−2	−6	0

−2 is a zero.

c. $x^3 - 10x - 12 = 0$
$(x+2)(x^2 - 2x - 6) = 0$
$x = \dfrac{2 \pm \sqrt{4+24}}{2} = \dfrac{2 \pm \sqrt{28}}{2}$
$= \dfrac{2 \pm 2\sqrt{7}}{2} = 1 \pm \sqrt{7}$
The solution set is $\left\{-2, 1+\sqrt{7}, 1-\sqrt{7}\right\}$.

19. $6x^3 + 25x^2 - 24x + 5 = 0$

a. $p: \pm 1, \pm 5$
$q: \pm 1, \pm 2, \pm 3, \pm 6$
$\dfrac{p}{q}: \pm 1, \pm 5, \pm \dfrac{1}{2}, \pm \dfrac{5}{2}, \pm \dfrac{1}{3}, \pm \dfrac{5}{3}, \pm \dfrac{1}{6}, \pm \dfrac{5}{6}$

b.

$$\begin{array}{r|rrrr} -5 & 6 & 25 & -24 & 5 \\ & & -30 & 25 & -5 \\ \hline & 6 & -5 & 1 & 0 \end{array}$$

–5 is a zero.

c. $6x^3 + 25x^2 - 24x + 5 = 0$

$(x+5)(6x^2 - 5x + 1) = 0$

$(x+5)(2x-1)(3x-1) = 0$

$x + 5 = 0 \quad 2x - 1 = 0 \quad 3x - 1 = 0$

$x = -5, \qquad x = \dfrac{1}{2}, \qquad x = \dfrac{1}{3}$

The solution set is $\left\{-5, \dfrac{1}{2}, \dfrac{1}{3}\right\}$.

21. $x^4 - 2x^3 - 5x^2 + 8x + 4 = 0$

a. $p: \pm 1, \pm 2, \pm 4$

$q: \pm 1$

$\dfrac{p}{q}: \pm 1, \pm 2, \pm 4$

b.

$$\begin{array}{r|rrrrr} 2 & 1 & -2 & -5 & 8 & 4 \\ & & 2 & 0 & -10 & -4 \\ \hline & 1 & 0 & -5 & -2 & 0 \end{array}$$

2 is a zero.

c. $x^4 - 2x^3 - 5x^2 + 8x + 4 = 0$

$(x-2)(x^3 - 5x - 2) = 0$

$$\begin{array}{r|rrrr} -2 & 1 & 0 & -5 & -2 \\ & & -2 & 4 & 2 \\ \hline & 1 & -2 & -1 & 0 \end{array}$$

–2 is a zero of $x^3 - 5x - 2 = 0$.

$(x-2)(x+2)\left(x^2 - 2x - 1\right) = 0$

$x = \dfrac{2 \pm \sqrt{4+4}}{2} = \dfrac{2 \pm \sqrt{8}}{2} = \dfrac{2 \pm 2\sqrt{2}}{2}$

$= 1 \pm \sqrt{2}$

The solution set is

$\left\{-2, 2, 1 + \sqrt{2}, 1 - \sqrt{2}\right\}$.

23. $f(x) = x^3 + 2x^2 + 5x + 4$

Since $f(x)$ has no sign variations, no positive real roots exist.

$f(-x) = -x^3 + 2x^2 - 5x + 4$

Since $f(-x)$ has 3 sign variations, 3 or 1 negative real roots exist.

25. $f(x) = 5x^3 - 3x^2 + 3x - 1$

Since $f(x)$ has 3 sign variations, 3 or 1 positive real roots exist.

$f(-x) = -5x^3 - 3x^2 - 3x - 1$

Since $f(-x)$ has no sign variations, no negative real roots exist.

27. $f(x) = 2x^4 - 5x^3 - x^2 - 6x + 4$

Since $f(x)$ has 2 sign variations, 2 or 0 positive real roots exist.

$f(-x) = 2x^4 + 5x^3 - x^2 + 6x + 4$

Since $f(-x)$ has 2 sign variations, 2 or 0 negative real roots exist.

29. $f(x) = x^3 - 4x^2 - 7x + 10$

$p: \pm 1, \pm 2, \pm 5, \pm 10$

$q: \pm 1$

$\dfrac{p}{q}: \pm 1, \pm 2, \pm 5, \pm 10$

Since $f(x)$ has 2 sign variations, 0 or 2 positive real zeros exist.

$f(-x) = -x^3 - 4x^2 + 7x + 10$

Since $f(-x)$ has 1 sign variation, exactly one negative real zeros exists.

$$\begin{array}{r|rrrr} -2 & 1 & -4 & -7 & 10 \\ & & -2 & 12 & -10 \\ \hline & 1 & -6 & 5 & 0 \end{array}$$

–2 is a zero.

$$f(x) = (x+2)\left(x^2 - 6x + 5\right)$$
$$= (x+2)(x-5)(x-1)$$
$x = -2, x = 5, x = 1$
The solution set is $\{-2, 5, 1\}$.

31. $2x^3 - x^2 - 9x - 4 = 0$
$p: \pm 1, \pm 2, \pm 4$
$q: \pm 1, \pm 2$
$\dfrac{p}{q}: \pm 1, \pm 2, \pm 4 \pm \dfrac{1}{2}$

1 positive real root exists.
$f(-x) = -2x^3 - x^2 + 9x - 4$ 2 or no negative real roots exist.

$-\frac{1}{2}$	2	-1	-9	-4
		-1	1	4
	2	-2	-8	0

$-\dfrac{1}{2}$ is a root.

$$\left(x + \frac{1}{2}\right)\left(2x^2 - 2x - 8\right) = 0$$
$$2\left(x + \frac{1}{2}\right)\left(x^2 - x - 4\right) = 0$$
$$x = \frac{1 \pm \sqrt{1+16}}{2} = \frac{1 \pm \sqrt{17}}{2}$$

The solution set is
$$\left\{ -\frac{1}{2}, \frac{1+\sqrt{17}}{2}, \frac{1-\sqrt{17}}{2} \right\}.$$

33. $f(x) = x^4 - 2x^3 + x^2 + 12x + 8$
$p: \pm 1, \pm 2, \pm 4, \pm 8$
$q: \pm 1$
$\dfrac{p}{q}: \pm 1, \pm 2, \pm 4, \pm 8$

Since $f(x)$ has 2 sign changes, 0 or 2 positive roots exist.

$$f(-x) = (-x)^4 - 2(-x)^3 + (-x)^2 - 12x + 8$$
$$= x^4 + 2x^3 + x^2 - 12x + 8$$

Since $f(-x)$ has 2 sign changes, 0 or 2 negative roots exist.

-1	1	-2	1	12	8
		-1	4	-4	-8
	1	-3	4	8	0

-1	1	-3	4	8
		-1	4	-8
	1	-4	8	0

$$0 = x^2 - 4x + 8$$
$$x = \frac{-(-4) \pm \sqrt{(-4)^2 - 4(1)(8)}}{2(1)}$$
$$x = \frac{4 \pm \sqrt{6 - 32}}{2}$$
$$x = \frac{4 \pm \sqrt{-16}}{2}$$
$$x = \frac{4 \pm 4i}{2}$$
$$x = 2 \pm 2i$$

The solution set is $\{-1, -1, 2+2i, 2-2i\}$.

35. $x^4 - 3x^3 - 20x^2 - 24x - 8 = 0$
$p: \pm 1, \pm 2, \pm 4, \pm 8$
$q: \pm 1$
$\dfrac{p}{q}: \pm 1, \pm 2, \pm 4 \pm 8$

1 positive real root exists.
3 or 1 negative real roots exist.

-1	1	-3	-20	-24	-8
		-1	4	16	8
	1	-4	-16	-8	0

$$(x+1)\left(x^3 - 4x^2 - 16x - 8\right) = 0$$

$$\begin{array}{r|rrrr} -2 & 1 & -4 & -16 & -8 \\ & & -2 & 12 & 8 \\ \hline & 1 & -6 & -4 & 0 \end{array}$$

$(x+1)(x+2)\left(x^2 - 6x - 4\right) = 0$

$x = \dfrac{6 \pm \sqrt{36+16}}{2} = \dfrac{6 \pm \sqrt{52}}{2}$

$= \dfrac{6 \pm 2\sqrt{13}}{2} = \dfrac{3 \pm \sqrt{13}}{2}$

The solution set is

$\left\{-1,\, -2,\, 3 \pm \sqrt{13},\, 3 - \sqrt{13}\right\}.$

37. $f(x) = 3x^4 - 11x^3 - x^2 + 19x + 6$

$p: \pm 1, \pm 2, \pm 3, \pm 6$

$q: \pm 1, \pm 3$

$\dfrac{p}{q}: \pm 1, \pm 2, \pm 3, \pm 6, \pm \dfrac{1}{3}, \pm \dfrac{2}{3}$

2 or no positive real zeros exists.

$f(-x) = 3x^4 + 11x^3 - x^2 - 19x + 6$

2 or no negative real zeros exist.

$$\begin{array}{r|rrrrr} -1 & 3 & -11 & -1 & 19 & 6 \\ & & -3 & 14 & -13 & -6 \\ \hline & 3 & -14 & 13 & 6 & 0 \end{array}$$

$f(x) = (x+1)\left(3x^3 - 14x^2 + 13x + 6\right)$

$$\begin{array}{r|rrrr} 2 & 3 & -14 & 13 & 6 \\ & & 6 & -16 & -6 \\ \hline & 3 & -8 & -3 & 0 \end{array}$$

$f(x) = (x+1)(x-2)\left(3x^2 - 8x - 3\right)$

$ = (x+1)(x-2)(3x+1)(x-3)$

$x = -1,\ x = 2\ x = -\dfrac{1}{3},\ x = 3$

The solution set is $\left\{-1,\, 2,\, -\dfrac{1}{3},\, 3\right\}.$

39. $4x^4 - x^3 + 5x^2 - 2x - 6 = 0$

$p: \pm 1, \pm 2, \pm 3, \pm 6$

$q: \pm 1, \pm 2, \pm 4$

$\dfrac{p}{q}: \pm 1, \pm 2, \pm 3, \pm 6, \pm \dfrac{1}{2}, \pm \dfrac{3}{2}, \pm \dfrac{1}{4}, \pm \dfrac{3}{4}$

3 or 1 positive real roots exists.

1 negative real root exists.

$$\begin{array}{r|rrrrr} 1 & 4 & -1 & 5 & -2 & -6 \\ & & 4 & 3 & 8 & 6 \\ \hline & 4 & 3 & 8 & 6 & 0 \end{array}$$

$(x-1)(4x^3 + 3x^2 + 8x + 6) = 0$

$4x^3 + 3x^2 + 8x + 6 = 0$ has no positive real roots.

$$\begin{array}{r|rrrr} -\frac{3}{4} & 4 & 3 & 8 & 6 \\ & & -3 & 0 & -6 \\ \hline & 4 & 0 & 8 & 0 \end{array}$$

$(x-1)\left(x + \dfrac{3}{4}\right)\left(4x^2 + 8\right) = 0$

$4(x-1)\left(x + \dfrac{3}{4}\right)\left(x^2 + 2\right) = 0$

$x^2 + 2 = 0$

$x^2 = -2$

$x = \pm i\sqrt{2}$

The solution set is $\left\{1,\, -\dfrac{3}{4},\, i\sqrt{2},\, -i\sqrt{2}\right\}.$

41. $2x^5 + 7x^4 - 18x^2 - 8x + 8 = 0$

$p: \pm 1, \pm 2, \pm 4, \pm 8$

$q: \pm 1, \pm 2$

$\dfrac{p}{q}: \pm 1, \pm 2, \pm 4, \pm 8, \pm \dfrac{1}{2}$

2 or no positive real roots exists.

3 or 1 negative real root exist.

$$\begin{array}{r|rrrrrr} -2 & 2 & 7 & 0 & -18 & -8 & 8 \\ & & -4 & -6 & 12 & 12 & -8 \\ \hline & 2 & 3 & -6 & -6 & 4 & 0 \end{array}$$

$(x+2)(2x^4 + 3x^3 - 6x^2 - 6x + 4) = 0$
$4x^3 + 3x^2 + 8x + 6 = 0$ has no positive real
roots.

-2	2	3	-6	-6	4
		-4	2	8	-4
	2	-1	-4	2	0

$(x+2)^2 (2x^3 - x^2 - 4x + 2)$

$\frac{1}{2}$	2	-1	-4	2
		1	0	2
	2	0	-4	0

$(x+2)^2 \left(x - \frac{1}{2} \right)(2x^2 - 4) = 0$

$2(x+2)^2 \left(x - \frac{1}{2} \right)(x^2 - 2) = 0$

$x^2 - 2 = 0$

$x^2 = 2$

$x = \pm\sqrt{2}$

The solution set is $\left\{ -2, \frac{1}{2}, \sqrt{2}, -\sqrt{2} \right\}$.

43. a. $f(x) = 27$, $x = 40$ People in the arts
complete 27% of their work in their 40's.

b. The polynomial will have a degree 2 with
a negative leading coefficient.

45. $14W^3 - 17W^2 - 16W + 34 = 211$
$14W^3 - 17W^2 - 16W - 177 = 0$
$p: \pm 1, \pm 3, \pm 59, \pm 177$
$q: \pm 1, \pm 2, \pm 7, \pm 14$

3	14	-17	-16	-177
		42	75	177
	14	25	59	0

$(x-3)(14x^2 + 25x + 59) = 0$
$b^2 - 4ac = 625 - 3304 < 0$
$W = 3$ mm
The abdominal width is 3 millimeters.

47. $V = lwh$
$72 = (h+7)(2h)(h)$
$72 = 2h^2(h+7)$
$2h^3 + 14h^2 - 72 = 0$
$h^3 + 7h^2 - 36 = 0$

2	1	7	0	-36
		2	18	36
	1	9	18	0

$(h-2)(h^2 + 9h + 18) = 0$
$(h-2)(h+3)(h+6) = 0$
$h = 2 \quad h = -3 \quad h = -6$
$h = -3$ and $h = -6$ do not make sense.
$h = 2$
$h + 7 = 9$
$2h = 4$
The dimensions are 2 in. by 9 in. by 4 in.

49.–55. Answers may vary.

57. $6x^3 - 19x^2 + 16x - 4 = 0$
$p: \pm 1, \pm 2, \pm 4$
$q: \pm 1, \pm 2, \pm 3, \pm 6$
$\frac{p}{q}: \pm 1, \pm 2, \pm 4, \pm\frac{1}{2}, \pm\frac{1}{3}, \pm\frac{2}{3}, \pm\frac{4}{3}, \pm\frac{1}{6}$

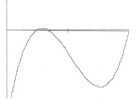

From the graph, we see that the solutions are
$\frac{1}{2}, \frac{2}{3}$ and 2.

59. $4x^4 + 4x^3 + 7x^2 - x - 2 = 0$
$p: \pm 1, \pm 2$

$q: \pm 1, \pm 2, \pm 4$

$\dfrac{p}{q}: \pm 1, \pm 2, \pm \dfrac{1}{2}, \pm \dfrac{1}{4}$

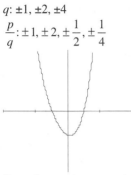

From the graph, we see that the solutions are $-\dfrac{1}{2}$ and $\dfrac{1}{2}$.

61. $f(x) = x^5 - x^4 + x^3 - x^2 + x - 8$

$f(x)$ has 5 sign variations, so either 5, 3, or 1 positive real roots exist.

$f(-x) = -x^5 - x^4 - x^3 - x^2 - x - 8$

$f(-x)$ has no sign variations, so no negative real roots exist.

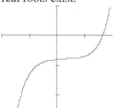

63. a. False; the equation has 0 sign variations, so no positive roots exist.

b. False; Descartes's Rule gives the possible number of roots.

c. False; Every polynomial equation of degree 3 has at least one <u>real</u> root.

d. True

(d) is true.

65. $(2x+1)(x+5)(x+2) - 3x(x+5) = 208$

$\left(2x^2 + 11x + 5\right)(x+2) - 3x^2 - 15x = 208$

$2x^3 + 4x^2 + 11x^2 + 22x + 5x$

$+10 - 3x^2 - 15x = 208$

$2x^3 + 15x^2 + 27x - 3x^2 - 15x - 198 = 0$

$2x^3 + 12x^2 + 12x - 198 = 0$

$2\left(x^3 + 6x^2 + 6x - 99\right) = 0$

3	1	6	6	−99
		3	27	99
	1	9	33	0

$x^2 + 9x + 33 = 0$

$b^2 - 4ac = -51$

$x = 3$ in.

Section 3.5

Check Point Exercises

1.

−7	2	11	−7	−6
		−14	21	−98
	2	−3	14	−104

The signs alternate.

2	2	11	−7	−6
		4	30	46
	2	15	23	40

All the numbers are nonnegative. Thus, −7 is a lower bound and 2 is an upper bound.

2. $f(-3) = 3(-3)^3 - 10(-3) + 9 = -42$

$f(-2) = 3(-2)^3 - 10(-2) + 9 = 5$

The sign change shows there is a zero between −3 and −2.

3. $(x - 2 + i)(x - 2 - i) = x^2 - 2x - ix - 2x + 4$
$+ 2i + ix - 2i - i^2 = x^2 - 4x + 5$

$$x^2 - 4x + 5 \overline{)x^4 - 8x^3 + 0x^2 + 64x - 105}$$
$$\underline{x^4 - 4x^3 + 5x^2}$$
$$-4x^3 - 5x^2 + 64x$$
$$\underline{-4x^3 + 16x^2 - 20x}$$
$$-21x^2 + 84x - 105$$
$$\underline{-21x^2 + 84x - 105}$$
$$0$$

quotient: $x^2 - 4x - 21$

$x^2 - 4x - 21 = 0$
$(x - 7)(x + 3) = 0$
$x = 7$ or $x = -3$
The solution set is $\{-3, 7, 2 + i, 2 - i\}$.

4. a. $x^4 - 4x^2 - 5 = \left(x^2 - 5\right)\left(x^2 + 1\right)$

b. $\left(x + \sqrt{5}\right)\left(x - \sqrt{5}\right)\left(x^2 + 1\right)$

c $\left(x + \sqrt{5}\right)\left(x - \sqrt{5}\right)(x + i)(x - i)$

5. $(x + 3)(x - i)(x + i) = (x + 3)(x^2 + 1)$
$f(x) = a_n(x + 3)(x^2 + 1)$
$f(1) = a_n(1 + 3)(1^2 + 1) = 8a_n = 8$
$a_n = 1$
$f(x) = (x + 3)(x^2 + 1)$ or $x^3 + 3x^2 + x + 3$

Exercise Set 3.5

1. $x^4 - 5x^3 + 11x^2 + 33x - 18 = 0$

-4	1	-5	11	33	-18
		-4	36	-188	620
	1	-9	47	-155	602

Since signs alternate, -4 is a lower bound.

7	1	-5	11	33	-18
		7	14	175	1456
	1	2	25	208	1438

Since no sign is negative, 7 is an upper bound.

3. $2x^3 + 5x^2 - 8x - 7 = 0$

-4	2	5	-8	7
		-8	12	-16
	2	-3	4	-9

Since signs alternate, -4 is a lower bound.

2	2	5	-8	7
		4	18	20
	2	9	10	27

Since no sign is negative, 2 is an upper bound.

5. $x^4 + 3x^3 + 2x^2 - 5x + 12 = 0$

a. p: $\pm 1, \pm 2, \pm 3, \pm 4, \pm 6, \pm 12$
q: ± 1
$\dfrac{p}{q}$: $\pm 1, \pm 2, \pm 3, \pm 4, +6, \pm 12$

b.

1	1	3	2	-5	12
		1	4	6	1
	1	4	6	1	13

1 is not a root.
1 is an upper bound.

c. Eliminate all positive possible rational roots.

d.

-3	1	3	2	-5	12
		-3	0	-6	33
	1	0	2	-11	45

-3 is not a root.
-3 is a lower bound.

e. Eliminate –3, –4, –6 and –12.

7. $f(x) = x^3 - x - 1$

$f(1) = -1$

$f(2) = 5$

$f(1.3) = -0.103$

$f(1.4) = 0.344$

$f(1.35) = 0.11038$

To the nearest tenth, the zero is 1.3.

9. $f(x) = 2x^4 - 4x^2 + 1$

$f(-1) = -1$

$f(0) = 1$

$f(-0.5) = 0.125$

$f(-0.6) = -0.1808$

$f(-0.55) = -0.027$

To the nearest tenth, the zero is –0.5.

11. $f(x) = x^3 + x^2 - 2x + 1$

$f(-3) = -11$

$f(-2) = 1$

$f(-2.2) = -0.408$

$f(-2.1) = 0.349$

$f(-2.15) = -0.0159$

To the nearest tenth, the zero is –2.1.

13. $f(x) = 3x^3 - 10x + 9$

$f(-3) = -42$

$f(-2) = 5$

$f(-2.1) = 2.217$

$f(-2.2) = -0.944$

$f(-2.15) = 0.68488$

To the nearest tenth, the zero is –2.2.

15. $x = -2i$, so $x = 2i$ also.

$(x + 2i)(x - 2i) = x^2 + 4$

$$x^2 + 4 \overline{)\,x^3 + 4x - 2x^2 - 8\,}$$
$$\underline{x^3 + 4x}$$
$$-2x^2 - 8$$
$$\underline{-2x^2 - 8}$$
$$0$$

quotient: $x - 2$

$x - 2 = 0$

$x = 2$

Solution: $\{-2i, 2i, 2\}$

17. $x = (1 + i)$, so $x = (1 - i)$ also.

$(x - 1 - i)(x - 1 + i)$

$= x^2 - x + ix - x + 1 - i - ix + i - i^2$

$= x^2 - 2x + 2$

$$x^2 - 2x + 2 \overline{)\,3x^3 - 7x^2 + 8x - 2\,}$$
$$\underline{3x^3 - 6x^2 + 6x}$$
$$-x^2 + 2x - 2$$
$$\underline{-x^2 + 2x - 2}$$
$$0$$

quotient: $3x - 1$

$3x - 1 = 0$

$x = \dfrac{1}{3}$

Solution: $\left\{ 1 - i,\, 1 + i,\, \dfrac{1}{3} \right\}$

19. $x = 2 - i$, so $x = 2 + i$ also.

$(x - 2 + i)(x - 2 - i)$

$= x^2 - 2x - ix - 2x + 4 + 2i + ix - 2i - i^2$

$= x^2 - 4x + 5$

$$x^2 - 4x + 5 \overline{)\,x^4 + 0x^3 - 6x^2 + 0x + 25\,}$$
$$\underline{x^4 - 4x^3 + 5x^2}$$
$$4x^3 - 11x^2 + 0x$$
$$\underline{4x^3 - 16x^2 + 20x}$$
$$5x^2 - 20x + 25$$
$$\underline{5x^2 - 20x + 25}$$
$$0$$

quotient: $x^2 + 4x + 5$

$x^2 + 4x + 5 = 0$

$x = \dfrac{-4 \pm \sqrt{16 - 4(5)}}{2} = \dfrac{-4 \pm \sqrt{-4}}{2}$

$= \dfrac{-4 \pm 2i}{2} = -2 \pm i$

The solution set is

$\{2 - i, 2 + i, -2 + i, -2 - i\}$.

21. $x = 2 - i$, so $x = 2 + i$ also.

$(x - 2 + i)(x - 2 - i)$

$$= x^2 - 2x - xi - 2x + 4 + 2i + ix - 2i - i^2$$
$$= x^2 - 4x + 5$$

$$
\begin{array}{r}
x^2 - 4x + 5 \\
x^2 - 4x + 5 \overline{\smash{\big)}\, x^4 - 8x^3 + 0x^2 + 64x - 105} \\
\underline{x^4 - 4x^3 + 5x^2} \\
-4x^3 - 5x^2 + 64x \\
\underline{-4x^3 + 16x^2 - 20x} \\
-21x^2 + 84x - 105 \\
\underline{-21x^2 + 84x - 105} \\
0
\end{array}
$$

$$x^2 - 4x - 21 = 0$$
$$(x - 7)(x + 3) = 0$$
$$x = 7,\ x = -3$$

The solution set is $\{2 + i,\ 2 - i,\ -3,\ 7\}$.

23. $x^4 - x^2 - 20$

　a. $\left(x^2 - 5\right)\left(x^2 + 4\right)$

　b. $\left(x + \sqrt{5}\right)\left(x - \sqrt{5}\right)\left(x^2 + 4\right)$

　c. $\left(x + \sqrt{5}\right)\left(x - \sqrt{5}\right)(x + 2i)(x - 2i)$

25. $x^4 + x^2 - 6$

　a. $\left(x^2 - 2\right)\left(x^2 + 3\right)$

　b. $\left(x + \sqrt{2}\right)\left(x - \sqrt{2}\right)\left(x^2 + 3\right)$

　c. $\left(x + \sqrt{2}\right)\left(x - \sqrt{2}\right)\left(x + i\sqrt{3}\right)\left(x - i\sqrt{3}\right)$

27. $x^4 - 2x^3 + x^2 - 8x - 12$

　a.
$$
\begin{array}{r}
x^2 - 2x - 3 \\
x^2 + 4 \overline{\smash{\big)}\, x^4 - 2x^3 + x^2 + 8x - 12} \\
\underline{x^4 \qquad\quad - 4x^2} \\
-2x^3 - 3x^2 + 8x \\
\underline{-2x^3 \qquad\quad - 8x} \\
-3x^2 \quad - 12 \\
\underline{-3x^2 \quad - 12} \\
\end{array}
$$

$$\left(x^2 - 2x - 3\right)\left(x^2 + 4\right)$$
$$(x - 3)\,(x + 1)\left(x^2 + 4\right)$$

　b. $(x - 3)\,(x + 1)\left(x^2 + 4\right)$

　c. $(x - 3)\,(x + 1)\,(x + 2i)\,(x - 2i)$

29. $(x - 1)\,(x + 5i)\,(x - 5i)$
$$= (x - 1)\left(x^2 + 25\right)$$
$$= x^3 + 25x - x^2 - 25$$
$$= x^3 - x^2 + 25x - 25$$
$$f(x) = a_n\!\left(x^3 - x^2 + 25x - 25\right)$$
$$f(-1) = a_n(-1 - 1 - 25 - 25)$$
$$-104 = a_n(-52)$$
$$a_n = 2$$
$$f(x) = 2\!\left(x^3 - x^2 + 25x - 25\right)$$
$$f(x) = 2x^3 - 2x^2 + 50x - 50$$

31. $(x+5)(x-4-3i)(x-4+3i)$

$= (x+5)\left(x^2 - 4x + 3ix - 4x + 16 - 12i\right.$

$\left. -3ix + 12i - 9i^2\right)$

$= (x+5)\left(x^2 - 8x + 25\right)$

$= \left(x^3 - 8x^2 + 25x + 5x^2 - 40x + 125\right)$

$= x^3 - 3x^2 - 15x + 125$

$f(x) = a_n(x^3 - 3x^2 - 15x + 125)$

$f(2) = a_n\left(2^3 - 3(2)^2 - 15(2) + 125\right)$

$91 = a_n(91)$

$a_n = 1$

$f(x) = 1\left(x^3 - 3x^2 - 15x + 125\right)$

$f(x) = x^3 - 3x^2 - 15x + 125$

33. $(x-i)(x+i)(x-3i)(x+3i)$

$= \left(x^2 - i^2\right)\left(x^2 - 9i^2\right)$

$= \left(x^2 + 1\right)\left(x^2 + 9\right)$

$= x^4 + 10x^2 + 9$

$f(x) = a_n(x^4 + 10x^2 + 9)$

$f(-1) = a_n((-1)^4 + 10(-1)^2 + 9)$

$20 = a_n(20)$

$a_n = 1$

$f(x) = x^4 + 10x^2 + 9$

35. $(x+2)\ (x-5)\ (x-3+2i)\ (x-3-2i)$

$= \left(x^2 - 3x - 10\right)$

$\quad \left(x^2 - 3x - 2ix - 3x + 9 + 6i + 2ix - 6i - 4i\right)$

$= \left(x^2 - 3x - 10\right)\left(x^2 - 6x + 13\right)$

$= x^4 - 6x + 13x^2 - 3x^3 + 18x^2$

$\quad -39x - 10x^2 + 60x - 130$

$= x^4 - 9x^3 + 21x^2 + 21x - 130$

$f(x) = a_n\left(x^4 - 9x^3 + 21x^2 + 21x - 130\right)$

$f(1) = a_n(1 - 9 + 21 + 21 - 130)$

$-96 = a_n(-96)$

$a_n = 1$

$f(x) = x^4 - 9x^3 + 21x^2 + 21x - 130$

37. $f(x) = x^3 - x^2 + 25x - 25$

$p: \pm 1, \pm 5, \pm 25$

$q: \pm 1$

$\dfrac{p}{q}: \pm 1, \pm 5, \pm 25$

$$
\begin{array}{r|rrrr}
1 & 1 & -1 & 25 & -25 \\
  &   & 1 & 0 & 25 \\
\hline
  & 1 & 0 & 25 & 0 \\
\end{array}
$$

$x = 1$

$x^2 + 25 = 0$

$x^2 = -25$

$x = \pm\sqrt{-25} = \pm 5i$

$f(x) = (x-1)(x-5i)(x+5i)$

39. $f(x) = x^3 - 8x^2 + 25x - 26$

$p: \pm 1, \pm 2, \pm 13, \pm 26$

$q: \pm 1$

$p: \pm 1, \pm 2, \pm 13, \pm 26$

$q:$

$$
\begin{array}{r|rrrr}
2 & 1 & -8 & 25 & -26 \\
  &   & 2 & -12 & 26 \\
\hline
  & 1 & -6 & 13 & 0 \\
\end{array}
$$

$$x = 2$$
$$x^2 - 6x + 13 = 0$$
$$x = \frac{6 \pm \sqrt{36 - 52}}{2} = \frac{6 \pm \sqrt{-16}}{2}$$
$$= \frac{6 \pm 4i}{2} = 3 \pm 2i$$
$$f(x) = (x - 2)(x - 3 + 2i)(x - 3 - 2i)$$

41. $f(x) = x^4 + 37x^2 + 36$
$$x^4 + 37x^2 + 36 = 0$$
$$\left(x^2 + 36\right)\left(x^2 + 1\right) = 0$$
$$x^2 = -36 \qquad x^2 = -1$$
$$x = \pm 6i \qquad x = \pm i$$
$$f(x) = (x - 6i)(x + 6i)(x - i)(x + i)$$

43. $f(x) = 16x^4 + 36x^3 + 16x^2 + x - 30$
p: $\pm 1, \pm 2, \pm 3, \pm 5, \pm 6, \pm 10, \pm 15, \pm 30$
q: $\pm 1, \pm 2, \pm 4, \pm 8, \pm 16$
$\dfrac{p}{q}$: $\pm 1, \pm 2, \pm 3, \pm 5, \pm 6, \pm 10, \pm 15, \pm 30,$

$$\pm \frac{1}{2}, \pm \frac{3}{2}, \pm \frac{5}{2}, \pm \frac{15}{2}, \pm \frac{1}{4}, \pm \frac{3}{4}, \pm \frac{5}{4},$$
$$\pm \frac{15}{4}, \pm \frac{30}{4}, \pm \frac{1}{8}, \pm \frac{3}{8}, \pm \frac{5}{8}, \pm \frac{15}{8},$$
$$\pm \frac{30}{8}, \pm \frac{1}{16}, \pm \frac{3}{16}, \pm \frac{5}{16}, \pm \frac{15}{16}$$

-2	16	36	16	1	-30
		-32	-8	-16	30
	16	4	8	-15	0

$$x = -2$$
$$0 = 16x^3 + 4x^2 + 8x - 15$$

$\frac{3}{4}$	16	4	8	-15
		12	12	15
	16	16	20	0

$$x = \frac{3}{4}$$
$$16x^2 + 16x + 20 = 0$$
$$x = \frac{-16 \pm \sqrt{-1024}}{32} = \frac{-16 \pm 32i}{32}$$
$$x = -\frac{1}{2} \pm i$$

$$f(x)$$
$$= (x + 2)(4x - 3)(2x + 1 - 2i)(2x + 1 + 2i)$$

45. If you are 25, the equivalent age for dogs is 3 years.

47. Answers may vary.

49.
$$1382 = -0.219x^3 + 4.885x^2 + 35.14x + 503.14$$
$$0 = -0.219x^3 + 4.885x^2 + 35.14x - 878.86$$

14	-0.219	4.885	35.14	503.14
		-3.066	25.466	848.484
	-0.219	1.819	60.606	-1351.624

15	-0.219	4.885	35.14	503.14
		-3.285	24	887.1
	-0.219	1.6	59.14	1390.2

The sign change in the remainders shows there is a root between 14 and 15.

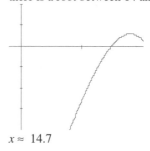

$$x \approx 14.7$$

51.–53. Answers may vary.

55. $f(x) = 2x^3 + x^2 - 14x - 7$

$$
\begin{array}{r|rrrr}
-3 & 2 & 1 & -14 & -7 \\
 & & -6 & 15 & -3 \\
\hline
 & 2 & -5 & 1 & -10
\end{array}
$$

$$
\begin{array}{r|rrrr}
3 & 2 & 1 & -14 & -7 \\
 & & 6 & 21 & 21 \\
\hline
 & 2 & 7 & 7 & 14
\end{array}
$$

-3 is a lower bound; 3 is an upper bound.

57. $f(x) = -0.00002x^3 + 0.008x^2 - 0.3x + 6.95$

a. $f(x) = -0.00002x^3 + 0.008x^2 - 0.3x + 6.95$

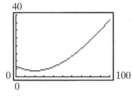

The graph suggests that people visit a physician more often as they age.

b. $f(x) = -0.00002x^3 + 0.008x^2 - 0.3x + 6.95$
$13.43 = -0.00002x^3 + 0.008x^2 - 0.3x + 6.95$
$0 = -0.00002x^3 + 0.008x^2 - 0.3x - 6.48$
$x = 60$; 60 years of age

c. Use Trace to find the value of the function at $y = 13.43$.

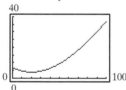

59. $f(x) = 3x^5 - 2x^4 + 6x^3 - 4x^2 - 24x + 16$

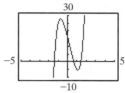

3 real zeros
2 nonreal complex zeros

61. $f(x) = x^6 - 64$

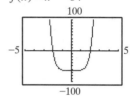

2 real zeros
4 nonreal complex zeros

63. Because the polynomial has no obvious changes of direction but the graph is obviously not linear, the smallest degree is 3.

65. Two roots appear twice, the smallest degree is 5.

67. Answers may vary.

Section 3.6

Check Point Exercises

1. a. $x - 5 = 0$
  $x = 5$
  $\{x | x \neq 5\}$

b. $x^2 - 25 = 0$
  $x^2 = 25$
  $x = \pm 5$
  $\{x \mid x \neq 5, x \neq -5\}$

c.　The denominator cannot equal zero.
　　All real numbers.

2. a.　$x^2 - 1 = 0$
　　　　$x^2 = 1$
　　　　$x = 1, \ x = -1$

b.　$g(x) = \dfrac{x-1}{x^2-1} = \dfrac{x-1}{(x-1)(x+1)} = \dfrac{1}{x+1}$
　　　$x = -1$

c.　The denominator cannot equal zero. No
　　　vertical asymptotes

3. a.　Since $n = m, \ y = \dfrac{9}{3} = 3$ is a horizontal
　　　asymptote.

b.　Since $n < m, \ y = 0$ is a horizontal
　　　asymptote.

c.　Since $n > m$, there is no horizontal
　　　asymptote.

4.　$f(x) = \dfrac{3x}{x-2}$

$f(-x) = \dfrac{3(-x)}{-x-2} = \dfrac{3x}{x+2}$

no symmetry

$f(0) = \dfrac{3(0)}{0-2} = 0$

The y-intercept is 0.
$3x = 0$
　$x = 0$
The x-intercept is 0.
Vertical asymptote:
$x - 2 = 0$
　$x = 2$
Horizontal asymptote:

$y = \dfrac{3}{1} = 3$

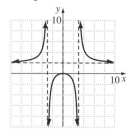

5.　$f(x) = \dfrac{2x^2}{x^2-9}$

$f(-x) = \dfrac{2(-x)^2}{(-x)^2-9} = \dfrac{2x^2}{x^2-9} = f(x)$

The y-axis symmetry.

$f(0) = \dfrac{2(0)^2}{0^2-9} = 0$

The y-intercept is 0.
$2x^2 = 0$
　$x = 0$
The x-intercept is 0.
vertical asymptotes:
$x^2 - 9 = 0$
$x = 3, \ x = -3$
horizontal asymptote:

$y = \dfrac{2}{1} = 2$

6.　$f(x) = \dfrac{x^4}{x^2+2}$

$f(-x) = \dfrac{(-x)^4}{(-x)^2+2} = \dfrac{x^4}{x^2+2} = f(x)$

y-axis symmetry

$$f(0) = \frac{0^4}{0^2 + 2} = 0$$

The y-intercept is 0.

$$x^4 = 0$$
$$x = 0$$

The x-intercept is 0.

vertical asymptotes:

$$x^2 + 2 = 0$$
$$x^2 = -2$$

no vertical asymptotes

horizontal asymptote:

Since $n > m$, there is no horizontal asymptote.

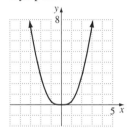

7.

$$\begin{array}{r|rrr} 2 & 2 & -5 & 7 \\ & & 4 & -2 \\ \hline & 2 & -1 & 5 \end{array}$$

the equation of the slant asymptote is
$y = 2x - 1$.

8. a. $C = 600{,}000 + 500x$

b. $\overline{C} = \dfrac{600{,}000 + 500x}{x}$

c. $\overline{C} = \dfrac{600{,}000 + 500(1000)}{1000} = 1100$

The cost per computer to replace 1000 computers would be $1100.

$$\overline{C} = \frac{600{,}000 + 500(10000)}{10000} = 560$$

The cost per computer to replace 10,000 computers would be $560.

$$\overline{C} = \frac{600{,}000 + 500(100{,}000)}{100{,}000} = 506$$

The cost per computer to replace 100,000 computers would be $506.

d. $y = 500$

The more computers the company replaces, the closer the average cost comes to $500.

Exercise Set 3.6

1. $f(x) = \dfrac{5x}{x - 4}$

     $\{x \mid x \neq 4\}$

3. $g(x) = \dfrac{3x^2}{(x - 5)(x + 4)}$

     $\{x \mid x \neq 5, x \neq -4\}$

5. $h(x) = \dfrac{x + 7}{x^2 - 49}$

     $x^2 - 49 = (x - 7)(x + 7)$

     $\{x \mid x \neq 7, x \neq -7\}$

7. $f(x) = \dfrac{x + 7}{x^2 + 49}$

     all real numbers

9. $-\infty$

11. $-\infty$

13. 0

15. $+\infty$

17. $-\infty$

19. 1

21. $f(x) = \dfrac{x}{x+4}$

$x + 4 = 0$

$x = -4$

vertical asymptote: $x = -4$

23. $g(x) = \dfrac{x+3}{x(x+4)}$

$x(x+4) = 0$

$x = 0, x = -4$

vertical asymptotes: $x = 0$, $x = -4$

25. $h(x) = \dfrac{x}{x(x+4)} = \dfrac{1}{x+4}$

$x + 4 = 0$

$x = -4$

vertical asymptote: $x = -4$

27. $r(x) = \dfrac{x}{x^2+4}$

$x^2 + 4$ has no real zeros

There are no vertical asymptotes.

29. $f(x) = \dfrac{12x}{3x^2+1}$

$n < m$

horizontal asymptote: $y = 0$

31. $g(x) = \dfrac{12x^2}{3x^2+1}$

$n = m,$

horizontal asymptote: $y = \dfrac{12}{3} = 4$

33. $h(x) = \dfrac{12x^3}{3x^2+1}$

$n > m$

no horizontal asymptote

35. $f(x) = \dfrac{-2x+1}{3x+5}$

$n = m$

horizontal asymptote: $y = -\dfrac{2}{3}$

37. $f(x) = \dfrac{4x}{x-2}$

$f(-x) = \dfrac{4(-x)}{(-x)-2} = \dfrac{4x}{x+2}$

$f(-x) \neq f(x), f(-x) \neq -f(x)$

no symmetry

y-intercept: $y = \dfrac{4(0)}{0-2} = 0$

x-intercept: $4x = 0$

$x = 0$

vertical asymptote:

$x - 2 = 0$

$x = 2$

horizontal asymptote:

$n = m$, so $y = \dfrac{4}{1} = 4$

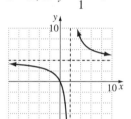

39. $f(x) = \dfrac{2x}{x^2-4}$

$f(-x) = \dfrac{2(-x)}{(-x)^2-4} = -\dfrac{2x}{x^2-4} = -f(x)$

Origin symmetry

y-intercept: $\dfrac{2(0)}{0^2-4} = \dfrac{0}{-4} = 0$

x-intercept:

$2x = 0$

$x = 0$

vertical asymptotes:

$x^2 - 4 = 0$

$x = \pm 2$

horizontal asymptote:

$n < m$ so $y = 0$

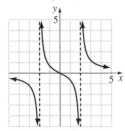

41. $f(x) = \dfrac{2x^2}{x^2 - 1}$

$f(-x) = \dfrac{2(-x)^2}{(-x)^2 - 1} = \dfrac{2x^2}{x^2 - 1} = f(x)$

y-axis symmetry

y-intercept: $y = \dfrac{2(0)^2}{0^2 - 1} = \dfrac{0}{1} = 0$

x-intercept:

$2x^2 = 0$

$x = 0$

vertical asymptote:

$x^2 - 1 = 0$

$x^2 = 1$

$x = \pm 1$

horizontal asymptote:

$n = m$, so $y = \dfrac{2}{1} = 2$

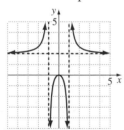

43. $f(x) = \dfrac{-x}{x + 1}$

$f(-x) = \dfrac{-(-x)}{(-x) + 1} = \dfrac{x}{-x + 1}$

$f(-x) \neq f(x), f(-x) \neq -f(x)$

no symmetry

y-intercept: $y = \dfrac{-(0)}{0 + 1} = \dfrac{0}{1} = 0$

x-intercept:

$-x = 0$

$x = 0$

vertical asymptote:

$x + 1 = 0$

$x = -1$

horizontal asymptote:

$n = m$, so $y = \dfrac{-1}{1} = -1$

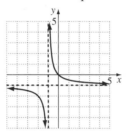

45. $f(x) = -\dfrac{1}{x^2 - 4}$

$f(-x) = -\dfrac{1}{(-x)^2 - 4} = -\dfrac{1}{x^2 - 4} = f(x)$

y-axis symmetry

y-intercept: $y = -\dfrac{1}{0^2 - 4} = \dfrac{1}{4}$

x-intercept: $-1 \neq 0$

no x-intercept

vertical asymptotes:

$x^2 - 4 = 0$

$x^2 = 4$

$x = \pm 2$

horizontal asymptote:

$n < m$ or $y = 0$

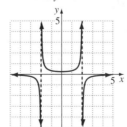

47. $f(x) = \dfrac{2}{x^2 + x - 2}$

$f(-x) = -\dfrac{2}{(-x)^2 - x - 2} = \dfrac{2}{x^2 - x - 2}$

$f(-x) \neq f(x), f(-x) \neq -f(x)$

no symmetry

y-intercept: $y = \dfrac{2}{0^2 + 0 - 2} = \dfrac{2}{-2} = -1$

x-intercept: none

vertical asymptotes:

$x^2 + x - 2 = 0$

$(x + 2)(x - 1) = 0$

$x = -2, x = 1$

horizontal asymptote:

$n < m$ so $y = 0$

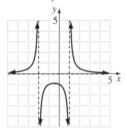

49. $f(x) = \dfrac{2x^2}{x^2 + 4}$

$f(-x) = \dfrac{2(-x)^2}{(-x)^2 + 4} = \dfrac{2x^2}{x^2 + 4} = f(x)$

y axis symmetry

y-intercept: $y = \dfrac{2(0)^2}{0^2 + 4} = 0$

x-intercept: $2x^2 = 0$

$x = 0$

vertical asymptote: none

horizontal asymptote:

$n = m$, so $y = \dfrac{2}{1} = 2$

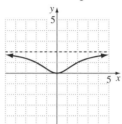

51. $f(x) = \dfrac{x + 2}{x^2 + x - 6}$

$f(-x) = \dfrac{-x + 2}{(-x)^2 - (-x) - 6} = \dfrac{-x + 2}{x^2 + x - 6}$

$f(-x) \neq f(x), f(-x) \neq -f(x)$

no symmetry

y-intercept: $y = \dfrac{0 + 2}{0^2 + 0 - 6} = -\dfrac{2}{6} = -\dfrac{1}{3}$

x-intercept:

$x + 2 = 0$

$x = -2$

vertical asymptotes:

$x^2 + x - 6 = 0$

$(x + 3)(x - 2)$

$x = -3, x = 2$

horizontal asymptote:

$n < m$, so $y = 0$

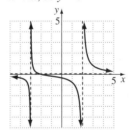

53. $f(x) = \dfrac{x^4}{x^2 + 2}$

$f(-x) = \dfrac{(-x)^4}{(-x)^2 + 2} = \dfrac{x^4}{x^2 + 2} = f(x)$

y-axis symmetry

y-intercept: $y = \dfrac{0^4}{0^2 + 2} = 0$

x-intercept: $x^4 = 0$

$x = 0$

vertical asymptote: none

horizontal asymptote:

$n > m$, so none

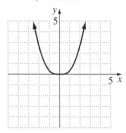

55. $f(x) = \dfrac{x^2 + x - 12}{x^2 - 4}$

$f(-x) = \dfrac{(-x)^2 - x - 12}{(-x)^2 - 4} = \dfrac{x^2 - x - 12}{x^2 - 4}$

$f(-x) \neq f(x), f(-x) \neq -f(x)$

no symmetry

y-intercept: $y = \dfrac{0^2 + 0 - 12}{0^2 - 4} = 3$

x-intercept: $x^2 + x - 12 = 0$

$\qquad\qquad (x - 3)(x + 4) = 0$

$\qquad\qquad\qquad x = 3, x = -4$

vertical asymptotes:

$\qquad x^2 - 4 = 0$

$(x - 2)(x + 2) = 0$

$\qquad\qquad x = 2, x = -2$

horizontal asymptote:

$n = m$, so $y = \dfrac{1}{1} = 1$

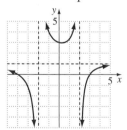

57. $f(x) = \dfrac{3x^2 + x - 4}{2x^2 - 5x}$

$f(-x) = \dfrac{3(-x)^2 - x - 4}{2(-x)^2 + 5x} = \dfrac{3x^2 - x - 4}{2x^2 + 5x}$

$f(-x) \neq f(x), f(-x) \neq -f(x)$

no symmetry

y-intercept: $y = \dfrac{3(0)^2 + 0 - 4}{2(0)^2 - 5(0)} = \dfrac{-4}{0}$

no y-intercept

x-intercepts:

$\qquad 3x^2 + x - 4 = 0$

$(3x + 4)(x - 1) = 0$

$\qquad 3x + 4 = 0 \;\; x - 1 = 0$

$\qquad\qquad 3x = -4$

$\qquad\qquad\quad x = -\dfrac{4}{3}, x = 1$

vertical asymptotes:

$2x^2 - 5x = 0$

$x(2x - 5) = 0$

$x = 0, 2x = 5$

$\qquad x = \dfrac{5}{2}$

horizontal asymptote:

$n = m$, so $y = \dfrac{3}{2}$

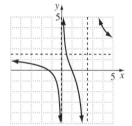

59. a. Slant asymptote:

$\qquad f(x) = x - \dfrac{1}{x}$

$\qquad y = x$

b. $f(x) = \dfrac{x^2 - 1}{x}$

$f(-x) = \dfrac{(-x)^2 - 1}{(-x)} = \dfrac{x^2 - 1}{-x} = -f(x)$

Origin symmetry

y-intercept: $y = \dfrac{0^2 - 1}{0} = \dfrac{-1}{0}$

no y-intercept

x-intercepts: $x^2 - 1 = 0$

$x = \pm 1$

vertical asymptote: $x = 0$

horizontal asymptote:

$n < m$, so none exist.

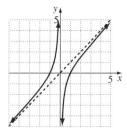

61. a.   Slant asymptote:

$f(x) = x + \dfrac{1}{x}$

$y = x$

b. $f(x) = \dfrac{x^2 + 1}{x}$

$f(-x) = \dfrac{(-x)^2 + 1}{-x} = \dfrac{x^2 + 1}{-x} = -f(x)$

Origin symmetry

y-intercept: $y = \dfrac{0^2 + 1}{0} = \dfrac{1}{0}$

no y-intercept

x-intercept:

$x^2 + 1 = 0$

$x^2 = -1$

no x-intercept

vertical asymptote: $x = 0$

horizontal asymptote:

$n > m$, so none exist.

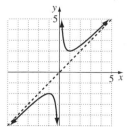

63. a.   Slant asymptote:

$f(x) = x + 4 + \dfrac{6}{x - 3}$

$y = x + 4$

b. $f(x) = \dfrac{x^2 + x - 6}{x - 3}$

$f(-x) = \dfrac{(-x)^2 + (-x) - 6}{-x - 3} = \dfrac{x^2 - x - 6}{-x - 3}$

$f(-x) \neq g(x), \; g(-x) \neq -g(x)$

No symmetry

y-intercept: $y = \dfrac{0^2 + 0 - 6}{0 - 3} = \dfrac{-6}{-3} = 2$

x-intercept:

$x^2 + x - 6 = 0$

$(x + 3)(x - 2) = 0$

$x = -3$ and $x = 2$

vertical asymptote:

$x - 3 = 0$

$x = 3$

horizontal asymptote:

$n > m$, so none exist.

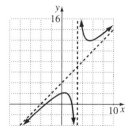

65. $f(x) = \dfrac{x^3 + 1}{x^2 + 2x}$

   a. slant asymptote:

$$\require{enclose}
\begin{array}{r}
x - 2 \\
x^2 + 2x \enclose{longdiv}{x^3 \qquad\ + 1} \\
\underline{x^3 + 2x^2} \\
-2x^2 \\
\underline{-2x^2 + 4x} \\
-4x + 1
\end{array}$$

$$y = x - 2$$

   b.

$$f(-x) = \dfrac{(-x)^3 + 1}{(-x)^2 + 2(-x)} = \dfrac{-x^3 + 1}{x^2 - 2x}$$

$$f(-x) \neq f(x), \quad f(-x) \neq -f(x)$$

no symmetry

y-intercept: $y = \dfrac{0^3 + 1}{0^2 + 2(0)} = \dfrac{1}{0}$

no y-intercept

x-intercept: $x^3 + 1 = 0$

$$x^3 = -1$$

$$x = -1$$

vertical asymptotes:

$$x^2 + 2x = 0$$

$$x(x + 2) = 0$$

$$x = 0, \quad x = -2$$

horizontal asymptote:

$n > m$, so none

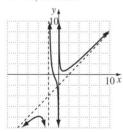

67. a. $C(x) = 100x + 100,000$

   b. $\overline{C}(x) = \dfrac{100x + 100,000}{x}$

   c. $\overline{C}(500) = \dfrac{100(500) + 100,000}{500} = \$300$

When 500 bicycles are manufactured, it cost \$300 to manufacture each.

$$\overline{C}(1000) = \dfrac{100(1000) + 100,000}{1000} = \$200$$

When 1000 bicycles are manufactured, it cost \$200 to manufacture each.

$$\overline{C}(2000) = \dfrac{100(2000) + 100,000}{2000} = \$150$$

When 2000 bicycles are manufactured, it cost \$150 to manufacture each.

$$\overline{C}(4000) = \dfrac{100(4000) + 100,000}{4000} = \$125$$

When 4000 bicycles are manufactured, it cost \$125 to manufacture each. The average cost decreases as the number of bicycles manufactured increases.

   d. $n = m$, so $y = \dfrac{100}{1} = 100$.

As greater numbers of bicycles are manufactured, the average cost approaches \$100.

69. a. $M(x) = \dfrac{190.9x + 2413.99}{0.234x + 12.54}$

   b. $2004 - 1985 = 19$

$$M(19) = \dfrac{190.9(19) + 2413.99}{0.234(19) + 12.54} = 355.65$$

The average amount a student will spend on text books in 2004 will be \$355.65.

   c. $y = \dfrac{190.9}{0.234} \approx 816$

The average cost approaches \$816.

71. $P(10) = \dfrac{100(10-1)}{10} = 90$ (10, 90)

For a disease that smokers are 10 times more likely to contact than non-smokers, 90% of the deaths are smoking related.

73. $y = 100$ As incidence of the diseases increases, the percent of death approaches, but never gets to be, 100%.

75. a. after 1 day: 35 words
after 5 days: about 12 words
after 15 days: about 7 words

b. $N(t) = \dfrac{5t + 30}{t}$, $t \geq 1$

$N(1) = \dfrac{5 + 30}{t} = 35$ words

This is the same as the estimate for the graph.

$N(5) = \dfrac{25 + 30}{5} = 11$ words

This is a little less than the estimate from the graph.

$N(15) = 7$ words

This is the same as the estimate from the graph.

c. The graph indicates that the students will remember 5 words over a long period of time.

d. $n = m$, so $y = \dfrac{5}{1} = 5$

The horizontal asymptote indicates that the students will remember 5 words over a long period of time.

77.–85. Answers may very.

87.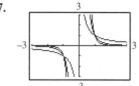

The graph approaches the horizontal asymptote faster and the vertical asymptote slower as *n* increases.

89. $f(x) = \dfrac{x^2 - 4x + 3}{x - 2}$

$g(x) = \dfrac{x^2 - 5x + 6}{x - 2}$

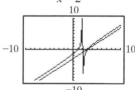

$g(x)$ is the graph of a line where $f(x)$ is the graph of a rational function with a slant asymptote.
In $g(x)$, $x - 2$ is a factor of $x^2 - 5x + 6$.

91. a. False

b. False; the graph of a rational function may not have a *y*-intercept when the *y*-axis is a vertical asymptote.

c. False; the graph can have 1 or no horizontal asymptotes.

d. True; the function is undefined for *x* values at a vertical asymptote.

(d) is true.

93.–95. Answers may very.

Section 3.7

Check Point Exercises

1. **a.** $L = kN$

   b. $L = 4N$

   c. $L = 4(17) = 68$
      Sain's moustache grew to 68 inches.

2. **a.** $W = kL$

   b. $75 = k(6)$
      $k = \dfrac{75}{6}$

   c. $W = kL$
      $W = \left(\dfrac{75}{6}\right)L = \dfrac{75L}{6}$

   d. $W = \dfrac{75(16)}{6} = 200$
      A 16-foot canoe weighs 200 pounds.

3. $P = kD$
    $25 = k(60)$
    $k = \dfrac{25}{60} = \dfrac{5}{12}$
    $P = \dfrac{5}{12}D$
    $P = \dfrac{5}{12}(330) = 137.5$
   The pressure will be 137.5 pounds per
   square inch.

4. $d = kv^2$
    $200 = k(60)^2$
    $k = \dfrac{200}{3600} = \dfrac{1}{18}$
    $d = \dfrac{1}{18}v^2$
    $d = \dfrac{1}{18}(100)^2 \approx 556$
   About 556 feet are required.

5. $P = \dfrac{k}{s}$
    $19.5 = \dfrac{k}{4}$
    $78 = k$
    $P = \dfrac{78}{s}$
    $P = \dfrac{78}{3}$
    $P = 26$
   The new pressure is about 4.36 pounds per
   square inch.

6. $M = \dfrac{kP}{W}$
    $32 = \dfrac{k16}{4}$
    $k = 8$
    $M = \dfrac{8P}{W}$
    $M = \dfrac{8(24)}{8} = 24$
   It will take 24 minutes.

7. $V = khr^2$
    $120\pi = k(10)(6)^2$
    $k = \dfrac{120\pi}{360} = \dfrac{\pi}{3}$
    $V = \dfrac{\pi hr^2}{3}$
    $V = \dfrac{\pi(2)(12)^2}{3} = 96\pi$
   The volume of the cone is 96π cubic feet.

Exercise Set 3.7

1. $g = kh$

3. $a = kb^2$

5. $r = \dfrac{k}{t}$

7. $a = \dfrac{k}{b^3}$

9. $r = \dfrac{ks}{v}$

11. $s = kgt^2$

13. $y = kx$
$75 = k \cdot 3$
$k = 25$

15. $y = kx^2$
$45 = k \cdot 3^2$
$9k = 45$
$k = 5$

17. $W = \dfrac{k}{r}$
$500 = \dfrac{k}{10}$
$k = 5000$

19. $A = \dfrac{kB}{C}$
$9 = \dfrac{k \cdot 12}{4}$
$k = 9 \cdot \dfrac{4}{12}$
$k = 3$

21. $a = kbc$
$72 = k \cdot 18 \cdot 2$
$36k = 72$
$k = 2$

23. $y = kx$
$35 = k \cdot 5$
$k = 7$
$y = 7x$
$y = 7 \cdot 12$
$y = 84$

25. $y = \dfrac{k}{x}$
$10 = \dfrac{k}{5}$
$k = 50$
$y = \dfrac{50}{x}$
$y = \dfrac{50}{2}$
$y = 25$

27. $y = \dfrac{kx}{z^2}$
$20 = \dfrac{k \cdot 50}{5^2} = \dfrac{50k}{25} = 2k$
$20 = 2k$
$k = 10$
$y = \dfrac{10x}{z^2}$
$y = \dfrac{10 \cdot 3}{6^2} = \dfrac{30}{36} = \dfrac{5}{6}$
$y = \dfrac{5}{6}$

29. $y = hxz$
$25 = k \cdot 2 \cdot 5$
$k = \dfrac{25}{10} = 2.5$
$y = 2.5xz$
$y = 2.5(8)(12)$
$y = 240$

31. a. $L = kW$

b. $L = 0.02W$

c. $L = 0.02(52)$
$\quad = 1.04$
Your fingernail length will be
1.04 inches.

33. $C = kM$

$400 = k \cdot 3000$

$k = \dfrac{400}{3000} = \dfrac{2}{15}$

$C = \dfrac{2}{15} M$

$C = \dfrac{2}{15} \cdot 450 = 60$

The cost is $60.

35. $s = kM$

$1502.2 = k(2.03)$

$k = 740$

$s = 740M$

$s = 740(3.3)$

$\quad = 2442$

The Blackbird's speed is 2442 miles per hour.

37. $W = kh^3$

$170 = k \cdot 70^3$

$343,000k = 170$

$k = \dfrac{17}{34,300}$

$W = \dfrac{17}{34,300} h^3$

$W = \dfrac{17}{34,300}(107)^3$

$W \approx 607$

Mr. Wadlow weighed approximately 607 pounds.

39. $t = \dfrac{k}{r}$

$1.5 = \dfrac{k}{20}$

$k = 30$

$t = \dfrac{30}{r}$

$t = \dfrac{30}{60} = 0.5$

It will take half an hour.

41. $v = \dfrac{k}{p}$

$32 = \dfrac{k}{8}$

$k = 256$

$v = \dfrac{256}{p}$

$40 = \dfrac{256}{p}$

$40p = 256$

$p = 6.4$

The pressure is 6.4 pounds.

43. $i = \dfrac{kw}{h}$

$21 = \dfrac{k \cdot 150}{70}$

$1470 = 150k$

$k = 9.8$

$i = \dfrac{9.8w}{h}$

$i = \dfrac{9.8(240)}{74} \approx 31.78$

index: about 32

This person is not in the desirable range.

45. $I = \dfrac{k}{d^2}$

$25 = \dfrac{k}{4^2}$

$k = 400$

$I = \dfrac{400}{d^2}$

$I = \dfrac{400}{6^2} \approx 11.11$

The illumination is about 11.11 foot-candles.

47. $e = kmv^2$

$36 = k \cdot 8 \cdot 3^2$

$72k = 36$

$k = 0.5$

$e = 0.5mv^2$

$e = 0.5(4)6^2 = 72$

The kinetic energy is 72 ergs.

49.
$$\frac{c}{p} = \frac{kp_1 \cdot p_2}{d^2}$$
$$158,233 = \frac{k(2538)(1818)}{(108)^2}$$
$$k \approx 400$$
$$c = \frac{(400)(1225)(2970)}{(3403)^2}$$
$$c \approx 126$$
About 126 phone calls per day are made.

51.–57. Answers may vary.

59. $p = kv^2$
$$p = k(2v)^2$$
$$p = k \cdot 4v^2$$
$$p = 4kv^2$$
The destructive power is four times as much.

61. $h = \dfrac{kv^2}{r}$
$$3h = \frac{3kv^2}{r} = \frac{kv^2}{\dfrac{r}{3}}$$

Reduce the resistance by a factor of $\dfrac{1}{3}$.

Review Exercises

1. $f(x) = -2(x-1)^2 + 3$

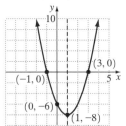

axis of symmetry: $x = 1$

2. $f(x) = (x+4)^2 - 2$

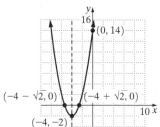

axis of symmetry: $x = -4$

3. $f(x) = -x^2 + 2x + 3$
$$= -\left(x^2 - 2x + 1\right) + 3 + 1$$
$$f(x) = -(x-1)^2 + 4$$

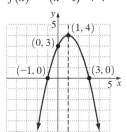

axis of symmetry: $x = 1$

4. $f(x) = 2x^2 - 4x - 6$
$$f(x) = 2\left(x^2 - 2x + 1\right) - 6 - 2$$
$$2(x-1)^2 - 8$$

axis of symmetry: $x = 1$

5. $s(t) = -16t^2 + 64t + 80$
$$t = -\frac{b}{2a} = -\frac{64}{2(-16)} = 2$$

It reaches its maximum height after 2 seconds.

$s(2) = -16(2)^2 + 64(2) + 80 = 144$
The maximum height is 144 feet.

6. Vertex (20, 5.4) In 1980, the divorce was at a maximum with 5.4 divorces for every 1000 in the population.

7. $A = x(1000 - 2x)$
$A = -2x^2 + 1000x$
$x = \dfrac{-1000}{2(-2)} = 250$
length $= 1000 - 2(250) = 500$

The maximum field will have sides of 250 yards and a length of 500 yards for an area of 125,000 square yards.

8. $f(x) = -x^3 + 12x^2 - x$
The graph rises to the left and falls to the right and goes through the origin, so graph (c) is the best match.

9. $g(x) = x^6 - 6x^4 + 9x^2$
The graph rises to the left and rises to the right, so graph (b) is the best match.

10. $h(x) = x^5 - 5x^3 + 4x$
The graph falls to the left and rises to the right and crosses the *y*-axis at zero, so graph (a) is the best match.

11. $f(x) = -x^4 + 1$
f(*x*) falls to the left and to the right so graph (d) is the best match.

12. $f(x) = -0.0013x^3 + 0.78x^2 - 1.43x + 18.1$
Because the degree is odd and the leading coefficient is negative, the graph falls to the right. Therefore, the model indicates that the percentage of families below the poverty level will eventually be negative, which is impossible.

13. $N(t) = -\dfrac{3}{4}t^4 + 3t^3 + 5$
Since the degree is even and the leading coefficient is negative, the graph falls to the right. Therefore, the model indicates a patient will eventually have a negative number of viral bodies, which is impossible.

14. $f(x) = -2(x-1)(x+2)^2(x+5)^3$
x = 1, multiplicity 1, the graph crosses the *x*-axis
x = –2, multiplicity 2, the graph touches the *x*-axis
x = –5, multiplicity 5, the graph crosses the *x*-axis

15. $f(x) = x^3 - 5x^2 - 25x + 125$
$\qquad = x^2(x-5) - 25(x-5)$
$\qquad = (x^2 - 25)(x-5)$
$\qquad = (x+5)(x-5)^2$
x = –5, multiplicity 1, the graph crosses the *x*-axis
x = 5, multiplicity 2, the graph touches the *x*-axis

16. $f(x) = x^3 - x^2 - 9x + 9$

a. Since *n* is odd and $a_n > 0$, the graph falls to the left and rises to the right.

b. $f(-x) = (-x)^3 - (-x)^2 - 9(-x) + 9$
$\qquad = -x^3 - x^2 + 9x + 9$
$f(-x) \neq f(x), f(-x) \neq -f(x)$
no symmetry

c. $f(x) = (x-3)(x+3)(x-1)$

zeros: 3, −3, 1

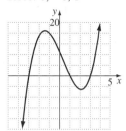

17. $f(x) = 4x - x^3$

a. Since n is odd and $a_n < 0$, the graph rises to the left and falls to the right.

b. $f(-x) = -4x + x^3$
$f(-x) = -f(x)$
origin symmetry

c. $f(x) = x(x^2 - 4) = x(x-2)(x+2)$
zeros: $x = 0, 2, -2$

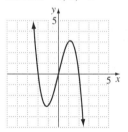

18. $f(x) = 2x^3 + 3x^2 - 8x - 12$

a. Since h is odd and $a_n > 0$, the graph falls to the left and rises to the right.

b. $f(-x) = -2x^3 + 3x^2 + 8x - 12$
$f(-x) \neq f(x), \; f(-x) = -f(x)$
no symmetry

c. $f(x) = (x-2)(x+2)(2x+3)$

zeros: $x = 2, -2, -\dfrac{3}{2}$

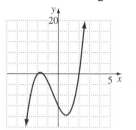

19. $g(x) = -x^4 + 25x^2$

a. The graph falls to the left and to the right.

b. $f(-x) = -(-x)^4 + 25(-x)^2$
$\qquad = -x^4 + 25x^2 = f(x)$
y-axis symmetry

c. $-x^4 + 25x^2 = 0$
$-x^2\left(x^2 - 25\right) = 0$
$-x^2(x-5)(x+5) = 0$
zeros: $x = -5, 0, 5$

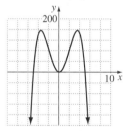

20. $f(x) = -x^4 + 6x^3 - 9x^2$

a. The graph falls to the left and to the right.

b. $f(-x) = -(-x)^4 + 6(-x)^3 - 9(-x)$
$\qquad = -x^4 - 6x^3 - 9x^2 \; f(-x) \neq f(x)$
$f(-x) \neq -f(x)$
no symmetry

c. $= -x^2\left(x^2 - 6x + 9\right) = 0$

$-x^2(x-3)(x-3) = 0$

zeros: $x = 0, 3$

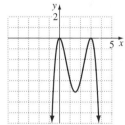

21. $f(x) = 3x^4 - 15x^3$

a. The graph rises to the left and to the right.

b. $f(-x) = 3(-x)^4 - 15(-x)^2 = 3x^4 + 15x^3$
$f(-x) \neq f(x),\ f(-x) \neq -f(x)$
no symmetry

c $3x^4 - 15x^3 = 0$
$3x^3(x-5) = 0$
zeros: $x = 0, 5$

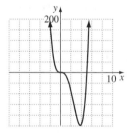

22. $x+1\overline{)4x^3 - 3x^2 - 2x + 1}$

$$\underline{4x^3 + 4x^2}$$
$$-7x^2 - 2x$$
$$\underline{-7x^2 - 7x}$$
$$5x + 1$$
$$\underline{5x + 5}$$
$$-4$$

with quotient on top: $4x^2 - 7x + 5$

Quotient: $4x^2 - 7x + 5 - \dfrac{4}{x+1}$

23. $5x-3\overline{)10x^3 - 26x^2 + 17x - 13}$

quotient: $2x^2 - 4x + 1$

$$\underline{10x^3 + \ 6x^2}$$
$$-20x^2 + 17x$$
$$\underline{-20x^2 + 12x}$$
$$5x - 13$$
$$\underline{5x - \ 3}$$
$$-10$$

Quotient: $2x^2 - 4x + 1 - \dfrac{10}{5x - 3}$

24. $2x^2+1\overline{)4x^4 + 6x^3 + 3x - 1}$

quotient: $2x^2 + 3x - 1$

$$\underline{4x^2 + 2x^2}$$
$$6x^3 - 2x^2 + 3x$$
$$\underline{6x^2 + 3x}$$
$$-2x^2 - 1$$
$$\underline{-2x^2 - 1}$$
$$0$$

25. $(3x^4 + 11x^3 - 20x^3 + 7x + 35) \div (x + 5)$

-5	3	11	-20	7	35
		-15	20	0	-35
	3	-4	0	7	0

Quotient: $3x^3 - 4x^2 + 7$

26. $(3x^4 - 2x^2 - 10x) \div (x - 2)$

2	3	0	-2	-10	0
		6	12	20	20
	3	6	10	10	20

Quotient: $3x^3 + 6x^2 + 10x + 10 + \dfrac{20}{x - 2}$

27. $f(x) = 2x^3 - 7x^2 + 9x - 3$

-13	2	-7	9	-3

$$\begin{array}{r} \underline{ \quad -26 \quad 429 \quad -5694} \\ 2 \quad -33 \quad 438 \quad -5697 \end{array}$$

Quotient: $f(-13) = -5697$

28. $f(x) = 2x^3 + x^2 - 13x + 6$

$$\begin{array}{r|rrrr} 2 & 2 & 1 & -13 & 6 \\ & & 4 & 10 & -6 \\ \hline & 2 & 5 & -3 & 0 \end{array}$$

$f(x) = (x-2)(2x^2 + 5x - 3)$
$\quad\;\; = (x-2)(2x-1)(x+3)$

Zeros: $x = 2, \dfrac{1}{2}, -3$

29. $x^3 - 17x + 4 = 0$

$$\begin{array}{r|rrrr} 4 & 1 & 0 & -17 & 4 \\ & & 4 & 16 & -4 \\ \hline & 1 & 4 & -1 & 0 \end{array}$$

$(x-4)\left(x^2 + 4x - 1\right) = 0$

$x = \dfrac{-4 \pm \sqrt{16+4}}{2} = \dfrac{-4 \pm 2\sqrt{5}}{2} = -2 \pm \sqrt{5}$

The solution set is $\left\{4, -2 \pm \sqrt{5}, -2 - \sqrt{5}\right\}$.

30. $f(x) = x^4 - 6x^3 + 14x^2 - 14x + 5$
$p: \pm 1, \pm 5$
$q: \pm 1$
$\dfrac{p}{q}: \pm 1, \pm 5$

31. $f(x) = 3x^5 - 2x^4 - 15x^3 + 10x^2 + 12x - 8$
$p: \pm 1, \pm 2, \pm 4, \pm 8$
$q: \pm 1, \pm 3$
$\dfrac{p}{q}: \pm 1, \pm 2, \pm 4, \pm 8, \pm \dfrac{8}{3}, \pm \dfrac{4}{3}, \pm \dfrac{2}{3}, \pm \dfrac{1}{3}$

32. $f(x) = 3x^4 - 2x^3 - 8x + 5$
$f(x)$ has 2 sign variations, so $f(x) = 0$ has 2 or 0 positive solutions.

$f(-x) = 3x^4 + 2x^3 + x + 5$
$f(-x)$ has no sign variations, so $f(x) = 0$ has no negative solutions.

33. $f(x) = 2x^5 - 3x^3 - 5x^2 + 3x - 1$
$f(x)$ has 3 sign variations, so $f(x) = 0$ has 3 or 1 positive real roots.
$f(-x) = -2x^5 + 3x^3 - 5x^2 - 3x - 1$
$f(-x)$ has 2 sign variations, so
$f(x) = 0$ has 2 or 0 negative solutions.

34. $f(x) = f(-x) = 2x^4 + 6x^2 + 8$
No sign variations exist for either $f(x)$ or $f(-x)$, so no real roots exist.

35. $f(x) = x^3 + 3x^2 - 4$

a. $p: \pm 1, \pm 2, \pm 4$
$q: \pm 1$
$\dfrac{p}{q}: \pm 1, \pm 2, \pm 4$

b. 1 sign variation $\Rightarrow$ 1 positive real zero
$f(-x) = -x^3 + 3x^2 - 4$
2 sign variations $\Rightarrow$ 2 or no negative real zeros

c.
$$\begin{array}{r|rrrr} 1 & 1 & 3 & 0 & -4 \\ & & 1 & 4 & 4 \\ \hline & 1 & 4 & 4 & 0 \end{array}$$
1 is a zero.

d. $(x-1)(x^2 + 4x + 4) = 0$
$(x-1)(x+2)^2 = 0$
$x = 1$ or $x = -2$
The solution set is $\{1, -2\}$.

36. $f(x) = 6x^3 + x^2 - 4x + 1$

a. p: ± 1

     q: ± 1, ± 2, ± 3, ± 6

     $\dfrac{p}{q}$: $\pm 1, \pm \dfrac{1}{2}, \pm \dfrac{1}{3}, \pm \dfrac{1}{6}$

b. $f(x) = 6x^3 + x^2 - 4x + 1$

     2 sign variations; 2 or 0 positive real zeros.

     $f(-x) = -6x^3 + x^2 + 4x + 1$

     1 sign variation; 1 negative real zero.

c.

$$
\begin{array}{r|rrrr}
-1 & 6 & 1 & -4 & 1 \\
   &   & -6 & 5 & -1 \\
\hline
   & 6 & -5 & 1 & 0
\end{array}
$$

     -1 is a zero.

d. $6x^3 + x^2 - 4x + 1 = 0$

     $(x+1)(6x^2 - 5x + 1) = 0$

     $(x+1)(3x-1)(2x-1) = 0$

     $x = -1$ or $x = \dfrac{1}{3}$ or $x = \dfrac{1}{2}$

     The solution set is $\left\{ -1, \dfrac{1}{3}, \dfrac{1}{2} \right\}$.

37. $f(x) = 8x^3 - 36x^2 + 46x - 15$

a. p: ± 1, ± 3, ± 5, ± 15

     q: ± 1, ± 2, ± 4, ± 8

     $\dfrac{p}{q}$: $\pm 1, \pm 3, \pm 5, \pm 15, \pm \dfrac{1}{2}, \pm \dfrac{1}{4}, \pm \dfrac{1}{8},$

         $\pm \dfrac{3}{2}, \pm \dfrac{3}{4}, \pm \dfrac{3}{8}, \pm \dfrac{5}{2}, \pm \dfrac{5}{4},$

         $\pm \dfrac{5}{8}, \pm \dfrac{15}{2}, \pm \dfrac{15}{4}, \pm \dfrac{15}{8}$

b. $f(x) = 8x^3 - 36x^2 + 46x - 15$

     3 sign variations; 3 or 1 positive real solutions.

     $f(-x) = -8x^3 - 36x^2 - 46x - 15$

     0 sign variations; no negative real solutions.

c.

$$
\begin{array}{r|rrrr}
\frac{1}{2} & 8 & -36 & 46 & -15 \\
   &   & 4 & -16 & 15 \\
\hline
   & 8 & -32 & 30 & 0
\end{array}
$$

     $\dfrac{1}{2}$ is a zero.

d. $8x^3 - 36x^2 + 46x - 15 = 0$

     $\left(x - \dfrac{1}{2} \right)(8x^2 - 32x + 30) = 0$

     $2\left(x - \dfrac{1}{2} \right)(4x - 16x + 15) = 0$

     $2\left(x - \dfrac{1}{2} \right)(2x - 5)(2x - 3) = 0$

     $x = \dfrac{1}{2}$ or $x = \dfrac{5}{2}$ or $x = \dfrac{3}{2}$

     The solution set is $\left\{ \dfrac{1}{2}, \dfrac{3}{2}, \dfrac{5}{2} \right\}$.

38. $f(x) = x^4 - x^3 - 7x^2 + x + 6$

a. p: ± 1, ± 2, ± 3, ± 6

     q: ± 1

     $\dfrac{p}{q}$: $\pm 1, \pm 2, \pm 3, \pm 6$

b. $f(x) = x^4 - x^3 - 7x^2 + x + 6$

     2 sign variations; 2 or zero positive real solutions.

     $f(-x) = x^4 + x^3 - 7x^2 - x + 6$

     2 sign variations; 2 or zero negative real solutions.

c.

$$
\begin{array}{r|rrrrr}
-2 & 1 & -1 & -7 & 1 & 6 \\
   &   & -2 & 6 & 2 & -6 \\
\hline
   & 1 & -3 & -1 & 3 & 0
\end{array}
$$

     -2 is a zero.

d. $x^4 - x^3 - 7x^2 + x + 6 = 0$
$(x+2)(x^3 - 3x^2 - x + 3) = 0$
$(x+2)[x^2(x-3) - (x-3)] = 0$
$(x+2)(x-3)(x^2 - 1) = 0$
$(x+2)(x-3)(x-1)(x+1) = 0$
$x = -2$ or $x = 3$ or $x = 1$ or $x = -1$
The solution set is $\{-2, -1, 1, 3\}$.

39. $4x^4 + 7x^2 - 2 = 0$

a. $p: \pm 1, \pm 2$
$q: \pm 1, \pm 2, \pm 4$
$\dfrac{p}{q}: \pm 1, \pm 2, \pm \dfrac{1}{2}, \pm \dfrac{1}{4}$

b. 1 sign variation; 1 positive real root
$f(-x) = 4x^4 + 7x^2 - 2$
1 sign variation; 1 negative real root

c.
$$\begin{array}{r|rrrrr}
\frac{1}{2} & 4 & 0 & 7 & 0 & -2 \\
 & & 2 & 1 & 4 & 2 \\
\hline
 & 4 & 2 & 8 & 4 & 0
\end{array}$$
$(2x - 1)\left(4x^3 + 2x^2 + 8x + 4\right) = 0$
$\dfrac{1}{2}$ is a zero.

d.
$$\begin{array}{r|rrrr}
-\frac{1}{2} & 4 & 2 & 8 & 4 \\
 & & -2 & 0 & -4 \\
\hline
 & 4 & 0 & 8 & 0
\end{array}$$
$(2x - 1)(2x + 1)(4x^2 + 8) = 0$
$4(2x - 1)(2x + 1)(x^2 + 2) = 0$
$x^2 = -2$
$x = \pm i\sqrt{2}$
The solution set is $\left\{\dfrac{1}{2}, -\dfrac{1}{2}, i\sqrt{2}, -i\sqrt{2}\right\}$.

40. $f(x) = 2x^4 + x^3 - 9x^2 - 4x + 4$

a. $p: \pm 1, \pm 2, \pm 4$
$q: \pm 1, \pm 2$
$\dfrac{p}{q} = \pm 1, \pm 2, \pm 4, \pm \dfrac{1}{2}$

b. 2 sign variations; 2 or no positive zeros
$f(-x) = 2x^4 - x^3 - 9x^2 + 4x + 4$
2 sign variations; 2 or no negative zeros

c.
$$\begin{array}{r|rrrrr}
2 & 2 & 1 & -9 & -4 & 4 \\
 & & 4 & 10 & 2 & -4 \\
\hline
 & 2 & 5 & 1 & -2 & 0
\end{array}$$
2 is a zero.

d. $f(x) = (x - 2)\left(2x^3 + 5x^2 + x - 2\right)$
$$\begin{array}{r|rrrr}
-2 & 2 & 5 & 1 & -2 \\
 & & -4 & -2 & 2 \\
\hline
 & 2 & 1 & -1 & 0
\end{array}$$
$f(x) = (x - 2)(x + 2)(2x^2 + x - 1)$
$= (x - 2)(x + 2)(2x - 1)(x + 1)$
$x = 2, -2, \dfrac{1}{2}, -1$
The solution set is $\left\{2, -2, \dfrac{1}{2}, -1\right\}$.

41. $2x^4 - 7x^3 - 5x^2 + 28x - 12 = 0$
$$\begin{array}{r|rrrrr}
-2 & 2 & -7 & -5 & 28 & -12 \\
 & & -4 & 22 & -34 & 12 \\
\hline
 & 2 & -11 & 17 & -6 & 0
\end{array}$$
-2 is a root and a lower bound.

$$\begin{array}{r|rrrrr}
6 & 2 & -7 & -5 & 28 & -12 \\
 & & 12 & 30 & 150 & 1068 \\
\hline
 & 2 & 5 & 25 & 178 & 1056
\end{array}$$

6 is an upper bound, but not a zero.

p: ±1, ±2, ±3, ±4, +6, ±12

q: ±1, ±2

$\dfrac{p}{q}$: ±1, ±2, ±3, ±4, ±6, ±12, ±$\dfrac{1}{2}$, ±$\dfrac{3}{2}$

Possible roots are: ±1, ±2, 3, 4, ±$\dfrac{1}{2}$, ±$\dfrac{3}{2}$

42. $2x^4 - x^3 - 5x^2 + 10x + 12 = 0$

    a. p: ±1, ±2, ±3, ±4, ±6, ±12

       q: ±1, ±2

       $\dfrac{p}{q}$: ±1, ±2, ±3, ±4, ±6, ±12, ±$\dfrac{1}{2}$, ±$\dfrac{3}{2}$

    b.

2	2	−1	−5	10	12
		4	6	2	24
	2	3	1	12	36

       2 is not a root but is an upper bound.

    c.

−2	2	−1	−5	10	12
		−4	10	−10	0
	2	−5	5	0	12

       −2 is not a root but is a lower bound.

    d. Possible roots are ±1, ±$\dfrac{1}{2}$, and ±$\dfrac{3}{2}$.

43. $f(x) = x^3 - 2x - 1$

$f(1) = (1)^3 - 2(1) - 1 = -2$

$f(2) = (2)^3 - 2(2) - 1 = 3$

Continue to use the Intermediate Value Theorem:

$f(1.5) = -0.625$

$f(1.6) = -0.104$

$f(1.7) = 0.513$

$f(1.65) = 0.192125$

$x \approx 1.6$

44. $f(x) = 3x^3 + 2x^2 - 8x + 7$

$f(-3) = 3(-3)^3 + 2(-3)^2 - 8(-3) + 7 = -32$

$f(-2) = 3(-2)^3 + 2(-2)^2 - 8(-2) + 7 = 7$

Continue to use the Intermediate Value Theorem:

$f(-2.4) = -3.752$

$f(-2.3) = -0.521$

$f(-2.2) = 2.336$

$f(-2.25) = 0.953125$

$x \approx -2.3$

45. $(x - 6 - 5i)(x - 6 + 5i)$

$= x^2 - 6x - 6x + 36 - 25i^2$

$= x^2 - 12x + 61$

$$
\require{enclose}
\begin{array}{r}
4x + 1 \\
x^2 - 12x + 61 \enclose{longdiv}{4x^3 - 47x^2 + 232x + 61} \\
\underline{4x^3 - 48x^2 + 244x} \\
x^2 - 12x + 61 \\
\underline{x^2 - 12x + 61} \\
0
\end{array}
$$

$4x + 1 = 0$

$x = -\dfrac{1}{4}$

The solution set is $\left\{ -\dfrac{1}{4},\ 6 \pm 5i,\ 6 - 5i \right\}$.

46. $(x - 1 + 3i)(x - 1 - 3i) = x^2 - 2x + 1 - 9i^2$

$= x^2 - 2x + 10$

$$
\require{enclose}
\begin{array}{r}
x^2 - 2x + 2 \\
x^2 - 2x + 10 \enclose{longdiv}{x^4 - 4x^3 + 16x^2 - 24x + 20} \\
\underline{x^4 - 2x^3 + 10x^2} \\
-2x^3 + 6x^2 - 24x \\
\underline{-2x^3 + 4x^2 - 20x} \\
2x^2 - 4x + 20 \\
\underline{2x^2 - 4x + 20} \\
0
\end{array}
$$

$x^2 - 2x + 2 = 0$

$x = \dfrac{2 \pm \sqrt{4 - 4(1)(2)}}{2}$

$x = \dfrac{2 \pm 2i}{2} = 1 \pm i$

The solution set is $\{1 + 3i,\ 1 - 3i,\ 1 + i,\ 1 - i\}$.

47. $(x - 4 - 7i)(x - 4 + 7i) = x^2 - 8x + 16 + 49$
$$= x^2 - 8x + 65$$

$$
\begin{array}{r}
2x^2 - x - 1 \\
x^2 - 8x + 65\overline{\smash{\big)}\,2x^4 - 17x^3 + 137x^2 - 57x - 65} \\
\underline{2x^4 - 16x^3 + 130x^2} \\
-x^3 + 7x^2 - 57x \\
\underline{-x^3 + 8x^2 - 65x} \\
-x^2 + 8x - 65 \\
\underline{-x^2 + 8x - 65} \\
0
\end{array}
$$

$$2x^2 - x - 1 = 0$$
$$x = \frac{1 \pm \sqrt{1 - 4(2)(-1)}}{4}$$
$$x = \frac{1 \pm 3}{4}$$
$$x = 1, \ -\frac{1}{2}$$

The solution set is $\left\{-\dfrac{1}{2}, 1, 4 + 7i, 4 - 7i\right\}$.

48. $f(x) = a_n(x - 2)(x - 2 + 3i)(x - 2 - 3i)$
$$f(x) = a_n(x - 2)\left(x^2 - 4x + 13\right)$$
$$f(1) = a_n(1 - 2)\left[1^2 - 4(1) + 13\right]$$
$$-10 = -10a_n$$
$$a_n = 1$$
$$f(x) = 1(x - 2)\left(x^2 - 4x + 13\right)$$
$$f(x) = x^3 - 4x^2 + 13x - 2x^2 + 8x - 26$$
$$f(x) = x^3 - 6x^2 + 21x - 26$$

49. $f(x) = a_n(x - i)(x + i)(x + 3)^2$
$$f(x) = a_n\left(x^2 + 1\right)\left(x^2 + 6x + 9\right)$$
$$f(-1) = a_n\left[(-1)^2 + 1\right]\left[(-1)^2 + 6(-1) + 9\right]$$
$$16 = 8a_n$$
$$a_n = 2$$
$$f(x) = 2\left(x^2 + 1\right)\left(x^2 + 6x + 9\right)$$
$$f(x) = 2\left(x^4 + 6x^3 + 9x^2 + x^2 + 6x + 9\right)$$
$$f(x) = 2x^4 + 12x^3 + 20x^2 + 12x + 18$$

50. $f(x) = a_n(x + 2)(x - 3)(x - 1 - 3i)(x - 1 + 3i)$
$$f(x) = a_n\left(x^2 - x - 6\right)\left(x^2 - 2x + 10\right)$$
$$f(x) = a_n\left(\begin{array}{l} x^4 - 2x^3 + 10x^2 - x^3 + \\ 2x^2 - 10x - 6x^2 + 12x - 60 \end{array}\right)$$
$$f(x) = a_n\left(x^4 - 3x^3 + 6x^2 + 2x - 60\right)$$
$$f(2) = a_n\left[(2)^4 - 3(2)^3 + 6(2)^2 + 2(2) - 60\right]$$
$$-40 = -40a_n$$
$$a_n = 1$$
$$f(x) = x^4 - 3x^3 + 6x^2 + 2x - 60$$

51. $f(x) = 2x^4 + 3x^3 + 3x - 2$
$p: \pm 1, \pm 2$
$q: \pm 1, \pm 2$
$\dfrac{p}{q}: \pm 1, \pm 2, \ \pm\dfrac{1}{2}$

$$
\begin{array}{r|rrrrr}
-2 & 2 & 3 & 0 & 3 & -2 \\
& & -4 & 2 & -4 & 2 \\
\hline
& 2 & -1 & 2 & -1 & 0
\end{array}
$$

$$2x^4 + 3x^3 + 3x - 2 = 0$$
$$(x + 2)(2x^3 - x^2 + 2x - 1) = 0$$
$$(x + 2)[x^2(2x - 1) + (2x - 1)] = 0$$
$$(x + 2)(2x - 1)(x^2 + 1) = 0$$
$$x = -2, \ x = \frac{1}{2} \text{ or } x = \pm i$$

The zeros are $-2, \ \dfrac{1}{2}, \ \pm i$.
$$f(x) = (x - i)(x + i)(x + 2)\left(x - \frac{1}{2}\right)$$

52. $g(x) = x^4 - 6x^3 + x^2 + 24x + 16$

p: ±1, ±2, ±4, ±8, ±16

q: ±1

$\dfrac{p}{q}$: ±1, ±2, ±4, ±8, ±16

$$
\begin{array}{r|rrrrr}
-1 & 1 & -6 & 1 & 24 & 16 \\
   &   & -1 & 7 & -8 & -16 \\
\hline
   & 1 & -7 & 8 & 16 & 0
\end{array}
$$

$x^4 - 6x^3 + x^2 + 24x + 16 = 0$

$(x+1)(x^3 - 7x^2 + 8x + 16) = 0$

$$
\begin{array}{r|rrrr}
-1 & 1 & -7 & 8 & 16 \\
   &   & -1 & 8 & -16 \\
\hline
   & 1 & -8 & 16 & 0
\end{array}
$$

$(x+1)^2(x^2 - 8x + 16) = 0$

$(x+1)^2(x-4)^2 = 0$

$x = -1$ or $x = 4$

$g(x) = (x+1)^2(x-4)^2$

53. 4 real zeros, one with multiplicity two

54. 3 real zeros; 2 nonreal complex zeros

55. 2 real zeros, one with multiplicity two; 2 nonreal complex zeros

56. 1 real zero; 4 nonreal complex zeros

57. $f(x) = \dfrac{2x}{x^2 - 9}$

Symmetry: $f(-x) = -\dfrac{2x}{x^2 - 9} = -f(x)$

origin symmetry

x-intercept:

$0 = \dfrac{2x}{x^2 - 9}$

$2x = 0$

$x = 0$

y-intercept: $y = \dfrac{2(0)}{0^2 - 9} = 0$

Vertical asymptote:

$x^2 - 9 = 0$

$(x-3)(x+3) = 0$

$x = 3$ and $x = -3$

Horizontal asymptote:

$n < m$, so $y = 0$

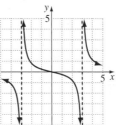

58. $g(x) = \dfrac{2x - 4}{x + 3}$

Symmetry: $g(-x) = \dfrac{-2x - 4}{x + 3}$

$g(-x) \neq g(x)$, $g(-x) \neq -g(x)$

No symmetry

x-intercept:

$2x - 4 = 0$

$x = 2$

y-intercept: $y = \dfrac{2(0) - 4}{(0) + 3} = -\dfrac{4}{3}$

Vertical asymptote:

$x + 3 = 0$

$x = -3$

Horizontal asymptote:

$n = m$, so $y = \dfrac{2}{1} = 2$

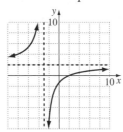

59. $h(x) = \dfrac{x^2 - 3x - 4}{x^2 - x - 6}$

Symmetry: $h(-x) = \dfrac{x^2 + 3x - 4}{x^2 + x - 6}$

$h(-x) \neq h(x), \ h(-x) \neq -h(x)$
No symmetry
x-intercepts:
$x^2 - 3x - 4 = 0$
$(x - 4)(x + 1)$
$x = 4 \quad x = -1$
y-intercept: $y = \dfrac{0^2 - 3(0) - 4}{0^2 - 0 - 6} = \dfrac{2}{3}$
Vertical asymptotes:
$x^2 - x - 6 = 0$
$(x - 3)(x + 2) = 0$
$x = 3, -2$

Horizontal asymptote:
$n = m$, so $y = \dfrac{1}{1} = 1$

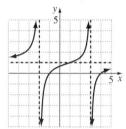

60. $r(x) = \dfrac{x^2 + 4x + 3}{(x + 2)^2}$

Symmetry: $r(-x) = \dfrac{x^2 - 4x + 3}{(-x + 2)^2}$

$r(-x) \neq r(x), \ r(-x) \neq -r(x)$
No symmetry
x-intercepts:
$x^2 + 4x + 3 = 0$
$(x + 3)(x + 1) = 0$
$x = -3, -1$
y-intercept: $y = \dfrac{0^2 + 4(0) + 3}{(0 + 2)^2} = \dfrac{3}{4}$
Vertical asymptote:
$x + 2 = 0$
$x = -2$
Horizontal asymptote:

$n = m$, so $y = \dfrac{1}{1} = 1$

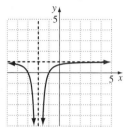

61. $y = \dfrac{x^2}{x + 1}$

Symmetry: $f(-x) = \dfrac{x^2}{-x + 1}$

$f(-x) \neq f(x), \ f(-x) \neq -f(x)$
No symmetry
x-intercept:
$x^2 = 0$
$x = 0$
y-intercept: $y = \dfrac{0^2}{0 + 1} = 0$
Vertical asymptote:
$x + 1 = 0$
$x = -1$
$n > m$, no horizontal asymptote.
Slant asymptote:
$y = x - 1 + \dfrac{1}{x + 1}$
$y = x - 1$

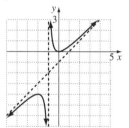

62. $y = \dfrac{x^2 + 2x - 3}{x - 3}$

Symmetry: $f(-x) = \dfrac{x^2 - 2x - 3}{-x - 3}$

$f(-x) \neq f(x), \ f(-x) \neq -f(x)$
No symmetry

x-intercepts:

$x^2 + 2x - 3 = 0$

$(x + 3)(x - 1) = 0$

$x = -3, 1$

y-intercept: $\quad y = \dfrac{0^2 + 2(0) - 3}{0 - 3} = \dfrac{-3}{-3} = 1$

Vertical asymptote:

$x - 3 = 0$

$x = 3$

Horizontal asymptote:

$n > m$, so no horizontal asymptote.

slant asymptote:

$y = x + 5 + \dfrac{12}{x - 3}$

$y = x + 5$

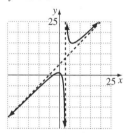

63. $\quad f(x) = \dfrac{-2x^3}{x^2 + 1}$

Symmetry: $\quad f(-x) = \dfrac{2}{x^2 + 1} = -f(x)$

Origin symmetry

x-intercept:

$-2x^3 = 0$

$x = 0$

y-intercept: $\quad y = \dfrac{-2(0)^3}{0^2 + 1} = \dfrac{0}{1} = 0$

Vertical asymptote:

$x^2 + 1 = 0$

$x^2 = -1$

No vertical asymptote.

Horizontal asymptote:

$n > m$, so no horizontal asymptote.

Slant asymptote:

$f(x) = -2x + \dfrac{2x}{x^2 + 1}$

$y = -2x$

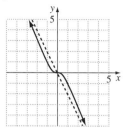

64. $\quad g(x) = \dfrac{4x^2 - 16x + 16}{2x - 3}$

Symmetry: $\quad g(-x) = \dfrac{4x^2 + 16x + 16}{-2x - 3}$

$g(-x) \neq g(x),\ g(-x) \neq -g(x)$

No symmetry

x-intercept:

$4x^2 - 16x + 16 = 0$

$4(x - 2)^2 = 0$

$x = 2$

y-intercept:

$y = \dfrac{4(0)^2 - 16(0) + 16}{2(0) - 3} = -\dfrac{16}{3}$

Vertical asymptote:

$2x - 3 = 0$

$x = \dfrac{3}{2}$

Horizontal asymptote:

$n > m$, so no horizontal asymptote.

Slant asymptote:

$g(x) = 2x - 5 + \dfrac{1}{2x - 3}$

$y = 2x - 5$

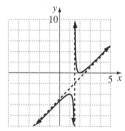

65. a. $\quad C(x) = 50,000 + 25x$

b. $\overline{C} = \dfrac{25x + 50,000}{x}$

c. $\overline{C}(50) = \dfrac{25(50) + 50,000}{50} = 1025$

When 50 calculators are manufactured, it costs \$1025 to manufacture each.

$\overline{C}(100) = \dfrac{25(100) + 50,000}{100} = 525$

When 100 calculators are manufactured, it costs \$525 to manufacture each.

$\overline{C}(1000) = \dfrac{25(1000) + 50,000}{1000} = 75$

When 1,000 calculators are manufactured, it costs \$75 to manufacture each.

$\overline{C}(100,000) = \dfrac{25(100,000) + 50,000}{100,000} = 25.5$

When 100,000 calculators are manufactured, it costs \$25.50 to manufacture each.

d. $n = m$, so $y = \dfrac{25}{1} = 25$ is the horizontal asymptote. Minimum costs will approach \$25.

66. a. $C(90) - C(50) = \dfrac{200(90)}{100 - 90} - \dfrac{200(50)}{100 - 50}$

$C(90) - C(50) = 1800 - 200$

$C(90) - C(50) = 1600$

The difference in cost of removing 90% versus 50% of the contaminants is 16 million dollars.

b. $x = 100$; No amount of money can remove 100% of the contaminants, since $C(x)$ increases without bound as x approaches 100.

67. $f(x) = \dfrac{150x + 120}{0.05x + 1}$

$n = m$, so $y = \dfrac{150}{0.05} = 3000$

The number of fish available in the pond approaches 3,000,000.

68. $P(x) = \dfrac{72,900}{100x^2 + 729}$

$n < m$ so $y = 0$

As the number of years of education increases the percentage rate of unemployment approaches zero.

69. a. $q(x) = \dfrac{1.96x + 3.14}{3.04x + 21.79}$

b. $y = \dfrac{1.96}{3.04} = 0.645$

The percentage of inmates that are in for violent crimes will approach 64.5%.

c. Answers may vary.

70. $b = ke$

$98 = k \cdot 1400$

$k = 0.07$

$b = 0.07e$

$b = 0.07(2200) = \$154$

71. $d = kt^2$

$144 = k(3)^2$

$k = 16$

$d = 16t^2$

$d = 16(10)^2 = 1,600 \text{ ft}$

72. $t = \dfrac{k}{r}$

$4 = \dfrac{k}{50}$

$k = 200$

$t = \dfrac{200}{r}$

$t = \dfrac{200}{40} = 5$ hours

73. $l = \dfrac{k}{d^2}$

$28 = \dfrac{k}{8^2}$

$k = 1792$

$l = \dfrac{1792}{d^2}$

$l = \dfrac{1792}{4^2} = 112$ decibels

74. $t = \dfrac{kc}{w}$

$10 = \dfrac{k \cdot 30}{6}$

$10 = 5h$

$h = 2$

$t = \dfrac{2c}{w}$

$t = \dfrac{2(40)}{5} = 16$ hours

75. $V = khB$

$175 = k \cdot 15 \cdot 35$

$k = \dfrac{1}{3}$

$V = \dfrac{1}{3} hB$

$V = \dfrac{1}{3} \cdot 20 \cdot 120 = 800$ ft^3

Chapter 3 Test

1. $f(x) = (x+1)^2 + 4$

vertex: $(-1, 4)$

axis of symmetry: $x = -1$

x-intercepts:

$(x+1)^2 + 4 = 0$

$x^2 + 2x + 5 = 0$

$x = \dfrac{-2 \pm \sqrt{4 - 20}}{2} = -1 \pm 2i$

no x-intercepts

y-intercept:

$f(0) = (0+1)^2 + 4 = 5$

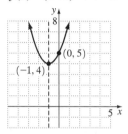

2. $f(x) = x^2 - 2x - 3$

$x = \dfrac{-b}{2a} = \dfrac{2}{2} = 1$

$f(1) = 1^2 - 2(1) - 3 = -4$

vertex: $(1, -4)$

axis of symmetry $x = 1$

x-intercepts:

$x^2 - 2x - 3 = 0$

$(x - 3)(x + 1) = 0$

$x = 3$ or $x = -1$

y-intercept:

$f(0) = 0^2 - 2(0) - 3 = -3$

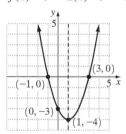

3. $f(x) = -2x^2 + 12x - 16$

Since the coefficient of x^2 is negative, the graph of $f(x)$ opens down and $f(x)$ has a maximum point.

$$x = \frac{-12}{2(-2)} = 3$$

$$f(3) = -2(3)^2 + 12(3) - 16$$
$$= -18 + 36 - 16$$
$$= 2$$

maximum point: (3, 2)

4. $f(x) = -x^2 + 46x - 360$

$$x = -\frac{b}{2a} = \frac{-46}{-2} = 23$$

23 VCRs will maximize profit.

$$f(23) = -(23)^2 + 46(23) - 360 = 169$$

Maximum daily profit = $16,900.

5. a. $\qquad f(x) = x^3 - 5x^2 - 4x + 20$

$$x^3 - 5x^2 - 4x + 20 = 0$$
$$x^2(x - 5) - 4(x - 5) = 0$$
$$(x - 5)(x - 2)(x + 2) = 0$$
$$x = 5, 2, -2$$

The solution set is {5, 2, –2}.

b. The degree of the polynomial is odd and the leading coefficient is positive. Thus the graph falls to the left and rises to the right.

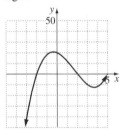

6. $f(x) = x^5 - x$

Since the degree of the polynomial is odd and the leading coefficient is positive, the graph of *f* should fall to the left and rise to the right. The *x*-intercepts should be –1 and 1.

7. a. The integral root appears to be 2.

b.
$$\begin{array}{r|rrrr}
2 & 6 & -19 & 16 & -4 \\
  &   & 12 & -14 & 4 \\
\hline
  & 6 & -7 & 2 & 0
\end{array}$$

$$6x^2 - 7x + 2 = 0$$
$$(3x - 2)(2x - 1) = 0$$
$$x = \frac{2}{3} \text{ or } x = \frac{1}{2}$$

The other two roots are $\frac{1}{2}$ and $\frac{2}{3}$.

8. $2x^3 + 11x^2 - 7x - 6 = 0$

p: ±1, ±2, ±3, ±6

q: ±1, ±2

$\dfrac{p}{q}$: ±1, ±2, ±3, ±6, ±$\dfrac{1}{2}$, ±$\dfrac{3}{2}$

9. $f(x) = 3x^5 - 2x^4 - 2x^2 + x - 1$

$f(x)$ has 3 sign variations.

$f(-x) = -3x^5 - 2x^4 - 2x^2 - x - 1$

$f(-x)$ has no sign variations.

There are 3 or 1 positive real solutions and no negative real solutions.

10. $x^3 + 6x^2 - x - 30 = 0$

p: ±1, ±2, ±3, ±5, ±6, ±10, ±15, ±30

q: ±1

$\dfrac{p}{q}$: ±1, ±2, ±3, ±5, ±6, ±10, ±15, ±30

$$\begin{array}{r|rrrr}
-5 & 1 & 6 & -1 & -30 \\
   &   & -5 & -5 & 30 \\
\hline
   & 1 & 1 & -6 & 0
\end{array}$$

$$x^3 + 6x^2 - x - 30 = 0$$
$$(x + 5)(x^2 + x - 6) = 0$$
$$(x + 5)(x + 3)(x - 2) = 0$$
$$x = -5 \text{ or } x = -3 \text{ or } x = 2$$

The solution set is {–5, –3, 2}.

11. $f(x) = 2x^4 - x^3 - 13x^2 + 5x + 15$

   a. p: $\pm 1, \pm 3, \pm 5, \pm 15$

      q: $\pm 1, \pm 2$

      $\dfrac{p}{q}$: $\pm 1, \pm 3, \pm 5, \pm 15, \pm \dfrac{1}{2}, \pm \dfrac{3}{2}, \pm \dfrac{5}{2}, \pm \dfrac{15}{2}$

   b.

$$
\begin{array}{r|rrrrr}
-1 & 2 & -1 & -13 & 5 & 15 \\
   &   & -2 & 3 & 10 & -15 \\
\hline
   & 2 & -3 & -10 & 15 & 0
\end{array}
$$

$$(x+1)(2x^3 - 3x^2 - 10x + 15) = 0$$
$$(x+1)[x^2(2x-3) - 5(2x-3)] = 0$$
$$(x+1)(2x-3)\left(x^2 - 5\right) = 0$$

$$x = -1 \text{ or } x = \frac{3}{2} \text{ or } x = \pm\sqrt{5}$$

The solution set is $\left\{-1, \dfrac{3}{2}, \sqrt{5}, -\sqrt{5}\right\}$.

12. $3x^4 + 4x^3 - 7x^2 - 2x - 3 = 0$

$$
\begin{array}{r|rrrrr}
-3 & 3 & 4 & -7 & -2 & -3 \\
   &   & -9 & 15 & -24 & 78 \\
\hline
   & 3 & -5 & 8 & -26 & 75
\end{array}
$$

-3 is a lower bound.

$$
\begin{array}{r|rrrrr}
2 & 3 & 4 & -7 & -2 & -3 \\
  &   & 6 & 20 & 26 & 48 \\
\hline
  & 3 & 10 & 13 & 24 & 45
\end{array}
$$

2 is an upper bound.

13. $(x - 1 + i)(x - 1 - i) = x^2 - 2x + 2$

$$
\begin{array}{r}
x^2 - 5x + 6 \\
x^2 - 2x + 2 \overline{\smash{\big)}\, x^4 - 7x^3 + 18x^2 - 22x + 12} \\
\underline{x^4 - 2x^3 + 2x^2} \\
-5x^3 + 16x^2 - 22x \\
\underline{-5x^3 + 10x^2 - 10x} \\
6x^2 - 12x + 12 \\
\underline{6x^2 - 12x + 12} \\
0
\end{array}
$$

$$x^2 - 5x + 6 = 0$$
$$(x - 3)(x - 2) = 0$$
$$x = 3 \text{ or } x = 2$$

The solution set is $\{2, 3, 1 + i, 1 - i\}$.

14. $f(x)$ has zeros at -2 and 1. The zero at -2 has multiplicity of 2.

$$x^3 + 3x^2 - 4 = (x - 1)(x + 2)^2$$

15. $f(x) = \dfrac{x}{x^2 - 16}$

domain: $\{x \mid x \neq 4, x \neq -4\}$

Symmetry: $f(-x) = \dfrac{-x}{x^2 - 16} = -f(x)$

y-axis symmetry

x-intercept: $x = 0$

y-intercept: $y = \dfrac{0}{0^2 - 16} = 0$

Vertical asymptotes:

$$x^2 - 16 = 0$$
$$(x - 4)(x + 4) = 0$$
$$x = 4, -4$$

Horizontal asymptote:

$n < m$, so $y = 0$ is the horizontal asymptote.

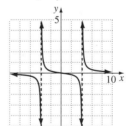

16. $f(x) = \dfrac{x^2 - 9}{x - 2}$

domain: $\{x \mid x \neq 2\}$

Symmetry: $f(-x) = \dfrac{x^2 - 9}{-x - 2}$

$f(-x) \neq f(x), f(-x) \neq -f(x)$

No symmetry

x-intercepts:

$x^2 - 9 = 0$

$(x - 3)(x + 3) = 0$

$x = 3, -3$

y-intercept: $y = \dfrac{0^2 - 9}{0 - 2} = \dfrac{9}{2}$

Vertical asymptote:

$x - 2 = 0$

$x = 2$

Horizontal asymptote:

$n > m$, so no horizontal asymptote exists.

Slant asymptote: $f(x) = x + 2 - \dfrac{5}{x - 2}$

$y = x + 2$

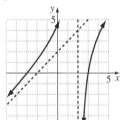

17. $f(x) = \dfrac{x + 1}{x^2 + 2x - 3}$

$x^2 + 2x - 3 = (x + 3)(x - 1)$

domain: $\{x \mid x = -3, x \neq 1\}$

Symmetry: $f(-x) = \dfrac{-x + 1}{x^2 - 2x - 3}$

$f(-x) \neq f(x), f(-x) \neq -f(x)$

No symmetry

x-intercept:

$x + 1 = 0$

$x = -1$

y-intercept: $y = \dfrac{0 + 1}{0^2 + 2(0) - 3} = -\dfrac{1}{3}$

Vertical asymptotes:

$x^2 + 2x - 3 = 0$

$(x + 3)(x - 1) = 0$

$x - 3, 1$

Horizontal asymptote:

$n < m$, so $y = 0$ is the horizontal asymptote.

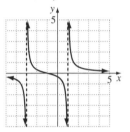

18. $f(x) = \dfrac{4x^2}{x^2 + 3}$

domain: all real numbers

Symmetry: $f(-x) = \dfrac{4x^2}{x^2 + 3} = f(x)$

y-axis symmetry

x-intercept:

$4x^2 = 0$

$x = 0$

y-intercept: $y = \dfrac{4(0)^2}{0^2 + 3} = 0$

Vertical asymptote:

$x^2 + 3 = 0$

$x^2 = -3$

No vertical asymptote.

Horizontal asymptote:

$n = m$, so $y = \dfrac{4}{1} = 4$ is the horizontal

asymptote.

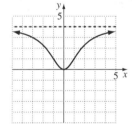

19. a. When $x = 5$, $y = .9$

After 5 learning tries, 90% of the responses were correct.

b. When $x = 11$, $y = .95$

After 5 learning tries, 95% of the responses were correct.

c. $y = .9/.9 = 1$

As the number of learning tries increases, the correct responses approaches 100%.

20. $I = \dfrac{k}{d^2}$

$20 = \dfrac{k}{d^2}$

$k = 4500$

$I = \dfrac{4500}{d^2}$

$I = \dfrac{4500}{10^2} = 45$ foot-candles

Cumulative Review Exercises (Chapters P–3)

1. $\dfrac{1}{2-\sqrt{3}} \cdot \dfrac{2+\sqrt{3}}{2+\sqrt{3}} = \dfrac{2+\sqrt{3}}{4-3} = 2+\sqrt{3}$

2. $3\left(x^2 - 3x + 1\right) - 2\left(3x^2 + x - 4\right)$

$= 3x^2 - 9x + 3 - 6x^2 - 2x + 8$

$= -3x^2 - 11x + 11$

3. $3\sqrt{8} + 5\sqrt{50} - 4\sqrt{32}$

$= 3\sqrt{4 \cdot 2} + 5\sqrt{25 \cdot 2} - 4\sqrt{16 \cdot 2}$

$= 3 \cdot 2\sqrt{2} + 5 \cdot 5\sqrt{2} - 4 \cdot 4\sqrt{2}$

$= 6\sqrt{2} + 25\sqrt{2} - 16\sqrt{2}$

$= 15\sqrt{2}$

4. $x^7 - x^5 = x^5\left(x^2 - 1\right)$

$= x^5(x-1)(x+1)$

5. $|2x - 1| = 3$

$2x - 1 = 3$

$2x = 4$

$x = 2$

$2x - 1 = -3$

$2x = -2$

$x = -1$

The solution set is $\{2, -1\}$.

6. $3x^2 - 5x + 1 = 0$

$x = \dfrac{5 \pm \sqrt{25 - 12}}{6} = \dfrac{5 \pm \sqrt{13}}{6}$

The solution set is $\left\{ \dfrac{5 + \sqrt{13}}{6}, \dfrac{5 - \sqrt{13}}{6} \right\}$.

7. $9 + \dfrac{3}{x} = \dfrac{2}{x^2}$

$9x^2 + 3x = 2$

$9x^2 + 3x - 2 = 0$

$(3x - 1)(3x + 2) = 0$

$3x - 1 = 0 \qquad 3x + 2 = 0$

$x = \dfrac{1}{3} \qquad$ or $\qquad x = -\dfrac{2}{3}$

The solution set is $\left\{ \dfrac{1}{3}, -\dfrac{2}{3} \right\}$.

8. $x^3 + 2x^2 - 5x - 6 = 0$

$p: \pm 1, \pm 2, \pm 3, \pm 6$

$q: \pm 1$

$\dfrac{p}{q}: \pm 1, \pm 2, \pm 3, \pm 6$

$$
\begin{array}{r|rrrr}
-3 & 1 & 2 & -5 & -6 \\
   &   & -3 & 3 & 6 \\
\hline
   & 1 & -1 & -2 & 0
\end{array}
$$

$x^3 + 2x^2 - 5x - 6 = 0$

$(x + 3)(x^2 - x - 2) = 0$

$(x + 3)(x + 1)(x - 2) = 0$

$x = -3$ or $x = -1$ or $x = 2$

The solution set is $\{-3, -1, 2\}$.

9. $|2x - 5| > 3$

$2x - 5 > 3$

$\quad 2x > 8$

$\qquad x > 4$

$2x - 5 < -3$

$\quad 2x < 2$

$\qquad x < 1$

$(-\infty,\ 1)$ or $(4,\ \infty)$

10. $\qquad 3x^2 > 2x + 5$

$3x^2 - 2x - 5 > 0$

$3x^2 - 2x - 5 = 0$

$(3x - 5)(x + 1) = 0$

$x = \dfrac{5}{3}$ or $x = -1$

Test intervals are $(-\infty, -1)$,

$\left(-1, \dfrac{5}{3}\right), \left(\dfrac{5}{3}, \infty\right)$.

Testing points, the solution is

$(-\infty,\ -1)$ or $\left(\dfrac{5}{3},\ \infty\right)$.

11. $\qquad x^2 + y^2 - 2x + 4y - 4 = 0$

$x^2 - 2x + 1 + y^2 + 4y + 4 = 4 + 1 + 4$

$\qquad (x - 1)^2 + (y + 2)^2 = 9$

center: $(1, -2)$

radius: 3

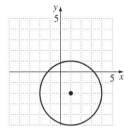

12. $\qquad V = C(1 - t)$

$\dfrac{V}{C} = 1 - t$

$\dfrac{V}{C} - 1 = -t$

$\qquad t = 1 - \dfrac{V}{C}$

13. $f(x) = \sqrt{45 - 9x}$

$45 - 9x \geq 0$

$45 \geq 9x$

$5 \geq x$

Domain: $(-\infty, 5]$

14. $(f - g)(x) = x^2 + 2x - 5 - (4x - 1)$

$\qquad\qquad = x^2 + 2x - 5 - 4x + 1$

$\qquad\qquad = x^2 - 2x - 4$

15. $(f \circ g)(x) = (4x - 1)^2 + 2(4x - 1) - 5$

$\qquad\qquad = 16x^2 - 8x + 1 + 8x - 2 - 5$

$\qquad\qquad = 16x^2 - 6$

16. $g(f(-3))$

$f(-3) = (-3)^2 + 2(-3) - 5$

$\qquad = 9 - 6 - 5 = -2$

$g(-2) = 4(-2) - 1 = -8 - 1 = -9$

17. $f(x) = x^3 - 4x^2 - x + 4$

a. $x^3 - 4x^2 - x + 4 = 0$

$x^2(x-4) - (x-4) = 0$

$\left(x^2 - 1\right)(x-4) = 0$

$(x-1)(x+1)(x-4) = 0$

$x = -1, 1, 4$

The solution set is $\{-1, 1, 4\}$.

b. The graph falls to the left and rises to the right.

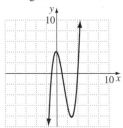

18. $f(x) = x^2 + 2x - 8$

$x = \dfrac{-b}{2a} = \dfrac{-2}{2} = -1$

$f(-1) = (-1)^2 + 2(-1) - 8$

$ = 1 - 2 - 8 = -9$

vertex: $(-1, -9)$

x-intercepts:

$x^2 + 2x - 8 = 0$

$(x+4)(x-2) = 0$

$x = -4$ or $x = 2$

y-intercept: $f(0) = -8$

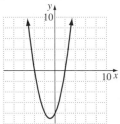

19. $f(x) = x^2(x-3)$

zeros: $x = 0$ (multiplicity 2) and $x = 3$

y-intercept: $y = 0$

$f(x) = x^3 - 3x^2$

$n = 3$, $a_n = 0$ so the graph falls to the left and rises to the right.

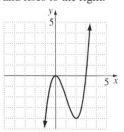

20. $f(x) = \dfrac{x-1}{x-2}$

vertical asymptote: $x = 2$

horizontal asymptote: $y = 1$

x-intercept: $x = 1$

y-intercept: $y = \dfrac{1}{2}$

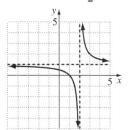

Chapter 4

Section 4.1

Check Point Exercises

1. Substitute 60 for x and evaluate the function at 60. $f(60) = 13.49(0.967)^{-60} - 1 \approx 1$
   Thus, one O-ring is expected to fail at a temperature of $60°F$.

2. Begin by setting up a table of coordinates.

x	$f(x) = 3^x$
-3	$f(-3) = 3^{-3} = \frac{1}{27}$
-2	$f(-2) = 3^{-2} = \frac{1}{9}$
-1	$f(-1) = 3^{-1} = \frac{1}{3}$
0	$f(0) = 3^0 = 1$
1	$f(1) = 3^1 = 3$
2	$f(2) = 3^2 = 9$
3	$f(3) = 3^3 = 27$

   Plot these points, connecting them with a continuous curve.

   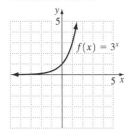

3. Note that the function $g(x) = 3^{x-1}$ has the general form $g(x) = b^{x+c}$ where $c = -1$. Because $c < 0$, we graph $g(x) = 3^{x-1}$ by shifting the graph of $f(x) = 3^x$ one unit to the right. Construct a table showing some of the coordinates for f and g.

x	$f(x) = 3^x$	$g(x) = 3^{x-1}$
-2	$3^{-2} = \frac{1}{9}$	$3^{-2-1} = 3^{-3} = \frac{1}{27}$
-1	$3^{-1} = \frac{1}{3}$	$3^{-1-1} = 3^{-2} = \frac{1}{9}$
0	$3^0 = 1$	$3^{0-1} = 3^{-1} = \frac{1}{3}$
1	$3^1 = 3$	$3^{1-1} = 3^0 = 1$
2	$3^2 = 9$	$3^{2-1} = 3^1 = 3$

   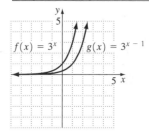

4. Note that the function $g(x) = 2^x + 1$ has the general form $g(x) = b^x + c$ where $c = 1$. Because $c > 0$, we graph $g(x) = 2^x + 1$ by shifting the graph of $f(x) = 2^x$ up one unit. Construct a table showing some of the coordinates for f and g.

x	$f(x) - 2^x$	$g(x) = 2^x + 1$
-2	$2^{-2} = \frac{1}{4}$	$2^{-2} + 1 = \frac{1}{4} + 1 = \frac{5}{4}$
-1	$2^{-1} = \frac{1}{2}$	$2^{-1} + 1 = \frac{1}{2} + 1 = \frac{3}{2}$
0	$2^0 = 1$	$2^0 + 1 = 1 + 1 = 2$
1	$2^1 = 2$	$2^1 + 1 = 2 + 1 = 3$
2	$2^2 = 4$	$2^2 + 1 = 4 + 1 = 5$

   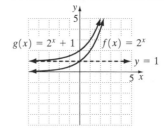

5. Because 2050 is 50 years after 2000, substitute 50 for x.

$$f(50) = 6e^{0.013(50)} = 6e^{0.65} \approx 11.49$$

The world population is 2050 will be approximately 11.49 billion.

6. a. $A = 10,000\left(1 + \dfrac{0.08}{4}\right)^{4 \cdot 5} \approx 14,859.47$

The balance in this account after 5 years is \$14,859.47.

b. $A = 10,000e^{0.08(5)} \approx 14,918.25$

The balance in this account after 5 years is \$14,918.25.

Exercise Set 4.1

1. $2^{3.4} \approx 10.556$

3. $3^{\sqrt{5}} \approx 11.665$

5. $4^{-1.5} = 0.125$

7. $e^{2.3} \approx 9.974$

9. $e^{-0.95} \approx 0.387$

11.

x	$f(x) = 4^x$
-2	$4^{-2} = \frac{1}{16}$
-1	$4^{-1} = \frac{1}{4}$
0	$4^0 = 1$
1	$4^1 = 4$
2	$4^2 = 16$

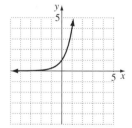

13.

x	$g(x) = \left(\frac{3}{2}\right)^x$
-2	$\left(\frac{3}{2}\right)^{-2} = \frac{4}{9}$
-1	$\left(\frac{3}{2}\right)^{-1} = \frac{2}{3}$
0	$\left(\frac{3}{2}\right)^0 = 1$
1	$\left(\frac{3}{2}\right)^1 = \frac{3}{2}$
2	$\left(\frac{3}{2}\right)^2 = \frac{9}{4}$

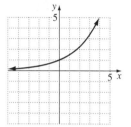

15.

x	$h(x) = \left(\frac{1}{2}\right)^x$
-2	$\left(\frac{1}{2}\right)^{-2} = 4$
-1	$\left(\frac{1}{2}\right)^{-1} = 2$
0	$\left(\frac{1}{2}\right)^0 = 1$
1	$\left(\frac{1}{2}\right)^1 = \frac{1}{2}$
2	$\left(\frac{1}{2}\right)^2 = \frac{1}{4}$

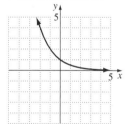

17.

x	$f(x) = (0.6)^x$
-2	$(0.6)^{-2} = 2.\overline{7}$
-1	$(0.6)^{-1} = 1.\overline{6}$
0	$(0.6)^0 = 1$
1	$(0.6)^1 = 0.6$
2	$(0.6)^2 = 0.36$

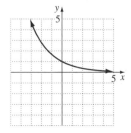

19. This is the graph of $f(x) = 3^x$ reflected about the *x*-axis and about the *y*-axis, so the function is $H(x) = -3^{-x}$.

21. This is the graph of $f(x) = 3^x$ reflected about the *x*-axis, so the function is $F(x) = -3^x$.

23. This is the graph of $f(x) = 3^x$ shifted one unit downward, so the function is $h(x) = 3^x - 1$.

25. The graph of $g(x) = 2^{x+!}$ can be obtained by shifting the graph of $f(x) = 2^x$ one unit to the left.

x	$g(x) = 2^{x+1}$
-2	$2^{-2+1} = 2^{-1} = \frac{1}{2}$
-1	$2^{-1+1} = 2^0 = 1$
0	$2^{0+1} = 2^1 = 2$
1	$2^{1+1} = 2^2 = 4$
2	$2^{2+1} = 2^3 = 8$

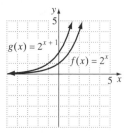

27. The graph of $g(x) = 2^x - 1$ can be obtained by shifting the graph of $f(x) = 2^x$ downward one unit.

x	$g(x) = 2^x - 1$
-2	$2^{-2} - 1 = \frac{1}{4} - 1 = -\frac{3}{4}$
-1	$2^{-1} - 1 = \frac{1}{2} - 1 = -\frac{1}{2}$
0	$2^0 - 1 = 1 - 1 = 0$
1	$2^1 - 1 = 2 - 1 = 1$
2	$2^2 - 1 = 4 - 1 = 3$

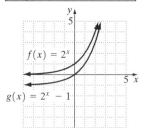

29. The graph of $h(x) = 2^{x+1} - 1$ can be obtained by shifting the graph of $f(x) = 2^x$ one unit to the left and one unit downward.

x	$h(x) = 2^{x+1} - 1$
-2	$2^{-2+1} - 1 = 2^{-1} - 1 = \frac{1}{2} - 1 = -\frac{1}{2}$
-1	$2^{-1+1} - 1 = 2^0 - 1 = 1 - 1 = 0$
0	$2^{0+1} - 1 = 2^1 - 1 = 2 - 1 = 1$
1	$2^{1+1} - 1 = 2^2 - 1 = 4 - 1 = 3$
2	$2^{2+1} - 1 = 2^3 - 1 = 8 - 1 = 7$

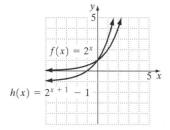

31. The graph of $g(x) = -2^x$ can be obtained by reflecting the graph of $f(x) = 2^x$ about the x-axis.

x	$g(x) = -2^x$
-2	$-2^{-2} = -\frac{1}{4}$
-1	$-2^{-1} = -\frac{1}{2}$
0	$-2^0 = -1$
1	$-2^1 = -2$
2	$-2^2 = -4$

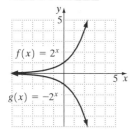

33. The graph of $g(x) = 2 \cdot 2^x$ can be obtained by vertically stretching the graph of

$f(x) = 2^x$ by a factor of two.

x	$g(x) = 2 \cdot 2^x$
-2	$2 \cdot 2^{-2} = 2 \cdot \frac{1}{4} = \frac{1}{2}$
-1	$2 \cdot 2^{-1} = 2 \cdot \frac{1}{2} = 1$
0	$2 \cdot 2^0 = 2 \cdot 1 = 2$
1	$2 \cdot 2^1 = 2 \cdot 2 = 4$
2	$2 \cdot 2^2 = 2 \cdot 4 = 8$

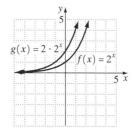

35. The graph of $g(x)$ can be obtained by reflecting $f(x)$ about the y-axis.

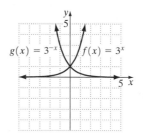

37. The graph of $g(x)$ can be obtained by horizontally stretching $f(x)$.

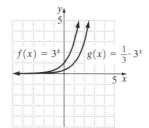

39. The graph of $g(x)$ can be obtained by moving the graph of $f(x)$ one space to the right and one space up.

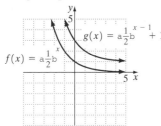

41. a. $A = 10,000\left(1 + \dfrac{0.055}{2}\right)^{2(5)}$

$\approx 13,116.51$

b. $A = 10,000\left(1 + \dfrac{0.055}{4}\right)^{4(5)}$

$\approx \$13,140.67$

c. $A = 10,000\left(1 + \dfrac{0.055}{12}\right)^{12(5)}$

$\approx 13,157.04$

d. $A = 10,000e^{0.055(5)}$

$\approx 13,165.31$

43. $A = 12,000\left(1 + \dfrac{0.07}{12}\right)^{12(3)}$

$\approx 14,795.11$ (7% yield)

$A = 12,000e^{0.0685(3)}$

$\approx 14,737.67$ (6.85% yield)

Investing \$12,000 for 3 years at 7% compounded monthly yields the greatest return.

45. a. $f(0) = 67.38(1.026)^0 = 67.38$

67.38 million

b. $f(27) = 67.38(1.026)^{27}$

≈ 134.7441 million

c. $f(54) = 67.38(1.026)^{54}$

≈ 269.4564 million

d. $f(81) = 67.38(1.026)^{81}$

≈ 538.8492 million

e. The population appears to double every 27 years.

47. $f(10) = \dfrac{400}{1 + 399(.67)^{10}} \approx 48$

At ten minutes after 8:00, 48 have heard the rumor.

49. $\$65,000(1 + 0.06)^{10} \approx 116,405.10$

The house will be worth \$116,405.10.

51. $2^{1.7} \approx 3.249009585$

$2^{1.73} \approx 3.317278183$

$2^{1.732} \approx 3.321880096$

$2^{1.73205} \approx 3.321995226$

$2^{1.7320508} \approx 3.321997068$

$2^{\sqrt{3}} \approx 3.321997085$

The closer the exponent is to $\sqrt{3}$, the closer the value is to $2^{\sqrt{3}}$.

53. $2006 - 1992 = 14$

$f(14) = 36.1e^{0.113(14)} \approx 175.6$ million

In the year 2006, approximately 175.6 million Americans will be enrolled in HMOs.

55. a. $f(0) = 80e^{-0.5(0)} + 20$

$= 80e^0 + 20$

$= 80(1) + 20$

$= 100$

100% of the material is remembered at the moment it is first learned.

b. $f(1) = 80e^{-0.5(1)} + 20 \approx 68.5$

68.5% of the material is remembered 1 week after it is first learned.

c. $f(4) = 80e^{-0.5(4)} + 20 \approx 30.8$

30.8% of the material is remembered 4 week after it is first learned.

d. $f(52) = 80e^{-0.5(52)} + 20 \approx 20$

20% of the material is remembered 1 year after it is first learned.

57. a. $N(0) = \dfrac{30,000}{1 + 20e^{-1.5(0)}} = 1428.57$

About 1429 people became ill.

b. $N(3) = \dfrac{30,000}{1 + 20e^{-1.5(3)}} \approx 24,546.30$

About 24,546 people were ill by the end of the third week.

c. The growth of the epidemic is limited by the size of the population. The horizontal asymptote shows that the epidemic will grow to the limiting size of the population, so that the entire population will eventually become ill.

59.–63. Answers may vary.

65.

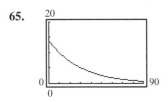

When $x = 31$, $y \approx 3.77$. NASA would not have launched the *Challenger*, since nearly 4 O-rings are expected to fail.

67. a.

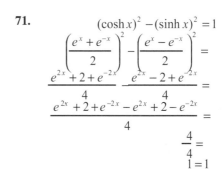

b.

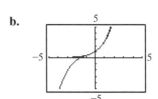

c.

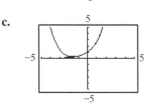

d. Answers may vary.

69. $y = 3^x$ is (d). y increases as x increases, but not as quickly as $y = 5^x$. $y = 5^x$ is (c).

$y = \left(\frac{1}{3}\right)^x$ is (a). $y = \left(\frac{1}{3}\right)^x$ is the same as $y = 3^{-x}$, so it is (d) reflected about the y-axis. $y = \left(\frac{1}{5}\right)^x$ is (b). $y = \left(\frac{1}{5}\right)^x$ is the same as $y = 5^{-x}$, so it is (c) reflected about the y-axis.

71.
$$(\cosh x)^2 - (\sinh x)^2 = 1$$
$$\left(\frac{e^x + e^{-x}}{2}\right)^2 - \left(\frac{e^x - e^{-x}}{2}\right)^2 =$$
$$\frac{e^{2x} + 2 + e^{-2x}}{4} - \frac{e^{2x} - 2 + e^{-2x}}{4} =$$
$$\frac{e^{2x} + 2 + e^{-2x} - e^{2x} + 2 - e^{-2x}}{4} =$$
$$\frac{4}{4} =$$
$$1 = 1$$

Section 4.2

Check Point Exercises

1. a. $3 = \log_7 x$ means $7^3 = x$.

b. $2 = \log_b 25$ means $b^2 = 25$.

c. $\log_4 26 = y$ means $4^y = 26$.

2. a. $2^5 = x$ means $5 = \log_2 x$.

b. $b^3 = 27$ means $3 = \log_b 27$.

c. $e^y = 33$ means $y = \log_e 33$.

3. a. Question: 10 to what power gives 100?
$\log_{10} 100 = 2$ because $10^2 = 100$.

b. Question: 3 to what power gives 3?
$\log_3 3 = 1$ because $3^1 = 3$.

c. Question: 36 to what power gives 6?
$\log_{36} 6 = \dfrac{1}{2}$ because $36^{\frac{1}{2}} = \sqrt{36} = 6$

4. a. Because $\log_b b = 1$, we conclude
$\log_9 9 = 1$.

b. Because $\log_b 1 = 0$, we conclude
$\log_8 1 = 0$.

5. a. Because $\log_b b^x = x$, we conclude
$\log_7 7^8 = 8$.

b. Because $b^{\log_b x} = x$, we conclude
$3^{\log_3 17} = 17$.

6. First, set up a table of coordinates for
$f(x) = 3^x$.

x	-2	-1	0	1	2	3
$f(x) = 3^x$	$\frac{1}{9}$	$\frac{1}{3}$	1	3	9	27

Reversing these coordinates gives the
coordinates for the inverse function
$g(x) = \log_3 x$.

x	$\frac{1}{9}$	$\frac{1}{3}$	1	3	9	27
$g(x) = \log_3 x$	-2	-1	0	1	2	3

The graph of the inverse can also be drawn
by reflecting the graph of $f(x) = 3^x$ about

the line $y = x$.

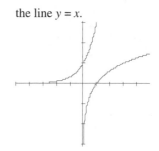

7. The domain of h consists of all x for which
$x - 5 > 0$. Solving this inequality for x, we
obtain $x > 5$. Thus, the domain of h is
$(5, \infty)$.

8. Substitute the boy's age, 10, for x and
evaluate the function at 10.
$f(10) = 29 + 48.8 \ \log(10 + 1)$
$\qquad = 29 + 48.8 \ \log(11)$
$\qquad \approx 80$
Thus, a 10-year-old boy is approximately
80% of his adult height.

9. Because $I = 10,000 \ I_0$,
$R = \log \dfrac{10,000 I_0}{I_0}$
$\quad = \log 10,000$
$\quad = 4$
The earthquake registered 4.0 on the Richter
scale.

10. a. The domain of f consists of all x for
which $4 - x > 0$. Solving this inequality
for x, we obtain $x < 4$. Thus, the
domain of f is $(-\infty, 4)$

b. The domain of g consists of all x for
which $x^2 > 0$. Solving this inequality
for x, we obtain $x < 0$ or $x > 0$. Thus the
domain of g is $(-\infty, 0)$ or $(0, \infty)$.

11. a. Because $\ln e^x = x$, we conclude
$\ln e^{25x} = 25x$.

b. Because $e^{\ln x} = x$, we conclude
$e^{\ln \sqrt{x}} = \sqrt{x}.$

12. Substitute 197 for P, the population in thousands. $W = 0.35 \ln 197 + 2.74 \approx 4.6$ The average walking speed in Jackson, Mississippi is approximately 4.6 feet per second.

Exercise Set 4.2

1. $2^4 = 16$

3. $3^2 = x$

5. $b^5 = 32$

7. $6^y = 216$

9. $\log_2 8 = 3$

11. $\log_2 \dfrac{1}{16} = -4$

13. $\log_8 2 = \dfrac{1}{3}$

15. $\log_{13} x = 2$

17. $\log_b 1000 = 3$

19. $\log_7 200 = y$

21. $\log_4 16 = 2$ because $4^2 = 16$.

23. $\log_2 64 = 6$ because $2^6 = 64$.

25. $\log_7 \sqrt{7} = \dfrac{1}{2}$ because $7^{\frac{1}{2}} = \sqrt{7}$.

27. $\log_2 \dfrac{1}{8} = -3$ because $2^{-3} = \dfrac{1}{8}$.

29. $\log_{64} 8 = \dfrac{1}{2}$ because $64^{\frac{1}{2}} = \sqrt{64} = 8$.

31. Because $\log_b b = 1$, we conclude
$\log_5 5 = 1.$

33. Because $\log_b 1 = 0$, we conclude
$\log_4 1 = 0.$

35. Because $\log_b b^x = x$, we conclude
$\log_5 5^7 = 7.$

37. Because $b^{\log_b x} = x$, we conclude
$8^{\log_8 19} = 19.$

39. First, set up a table of coordinates for
$f(x) = 4^x.$

x	-2	-1	0	1	2	3
$f(x) = 4x$	$\frac{1}{16}$	$\frac{1}{4}$	1	4	16	64

Reversing these coordinates gives the coordinates for the inverse function $g(x) = \log_4 x.$

x	$\frac{1}{16}$	$\frac{1}{4}$	1	4	16	64
$g(x) = \log_{4x}$	-2	-1	0	1	2	3

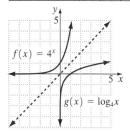

41. First, set up a table of coordinates for
$f(x) = \left(\dfrac{1}{2}\right)^x.$

x	-2	-1	0	1	2	3
$f(x) = \left(\frac{1}{2}\right)^x$	4	2	1	$\frac{1}{2}$	$\frac{1}{4}$	$\frac{1}{8}$

Reversing these coordinates gives the coordinates for the inverse function $g(x) = \log_{1/2} x.$

x	4	2	1	$\frac{1}{2}$	$\frac{1}{4}$	$\frac{1}{8}$
$g(x) = \log_{1/2} x$	-2	-1	0	1	2	3

51.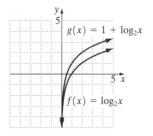

x-intercept: (0.5,0)
vertical asymptote: $x = 0$

53.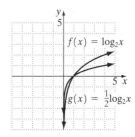

x-intercept: (1,0)
vertical asymptote: $x = 0$

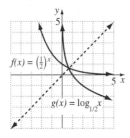

43. This is the graph of $f(x) = \log_3 x$ reflected about the x-axis and shifted up one unit, so the function is $H(x) = 1 - \log^x$.

45. This is the graph of $f(x) = \log_3 x$ shifted down one unit, so the function is $h(x) = \log_3 x - 1$.

47. This is the graph of $f(x) = \log_3 x$ shifted right one unit, so the function is $g(x) = \log_3(x - 1)$.

49.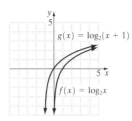

x-intercept: (0,0)
vertical asymptote: $x = -1$

55. The domain of f consists of all x for which $x + 4 > 0$. Solving this inequality for x, we obtain $x > -4$. Thus, the domain of f is $(-4, \infty)$.

57. The domain of f consists of all x for which $2 - x > 0$. Solving this inequality for x, we obtain $x < 2$. Thus, the domain of f is $(-\infty, 2)$.

59. The domain of f consists of all x for which $(x - 2)^2 > 0$. Solving this inequality for x, we obtain $x < 2$ or $x > 2$. Thus, the domain of f is $(-\infty, 2)$ or $(2, -\infty)$.

61. $\log 100 = \log_{10} 100 = 2$ because $10^2 = 100$.

63. Because $\log 10^x = x$, we conclude $\log 10^7 = 7$.

65. Because $10^{\log x} = x$, we conclude $10^{\log 33} = 33$.

67. $\ln 1 = 0$ because $e^0 = 1$.

69. Because $\ln e^x = x$, we conclude $\ln e^6 = 6$.

71. $\ln \dfrac{1}{e^6} = \ln e^{-6}$

Because $\ln e^x = x$ we conclude

$\ln e^{-6} = -6$, so $\ln \dfrac{1}{e^6} = -6$.

73. Because $e^{\ln x} = x$, we conclude $e^{\ln 125} = 125$.

75. Because $\ln e^x = x$, we conclude $\ln e^{9x} = 9x$.

77. Because $e^{\ln x} = x$, we conclude $e^{\ln 5x^2} = 5x^2$.

79. Because $10^{\log x} = x$, we conclude $10^{\log \sqrt{x}} = \sqrt{x}$.

81. $f(13) = 62 + 35\log(13-4) \approx 95.4$
She is approximately 95.4% of her adult height.

83. $f(16) = 2.05 + 1.3\ln(16) \approx 5.65$ billion
Approximately \$5.65 billion was spent in 2000.

85. $D = 10\log\left[10^{12}(6.3 \times 10^6)\right] \approx 188$

Yes, the sound can rupture the human eardrum.

87. a. $f(0) = 88 - 15\ln(0 + 1) = 88$
The average score on the original exam was 88.

    b. $f(2) = 88 - 15\ln(2 + 1) = 71.5$
$f(4) = 88 - 15\ln(4 + 1) = 63.9$

$f(6) = 88 - 15\ln(6 + 1) = 58.8$
$f(8) = 88 - 15\ln(8 + 1) = 55$
$f(10) = 88 - 15\ln(10 + 1) = 52$
$f(12) = 88 - 15\ln(12 + 1) = 49.5$

The average score after 2 months was about 71.5, after 4 months was about 63.9, after 6 months was about 58.8, after 8 months was about 55, after 10 months was about 52, and after one year was about 49.5.

   c.
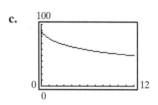

Material retention decreases as time passes.

89.–95. Answers may vary.

97.
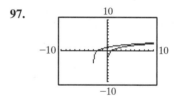

$g(x)$ is $f(x)$ shifted 3 units left.

99.
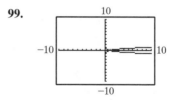

$g(x)$ is $f(x)$ reflected about the x-axis.

101.

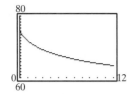

The score falls below 65 after 9 months.

103.

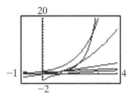

$$y = \ln x, \ y = \sqrt{x}, \ y = x,$$
$$y = x^2, \ y = e^x, \ y = x^x$$

105. $\dfrac{\log_3 81 - \log_\pi 1}{\log_{2\sqrt{2}} 8 - \log 0.001} = \dfrac{4 - 0}{2 - (-3)} = \dfrac{4}{5}$

107. $\log_4 60 < \log_4 64 = 3$ so $\log_4 60 < 3.$
$\log_3 40 > \log_3 27 = 3$ so $\log_3 40 > 3.$
$\log_4 60 < 3 < \log_3 40$
$\log_3 40 > \log_4 60$

Section 4.3

Check Point Exercises

1. a. $\log_6 (7 \cdot 11) = \log_6 7 + \log_6 11$

  b. $\log(100x) = \log 100 + \log x$
$$= 2 + \log x$$

2. a. $\log_8 \left(\dfrac{23}{x} \right) = \log_8 23 - \log_8 x$

  b. $\ln \left(\dfrac{e^5}{11} \right) = \ln e^5 - \ln 11$
$$= 5 - \ln 11$$

3. a. $\log_6 3^9 = 9 \log_6 3$

b. $\ln \sqrt[3]{x} = \ln x^{1/3}$
$$= \frac{1}{3} \ln x$$

4. a. $\log_b x^4 \sqrt[3]{y}$
$$= \log_b x^4 y^{1/3}$$
$$= \log_b x^4 + \log_b y^{1/3}$$
$$= 4 \log_b x + \frac{1}{3} \log_b y$$

  b. $\log_5 \dfrac{\sqrt{x}}{25 y^3}$
$$= \log_5 \dfrac{x^{1/2}}{25 y^3}$$
$$= \log_5 x^{1/2} - \log_5 25 y^3$$
$$= \log_5 x^{1/2} - \left(\log_5 25 + \log_5 y^3 \right)$$
$$= \frac{1}{2} \log_5 x - \left(\log_5 25 + 3 \log_5 y \right)$$
$$= \frac{1}{2} \log_5 x - \log_5 25 - 3 \log_5 y$$
$$= \frac{1}{2} \log_5 x - 2 - 3 \log_5 y$$

5. a. $\log 25 + \log 4 = \log(25 \cdot 4)$
$$= \log 100$$
$$= 2$$

  b. $\log(7x + 6) - \log x = \log \dfrac{7x + 6}{x}$

6. a. $\ln x^2 + \dfrac{1}{3} \ln(x + 5)$
$$= \ln x^2 + \ln(x + 5)^{1/3}$$
$$= \ln x^2 (x + 5)^{1/3}$$
$$= \ln x^2 \sqrt[3]{x + 5}$$

  b. $2 \log(x - 3) - \log x$
$$= \log(x - 3)^2 - \log x$$
$$= \log \dfrac{(x - 3)^2}{x}$$

c. $\dfrac{1}{4}\log_b x - 2\log_b 5 + 10\log_b y$

$$= \log_b x^{1/4} - \log_b 5^2 + \log_b y^{10}$$

$$= \log_b \dfrac{x^{1/4}\, y^{10}}{25}$$

7. $\log_7 2506 = \dfrac{\log 2506}{\log 7}$

$$\approx 4.02$$

8. $\log_7 2506 = \dfrac{\ln 2506}{\ln 7}$

$$\approx 4.02$$

Exercise Set 4.3

1. $\log_5(7\cdot 3) = \log_5 7 + \log_5 3$

3. $\log_7(7x) = \log_7 7 + \log_7 x$

$$= 1 + \log_7 x$$

5. $\log(1000x) = \log 1000 + \log x$

$$= 3 + \log x$$

7. $\log_7\left(\dfrac{7}{x}\right) = \log_7 7 - \log_7 x$

$$= 1 - \log_7 x$$

9. $\log\left(\dfrac{x}{100}\right) = \log x - \log 100$

$$= \log_x - 2$$

11. $\log_4\left(\dfrac{64}{y}\right) = \log_4 64 - \log_4 y$

$$= 3 - \log_4 y$$

13. $\ln\left(\dfrac{e^2}{5}\right) = \ln e^2 - \ln 5$

$$= 2\ln e - \ln 5$$
$$= 2 - \ln 5$$

15. $\log_b x^3 = 3\log_b x$

17. $\log N^{-6} = -6\log N$

19. $\ln \sqrt[5]{x} = \ln x^{(1/5)}$

$$= \dfrac{1}{5}\ln x$$

21. $\log_b x^2 y = \log_b x^2 + \log_b y$

$$= 2\log_b x + \log_b y$$

23. $\log_4\left(\dfrac{\sqrt{x}}{64}\right) = \log_4 x^{1/2} - \log_4 64$

$$= \dfrac{1}{2}\log_4 x - 3$$

25. $\log_6\left(\dfrac{36}{\sqrt{x+1}}\right) = \log_6 36 - \log_6(x+1)^{1/2}$

$$= 2 - \dfrac{1}{2}\log_6(x+1)$$

27. $\log_b\left(\dfrac{x^2 y}{z^2}\right) = \log_b\left(x^2 y\right) - \log_b z^2$

$$= \log_b x^2 + \log_b y - \log_b z^2$$
$$= 2\log_b x + \log_b y - 2\log_b z$$

29. $\log \sqrt{100x} = \log(100x)^{1/2}$

$$= \dfrac{1}{2}\log(100x)$$
$$= \dfrac{1}{2}(\log 100 + \log x)$$
$$= \dfrac{1}{2}(2 + \log x)$$
$$= 1 + \dfrac{1}{2}\log x$$

31. $\log\sqrt[3]{\dfrac{x}{y}} = \log\left(\dfrac{x}{y}\right)^{1/3}$

$$= \dfrac{1}{3}\left[\log\left(\dfrac{x}{y}\right)\right]$$
$$= \dfrac{1}{3}(\log x - \log y)$$
$$= \dfrac{1}{3}\log x - \dfrac{1}{3}\log y$$

33.

$$\log_b \frac{\sqrt{x}\,y^3}{z^3}$$

$$= \log_b x^{1/2} + \log_b y^3 - \log_b z^3$$

$$= \frac{1}{2}\log_b x + 3\log_b y - 3\log_b z$$

35.

$$\log_5 \sqrt[3]{\frac{x^2 y}{25}}$$

$$= \log_5 x^{2/3} + \log_5 y^{1/3} - \log_5 25^{1/3}$$

$$= \frac{2}{3}\log_5 x + \frac{1}{3}\log_5 y - \log_5 5^{2/3}$$

$$= \frac{2}{3}\log_5 x + \frac{1}{3}\log_5 y - \frac{2}{3}$$

37.

$$\ln\left[\frac{x^3 \sqrt{x^2+1}}{(x+1)^4}\right]$$

$$= \ln x^3 + \ln \sqrt{x^2+1} - \ln(x+1)^4$$

$$= 3\ln x + \frac{1}{2}\ln(x^2+1) - 4\ln(x+1)$$

39.

$$\log\left|\frac{10x^2 \sqrt[3]{1-x}}{7(x+1)^2}\right|$$

$$= \log 10 + \log x^2 + \log \sqrt[3]{1-x} - \log 7 - \log(x+1)^2$$

$$= 1 + 2\log x + \frac{1}{3}\log(1-x) - \log 7 - 2\log(x+1)$$

41.
$$\log 5 + \log 2 = \log(5\cdot 2)$$
$$= \log 10$$
$$= 1$$

43. $\ln x + \ln 7 = \ln(7x)$

45.
$$\log_2 96 - \log_2 3 = \log_2\left(\frac{96}{3}\right)$$
$$= \log_2 32$$
$$= 5$$

47. $\log(2x+5) - \log x = \log\left(\dfrac{2x+5}{x}\right)$

49.
$$\log x + 3\log y = \log x + \log y^3$$
$$= \log(xy^3)$$

51.
$$\frac{1}{2}\ln x + \ln y = \ln x^{1/2} + \ln y$$
$$= \ln\left(x^{\frac{1}{2}}y\right) \text{ or } \ln\left(\sqrt{x}\,y\right)$$

53.
$$2\log_b x + 3\log_b y = \log_b x^2 + \log_b y^3$$
$$= \log_b(x^2 y^3)$$

55.
$$5\ln x - 2\ln y = \ln x^5 - \ln y^2$$
$$= \ln\left(\frac{x^5}{y^2}\right)$$

57.
$$3\ln x - \frac{1}{3}\ln y = \ln x^3 - \ln y^{1/3}$$
$$= \ln\left(\frac{x^3}{y^{1/3}}\right) \text{ or } \ln\left(\frac{x^3}{\sqrt[3]{y}}\right)$$

59.
$$4\ln(x+6) - 3\ln x = \ln(x+6)^4 - \ln x^3$$
$$= \ln\frac{(x+6)^4}{x^3}$$

61.
$$3\ln x + 5\ln y - 6\ln z$$
$$= \ln x^3 + \ln y^5 - \ln z^6$$
$$= \ln\frac{x^3 y^5}{z^6}$$

63.
$$\frac{1}{2}\left(\log x + \log y\right)$$
$$= \frac{1}{2}(\log xy)$$
$$= \log(xy)^{1/2}$$
$$= \log \sqrt{xy}$$

65.
$$\frac{1}{2}(\log_5 x + \log_5 y) - 2\log_5 (x+1)$$
$$= \frac{1}{2}\log_5 xy - \log_5 (x+1)^2$$
$$= \log_5 (xy)^{1/2} - \log_5 (x+1)^2$$
$$= \log_5 \frac{(xy)^{1/2}}{(x+1)^2}$$
$$= \log_5 \frac{\sqrt{xy}}{(x+1)^2}$$

67.
$$\frac{1}{3}[2\ln(x+5) - \ln x - \ln(x^2 - 4)]$$
$$= \frac{1}{3}[\ln(x+5)^2 - \ln x - \ln(x^2 - 4)]$$
$$= \frac{1}{3}\left[\ln \frac{(x+5)^2}{x(x^2 - 4)}\right]$$
$$= \ln \left[\frac{(x+5)^2}{x(x^2 - 4)}\right]^{1/3}$$
$$= \ln \sqrt[3]{\frac{(x+5)^2}{x(x^2 - 4)}}$$

69.
$$\log x + \log 7 + \log(x^2 - 1) - \log(x+1)$$
$$= \log \frac{7x(x^2 - 1)}{(x+1)}$$
$$= \log \frac{7x(x-1)(x+1)}{x+1}$$
$$= \log[7x(x-1)]$$

71. $\log_5 13 = \dfrac{\log 13}{\log 5} \approx 1.5937$

73. $\log_{14} 87.5 = \dfrac{\ln 87.5}{\ln 14} \approx 1.6944$

75. $\log_{0.1} 17 = \dfrac{\log 17}{\log 0.1} \approx -1.2304$

77. $\log_\pi 63 = \dfrac{\ln 63}{\ln \pi} \approx 3.6193$

79.

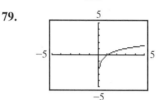

81.

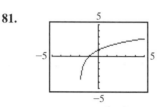

83. a. $D = 10\log\left(\dfrac{I}{I_0}\right)$

  b. $D_1 = 10\log\left(\dfrac{100I}{I_0}\right)$
$$= 10\log(100I - I_0)$$
$$= 10\log 100 + 10\log I - 10\log I_0$$
$$= 10(2) + 10\log I - 10\log I_0$$
$$= 20 + 10\log\left(\dfrac{I}{I_0}\right)$$

This is 20 more than the loudness level of the softer sound. This means that the 100 times louder sound will be 20 decibels louder.

85.–91. Answers may vary.

93. a. $y = \log_3 x = \dfrac{\ln x}{\ln 3}$

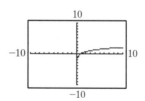

b.

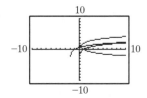

To obtain the graph of $y = 2 + \log_3 x$, shift the graph of $y = \log_3 x$ two units upward. To obtain the graph of $y = \log_3(x + 2)$, shift the graph of $y = \log_3 x$ two units left. To obtain the graph of $y = -\log_3 x$, reflect the graph of $y = \log_3 x$ about the x-axis.

95. $\log_3 x = \dfrac{\log x}{\log 3}$;

$\log_{25} x = \dfrac{\log x}{\log 25}$;

$\log_{100} x = \dfrac{\log x}{\log 100}$

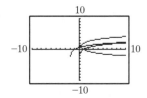

a. top graph: $y = \log_{100} x$
bottom graph: $y = \log_3 x$

b. top graph: $y = \log_3 x$
bottom graph: $y = \log_{100} x$

c. Comparing graphs of $\log_b x$ for $b > 1$, the graph of the equation with the largest b will be on the top in the interval $(0, 1)$ and on the bottom in the interval $(1, \infty)$.

97. a. Values of y may vary.

b. For $y = 3$, the graphs are:

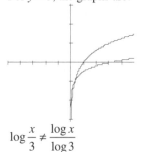

$\log \dfrac{x}{3} \neq \dfrac{\log x}{\log 3}$

99. a. Values of y may vary.
b. For $y = 6$, the graphs are:

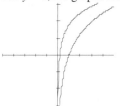

$\ln(6x) \neq (\ln x)(\ln 6)$

101. a. False;

$\log_7 49 - \log_7 7 = \log_7 \dfrac{49}{7} = \log_7 7 = 1$

$\dfrac{\log_7 49}{\log_7 7} = \dfrac{2}{1} = 2$

b. False;

$3\log_b x + 3\log_b y = \log_b(xy)^3$
$\neq \log_b\left(x^3 + y^3\right)$

c. False;

$\log_b(xy)^5 = 5\log_b(xy)$
$= 5(\log_b x + \log_b y)$
$\neq (\log_b x + \log_b y)^5$

d. True;

$\ln \sqrt{2} = \ln 2^{1/2}$
$= \dfrac{1}{2}\ln 2 = \dfrac{\ln 2}{2}$

(d) is true.

103. $\log_7 9 = \dfrac{\log 9}{\log 7} = \dfrac{\log 3^2}{\log 7} = \dfrac{2 \log 3}{\log 7}$

$= \dfrac{2A}{B}$

105. $\dfrac{\log_b (x+h) - \log_b x}{h}$

$= \dfrac{\log_b \dfrac{x+h}{x}}{h}$

$= \dfrac{\log_b \left(1 + \dfrac{h}{x}\right)}{h}$

$= \dfrac{1}{h} \log_b \left(1 + \dfrac{h}{x}\right)$

$= \log_b \left(1 + \dfrac{x}{h}\right)^{1/h}$

Section 4.4

Check Point Exercises

1. $5^x = 134$

$\ln 5^x = \ln 134$

$x \ln 5 = \ln 134$

$x = \dfrac{\ln 134}{\ln 5} \approx 3.04$

The solution set is $\left\{ \dfrac{\ln 134}{\ln 5} \right\}$,

approximately 3.04.

2. $7e^{2x} = 63$

$e^{2x} = 9$

$\ln e^{2x} = \ln 9$

$2x = \ln 9$

$x = \dfrac{\ln 9}{2} \approx 1.10$

The solution set is $\left\{ \dfrac{\ln 9}{2} \right\}$,

approximately 1.10.

3. $6^{3x-4} - 7 = 2081$

$6^{3x-4} = 2088$

$\ln 6^{3x-4} = \ln 2088$

$(3x - 4)\ln 6 = \ln 2088$

$3x \ln 6 - 4 \ln 6 = \ln 2088$

$3x \ln 6 = \ln 2088 + 4 \ln 6$

$x = \dfrac{\ln 2088 + 4 \ln 6}{3 \ln 6} \approx 2.76$

The solution set is $\left\{ \dfrac{\ln 2088 + 4 \ln 6}{3 \ln 6} \right\}$,

approximately 2.76.

4. $e^{2x} - 8e^x + 7 = 0$

$\left(e^x - 7\right)\left(e^x - 1\right) = 0$

$e^x - 7 = 0 \quad$ or $\quad e^x - 1 = 0$

$\qquad e^x = 7 \qquad\qquad e^x = 1$

$\ln e^x = \ln 7 \qquad \ln e^x = \ln 1$

$\qquad x = \ln 7 \qquad\qquad x = 0$

The solution set is $\{0, \ln 7\}$. The solutions

are 0 and (approximately) 1.95.

5. $\log_2 (x - 4) = 3$

$2^3 = x - 4$

$8 = x - 4$

$12 = x$

Check:

$\log_2 (x - 4) = 3$

$\log_2 (12 - 4) = 3$

$\log_2 8 = 3$

$3 = 3$

The solution set is $\{12\}$.

6. $\log x + \log(x - 3) = 1$

$\log x(x - 3) = 1$

$10^1 = x(x - 3)$

$10 = x^2 - 3x$

$0 = x^2 - 3x - 10$

$0 = (x - 5)(x + 2)$

$x - 5 = 0 \quad$ or $\quad x + 2 = 0$

$x = 5 \quad$ or $\qquad x = -2$

Check

Checking 5:

$\log 5 + \log(5 - 3) = 1$
$\log 5 + \log 2 = 1$
$\log(5 \cdot 2) = 1$
$\log 10 = 1$
$1 = 1$

Checking -2:
$\log x + \log(x - 3) = 1$
$\log(-2) + \log(-2 - 3) \overset{?}{=} 1$

Negative numbers do not have logarithms so -2 does not check.
The solution set is $\{5\}$.

7. $4 \ln 3x = 8$
$\ln 3x = 2$
$e^{\ln 3x} = e^2$
$3x = e^2$
$x = \dfrac{e^2}{3} \approx 2.46$

Check
$4 \ln 3x = 8$
$4 \ln 3 \left(\dfrac{e^2}{3} \right) = 8$
$4 \ln e^2 = 8$
$4(2) = 8$
$8 = 8$

The solution set is $\left\{ \dfrac{e^2}{3} \right\}$, approximately 2.46.

8. For a risk of 7%, let $R = 7$ in
$R = 6e^{12.77x}$
$6e^{12.77x} = 7$
$e^{12.77x} = \dfrac{7}{6}$
$\ln e^{12.77x} = \ln\left(\dfrac{7}{6}\right)$
$12.77x = \ln\left(\dfrac{7}{6}\right)$
$x = \dfrac{\ln\left(\dfrac{7}{6}\right)}{12.77} \approx 0.01$

For a blood alcohol concentration of 0.01, the risk of a car accident is 7%.

9. $A = P\left(1 + \dfrac{r}{n}\right)^{nt}$
$3600 = 1000\left(1 + \dfrac{0.08}{4}\right)^{4t}$
$1000\left(1 - \dfrac{0.08}{4}\right)^{4t} = 3600$
$1000(1 + 0.02)^{4t} = 3600$
$1000(1.02)^{4t} = 3600$
$(1.02)^{4t} = \ln 3.6$
$4t \ln(1.02) = \ln 3.6$
$t = \dfrac{\ln 3.6}{4 \ln 1.02}$
≈ 16.2

After approximately 16.2 years, the $1000 will grow to an accumulated value of $3600.

10. 　　　　$N = 461.87 + 299.4 \ln x$
$2000 = 461.87 + 299.4 \ln x$
$461.87 + 299.4 \ln x = 2000$
$299.4 \ln x = 1538.13$
$\ln x = \dfrac{1538.13}{299.4}$
$e^{\ln x} = e^{1538.13/299.4}$
$x = e^{1538.13/299.4}$
≈ 170

Approximately 170 years after 1979, in 2149, there will be 2 million U.S. workers in the environmental industry.

Exercise Set 4.4

1. 　　$10^x = 3.91$
$\ln 10^x = \ln 3.91$
$x \ln 10 = \ln 3.91$
$x = \dfrac{\ln 3.91}{\ln 10} \approx 0.59$

The solution set is $\left\{ \dfrac{\ln 3.91}{\ln 10} \right\}$, approximately 0.59.

3. $e^x = 5.7$

$\ln e^x = 5.7$

$x = \ln 5.7 \approx 1.74$

The solution set is $\{\ln 5.7\}$, approximately 1.74.

5. $5^x = 17$

$\ln 5^x = \ln 17$

$x \ln 5 = \ln 17$

$x = \dfrac{\ln 17}{\ln 5} \approx 1.76$

The solution set is $\left\{ \dfrac{\ln 17}{\ln 5} \right\}$, approximately 1.76.

7. $5e^x = 23$

$e^x = \dfrac{23}{5}$

$\ln e^x = \ln \dfrac{23}{5}$

$x = \ln \dfrac{23}{5} \approx 1.53$

The solution set is $\left\{ \ln \dfrac{23}{5} \right\}$, approximately 1.53.

9. $3e^{5x} = 1977$

$e^{5x} = 659$

$\ln e^{5x} = \ln 659$

$x = \dfrac{\ln 659}{5} \approx 1.30$

The solution set is $\left\{ \dfrac{\ln 659}{5} \right\}$, approximately 1.30.

11. $e^{1-5x} = 793$

$\ln e^{1-5x} = \ln 793$

$(1 - 5x)(\ln e) = \ln 793$

$1 - 5x = \ln 793$

$5x = 1 - \ln 793$

$x = \dfrac{1 - \ln 793}{5} \approx -1.14$

The solution set is $\left\{ \dfrac{1 - \ln 793}{5} \right\}$, approximately −1.14.

13. $e^{5x-3} - 2 = 10,476$

$e^{5x-3} = 10,478$

$\ln e^{5x-3} = \ln 10,478$

$(5x - 3)\ln e = \ln 10,478$

$5x - 3 = \ln 10,478$

$5x = \ln 10,478 + 3$

$x = \dfrac{\ln 10,478 + 3}{5} \approx 2.45$

The solution set is $\left\{ \dfrac{\ln 10,478 + 3}{5} \right\}$, approximately 2.45.

15. $7^{x+2} = 410$

$\ln 7^{x+2} = \ln 410$

$(x + 2)\ln 7 = \ln 410$

$x + 2 = \dfrac{\ln 410}{\ln 7}$

$x = \dfrac{\ln 410}{\ln 7} - 2 \approx 1.09$

The solution set is $\left\{ \dfrac{\ln 410}{\ln 7} - 2 \right\}$, approximately 1.09.

17. $7^{0.3x} = 813$

$\ln 7^{0.3x} = \ln 813$

$0.3x \ln 7 = \ln 813$

$x = \dfrac{\ln 813}{0.3 \ln 7} \approx 11.48$

The solution set is $\left\{ \dfrac{\ln 813}{0.3 \ln 7} \right\}$, approximately 11.48.

19.

$$5^{2x+3} = 3^{x-1}$$
$$\ln 5^{2x+3} = \ln 3^{x-1}$$
$$(2x+3)\ln 5 = (x-1)\ln 3$$
$$2x\ln 5 + 3\ln 5 = x\ln 3 - \ln 3$$
$$3\ln 5 + \ln 3 = x\ln 3 - 2x\ln 5$$
$$3\ln 5 + \ln 3 = x(\ln 3 - 2\ln 5)$$
$$\frac{3\ln 5 + \ln 3}{\ln 3 - 2\ln 5} = x$$
$$-2.80 \approx x$$

The solution set is $\left\{ \dfrac{3\ln 5 + \ln 3}{\ln 3 - 2\ln 5} \right\}$,

approximately –2.80.

21.

$$e^{2x} - 3e^x + 2 = 0$$
$$\left(e^x - 2\right)\left(e^x - 1\right) = 0$$

$$e^x - 2 = 0 \quad \text{or} \quad e^x - 1 = 0$$
$$e^x = 2 \qquad\qquad e^x = 1$$
$$\ln e^x = \ln 2 \qquad \ln e^x = \ln 1$$
$$x = \ln 2 \qquad\qquad x = 0$$

The solution set is {0, ln 2}. The solutions
are 0 and (approximately) 0.69.

23.

$$e^{4x} + 5e^{2x} - 24 = 0$$
$$\left(e^{2x} + 8\right)\left(e^{2x} - 3\right) = 0$$

$$e^{2x} + 8 = 0 \qquad \text{or } e^{2x} - 3 = 0$$
$$e^{2x} = -8 \qquad\qquad e^{2x} = 3$$
$$\ln e^{2x} = \ln(-8) \qquad \ln e^{2x} = \ln 3$$
$$2x = \ln(-8) \qquad 2x = \ln 3$$
$$\ln(-8) \text{ does not exist} \qquad x = \frac{\ln 3}{2}$$

$$x = \frac{\ln 3}{2} \approx 0.55$$

The solution set is $\left\{ \dfrac{\ln 3}{2} \right\}$,

approximately 0.55.

25.

$$3^{2x} + 3^x - 2 = 0$$
$$(3^x + 2)(3^x - 1) = 0$$
$$3^x + 2 = 0 \qquad\qquad 3^x - 1 = 0$$
$$3^x = -2 \qquad\qquad 3^x = 1$$
$$\log 3^x = \log(-2) \quad \log 3^x = \log 1$$
$$\text{can't do} \qquad\qquad x\log 3 = 0$$
$$x = \frac{0}{\log 3}$$
$$x = 0$$

The solution set is {0}.

27. $\log_3 x = 4$
$$x = 3^4$$
$$x = 81$$
The solution set is {81}.

29. $\log_4 (x+5) = 3$
$$x + 5 = 4^3$$
$$x + 5 = 64$$
$$x = 59$$
The solution set is {59}.

31. $\log_3 (x-4) = -3$
$$x - 4 = 3^{-3}$$
$$x - 4 = \frac{1}{27}$$
$$x = \frac{109}{27}$$

The solution set is $\left\{ \dfrac{109}{27} \right\}$.

33. $\log_4 (3x+2) = 3$
$$3x + 2 = 4^3$$
$$3x + 2 = 64$$
$$3x = 62$$
$$x = \frac{62}{3}$$

The solution set is $\left\{ \dfrac{62}{3} \right\}$.

35. $\log_5 x + \log_5(4x - 1) = 1$
$$\log_5\left(4x^2 - x\right) = 1$$
$$4x^2 - x = 5$$
$$4x^2 - x - 5 = 0$$
$$(4x - 5)(x + 1) = 0$$
$$x = \frac{5}{4} \text{ or } x = -1$$

$x = -1$ does not check because $\log_5(-1)$ does not exist.

The solution set is $\left\{\dfrac{5}{4}\right\}$.

37. $\log_3(x - 5) + \log_3(x + 3) = 2$
$$\log_3\left[(x - 5)(x + 3)\right] = 2$$
$$(x - 5)(x + 3) = 3^2$$
$$x^2 - 2x - 15 = 9$$
$$x^2 - 2x - 24 = 0$$
$$(x - 6)(x + 4) = 0$$
$$x = 6 \text{ or } x = -4$$

$x = -4$ does not check because $\log_3(-4 - 5)$ does not exist. The solution set is $\{6\}$.

39. $\log_2(x + 2) - \log_2(x - 5) = 3$
$$\log_2\left(\frac{x + 2}{x - 5}\right) = 3$$
$$\frac{x + 2}{x - 5} = 2^3$$
$$\frac{x + 2}{x - 5} = 8$$
$$x + 2 = 8(x - 5)$$
$$x + 2 = 8x - 40$$
$$7x = 42$$
$$x = 6$$

The solution set is $\{6\}$.

41. $2\log_3(x + 4) = \log_3 9 + 2$
$$2\log_3(x + 4) = 2 + 2$$
$$2\log_3(x + 4) = 4$$
$$\log_3(x + 4) = 2$$
$$3^2 = x + 4$$
$$9 = x + 4$$
$$5 = x$$

The solution set is $\{5\}$.

43. $\log_2(x - 6) + \log_2(x - 4) - \log_2 x = 2$
$$\log_2 \frac{(x - 6)(x - 4)}{x} = 2$$
$$\frac{(x - 6)(x - 4)}{x} = 2^2$$
$$x^2 - 10x + 24 = 4x$$
$$x^2 - 14x + 24 = 0$$
$$(x - 12)(x - 2) = 0$$
$$x - 12 = 0 \qquad x - 2 = 0$$
$$x = 12 \qquad x = 2$$

The solution set is $\{12\}$ since $\log_2(2\_6) = \log_2(\_4)$ is not possible.

45. $\ln x = 2$
$$e^{\ln x} = e^2$$
$$x = e^2 \approx 7.39$$
The solution set is $\left\{e^2\right\}$, approximately 7.39.

47. $5\ln 2x = 20$
$$\ln 2x = 4$$
$$e^{\ln 2x} = e^4$$
$$2x = e^4$$
$$x = \frac{e^4}{2} \approx 27.30$$
The solution set is $\left\{\dfrac{e^4}{2}\right\}$, approximately 27.30.

49. $6 + 2\ln x = 5$
$$2\ln x = -1$$
$$\ln x = -\frac{1}{2}$$
$$e^{\ln x} = e^{-1/2}$$
$$x = e^{-1/2} \approx 0.61$$
The solution set is $\left\{e^{-1/2}\right\}$, approximately 0.61.

51. $\ln\sqrt{x+3} = 1$

$e^{\ln\sqrt{x+3}} = e^1$

$\sqrt{x+3} = e$

$x+3 = e^2$

$x = e^2 - 3 \approx 4.39$

The solution set is $\{e^2 - 3\}$,
approximately 4.39.

53. $25 = 6e^{12.77x}$

$\dfrac{25}{6} = e^{12.77x}$

$\ln\dfrac{25}{6} = \ln e^{12.77x}$

$\ln\dfrac{25}{6} = 12.77x$

$\dfrac{\ln\dfrac{25}{6}}{12.77} = x$

$0.112 \approx x$

A blood alcohol level of about 0.112
corresponds to a 25% risk of a car accident.

55. a. $A = 18.9e^{0.005(0)}$

$A = 18.9$ million

b. $19.6 = 18.9e^{0.0055t}$

$\dfrac{19.6}{18.9} = e^{0.0055t}$

$\ln\dfrac{19.6}{18.9} = \ln e^{0.0055t}$

$\ln\dfrac{19.6}{18.9} = 0.0055t$

$\dfrac{\ln\dfrac{19.6}{18.9}}{0.0055} = t$

$6.6 \approx t$

In 2007 the population of New York will
reach 19.6 million.

57. $20,000 = 12,500\left(1 + \dfrac{0.0575}{4}\right)^{4t}$

$12,500(1.014375)^{4t} = 20,000$

$(1.014375)^{4t} = 1.6$

$\ln(1.014375)^{4t} = \ln 1.6$

$4t\ln(1.014375) = \ln 1.6$

$t = \dfrac{\ln 1.6}{4\ln 1.014375} \approx 8$

8 years

59. $1400 = 1000\left(1 + \dfrac{r}{360}\right)^{360\cdot 2}$

$\left(1 + \dfrac{r}{360}\right)^{720} = 1.4$

$\ln\left(1 + \dfrac{r}{360}\right)^{720} = \ln 1.4$

$720\ln\left(1 + \dfrac{r}{360}\right) = \ln 1.4$

$\ln\left(1 + \dfrac{r}{360}\right) = \dfrac{\ln 1.4}{720}$

$e^{\ln(1 + r/360)} = e^{(\ln 1.4)/720}$

$1 + \dfrac{r}{360} = e^{(\ln 1.4)/720} - 1$

$r = 360(e^{(\ln 1.4)/720}) - 1$

≈ 0.168

16.8%

61. accumulated amount $= 2(8000) = 16,000$

$16,000 = 8000e^{0.08t}$

$e^{0.08t} = 2$

$\ln e^{0.08t} = \ln 2$

$0.08t = \ln 2$

$t = \dfrac{\ln 2}{0.08}$

$t \approx 8.7$

The amount would double in 8.7 years.

63. accumulated amount $= 3(2350) = 7050$

$$7050 = 2350e^{r \cdot 7}$$
$$e^{7r} = 3$$
$$\ln e^{7r} = \ln 3$$
$$7r = \ln 3$$
$$r = \frac{\ln 3}{7} \approx 0.157$$

15.7%

65. $25,000 = 15,557 + 5259 \ln x$

$$5259 \ln x = 9443$$
$$\ln x = \frac{9443}{5259}$$
$$e^{\ln x} = e^{9443/5259}$$
$$x = e^{9443/5259} \approx 6$$

The average cost was \$25,000 6 years after 1989, in 1995.

67. $30 \log_2 x = 45$

$$\log_2 x = 1.5$$
$$x = 2^{1.5} \approx 2.8$$

Only half the students recall the important features of the lecture after 2.8 days. (2.8, 50)

69. $2.4 = -\log x$

$$\log x = -2.4$$
$$x = 10^{-2.4} \approx 0.004$$

The hydrogen ion concentration was $10^{-2.4}$, approximately 0.004 moles per liter.

71.–73. Answers may vary.

75.

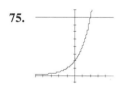

The intersection point is (2, 8).

Verify : $x = 2$

$$2^{x+1} = 8$$
$$2^{2+1} = 2$$
$$2^3 = 8$$
$$8 = 8$$

The solution set is $\{2\}$.

77.

The intersection point is (4, 2).

Verify : $x = 4$

$$\log_3(4 \cdot 4 - 7) = 2$$
$$\log_3 9 = 2$$
$$2 = 2$$

The solution set is $\{4\}$.

79.

The intersection point is (2, 1).

Verify : $x = 2$

$$\log(2 + 3) + \log 2 = 1$$
$$\log 5 + \log 2 = 1$$
$$\log(5 \cdot 2) = 1$$
$$\log 10 = 1$$
$$1 = 1$$

The solution set is $\{2\}$.

81.

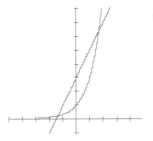

There are 2 points of intersection, approximately
(−1.391606, 0.21678798) and
(1.6855579, 6.3711158).
Verify $x \approx$ _1.391606
$$3^x = 2x + 3$$
$$3^{-1.391606} \approx 2(-1.391606) + 3$$
$$0.2167879803 \approx 0.216788$$
Verify $x \approx 1.6855579$
$$3^x = 2x + 3$$
$$3^{1.6855579} \approx 2(1.6855579) + 3$$
$$6.37111582 \approx 6.371158$$
The solution set is {−1.391606, 1.6855579}.

83.

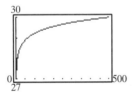

As the distance from the eye increases, barometric air pressure increases, leveling off at about 30 inches of mercury.

85.

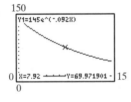

When $P = 70$, $t \approx 7.9$, so it will take about 7.9 minutes.
Verify:

$$70 = 45e^{-0.092(7.9)}$$
$$70 \approx 70.10076749$$
The runner's pulse will be 70 beats per minute after about 7.9 minutes.

87. a. False; $\log(x + 3) = 2$ means
$$x + 3 = 10^2$$

b. False; $\log(7x + 3) - \log(2x + 5) = 4$
means $\log \dfrac{7x + 3}{2x + 5} = 4$ which means
$$\dfrac{7x + 3}{2x + 5} = 10^4$$

c. True; $x = \dfrac{1}{k}\ln y$

$$kx = \ln y$$
$$e^{kx} = e^{\ln y}$$
$$e^{kx} = y$$

d. False; The equation $x^{10} = 5.71$ has no variable in an exponent so is not an exponential equation.

(c) is true

89.
$$(\ln x)^2 = \ln x^2$$
$$(\ln x)^2 = 2\ln x$$
$$(\ln x)^2 - 2\ln x = 0$$
$$\ln x(\ln x - 2) = 0$$
$$\ln x = 2$$
$$e^{\ln x} = e^2 \quad \text{or} \quad \begin{matrix}\ln x = 0 \\ x = 1\end{matrix}$$
$$x = e^2$$

The solution set is $\left\{ e^2 \right\}$

Check with graphing utility:

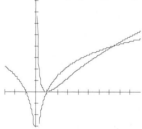

There are two points of intersection: $(1, 0)$ and approximately $(7.3890561, 4)$. Since $e^2 \approx 7.3890566099$, the graph verifies $x = 1$ and $x = e^2$, so the solution set is $\{1, e^2\}$ as determined algebraically.

91.
$$\ln(\ln x) = 0$$
$$e^{\ln(\ln x)} = e^0$$
$$\ln x = 1$$
$$e^{\ln x} = e^1$$
$$x = e$$

The solution set is $\{e\}$.

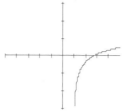

The graph of $\ln(\ln(x))$ crosses the graph $y = 0$ at approximately 2.718.

Section 4.5

Check Point Exercises

1. a. Use the exponential growth model $A = A_0 e^{kt}$ with 1990 corresponding to $t = 0$ when the population was 643 million:

$$A = 643 e^{kt}$$

Substitute $t = 2000 - 1990 = 10$ when the population was 813 million, so $A = 813$, to find k.

$$813 = 643 e^{k10}$$
$$\frac{813}{643} = e^{k10}$$
$$\ln \frac{813}{643} = \ln e^{k10}$$
$$\ln \frac{813}{643} = 10k$$
$$\frac{\ln \dfrac{813}{643}}{10} = k$$
$$0.023 \approx k$$

So the exponential growth function is $A = 643 e^{0.023t}$

b. Substitute 2000 for A in the model from part (a) and solve for t.

$$2000 = 643e^{0.023t}$$

$$\frac{2000}{643} = e^{0.023t}$$

$$\ln\frac{2000}{643} = \ln e^{0.023t}$$

$$\ln\frac{2000}{643} = 0.023t$$

$$\frac{\ln\dfrac{2000}{643}}{0.023} = t$$

$$49 \approx t$$

The population will reach 2000 million, or two billion, about 49 years after 1990, in 2039.

2. a. In the exponential decay model

$A = A_0 e^{kt}$, substitute $\dfrac{A_0}{2}$ for A since the amount present after 28 years is half the original amount.

$$\frac{A_0}{2} = A_0 e^{k \cdot 28}$$

$$e^{28k} = \frac{1}{2}$$

$$\ln e^{28k} = \ln\frac{1}{2}$$

$$28k = \ln\frac{1}{2}$$

$$k = \frac{\ln^{1/2}}{28} \approx -0.0248$$

So the exponential decay model is
$A = A_0 e^{-0.0248t}$

b. Substitute 60 for A_0 and 10 for A in the model from part (a) and solve for t.

$$10 = 60e^{-0.0248t}$$

$$e^{-0.0248t} = \frac{1}{6}$$

$$\ln e^{-0.0248t} = \ln\frac{1}{6}$$

$$-0.0248t = \ln\frac{1}{6}$$

$$t = \frac{\ln\dfrac{1}{6}}{-0.0248} \approx 72$$

The strontium-90 will decay to a level of 10 grams about 72 years after the accident.

3. a. The time prior to learning trials corresponds to $t = 0$.

$$f(0) = \frac{0.8}{1 + e^{-0.2(0)}} = 0.4$$

The proportion of correct responses prior to learning trials was 0.4.

b. Substitute 10 for t in the model:

$$f(10) = \frac{0.8}{1 + e^{-0.2(10)}} \approx 0.7$$

The proportion of correct responses after 10 learning trials was 0.7.

c. In the logistic growth model,

$f(t) = \dfrac{c}{1 + ae^{-bt}}$, the constant c represents the limiting size that $f(t)$ can attain. The limiting size of the proportion of correct responses as continued learning trials take place is 0.8.

4. $y = ab^x$ is equivalent to $y = ae^{(\ln b)x}$.

For $y = 4(7.8)^x$, $a = 4$, $b = 7.8$.

Thus, $y = 4(7.8)^x$ is equivalent to $y = 4e^{(\ln 7.8)x}$ in terms of a natural logarithm. Rounded to three decimal places, the model is approximately equivalent to $y = 4e^{2.054x}$.

Exercise Set 4.5

1. 1970 corresponds to $t = 0$.

$A = 203e^{0.011(0)}$

$A = 203$

In 1970, the population was 203 million.

3. Solve for t when $A = 300$.

$300 = 203e^{0.011t}$

$\dfrac{300}{203} = e^{0.011t}$

$\ln\dfrac{300}{203} = \ln e^{0.011t}$

$\ln\dfrac{300}{203} = 0.011t$

$\dfrac{\ln\dfrac{300}{203}}{0.011} = t$

$36 \approx t$

The population will be 300 million about 36 years after 1970, in 2006.

5. In the exponential growth model,

$A = A_0 e^{kt}$, k represents the growth rate. The population was increasing by about 2.6% each year.

7. $1624 = 574e^{0.026t}$

$\dfrac{116}{41} = e^{0.026t}$

$\ln\dfrac{116}{41} = \ln e^{0.026t}$

$\ln\dfrac{116}{41} = 0.026t$

$t = \dfrac{\ln\frac{116}{41}}{0.026} \approx 40$

The population will be 1624 million about 40 years after 1974, in 2014.

9. a. $A_0 = 158700$

$A = 158700e^{kt}$ for 2000,

$t = 5$, $A = 207200$

$207200 = 158700e^{k5}$

$\dfrac{207200}{158700} = e^{5k}$

$\ln\dfrac{207200}{158700} = \ln e^{5k}$

$\ln\dfrac{207200}{158700} = 5k$

$\dfrac{\ln\dfrac{207200}{158700}}{5} = k$

$0.0533 \approx k$

b. $300000 = 158700e^{0.0533t}$

$\dfrac{300000}{158700} = e^{0.0533t}$

$\ln\dfrac{300000}{158700} = \ln e^{0.0533t}$

$\ln\dfrac{300000}{158700} = 0.0533t$

$\dfrac{\ln\dfrac{300000}{158700}}{0.0533} = t$

$12 \approx t$

In 12 years after 1995, 2007, the price will

Be \$300,000.

11. $A_0 = 6.04$, in 2050, $t = 50$ and $A = 10$

$$10 = 6.04e^{k50}$$

$$\frac{10}{6.04} = e^{50k}$$

$$\ln\frac{10}{6.04} = \ln e^{50k}$$

$$\ln\frac{10}{6.04} = 50k$$

$$\frac{\ln\frac{10}{6.04}}{50} = k$$

$$0.01 \approx k$$

$$A = 6.04e^{0.01k}$$

13. $A = 16e^{-0.000121(5715)} \approx 8.01$

In 5715 years, 8.01 grams of carbon-14 will be present.

15. After 10 seconds, $\frac{16}{2}$ or 8 grams;

After 20 seconds, $\frac{8}{2}$ or 4 grams;

After 30 seconds, $\frac{4}{2}$ or 2 grams;

After 40 seconds, $\frac{2}{2}$ or 1 gram;

After 50 seconds, $\frac{1}{2}$ or 0.5 gram.

17. For an original amount of A_0, for the amount remaining is $A = 0.15A_0$.

$$0.15A_0 = A_0e^{-0.000121t}$$

$$0.15 = e^{-0.000121t}$$

$$\ln 0.15 = \ln e^{-0.000121t}$$

$$\ln 0.15 = -0.000121t$$

$$t = \ln\frac{0.15}{-0.000121} \approx 15,679$$

The paintings were about 15,679 years old.

19. a. Half the original amount corresponds to an amount remaining of $A = \frac{1}{2}A_0$. This amount corresponds to $t = 1.31$.

$$\frac{1}{2}A_0 = A_0e^{1.31k}$$

$$\frac{1}{2} = e^{1.31k}$$

$$\ln\frac{1}{2} = \ln e^{1.31k}$$

$$k = \frac{\ln\frac{1}{2}}{1.31} \approx -0.52912$$

The decay model is given by

$$A = A_0e^{-0.52912t}$$

b. $0.945A_0 = A_0e^{-0.52912t}$

$$0.945 = e^{-0.52912t}$$

$$\ln 0.945 = -0.52912t$$

$$t = \frac{\ln 0.945}{-0.52912} \approx 0.107$$

The bones of the dinosaur were about 0.107 billion, or 107 million years old.

21. The doubling of the original population corresponds to $A = 2A$.

$$2A_0 = A_0e^{kt}$$

$$2 = e^{kt}$$

$$\ln 2 = \ln e^{kt}$$

$$\ln 2 = kt$$

$$t = \frac{\ln 2}{k}$$

23. $t = \frac{\ln 2}{0.011} \approx 63$

It will take China about 63 years to double its population.

25. a. When the epidemic began, $t = 0$.

$$f(0) = \frac{100,000}{1 + 5000e^0} \approx 20$$

Twenty people became ill when the epidemic began.

b. $f(4) = \frac{100,000}{1 + 5,000e^{-4}} \approx 1080$

About 1080 people were ill at the end of the fourth week.

c. In the logistic growth model,
$$f(t) = \frac{c}{1 + ae^{-bt}},$$
the constant c represents the limiting size that $f(t)$ can attain. The limiting size of the population that becomes ill is 100,000 people.

27. $P(20) = \dfrac{0.9}{1 + 271e^{-0.122(20)}} \approx 0.037$

The probability that a 20-year-old has some coronary heart disease is about 3.7%.

29.
$$0.5 = \frac{1.9}{1 + 271e^{-0.122t}}$$
$$0.5\left(1 + 271e^{-0.122t}\right) = 0.9$$
$$1 + 271e^{-0.122t} = 1.8$$
$$271e^{-0.122t} = 0.8$$
$$e^{-0.122t} = \frac{0.8}{271}$$
$$\ln e^{-0.122t} = \ln \frac{0.8}{271}$$
$$-0.122t = \ln \frac{0.8}{271}$$
$$t = \frac{\ln \frac{0.8}{271}}{-0.122} \approx 48$$

The probability of some coronary heart disease is 0.5 at about age 48.

31. $y = 100(4.6)^x$ is equivalent to
$y = 100e^{(\ln 4.6)x}$;
Using $\ln 4.6 \approx 1.526$,
$y = 100e^{1.526x}$.

33. $y = 2.5(0.7)^x$ is equivalent to
$y = 2.5e^{(\ln 0.7)x}$;
Using $\ln 0.7 \approx -0.357$,
$y = 2.5e^{-0.357x}$.

35.–43. Answers may vary.

45. $y = 1.74(1.037)^x$
The correlation coefficient,

$r = 0.97$, is somewhat close to 1, indicating that the model is a good fit.

47. $y = 1.547 + 0.112x$
The correlation coefficient, $r = 0.99$, is close to 1, indicating that the model is a good fit.

49. $y = 1.547 + 0.112x$
The correlation coefficient, $r = 0.99$, is close to 1, indicating that the model is the best fit.
$$7.5 = 1.547 + 0.112x$$
$$5.953 = 0.112x$$
$$53.15 = x$$
$$1969 + 53 = 2022$$

51. $y = 0.06x^4 - 1.7x^3 + 14.2x^2 + 34x + 153; r = .9979$

53. Answers will vary.

Review Exercises

1. This is the graph of $f(x) = 4^x$ reflected about the y-axis, so the function is $g(x) = 4^{-x}$.

2. This is the graph of $f(x) = 4^x$ reflected about the x-axis and about the y-axis, so the function is $h(x) = -4^{-x}$.

3. This is the graph of $f(x) = 4^x$ reflected about the x-axis and about the y-axis then shifted upward 3 units, so the function is $r(x) = -4^{-x} + 3$.

4. This is the graph of $f(x) = 4^x$.

5.

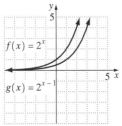

x	$f(x) = 2x$	$g(x) = 2^{x-1}$
-2	$2^{-2} = \frac{1}{4}$	$2^{-2-1} = 2^{-3} = \frac{1}{8}$
-1	$2^{-1} = \frac{1}{2}$	$2^{-1-1} = 2^{-2} = \frac{1}{4}$
0	$2^0 = 1$	$2^{0-1} = 2^{-1} = \frac{1}{2}$
1	$2^1 = 2$	$2^{1-1} = 2^0 = 1$
2	$2^2 = 4$	$2^{2-1} = 2^1 = 2$

The graph of $g(x)$ shifts the graph of $f(x)$ one unit to the right.

6.

x	$f(x) = 3^x$	$g(x) = 3^x - 1$
-2	$3^{-2} = \dfrac{1}{9}$	$3^{-2} - 1 = -\dfrac{8}{9}$
-1	$3^{-1} = \dfrac{1}{3}$	$3^{-1} - 1 = -\dfrac{2}{3}$
0	$3^0 = 1$	$3^0 - 1 = 0$
1	$3^1 = 3$	$3^1 - 1 = 2$
2	$3^2 = 9$	$3^2 - 1 = 8$

The graph of $g(x)$ reflects the graph of $f(x)$ about the x-axis.

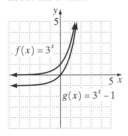

7.

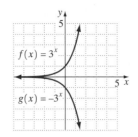

x	$f(x) = 3^x$	$g(x) = -3^x$
-2	$3^{-2} = \dfrac{1}{9}$	$-3^{-2} = -\dfrac{1}{9}$
-1	$3^{-1} = \dfrac{1}{3}$	$-3^{-1} = -\dfrac{1}{3}$
0	$3^0 = 1$	$-3^0 = -1$
1	$3^1 = 3$	$-3^1 = -3$
2	$3^2 = 9$	$-3^2 = -9$

The graph of $g(x)$ reflects the graph of $f(x)$ about the y – axis.

8.

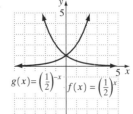

x	$f(x) = \left(\frac{1}{2}\right)^x$	$g(x) = \left(\frac{1}{2}\right)^{-x}$
-2	$\left(\frac{1}{2}\right)^{-2} = 4$	$\left(\frac{1}{2}\right)^{-(-2)} = \left(\frac{1}{2}\right)^2 = \frac{1}{4}$
-1	$\left(\frac{1}{2}\right)^{-1} = 2$	$\left(\frac{1}{2}\right)^{-1(-1)} = \left(\frac{1}{2}\right)^1 = \frac{1}{2}$
0	$\left(\frac{1}{2}\right)^0 = 1$	$\left(\frac{1}{2}\right)^{-(0)} = \left(\frac{1}{2}\right)^0 = 1$
1	$\left(\frac{1}{2}\right)^1 = \frac{1}{2}$	$\left(\frac{1}{2}\right)^{-1(1)} = \left(\frac{1}{2}\right)^{-1} = 2$
2	$\left(\frac{1}{2}\right)^2 = \frac{1}{4}$	$\left(\frac{1}{2}\right)^{-2(2)} = \left(\frac{1}{2}\right)^{-2} = 4$

The graph of $g(x)$ reflects the graph of $f(x)$ about the y-axis.

9. 5.5% compounded semiannually:
$$A = 5000\left(1 + \frac{0.055}{2}\right)^{2 \cdot 5} \approx 6558.26$$

5.25% compounded monthly:
$$A = 5000\left(1 + \frac{0.0525}{12}\right)^{12 \cdot 5} \approx 6497.16$$

5.5% compounded semiannually yields the greater return.

10. 7% compounded monthly:
$$A = 14,000\left(1 + \frac{0.07}{12}\right)^{12 \cdot 10} \approx 28,135.26$$

6.85% compounded continuously:
$$A = 14,000e^{0.0685(10)} \approx 27,772.81$$
7% compounded monthly yields the greater return.

11. **a.** When first taken out of the microwave, the temperature of the coffee was 200°.

     b. After 20 minutes, the temperature of the coffee was about 120°.
$$T = 70 + 130e^{-0.04855(20)} \approx 119.23$$
Using a calculator, the temperature is about 119°.

     c. The coffee will cool to about 70°; The temperature of the room is 70°.

12. $49^{1/2} = 7$

13. $4^3 = x$

14. $3^y = 81$

15. $\log_6 216 = 3$

16. $\log_b 625 = 4$

17. $\log_{13} 874 = y$

18. $\log_4 64 = 3$ because $4^3 = 64$.

19. $\log_5 \frac{1}{25} = -2$ because $5^{-2} = \frac{1}{25}$.

20. $\log_3(-9)$ cannot be evaluated since $\log_b x$ is defined only for $x > 0$.

21. $\log_{16} 4 = \frac{1}{2}$ because $16^{1/2} = \sqrt{16} = 4$.

22. Because $\log_b b = 1$, we conclude $\log_{17} 17 = 1$.

23. Because $\log_b b^x = x$, we conclude $\log_3 3^8 = 8$.

24. Because $\ln e^x = x$, we conclude $e^5 = 5$.

25. Because $\log_b = 1$, we conclude $\log_8 8 = 1$.
So, $\log_3(\log_8 8) = \log_3 1$.
Because $\log_b 1 = 0$ we conclude $\log_3 1 = 0$.
Therefore, $\log_3(\log_8 8) = 0$.

26.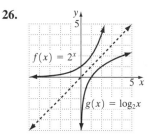

27.

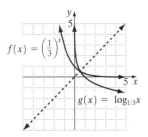

$f(x) = \left(\frac{1}{3}\right)^x$

$g(x) = \log_{1/3} x$

28. This is the graph of $f(x) = \log x$ reflected about the y-axis, so the function is $g(x) = \log(-x)$.

29. This is the graph of $f(x) = \log x$ shifted left 2 units, reflected about the y-axis, then shifted upward one unit, so the function is $r(x) = 1 + \log(2 - x)$.

30. This is the graph of $f(x) = \log x$ shifted left 2 units then reflected about the y-axis, so the function is $h(x) = \log(2 - x)$.

31. This is the graph of $f(x) = \log x$.

32.

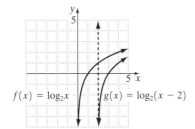

$f(x) = \log_2 x$ $g(x) = \log_2(x - 2)$

x-intercept: (3, 0)
vertical asymptote: $x = 2$

33.

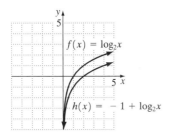

$f(x) = \log_2 x$

$h(x) = -1 + \log_2 x$

x-intercept: (2, 0)
vertical asymptote: $x = 0$

34.

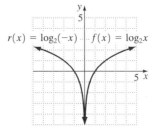

$r(x) = \log_2(-x)$ $f(x) = \log_2 x$

x-intercept: (−1, 0)
vertical asymptote: $x = 0$

35. The domain of f consists of all x for which $x + 5 > 0$.
Solving this inequality for x, we obtain $x > -5$.
Thus the domain of f is $(-5, \infty)$

36. The domain of f consists of all x for which $3 - x > 0$.
Solving this inequality for x, we obtain $x < 3$.
Thus, the domain of f is $(-\infty, 3)$.

37. The domain of f consists of all x for which $(x - 1)^2 > 0$.
Solving this inequality for x, we obtain $x < 1$ or $x > 1$. Thus, the domain of f is $(-\infty, 1)$ or $(1, \infty)$.

38. Because $\ln e^x = x$, we conclude $\ln e^{6x} = 6x$.

39. Because $e^{\ln x} = x$, we conclude $e^{\ln \sqrt{x}} = \sqrt{x}$.

40. Because $10^{\log x} = x$, we conclude $10^{\log 4x^2} = 4x^2$.

41.　$R = \log \dfrac{1000 I_0}{I_0} = \log 1000 = 3$

The Richter scale magnitude is 3.0.

42. a.　$f(0) = 76 - 18\log(0 + 1) = 76$

When first given, the average score was 76.

b.　$f(2) = 76 - 18\log(2 + 1) \approx 67$
$f(4) = 76 - 18\log(4 + 1) \approx 63$
$f(6) = 76 - 18\log(6 + 1) \approx 61$
$f(8) = 76 - 18\log(8 + 1) \approx 59$
$f(12) = 76 - 18\log(12 + 1) \approx 56$

After 2, 4, 6, 8, and 12 months, the average scores are about 67, 63, 61, 59, and 56, respectively.

c.

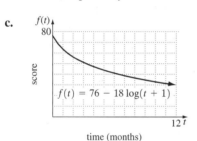

Retention decreases as time passes.

43.　$t = \dfrac{1}{0.06}\ln\left(\dfrac{12}{12 - 5}\right) \approx 8.98$

It will take about 9 weeks.

44.　$\log_6\left(36 x^3\right)$
$= \log_6 36 + \log_6 x^3$
$= \log_6 36 + 3\log_6 x$
$= 2 + 3\log_6 x$

45.　$\log_4 \dfrac{\sqrt{x}}{64} = \log_4 x^{1/2} - \log_4 64$
$\phantom{\log_4 \dfrac{\sqrt{x}}{64}} = \dfrac{1}{2}\log_4 x - 3$

46.　$\log_2 \dfrac{xy^2}{64} = \log_2 xy^2 - \log_2 64$
$\phantom{\log_2 \dfrac{xy^2}{64}} = \log_2 x + \log_2 y^2 - \log_2 64$
$\phantom{\log_2 \dfrac{xy^2}{64}} = \log_2 x + 2\log_2{}^{y-6}$

47.　$\ln 3\sqrt[3]{\dfrac{x}{e}}$
$= \ln\left(\dfrac{x}{e}\right)^{1/3}$
$= \dfrac{1}{3}\left[\ln x - \ln e\right]$
$= \dfrac{1}{3}\ln x - \dfrac{1}{3}\ln e$
$= \dfrac{1}{3}\ln x - \dfrac{1}{3}$

48.　$\log_b 7 + \log_b 3$
$= \log_b(7 \cdot 3)$
$= \log_b 21$

49.　$\log 3 - 3\log x$
$= \log 3 - \log x^3$
$= \log \dfrac{3}{x^3}$

50.　$3\ln x + 4\ln y$
$= \ln x^3 + \ln y^4$
$= \ln\left(x^3 y^4\right)$

51.　$\dfrac{1}{2}\ln x - \ln y$
$= \ln x^{1/2} - \ln y$
$= \ln \dfrac{\sqrt{x}}{y}$

52.　$\log_6 72{,}348 = \dfrac{\log 72{,}348}{\log 6} \approx 6.2448$

53.　$\log_4 0.863 = \dfrac{\ln 0.863}{\ln 4} \approx -0.1063$

54.　$8^x = 12{,}143$
$\ln 8^x = \ln 12{,}143$

$x \ln 8 = \ln 12{,}143$

$x = \dfrac{\ln 12{,}143}{\ln 8} \approx 4.523$

The solution set is $\left\{ \dfrac{\ln 12{,}143}{\ln 8} \right\}$,

approximately 4.52.

55. $9e^{5x} = 1269$

$e^{5x} = 141$

$\ln e^{5x} = \ln 141$

$5x = \ln 141$

$x = \dfrac{\ln 141}{5}$

The solution set is $\left\{ \dfrac{\ln 141}{5} \right\}$, approximately

0.99.

56. $e^{12-5x} - 7 = 123$

$e^{12-5x} = 130$

$\ln e^{12-5x} = \ln 130$

$12 - 5x = \ln 130$

$5x = 12 - \ln 130$

$x = \dfrac{12 - \ln 130}{5} \approx 1.426$

The solution set is $\{1.43\}$.

57. $5^{4x+2} = 37{,}500$

$\ln 5^{4x+2} = \ln 37{,}500$

$(4x+2)\ln 5 = \ln 37{,}500$

$4x \ln 5 + 2 \ln 5 = \ln 37{,}500$

$4x \ln 5 = \ln 37{,}500 - 2 \ln 5$

$x = \dfrac{\ln 37{,}500 - 2 \ln 5}{4 \ln 5}$

The solution set is $\left\{ \dfrac{\ln 37{,}500 - 2 \ln 5}{4 \ln 5} \right\}$,

approximately 1.14.

58. $e^{2x} - e^{x} - 6 = 0$

$\left(e^{x} - 3\right)\left(e^{x} + 2\right) = 0$

$e^{x} - 3 = 0$ or $e^{x} + 2 = 0$

$e^{x} = 3$ $\qquad\qquad e^{x} = -2$

$\ln e^{x} = \ln 3$ $\qquad \ln e^{x} - \ln(-2)$

$x = \ln 3$ $\qquad\qquad x = \ln(-2)$

$x = \ln 3 \approx 1.099$ $\ln(-2)$ does not exist.

The solution set is $\{\ln 3\}$,

approximately 1.10.

59. $\log_4 (3x - 5) = 3$

$3x - 5 = 4^3$

$3x - 5 = 64$

$3x = 69$

$x = 23$

The solutions set is $\{23\}$.

60. $\log_2 (x+3) + \log_2 (x-3) = 4$

$\log_2 (x+3)(x-3) = 4$

$\log_2 (x^2 - 9) = 4$

$x^2 - 9 = 2^4$

$x^2 - 9 = 16$

$x^2 = 25$

$x = \pm 5$

$x = -5$ does not check because $\log_2(-5+3)$

does not exist.

The solution set is $\{5\}$.

61. $\log_3 (x-1) - \log_3 (x+2) = 2$

$\log_3 \dfrac{x-1}{x+2} = 2$

$\dfrac{x-1}{x-2} = 3^2$

$\dfrac{x-1}{x+2} = 9$

$x - 1 = 9(x+2)$

$x - 1 = 9x + 18$

$8x = -19$

$x = -\dfrac{19}{8}$

$x = -\dfrac{19}{8}$ does not check because

$\log_3\left(-\dfrac{19}{8}-1\right)$ does not exist.

The solution set is $\varnothing$.

62. $\ln x = -1$

$x = e^{-1} = \dfrac{1}{e} \approx 0.368$

The solution set is $\left\{\dfrac{1}{e}\right\}$,

approximately 0.368.

63. $3 + 4\ln 2x = 15$

$4\ln 2x = 12$

$\ln 2x = 3$

$2^x = e^3$

$x = \dfrac{e^3}{2} \approx 10.043$

The solution set is $\left\{\dfrac{e^3}{2}\right\}$,

approximately 10.043

64. $13 = 10.1e^{0.005t}$

$e^{0.005t} = \dfrac{13}{10.1}$

$\ln e^{0.005t} = \ln \dfrac{13}{10.1}$

$0.005t = \ln \dfrac{13}{10.1}$

$t = \dfrac{\ln \dfrac{13}{10.1}}{0.005} \approx 50$

The population will reach 13 million about 50 years after 1992, in 2042.

65. $280 \cdot 2 = 364(1.005)^t$

$364(1.005)^t = 560$

$1.005^t = \dfrac{20}{13}$

$\ln 1.005^t = \ln \dfrac{20}{13}$

$t\ln 1.005 = \ln \dfrac{20}{13}$

$t = \dfrac{\ln \dfrac{20}{13}}{\ln 1.005} \approx 86$

The carbon dioxide concentration will be double the pre-industrial level about 86 years after 2000, in 2086.

66. $30,000 = 15,557 + 5259\ln x$

$5259\ln x = 14,443$

$\ln x = \dfrac{14,443}{5259}$

$x = e^{14,443/5259} \approx 16$

The average cost of a new car will reach \$30,000 about 16 years after 1989, in 2005.

67. $20,000 = 12,500\left(1 + \dfrac{0.065}{4}\right)^{4t}$

$12,500(1.01625)^{4t} = 20,000$

$(1.01625)^{4t} = 1.6$

$\ln(1.01625)^{4t} = \ln 1.6$

$4t\ln 1.01625 = \ln 1.6$

$t = \dfrac{\ln 1.6}{4\ln 1.01625} \approx 7.3$

It will take about 7.3 years.

68. $3 \cdot 50,000 = 50,000e^{0.075t}$

$50,000e^{0.075t} = 150,000$

$e^{0.075} = 3$

$\ln e^{0.075t} = \ln 3$

$0.075t = \ln 3$

$t = \dfrac{\ln 3}{0.075} \approx 14.6$

It will take about 14.6 years.

69. When an investment value triples, $A = 3P$.

$3P = Pe^{5r}$

$$e^{5r} = 3$$
$$\ln e^{5r} = \ln 3$$
$$5r = \ln 3$$
$$r = \frac{\ln 3}{5} \approx 0.2197$$

The interest rate would need to be about 21.97%

70. a.

$$35.3 = 22.4e^{k10}$$
$$\frac{35.3}{22.4} = e^{10k}$$
$$\ln \frac{35.3}{22.4} = \ln e^{10k}$$
$$\ln \frac{35.3}{22.4} = 10k$$
$$\frac{\ln \frac{35.3}{22.4}}{10} = k$$
$$0.045 \approx k$$
$$A = 22.4e^{0.045t}$$

b. $A = 22.4e^{0.045(26)} \approx 55.1$

In 2010, the population will be about 55.1 million.

c.

$$60 = 22.4e^{0.045t}$$
$$\frac{60}{22.4} = e^{0.045t}$$
$$\ln \frac{60}{22.4} = \ln e^{0.045t}$$
$$\ln \frac{60}{22.4} = 0.045t$$
$$\frac{\ln \frac{60}{22.4}}{0.045} = t$$
$$22 \approx t$$

The population will reach 60 million about 22 years after 1990, in 2012.

71. If the remaining amount is 15% of the original amount, them $A = 0.15A_0$.

$$0.15A_0 = A_0e^{-0.000121t}$$
$$e^{-0.00121t} = 0.15$$
$$\ln e^{-0.00121t} = \ln 0.15$$
$$-0.0012t = \ln 0.15$$
$$t = \frac{\ln 0.15}{-0.00121} \approx 15,679$$

At the time of discovery, the paintings were about 15,679 years old.

72. a. $f(0) = \dfrac{500,000}{1 + 2499e^{-0.92(0)}} = 200$

200 people became ill when the epidemic began.

b. $f(6) = \dfrac{500,000}{1 + 2499e^{-0.92(6)}} = 45,410$

45,410 were ill after 6 weeks.

c. 500,000

73. $y = 73(2.6)^x$ is equivalent to
$y = 73e^{(\ln 2.6)x}$; Using $\ln 2.6 \approx 0.956$;
$y = 73e^{0.956x}$.

74. $y = 6.5(0.43)^x$ is equivalent to
$y = 6.5e^{(\ln 0.43)x}$; Using $\ln 0.43 \approx -0.844$;
$y = 6.5e^{-0.844x}$.

75. The high projection might be best modeled by an exponential function, the medium projection by a linear function, and the low projection by a quadratic function; If the low projection is modeled by a quadratic function, the leading coefficient would be negative since the parabola opens downward.

76. linear model:
$y = 0.5055x - 8.5905$
$r = 0.9451995388$

quadratic model:
$$y = 0.0042934712x^2 - 0.1041729153x$$
$$+ 5.038408856$$
$$R^2 = 0.9883582557$$

exponential model:
$$y = 3.38051786(1.0235357)^x$$
$$r = 0.9945619484$$

logarithmic model:
$$y = -20.94062012 + 12.53110237 \ln x$$
$$r = 0.6748503469$$

The exponential model best fits the given data. 2050 is 151 years after 1899.
$$y = 3.38051786(1.0235357)^{151} \approx 113.4$$
In 2050, the projected U.S. population age 65 and over will be about 113.4 million.

Chapter 4 Test

1.

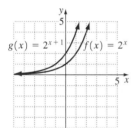

2.

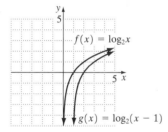

3. $125 = 5^3$

4. $\log_{36} 6 = \dfrac{1}{2}$

5. The domain of f consists of all x for which $3 - x > 0$. Solving this inequality for x, we

obtain $x < 3$.
Thus, the domain of f is $(-\infty, 3)$.

6. $\log_4\left(64x^5\right) = \log_4 64 + \log_4 x^5$
$$= 3 + 5\log_4 x$$

7. $\log_3 \dfrac{\sqrt[3]{x}}{81} = \log_3 x^{\frac{1}{3}} - \log_3 81$
$$= \dfrac{1}{3}\log_3 x - 4$$

8. $6\log x + 2\log y = \log x^6 + \log y^2$
$$= \log\left(x^6 y^2\right)$$

9. $\ln 7 - 3\ln x = \ln 7 - \ln x^3$
$$= \ln \dfrac{7}{x^3}$$

10. $\log_{15} 71 = \dfrac{\log 71}{\log 15} \approx 1.5741$

11. $5^x = 1.4$
$$\ln 5^x = \ln 1.4$$
$$x \ln 5 = \ln 1.4$$
$$x = \dfrac{\ln 1.4}{\ln 5} \approx 0.2091$$
The solution set is $\left\{ \dfrac{\ln 1.4}{\ln 5} \right\}$, approximately 0.2091.

12. $400e^{0.005x} = 1600$
$$e^{0.005x} = 4$$
$$\ln e^{0.005x} = \ln 4$$
$$0.005x = \ln 4$$
$$x = \dfrac{\ln 4}{0.005} \approx 277.2589$$
The solution set is $\left\{ \dfrac{\ln 4}{0.005} \right\}$, approximately 277.2589.

13. $e^{2x} - 6e^x + 5 = 0$
$$\left(e^x - 5\right)\left(e^x - 1\right) = 0$$

$$e^x - 5 = 0 \qquad \text{or} \quad e^x - 1 = 0$$
$$e^x = 5 \qquad\qquad\quad e^x = 1$$
$$\ln e^x = \ln 5 \qquad\quad \ln e^x = \ln 1$$
$$x = \ln 5 \qquad\qquad x = \ln 1$$
$$x \approx 1.6094 \qquad\qquad x = 0$$

The solution set is $\{0, \ln 5\};\ \ln \approx 1.6094.$

14. $\log_6(4x - 1) = 3$
$$4x - 1 = 6^3$$
$$4x - 1 = 216$$
$$4x = 217$$
$$x = \frac{217}{4}$$

The solution set is $\left\{\dfrac{217}{4}\right\}$.

15. $\log x + \log(x + 15) = 2$
$$\log(x^2 + 15x) = 2$$
$$x^2 + 15x = 10^2$$
$$x^2 + 15x - 100 = 0$$
$$(x + 20)(x - 5) = 0$$
$$x + 20 = 0 \text{ or } x - 5 = 0$$
$$x = -20 \qquad x = 5$$

$x = -20$ does not check because $\log(-20)$
does not exist.
The solution set is $\{5\}$.

16. $2 \ln 3x = 8$
$$\ln 3x = 4$$
$$3x = e^4$$
$$x = \frac{e^4}{3} \approx 18.1994$$

The solution set is $\left\{\dfrac{e^4}{3}\right\}$,
approximately 18.1994.

17. 6.5% compounded semiannually:
$$A = 3,000\left(1 + \frac{0.065}{2}\right)^{2(10)} \approx \$5,687.51$$

6% compounded continuously:
$$A = 3,000e^{0.06(10)} \approx \$5,466.36$$

6.5% compounded semiannually yields
about \$221 more than 6% compounded
continuously.

18. $D = 10 \log \dfrac{10^{12} I_0}{I_0}$
$$= 10 \log 10^{12}$$
$$= 10 \cdot 12$$
$$= 120$$

The loudness of the sound is 120 decibels.

19. a. In 1959, $t = 0$.
$$89.18e^{-0.004(0)} = 89.18$$
In 1959, about 89% of married men
were employed.

b. The percentage is decreasing since
$k = -0.004 < 1$.

c. $$77 = 89.18e^{-0.004t}$$
$$e^{-0.004t} = \frac{77}{89.18}$$
$$\ln e^{-0.004t} = \ln \frac{77}{89.18}$$
$$-0.004t = \ln \frac{77}{89.18}$$
$$t = \frac{\ln \frac{77}{89.18}}{-0.004} \approx 37$$

77% of U.S. married men were
employed about 37 years after 1959, in
1996.

20. In 1990, $t = 0$ and $A_0 = 509$
In 2000, $t = 2000 - 1990 = 10$ and
$A = 729$.

$$729 = 509e^{k10}$$
$$\frac{729}{509} = e^{10k}$$
$$\ln \frac{729}{509} = \ln e^{10k}$$
$$\ln \frac{729}{509} = 10k$$
$$\frac{\ln \dfrac{729}{509}}{10} = k$$
$$0.036 \approx k$$

The exponential growth function is
$A = 509e^{0.036t}$.

21. When the amount remaining is 5%,
$A = 0.05A_0$.
$$0.05A_0 = A_0 e^{-0.000121t}$$
$$e^{-0.000121t} = 0.05$$
$$\ln e^{-0.000121t} = \ln 0.05$$
$$-0.000121t = \ln 0.05$$
$$t = \frac{\ln 0.05}{-0.000121} \approx 24,758$$
The man died about 24,758 years ago.

22. a. $f(0) = \dfrac{140}{1 + 9e^{-0.165(0)}} = 14$

Fourteen elk were initially introduced to the habitat.

b. $f(10) = \dfrac{140}{1 + 9e^{-0.165(10)}} \approx 51$

After 10 years, about 51 elk are expected.

c. In the logistic growth model,
$f(t) = \dfrac{c}{1 + ae^{-bt}}$,
the constant c represents the limiting size that $f(t)$ can attain. The limiting size of the elk population is 140 elk.

Cumulative Review Exercises (Chapters 1–4)

1. $|3x - 4| = 2$
$$3x - 4 = 2 \qquad \text{or} \quad 3x - 4 = -2$$
$$3x = 6 \qquad\qquad\qquad 3x = 2$$
$$x = 2 \qquad\qquad\qquad x = \frac{2}{3}$$

The solution set is $\left\{ \dfrac{2}{3}, 2 \right\}$.

2. $\sqrt{2x - 5} - \sqrt{x - 3} = 1$
$$\sqrt{2x - 5} = 1 + \sqrt{x - 3}$$
$$\left(\sqrt{2x - 5} \right)^2 = \left(1 + \sqrt{x - 3} \right)^2$$
$$2x - 5 = 1 + 2\sqrt{x - 3} + x - 3$$
$$2x - 5 = x - 2 + 2\sqrt{x - 3}$$
$$x - 3 = 2\sqrt{x - 3}$$
$$(x - 3)^2 = \left(2\sqrt{x - 3} \right)^2$$
$$(x - 3)^2 = 4(x - 3)$$
$$x^2 - 6x + 9 = 4x - 12$$
$$x^2 - 10x + 21 = 0$$
$$(x - 3)(x - 7) = 0$$

$x = 3$ or $x = 7$
Both solutions satisfy the original equation when checked.
The solution set is $\{3, 7\}$.

3. $x^4 + x^3 - 3x^2 - x + 2 = 0$
$p: \pm 1, \pm 2$
$q: \pm 1$
$\dfrac{p}{q}: \pm 1, \pm 2$

-2	1	1	-3	-1	2
		-2	2	2	-2
	1	-1	-1	1	0

$$(x+2)(x^3 - x^2 - x + 1) = 0$$
$$(x+2)[x^2(x-1) - (x-1)] = 0$$
$$(x+2)(x^2 - 1)(x-1) = 0$$
$$(x+2)(x+1)(x-1)(x-1) = 0$$
$$(x+2)(x+1)(x-1)^2 = 0$$
$$x+2 = 0 \quad \text{or} \quad x+1 = 0 \quad \text{or} \quad x-1 = 0$$
$$x = -2 \qquad x = -1 \qquad x = 1$$
The solution set is $\{-2, -1, 1\}$.

4. $e^{5x} - 32 = 96$
$$e^{5x} = 128$$
$$\ln e^{5x} = \ln 128$$
$$5x = \ln 128$$
$$x = \frac{\ln 128}{5} \approx 0.9704$$
The solution set is $\left\{ \dfrac{\ln 128}{5} \right\}$,
approximately 0.9704.

5. $\log_2(x+5) + \log_2(x-1) = 4$
$$\log_2[(x+5)(x-1)] = 4$$
$$(x+5)(x-1) = 2^4$$
$$x^2 + 4x - 5 = 16$$
$$x^2 + 4x - 21 = 0$$
$$(x+7)(x-3) = 0$$
$$x+7 = 0 \quad \text{or} \quad x-3 = 0$$
$$x = -7 \qquad x = 3$$
$x = -7$ does not check because $\log_2(-7+5)$
does not exist.
The solution set is $\{3\}$.

6. $14 - 5x \geq -6$
$$-5x \geq -20$$
$$x \leq 4$$
The solution set is $(-\infty, 4]$.

7. $|2x - 4| \leq 2$
$$2x - 4 \leq 2 \quad \text{and} \quad 2x - 4 \geq -2$$
$$2x \leq 6 \qquad\qquad 2x \geq 2$$
$$x \leq 3 \qquad \text{and} \quad x \geq 1$$
The solution set is $[1, 3]$.

8. $m = \dfrac{3 - (-3)}{1 - 3} = \dfrac{6}{-2} = -3$
Using $(1, 3)$ point-slope form:
$$y - 3 = -3(x - 1)$$
slope-intercept form:
$$y - 3 = -3(x - 1)$$
$$y - 3 = -3x + 3$$
$$y = -3x + 6$$

9. $(f \circ g)(x) = f(x + 2)$
$$= (x + 2)^2$$
$$= x^2 + 4x + 4$$
$$(g \circ f)(x) = g(x^2)$$
$$= x^2 + 2$$

10. $f(x) = 2x - 7$
$$y = 2x - 7$$
$$x = 2y - 7$$
$$x + 7 = 2y$$
$$\frac{x + 7}{2} = y$$
$$f^{-1}(x) = \frac{x + 7}{2}$$

11.

$$\begin{array}{r}
x^2 + 3x - 3 \\
x+2 \overline{\smash{\big)}\, x^3 - 5x^2 + 3x - 10} \\
\underline{x^3 + 2x^2} \\
3x^2 + 3x \\
\underline{3x^2 + 6x} \\
-3x - 10 \\
\underline{-3x - 6} \\
-4
\end{array}$$

Quotient: $x^2 + 3x - 3 - \dfrac{4}{x + 2}$

12. $f(x) = 4x^3 - 7x - 3$
$$p = \pm 1, \pm 3$$
$$q = \pm 1, \pm 2, \pm 4$$
$$\frac{p}{q} = \pm 1, \pm \frac{1}{2}, \pm \frac{1}{4}, \pm 3, \pm \frac{3}{2}, \pm \frac{3}{4}$$

13. $y = kx^2$

$12 = k \cdot 3^2$

$k = \dfrac{12}{9} = \dfrac{4}{3}$

$y = \dfrac{4}{3}x^2$

$y = \dfrac{4}{3}(15)^2$

$y = 300$

14. If $1 + i$ is a root, $1 - i$ is a root.

$(x - 1 + i)(x - 1 - i)$

$= x^2 - x - xi - x + 1 + i + xi - i - i^2$

$= x^2 - 2x + 2$

$$x^2 - 2x + 2 \overline{\smash{)}\begin{array}{r} x - 2 \\ x^3 - 4x^2 + 6x - 4 \end{array}}$$
$$\underline{x^3 - 2x^2 + 2x}$$
$$-2x^2 + 4x - 4$$
$$\underline{-2x^2 + 4x - 4}$$
$$0$$

$x - 2 = 0$

$x = 2$

The solution set is $\{1 + i, 1 - i, 2\}$.

15. Circle with center: $(3, -2)$ and radius of 2

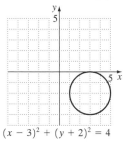

$(x - 3)^2 + (y + 2)^2 = 4$

16. Parabola with vertex: $(2, -1)$

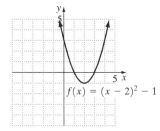

$f(x) = (x - 2)^2 - 1$

17. x-intercepts:

$x^2 - 1 = 0$

$x^2 = 1$

$x = \pm 1$

The x-intercepts are $(1, 0)$ and $(-1, 0)$.

vertical asymptotes:

$x^2 - 4 = 0$

$x^2 = 4$

$x = \pm 2$

The vertical asymptotes are $x = 2$ and $x = -2$.

Horizontal asymptote: $y = 1$

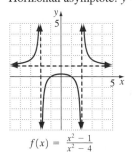

$f(x) = \dfrac{x^2 - 1}{x^2 - 4}$

18. x-intercepts:

$x - 2 = 0$ or $x + 1 = 0$

$x = 2$ or $x = -1$

The x-intercepts are $(2, 0)$ and $(-1, 0)$.

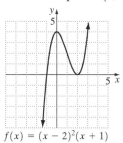

$f(x) = (x - 2)^2(x + 1)$

19. $40x + 10(1.5x) = 660$

$40x + 15x = 660$

$55x = 660$

$x = 12$

Your normal hourly salary is \$12 per hour.

20.

$$\frac{1}{2} = 1 - K \ln(3+1)$$

$$K \ln 4 = \frac{1}{2}$$

$$K = \frac{\frac{1}{2}}{\ln 4} \approx 0.361$$

$$F = 1 - 0.361\ln(t+1)$$

$$= 1 - 0.361\ln(6+1)$$

$$= 1 - 0.361\ln 7$$

$$\approx 0.361$$

About $\dfrac{361}{1000}$ of the people in the group

remember all the words in a list 6 hours
after memorizing them.

Chapter 5

Check Point Exercises

1. $2x = 3y = -4$
   $2(1) - 3(2) = -4$
   $2 - 6 = -4$
   $-4 = -4$ true
   $2x + y = 4$
   $2(1) + 2 = 4$
   $2 + 2 = 4$
   $4 = 4$
   $(1, 2)$ is a solution of the system.

2. $y = 5x - 13$
   $2x + 3y = 12$
   Substitute the expression $5x - 13$ for y in the second equation and solve for x.
   $2x + 3(5x - 13) = 12$
   $2x + 15x - 39 = 12$
   $17x = 51$
   $x = 3$
   Substitute 3 for x in the first equation.
   $y = 5(3) - 13 = 15 - 13 = 2$
   The solution set is $\{(3, 2)\}$.

3. $3x + 2y = -1$
   $x - y = 3$
   Solve the second equation for x.
   $x = y + 3$
   Substitute the expression $y + 3$ for x in the first equation and solve for x.
   $3(y + 3) + 2y = -1$
   $3y + 9 + 2y = -1$
   $5y = -10$
   $y = -2$
   Substitute –2 for y in the equation $x = y + 3$.
   $x = -2 + 3 = 1$
   The solution set is $\{(1, -2)\}$.

4. $4x + 5y = 3$
   $2x - 3y = 7$
   Eliminate x by multiplying the second equation by –2 and adding the resulting equations.
   $$\begin{array}{r} 4x + 5y = 3 \\ -4x + 6y = -14 \\ \hline 11y = -11 \\ y = -1 \end{array}$$
   Substitute –1 for y in the first equation.
   $4x + 5(-1) = 3$
   $4x - 5 = 3$
   $4x = 8$
   $x = 2$
   The solution set is $\{(2, -1)\}$.

5. $4x = 5 + 2y$
   $3y = 4 - 2x$
   Arrange the system so that variable terms appear on the left and constants appear on the right.
   $4x - 2y = 5$
   $2x + 3y = 4$
   Eliminate x by multiplying the second equation by –2 and adding the resulting equations.
   $$\begin{array}{r} 4x - 2y = 5 \\ -4x - 6y = -8 \\ \hline -8y = -3 \\ y = \dfrac{3}{8} \end{array}$$
   Substitute $\dfrac{3}{8}$ for y in the first equation.

$$4x = 5 + 2\left(\frac{3}{8}\right)$$

$$4x = 5 + \frac{6}{8} = \frac{46}{8} = \frac{23}{4}$$

$$x = \frac{23}{16}$$

The solution set is $\left\{\left(\frac{23}{16}, \frac{3}{8}\right)\right\}$.

6. The elimination method is used here to solve the system.

$$x + 2y = 4$$
$$3x + 6y = 13$$

Eliminate x by multiplying the first equation by -3 and adding the resulting equations.

$$-3x - 6y = -12$$
$$\underline{3x + 6y = 13}$$
$$0 = 1$$

The false statement $0 = 1$ indicates that the system has no solution. The solution set is the empty set, $\varnothing$.

7. The substitution method is used here to solve the system.

$$y = 4x - 4$$
$$8x - 2y = 8.$$

Substitute the expression $4x - 4$ for y in the second equation and solve for y.

$$8x - 2(4x - 4) = 8$$
$$8x - 8x + 8 = 8$$
$$8 = 8$$

This true statement indicates that the system has infinitely many solutions. The solution set is

$$\{(x, y) \mid y = 4x - 4\} \text{ or } \{(x, y) \mid 8x - 2y = 8\}.$$

8. a. $C = 300,000 + 30x$

  b. $R = 80x$

  c. $80x = 300,000 + 3x$
$$50x = 300,000$$
$$x = 6000$$
$$80(6000) = 48000$$

Break even point (6000, 48000)
The company will need to make 6000 pairs of shoes and earn \$48,000 to break even.

9. $N = -20p + 1000$
$N = 5p + 250$
Substitute $-20p + 1000$ for N in the second

equation.
$$-20p + 1000 = 5p + 250$$
$$750 = 25p$$
$$p = 30$$

Supply and demand are equal at \$30. To find the number of units supplied and sold each week at this price, substitute 30 for p in either the demand or the supply model.

$$N = -20(30) + 1000$$
$$= -600 + 1000$$
$$= 400$$

At a price of \$30, 400 units of the product can be supplied and sold.

Exercise Set 5.1

1. $x + 3y = 11$
$$2 + 3(3) = 11$$
$$2 + 9 \triangleq 11$$
$$11 = 11 \text{ true}$$
$$x - 5y = -13$$
$$2 - 5(3) \triangleq -13$$
$$2 - 15 = -13$$
$$-13 = -13 \text{ true}$$

$(2, 3)$ is a solution.

3. $2x + 3y = 17$
$$2(2) + 3(5) \triangleq 17$$
$$4 + 15 \triangleq 17$$
$$19 = 17 \text{ false}$$

$(2, 5)$ is not a solution.

5. $x + y = 4$
$$y = 3x$$

Substitute the expression $3x$ for y in the first equation and solve for x.

$$x + 3x = 4$$
$$4x = 4$$
$$x = 1$$

Substitute 1 for x in the second equation.
$$y = 3(1) = 3$$

The solution set is $\{(1, 3)\}$.

7. $x + 3y = 8$
$y = 2x - 9$
Substitute the expression $2x - 9$ for y in the first equation and solve for x.
$x + 3(2x - 9) = 8$
$x + 6x - 27 = 8$
$7x = 35$
$x = 5$
Substitute 5 for x in the second equation.
$y = 2(5) - 9 = 10 - 9 = 1$
The solution set is $\{(5, 1)\}$.

9. $x = 4y - 2$
$x = 6y + 8$
Substitute the expression $4y - 2$ for x in the second equation and solve for y.
$4y - 2 = 6y + 8$
$-10 = 2y$
$-5 = y$
Substitute –5 for y in the equation $x = 4y - 2$.
$x = 4(-5) - 2 = -22$
The solution set is $\{(-22, -5)\}$.

11. $5x + 2y = 0$
$x - 3y = 0$
Solve the second equation for x.
$x = 3y$
Substitute the expression $3y$ for x in the first equation and solve for y.
$5(3y) + 2y = 0$
$15y + 2y = 0$
$17y = 0$
$y = 0$
Substitute 0 for y in the equation $x = 3y$
$y = 3(0) = 0$
The solution set is $\{(0, 0)\}$.

13. $2x + 5y = -4$
$3x - y = 11$
Solve the second equation for y.
$-y = -3x + 11$

$y = 3x - 11$
Substitute the expression $3x - 11$ for y in the first equation and solve for x.
$2x + 5(3x - 11) = -4$
$2x + 15x - 55 = -4$
$17x = 51$
$x = 3$
Substitute 3 for x in the equation $y = 3x - 11$.
$y = 3(3) - 11 = 9 - 11 = -2$
The solution set is $\{(3, -2)\}$.

15. $2x - 3y = 8 - 2x$
$2x + 4y = x + 3y + 14$
Solve the second equation for y.
$y = -2x + 14$
Substitute the expression $-2x + 14$ for y in the first equation and solve for x.
$2x - 3(-2x + 14) = 8 - 2x$
$2x + 6x - 42 = 8 - 2x$
$8x - 42 = 8 - 2x$
$10x = 50$
$x = 5$
Substitute 5 for x in the equation $y = -2x + 14$.
$y = -2(5) + 14 = -10 + 14 = 4$
The solution set is $\{(5, 4)\}$.

17. $y = \dfrac{1}{3}x + \dfrac{2}{3}$

$y = \dfrac{5}{7}x - 2$

Substitute the expression $y = \dfrac{1}{3}x + \dfrac{2}{3}$ for y in the second equation and solve for x.
$\dfrac{1}{3}x + \dfrac{2}{3} = \dfrac{5}{7}x - 2$
$7x + 14 = 15x - 42$
$56 = 8x$
$7 = x$
Substitute 7 for x in the equation

$y = \dfrac{1}{3}x + \dfrac{2}{3}$ and solve for y.

$y = \dfrac{1}{3}(7) + \dfrac{2}{3} = \dfrac{7}{3} + \dfrac{2}{3} = \dfrac{9}{3} = 3$

The solution set is $\{(7, 3)\}$.

19. Eliminate y by adding the equations.

$x + y = 1$

$\underline{x - y = 3}$

$\quad 2x = 4$

$\quad\ x = 2$

Substitute 2 for x in the first equation.

$2 + y = 1$

$\quad y = -1$

The solution set is $\{(2, -1)\}$.

21. Eliminate y by adding the equations.

$2x + 3y = 6$

$\underline{2x - 3y = 6}$

$\quad\ 4x = 12$

$\quad\ \ x = 3$

Substitute 3 for x in the first equation.

$2(3) + 3y = 6$

$6 + 3y = 6$

$\quad\ 3y = 0$

$\quad\ \ y = 0$

The solution set is $\{(3, 0)\}$.

23. $x + 2y = 2$

$-4x + 3y = 25$

Eliminate x by multiplying the first equation by 4 and adding the resulting equations.

$4x + 8y = 8$

$\underline{-4x + 3y = 25}$

$\quad\ \ 11y = 33$

$\quad\quad\ y = 3$

Substitute 3 for y in the first equation.

$x + 2(3) = 2$

$x + 6 = 2$

$\quad\ x = -4$

The solution set is $\{(-4, 3)\}$.

25. $4x + 3y = 15$

$2x - 5y = 1$

Eliminate x by multiplying the second equation by -2 and adding the resulting equations.

$4x + 3y = 15$

$\underline{-4x + 10y = -2}$

$\quad\quad 13y = 13$

$\quad\quad\ \ y = 1$

Substitute 1 for y in the second equation.

$2x - 5(1) = 1$

$\quad\ 2x = 6$

$\quad\ \ x = 3$

The solution set is $\{(3, 1)\}$.

27. $3x - 4y = 11$

$2x + 3y = -4$

Eliminate x by multiplying the first equation by 2 and the second equation by -3. Add the resulting equations.

$6x - 8y = 22$

$\underline{-6x - 9y = 12}$

$\quad\ -17y = 34$

$\quad\quad\ y = -2$

Substitute -2 for y in the second equation.

$2x + 3(-2) = -4$

$2x - 6 = -4$

$\quad\ 2x = 2$

$\quad\ \ x = 1$

The solution set is $\{(1, -2)\}$.

29. $3x = 4y + 1$

$3y = 1 - 4x$

Arrange the system so that variable terms appear on the left and constants appear on the right.

$3x - 4y = 1$

$4x + 3y = 1$

Eliminate y by multiplying the first equation by 3 and the second equation by 4. Add the resulting equations.

$$9x - 12y = 3$$
$$\underline{16x + 12y = 4}$$
$$25x = 7$$
$$x = \frac{7}{25}$$

Substitute $\frac{7}{25}$ for x in the second equation.

$$3y = 1 - 4\left(\frac{7}{25}\right)$$
$$3y = \frac{-3}{25}$$
$$y = \frac{-1}{25}$$

The solution set is $\left\{\left(\frac{7}{25}, -\frac{1}{25}\right)\right\}$.

31. The substitution method is used here to solve the system.
$$x = 9 - 2y$$
$$x + 2y = 13$$
Substitute the expression $9 - 2y$ for x in the second equation and solve for y.
$$9 - 2y + 2y = 13$$
$$9 = 13$$
The false statement $9 = 13$ indicates that the system has no solution.
The solution set is the empty set, $\varnothing$.

33. The substitution method is used here to solve the system.
$$y = 3x - 5$$
$$21x - 35 = 7y$$
Substitute the expression $3x - 5$ for y in the second equation and solve for x.
$$21x - 35 = 7(3x - 5)$$
$$21x - 35 = 21x - 35$$
$$-35 = -35$$
This true statement indicates that the system has infinitely many solutions.

The solution set is $\left\{(x, y) \mid y = 3x - 5\right\}$ or $\left\{(x, y) \mid 21x - 35 = 7y\right\}$.

35. The elimination method is used here to solve the system.
$$3x - 2y = -5$$
$$4x + y = 8$$
Eliminate y by multiplying the second equation by 2 and adding the resulting equations.
$$3x - 2y = -5$$
$$\underline{8x + 2y = 16}$$
$$11x = 11$$
$$x = 1$$
Substitute 1 for x in the second equation.
$$4(1) + y = 8$$
$$y = 4$$
The solution set is $\{(1, 4)\}$.

37. The elimination method is used here to solve the system.
$$x + 3y = 2$$
$$3x + 9y = 6$$
Eliminate x by multiplying the first equation by -3 and adding the resulting equations.
$$-3x - 9y = -6$$
$$\underline{3x + 9y = 6}$$
$$0 = 0$$
This true statement indicates that the system has infinitely many solutions.
The solution set is $\left\{(x, y) \mid x + 3y = 2\right\}$ or $\left\{(x, y) \mid 3x + 9y = 6\right\}$.

39. First multiply each term in the first equation by 4 to eliminate the fractions.
$$\frac{x}{4} - \frac{y}{4} = -1$$
$$x - y = -4$$
Multiply the first equation by -1 and add to the second equation and solve for y.

$$-x + y = 4$$
$$x + 4y = -9$$
$$5y = -5$$
$$y = -1$$

Substitute –1 for y in the equation $x - y = -4$ and solve for x.
$$x - (-1) = -4$$
$$x + 1 = -4$$
$$x = -5$$

The solution set is $\{(-5, -1)\}$.

41. Rearrange the equations to get in the standard form.
$$2x - 3y = 4$$
$$4x + 5y = 3$$

Multiply the first equation by –2 and add to the second equation. Solve for y.
$$-4x + 6y = -8$$
$$4x + 5y = 3$$
$$11y = -5$$
$$y = -\frac{5}{11}$$

Multiply the first equation by 5 and the second equation by 3 and add the equations. Solve for x.
$$10x - 15y = 20$$
$$12x + 15y = 9$$
$$22x = 29$$
$$x = \frac{29}{22}$$

The solution set is $\left\{ \left(\dfrac{29}{22}, -\dfrac{5}{11} \right) \right\}$.

43. Add the equations to eliminate y.
$$x + y = 7$$
$$\underline{x - y = -1}$$
$$2x = 6$$
$$x = 3$$

Substitute 3 for x in the first equation.
$$3 + y = 7$$

$$y = 4$$

The numbers are 3 and 4.

45. $3x - y = 1$
$$x + 2y = 12$$

Eliminate y by multiplying the first equation by 2 and adding the resulting equations.
$$6x - 2y = 2$$
$$\underline{x + 2y = 12}$$
$$7x = 14$$
$$x = 2$$

Substitute 2 for x in the first equation.
$$3(2) - y = 1$$
$$6 - y = 1$$
$$-y = -5$$
$$y = 5$$

The numbers are 2 and 5.

47. a. $C = 18000 + 20x$

b. $R = 80x$

c. $80x = 18000 + 20x$
$$60x = 18000$$
$$x = 300$$
$$80(300) = 24000$$

The company must sell 300 canoes and make \$24,000 to break even.

49. a. $C = 30000 + 2500x$

b. $R = 3125x$

c. $3125x = 30000 + 2500x$
$$625x = 30000$$
$$x = 48$$
$$3125(48) = 150000$$

The play must have 48 sell-out performances and earn \$150,000 to break even.

51. $N = -25p + 7500$
$N = 5p + 6000$

a. Substitute 40 for p in the demand model.
$$N = -25(40) + 7500$$
$$= -1000 + 7500$$
$$= 6500$$
At \$40 a ticket, 6500 tickets can be sold.
Substitute 40 for p in the supply model.
$$N = 5(40) + 6000$$
$$= 200 + 6000$$
$$= 6200$$
At \$40 a ticket, 6200 tickets can be supplied.

b. Substitute $-25p + 7500$ for N in the second equation.
$$-25p + 7500 = 5p + 6000$$
$$1500 = 30p$$
$$50 = p$$
Supply and demand are equal at \$50 a ticket.
To find the number of tickets supplied and sold at this price, substitute 50 for p into either the demand or supply model.
$$N = -25(50) + 7500$$
$$= -1250 + 7500$$
$$= 6250$$
At a price of \$50, 6250 tickets can be supplied and sold.

53. $-.4x + 28 = 15 - .07x$
$$13 = .33x$$
$$39 \approx x$$
$$-.4(39) + 28 = 12.$$
In 39 years after 1965, 2004, there will be 12.4 deaths per thousand from gunshots and 12.4 deaths per thousand for car crashes.

55. a. $E = 508 + 25x$

b. $E = 345 + 9x$

c. $508 + 25x = 2(345 + 9x)$
$$508 + 25x = 690 + 18x$$
$$7x = 182$$
$$x = 26$$
26 years after 1985, in 2011, college graduates will be making twice as much as high school graduates. Weekly earnings for college graduates in 2011 will be \$1158, and \$579 for high school graduates.

57. $x + 2y = 1980$
$2x + y = 2670$
Multiply the first equation by -2 and add to the second equation. Solve for y.
$$-2x - 4y = -3960$$
$$2x + y = 2670$$
$$-3y = -1290$$
$$y = 430$$
Substitute 430 for y in the second equation and solve for x.
$$2x + 430 = 2670$$
$$2x = 2240$$
$$x = 1120$$
There are 1120 calories in a pan pizza and 430 calories in a beef burrito.

59. $x + y = 300 + 241$ or $x + y = 541$
$2x + 3y = 1257$
Multiply the first equation by -2 and add to the second equation. Solve for y.
$$-2x - 2y = -1082$$
$$2x + 3y = 1257$$
$$y = 175$$
Substitute 175 for y in the first equation and solve for x.
$$x + 175 = 541$$
$$x = 366$$
There are 366 mg in scrambled eggs and 175 mg in a Double Beef Whooper.

61. $x + y = 200$
$100x + 80y = 17000$

Multiply the first equation by -100 and add to the second equation. Solve for y.

$$-100x - 100y = -20000$$
$$100x + 80y = 17000$$
$$-20y = -3000$$
$$y = 150$$

Substitute 150 for y in the first equation and solve for x.

$$x + 150 = 200$$
$$x = 50$$

There are 50 rooms with kitchenettes and 150 rooms without.

63.
$$2x + 2y = 360$$
$$20x + 8(2y) = 3280$$

Multiply the first equation by $\_10$ and add to the second equation. Solve for y.

$$-20x - 20y = -3600$$
$$20x + 16y = 3280$$
$$-4y = -320$$
$$y = 80$$

Substitute 80 for y in the first equation and solve for x.

$$2x + 2(80) = 360$$
$$2x + 160 = 360$$
$$2x = 200$$
$$x = 100$$

The lot is 100 feet long and 80 feet wide.

65.
$$(x + y)2 = 16$$
$$(x - y)2 = 8$$

Multiply to remove the parentheses and then add the two equations together. Solve for x.

$$2x + 2y = 16$$
$$2x - 2y = 8$$
$$4x = 24$$
$$x = 6$$

Substitute 6 for x in the first equation and solve for y.

$$2(6) + 2y = 16$$
$$12 + 2y = 16$$
$$2y = 4$$
$$y = 2$$

The crew rows 6 mph and the current is 2 mph.

67. Since the angles x and $3y + 20$ form a straight line, they must add to $180°$. The angles x and y must add to $90°$.

$$x + 3y + 20 = 180 \text{ becomes } x + 3y = 160$$
$$x + y = 90$$

Multiply the second equation by -1 and add to the first equation. Solve for y.

$$-x - y = -90$$
$$x + 3y = 160$$
$$2y = 70$$
$$y = 35^O$$

Substitute 35 for y in the second equation and solve for x.

$$x + 35 = 90$$
$$x = 55^O$$

69.– 77. Answers may vary.

79.   Exercise 6

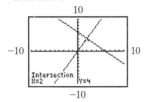

Exercise 8

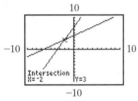

Exercise 10

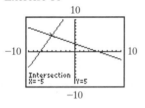

Exercise 12

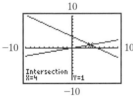

Exercise 14

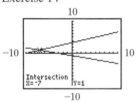

81.   Answers may vary.

83. x = first lucky number
y = second lucky number
$3x + 6y = 12$
$x + 2y = \ 5$

Eliminate x by multiplying the second equation by -3 and adding the resulting equations.

$$3x + 6y = 12$$
$$\underline{-3x - 6y = -15}$$
$$0 = -3$$

The false statement $0 = -3$ indicates that the system has no solution. Therefore, the twin who always lies is talking.

Section 5.2

Check Point Exercises

1. $x - 2y + 3z = 22$
$-1 - 2(-4) + 3(5) = 22$
$-1 + 8 + 15 = 22$
$22 = 22 \ \ \text{true}$
$2x - 3y - z = 5$
$2(-1) - 3(-4) - 5 = 5$
$-2 + 12 - 5 = 5$
$5 = 5 \ \ \text{true}$
$3x + y - 5z = -32$
$3(-1) - 4 - 5(5) = -32$
$-3 - 4 - 25 = -32$
$-32 = -32 \ \ \text{true}$
$(-1, -4, 5)$ is a solution of the system.

2. $x + 4y - z = 20$
$3x + 2y + z = 8$
$2x - 3y + 2z = -16$
Eliminate z from Equations 1 and 2 by adding Equation 1 and Equation 2.
$x + 4y - z = 20$
$\underline{3x + 2y + z = 8}$
$4x + 6y = 28 \ \ \text{Equation 4}$
Eliminate z from Equations 2 and 3 by multiplying Equation 2 by -2 and adding the resulting equation to Equation 3.
$-6x - 4y - 2z = -16$
$\underline{2x - 3y + 2z = -16}$
$-4x - 7y = -32 \ \ \text{Equation 5}$

Solve Equations 4 and 5 for x and y by adding Equation 4 and Equation 5.

$$4x + 6y = 28$$
$$\underline{-4x - 7y = -32}$$
$$-y = -4$$
$$y = 4$$

Substitute 4 for y in Equation 4 and solve for x.

$$4x + 6(4) = 28$$
$$4x + 24 = 28$$
$$4x = 4$$
$$x = 1$$

Substitute 1 for x and 4 for y in Equation 2 and solve for z.

$$3(1) + 2(4) + z = 8$$
$$3 + 8 + z = 8$$
$$11 + z = 8$$
$$z = -3$$

The solution set is $\{(1, 4, -3)\}$.

3. $2y - z = 7$
$$x + 2y + z = 17$$
$$2x - 3y + 2z = -1$$

Eliminate x and z from Equations 2 and 3 by multiplying Equation 2 by -2 and adding the resulting equation to Equation 3.

$$-2x - 4y - 2z = -34$$
$$\underline{2x - 3y + 2z = -1}$$
$$-7y = -35$$
$$y = 5$$

Substitute 5 for y in Equation 1 and solve for z.

$$2(5) - z = 7$$
$$10 - z = 7$$
$$-z = -3$$
$$z = 3$$

Substitute 5 for y and 3 for z in Equation 2 and solve for x.

$$x + 2(5) + 3 = 17$$
$$x + 10 + 3 = 17$$
$$x + 13 = 17$$
$$x = 4$$

The solution set is $\{(4, 5, 3)\}$.

4. $(1, 4), (2, 1), (3, 4)$
$$y = ax^2 + bx + c$$

Substitute 1 for x and 4 for y in
$$y = ax^2 + bx + c.$$
$$4 = a(1)^2 + b(1) + c$$
$$4 = a + b + c \quad \text{Equation 1}$$

Substitute 2 for x and 1 for y in
$$y = ax^2 + bx + c.$$
$$1 = a(2)^2 + b(2) + c$$
$$1 = 4a + 2b + c \quad \text{Equation 2}$$

Substitute 3 for x and 4 for y in
$$y = ax^2 + bx + c.$$
$$4 = a(3)^2 + b(3) + c$$
$$4 = 9a + 3b + c \quad \text{Equation 3}$$

Eliminate c from Equations 1 and 2 by multiplying Equation 2 by -1 and adding the resulting equation to Equation 1.

$$4 = a + b + c$$
$$\underline{-1 = -4a - 2b - c}$$
$$3 = -3a - b \qquad \text{Equation 4}$$

Eliminate c from Equation 2 and 3 by multiplying Equation 3 by -1 and adding the resulting equation to Equation 2.

$$1 = 4a + 2b + c$$
$$\underline{-4 = -9a - 3b - c}$$
$$-3 = -5a - b \qquad \text{Equation 5}$$

Solve Equations 4 and 5 for a and b by multiplying Equation 5 by -1 and adding the resulting equation to Equation 4.

$$3 = -3a - b$$
$$\underline{3 = 5a + b}$$
$$6 = 2a$$
$$a = 3$$

Substitute 3 for a in Equation 4 and solve for b.

$$3 = -3(3) - b$$
$$3 = -9 - b$$
$$12 = -b$$
$$b = -12$$

Substitute 3 for a and -12 for b in Equation 1 and solve for c.

$$4 = 3 - 12 + c$$
$$4 = -9 + c$$
$$c = 13$$

Substituting 3 for a, -12 for b, and 13 for c in the quadratic equation $y = ax^2 + bx + c$ gives

$$y = 3x^2 - 12x + 13.$$

Exercise Set 5.2

1. $x + y + z = 4$
$$2 - 1 + 3 \stackrel{\triangle}{=} 4$$
$$4 = 4 \text{ true}$$
$$x - 2y - z = 1$$
$$2(2) - 2(-1) - 3 = 1$$
$$4 + 2 - 3 = 1$$
$$1 = 1 \text{ true}$$
$$2x - y - 2z = -1$$
$$2(2) - (-1) - 2(3) \stackrel{\triangle}{=} -1$$
$$4 + 1 - 6 = -1$$
$$-1 = -1 \text{ false}$$

$(2, -1, 3)$ is a solution.

3. $x - 2y = 2$
$$4 - 2(1) = 2$$
$$4 - 2 = 2$$
$$2 = 2 \text{ true}$$
$$2x + 3y = 11$$
$$2(4) + 3(1) = 11$$
$$8 + 3 \stackrel{\triangle}{=} 11$$
$$11 = 11 \text{ true}$$
$$y - 4z = -7$$
$$1 - 4(2) \stackrel{\triangle}{=} -7$$
$$1 - 8 \stackrel{\triangle}{=} -7$$

$$-7 = -7 \text{ true}$$
$(4, 1, 2)$ is a solution.

5. $x + y + 2z = 11$
$$x + y + 3z = 14$$
$$x + 2y - z = 5$$

Eliminate x and y from Equations 1 and 2 by multiplying Equation 2 by -1 and adding the resulting equation to Equation 1.

$$-x - y - 3z = -14$$
$$\underline{x + y + 2z = 11}$$
$$-z = -3$$
$$z = 3$$

Substitute 3 for z in Equations 1 and 3.
$$x + y + 2(3) = 11$$
$$x + 2y - (3) = 5$$
Simplify:
$$x + y = 5 \qquad \text{Equation 4}$$
$$x + 2y = 8 \qquad \text{Equation 5}$$

Solve Equations 4 and 5 for x and y by multiplying Equation 5 by -1 and adding the resulting equation to Equation 4.

$$x + y = 5$$
$$\underline{-x - 2y = -8}$$
$$-y = -3$$
$$y = 3$$

Substitute 3 for z and 3 for y in Equation 2 and solve for x.
$$x + 3 + 3(3) = 14$$
$$x + 12 = 14$$
$$x = 2$$

The solution set is $\{(2, 3, 3)\}$.

7. $4x - y + 2z = 11$
$$x + 2y - z = -1$$
$$2x + 2y - 3z = -1$$

Eliminate y from Equation 1 and 2 by multiplying Equation 1 by 2 and adding the resulting equation to Equation 2 and 3.

$$8x - 2y + 4z = 22$$
$$\underline{x + 2y - z = -1}$$
$$9x + 3z = 21 \qquad \text{Equation 4}$$

Eliminate y from Equations 1 and 3 by multiplying Equation 1 by 2 and adding the resulting equation to Equation 3.

$$8x - 2y + 4z = 22$$
$$\underline{2x + 2y - 3z = -1}$$
$$10x + z = 21 \qquad \text{Equation 5}$$

Solve Equations 4 and 5 for x and z by multiplying Equation 5 by -3 and adding the resulting equation to Equation 4.

$$9x + 3z = 21$$
$$\underline{-30x - 3z = -63}$$
$$-21x = -42$$
$$x = 2$$

Substitute 2 for x in Equation 5 and solve for z. $10(2) + z = 21$

$$20 + z = 21$$
$$z = 1$$

Substitute 2 for x and 1 for z in Equation 2 and solve for y.

$$2 + 2y - 1 = -1$$
$$2y + 1 = -1$$
$$2y = -2$$
$$y = -1$$

The solution set is $\{(2, -1, 1)\}$.

9. $3x + 5y + 2z = 0$

    $12x - 15y + 4z = 12$

    $6x - 25y - 8z = 8$

    Eliminate z from Equations 1 and 3 by multiplying Equation 1 by -2 and adding the resulting equation to Equation 2.

    $$-6x - 10y - 4z = 0$$
    $$\underline{12x - 15y + 4z = 12}$$
    $$6x - 25y = 12 \qquad \text{Equation 4}$$

    Eliminate z from Equations 1 and 3 by multiplying Equation 1 by 4 and adding the

resulting equation to Equation 3.

$$12x + 20y + 8z = 0$$
$$\underline{6x - 25y - 8z = 8}$$
$$18x - 5y = 8 \qquad \text{Equation 5}$$

Solve Equations 4 and 5 for x and y by multiplying Equation 4 by -3 and adding the resulting equation to Equation 5.

$$-18x + 75y = -36$$
$$\underline{18x - 5y = 8}$$
$$70y = -28$$
$$y = -\frac{2}{5}$$

Substitute $-\frac{2}{5}$ for y in Equation 4 and solve for x.

$$6x - 25\left(-\frac{2}{5}\right) = 12$$
$$6x + 10 = 12$$
$$6x = 2$$
$$x = \frac{2}{6} = \frac{1}{3}$$

Substitute $\frac{1}{3}$ for x and $-\frac{2}{5}$ for y in Equation 1 and solve for z.

$$3\left(\frac{1}{3}\right) + 5\left(-\frac{2}{5}\right) + 2z = 0$$
$$1 - 2 + 2z = 0$$
$$2z - 1 = 0$$
$$2z = 1$$
$$z = \frac{1}{2}$$

The solution set is $\left\{\left(\frac{1}{3}, -\frac{2}{5}, \frac{1}{2}\right)\right\}$.

11. $2x - 4y + 3z = 17$

    $x + 2y - z = 0$

    $4x - y - z = 6$

    Eliminate z from Equations 1 and 2 by multiplying Equation 2 by 3 and adding the

271

resulting equation to Equation 1.

$2x - 4y + 3z = 17$

$3x + 6y - 3z = 0$

$\overline{\qquad 5x + 2y = 17 \qquad}$ Equation 4

Eliminate z from Equations 2 and 3 by multiplying Equation 2 by -1 and adding the resulting equation to Equation 3.

$-x - 2y + z = 0$

$\underline{4x - y - z = 6}$

$\qquad 3x - 3y = 6 \qquad$ Equation 5

Solve Equations 4 and 5 for x and y by multiplying Equation 5 by $\dfrac{2}{3}$ and adding the resulting equation to Equation 4.

$5x + 2y = 17$

$\underline{2x - 2y = 4}$

$\qquad 7x = 21$

$\qquad x = 3$

Substitute 3 for x in Equation 4 and solve for y.

$5(3) + 2y = 17$

$15 + 2y = 17$

$2y = 2$

$y = 1$

Substitute 3 for x and 1 for y in Equation 2 and solve for z.

$3 + 2(1) - z = 0$

$3 + 2 - z = 0$

$5 - z = 0$

$5 = z$

The solution set is $\left\{ (3, 1, 5) \right\}$.

13. $2x + y = 2$

$x + y - z = 4$

$3x + 2y + z = 0$

Eliminate z from Equations 2 and 3 by adding Equation 2 and Equation 3.

$x + y - z = 4$

$3x + 2y + z = 0$

$\overline{\qquad 4x + 3y = 4 \qquad}$ Equation 4

Solve Equations 1 and 4 for x and y by multiplying Equation 1 by -3 and adding the resulting equation to Equation 4.

$-6x - 3y = -6$

$\underline{4x + 3y = 4}$

$\qquad -2x = -2$

$\qquad x = 1$

Substitute 1 for x in Equation 1 and solve for y.

$2(1) + y = 2$

$2 + y = 2$

$y = 0$

Substitute 1 for x and 0 for y in Equation 2 and solve for z.

$1 + 0 - z = 4$

$1 - z = 4$

$-z = 3$

$z = -3$

The solution set is $\{(1, 0, -3)\}$.

15. $x + y = -4$

$y - z = 1$

$2x + y + 3z = -21$

Eliminate y from Equations 1 and 2 by multiplying Equation 1 by -1 and adding the resulting equation to Equation 2.

$-x - y = 4$

$\underline{y - z = 1}$

$-x - z = 5$ Equation 4

Eliminate y from Equations 2 and 3 by multiplying Equation 2 by -1 and adding the resulting equation to Equation 3.

$-y + z = -1$

$\underline{2x + y + 3z = -21}$

$\qquad 2x + 4z = -22$ Equation 5

Solve Equations 4 and 5 for x and z by multiplying Equation 4 by 2 and adding the resulting equation to Equation 5.

$$-2x - 2z = 10$$
$$\underline{2x + 4z = -22}$$
$$2z = -12$$
$$z = -6$$

Substitute -6 for z in Equation 2 and solve for y.

$$y - (-6) = 1$$
$$y + 6 = 1$$
$$y = -5$$

Substitute -5 for y in Equation 1 and solve for x

$$x + (-5) = -4$$
$$x = 1$$

The solution set is $\{(1, -5, -6)\}$.

17. $3(2x + y) + 5z = -1$
$\quad 2(x - 3y + 4z) = -9$
$\quad 4(1 + x) = -3(z - 3y)$

Simplify each equation.

$\quad 6x + 3y + 5z = -1 \quad$ Equation 4
$\quad 2x - 6y + 8z = -9 \quad$ Equation 5
$\quad 4 + 4x = -3z + 9y$
$\quad 4x - 9y + 3z = -4 \quad$ Equation 6

Eliminate x from Equations 4 and 5 by multiplying Equation 5 by -3 and adding the resulting equation to Equation 4.

$$-6x + 3y + 5z = -1$$
$$\underline{-6x + 18y - 24z = 27}$$
$$21y - 19z = 26 \quad \text{Equation 7}$$

Eliminate x from Equations 5 and 6 by multiplying Equation 5 by -2 and adding the resulting equation to Equation 6.

$$-4x + 12y - 16z = 18$$
$$\underline{4x - 9y + 3z = -4}$$
$$3y - 13z = 14 \quad \text{Equation 8}$$

Solve Equations 7 and 8 for y and z by multiplying Equation 8 by -7 and adding the resulting equation to Equation 7.

$$21y - 19z = 26$$
$$\underline{-21y + 91z = -98}$$
$$72z = -72$$
$$z = -1$$

Substitute -1 for z in Equation 8 and solve for y.

$$3y - 13(-1) = 14$$
$$3y + 13 = 14$$
$$3y = 1$$
$$y = \frac{1}{3}$$

Substitute $\dfrac{1}{3}$ for y and -1 for z in Equation 5 and solve for x.

$$2x - 6\left(\frac{1}{3}\right) + 8(-1) = -9$$
$$2x - 2 - 8 = -9$$
$$2x - 10 = -9$$
$$2x = 1$$
$$x = \frac{1}{2}$$

The solution set is $\left\{\left(\dfrac{1}{2}, \dfrac{1}{3}, -1\right)\right\}$.

19. $x + y + z = 16$
$\quad 2x + 3y + 4z = 46$
$\quad 5x - y = 31$

Eliminate z from Equations 1 and 2 by multiplying Equation 1 by -4 and adding the resulting equation to Equation 2.

$$-4x - 4y - 4z = -64$$
$$\underline{2x + 3y + 4z = 46}$$
$$-2x - y = -18 \quad \text{Equation 4}$$

Solve Equations 3 and 4 for x and y by multiplying Equation 4 by -1 and adding the resulting equation to Equation 3.

$5x - y = 31$

$\dfrac{2x + y = 18}{7x = 49}$

$x = 7$

Substitute 7 for x in Equation 3 and solve for y.

$5(7) - y = 31$

$35 - y = 31$

$-y = -4$

$y = 4$

Substitute 7 for x and 4 for y in Equation 1 and solve for z.

$7 + 4 + z = 16$

$z + 11 = 16$

$z = 5$

The numbers are 7, 4 and 5.

21. $(-1, 6), (1, 4), (2, 9)$

$y = ax^2 + bx + c$

Substitute -1 for x and 6 for y in

$y = ax^2 + bx + c$.

$6 = a(-1)^2 + b(-1) + c$

$6 = a - b + c$ Equation 1

Substitute 1 for x and 4 for y in

$y = ax^2 + bx + c$.

$4 = a(1)^2 + b(1) + c$

$4 = a + b + c$ Equation 2

Substitute 2 for x and 9 for y in

$y = ax^2 + bx + c$.

$9 = a(2)^2 + b(2) + c$

$9 = 4a + 2b + c$ Equation 3

Eliminate b from Equations 1 and 2 by adding Equation 1 and Equation 2.

$6 = a - b + c$

$\dfrac{4 = a + b + c}{10 = 2a + 2c}$ Equation 4

Eliminate b from Equations 1 and 3 by multiplying Equation 1 by 2 and adding the

resulting equation to Equation 3.

$12 = 2a - 2b + 2c$

$\dfrac{9 = 4a + 2b + c}{21 = 6a + 3c}$ Equation 5

Solve Equations 4 and 5 for a and c by multiplying Equation 4 by -3 and adding the resulting equation to Equation 5.

$-30 = -6a - 6c$

$\dfrac{21 = 6a + 3c}{-9 = -3c}$

$c = 3$

Substitute 3 for c in Equation 4 and solve for a.

$10 = 2a + 2(3)$

$10 = 2a + 6$

$4 = 2a$

$a = 2$

Substitute 2 for a and 3 for c in Equation 2 and solve for b.

$4 = 2 + b + 3$

$4 = b + 5$

$b = -1$

Substituting 2 for a, -1 for b, and 3 for c in

the quadratic equation $y = ax^2 + bx + c$

gives $y = 2x^2 - x + 3$.

23. $(-1, -4), (1, -2), (2, 5)$

Substitute -1 for x and -4 for y in
$y = ax^2 + bx + c.$
$-4 = a(-1)^2 + b(-1) + c$
$-4 = a - b + c$ Equation 1

Substitute 1 for x and -2 for y in
$y = ax^2 + bx + c.$
$-2 = a(1)^2 + b(1) + c$
$-2 = a + b + c$ Equation 2

Substitute 2 for x and 5 for y in
$y = ax^2 + bx + c.$
$5 = a(2)^2 + b(2) + c$
$5 = 4a + 2b + c$ Equation 3

Eliminate a and b from Equations 1 and 2 by multiplying Equation 1 by -1 and adding the resulting equation to Equation 2.

$\begin{array}{r} 4 = -a + b - c \\ \underline{-2 = a + b + c} \\ 2 = 2b \end{array}$

$b = 1$

Eliminate c from Equations 1 and 3 by multiplying Equation 1 by -1 and adding the resulting equation to Equation 3.

$\begin{array}{r} 4 = -a + b - c \\ \underline{5 = 4a + 2b + c} \\ 9 = 3a + 3b \end{array}$ Equation 4

Substitute 1 for b in Equation 4 and solve for a.
$9 = 3a + 3(1)$
$9 = 3a + 3$
$6 = 3a$
$a = 2$

Substitute 2 for a and 1 for b in Equation 2 and solve for c.
$-2 = 2 + 1 + c$
$-2 = c + 3$
$c = -5$

Substituting 2 for a, 1 for b, and -5 for c

in quadratic equation $y = ax^2 + bx + c$
gives $y = 2x^2 + x - 5$.

25. a. $(0, 1180)$ $(1, 1070)$ $(2, 1230)$

b. $1180 = a(0)^2 + b(0) + c$
$1180 = c$
$1070 = a(1)^2 + b(1) + c$
$1070 = a + b + c$

$1230 = a(2)^2 + b(2) + c$
$1230 = 4a + 2b + c$

c. Substitute 1180 for c in the second and third equations.
$a + b + 1180 = 1070$
$a + b = -110$

$4a + 2b + 1180 = 1230$
$4a + 2b = 50$

Multiply the first equation by -2 and add to the second equation. Solve for a.

$\begin{array}{r} -2a - 2b = 220 \\ \underline{4a + 2b = 50} \\ 2a = 270 \\ a = 135 \end{array}$

Substitute 135 for a in the first equation and solve for b.
$135 + b = -110$
$b = -245$

The quadratic equation is
$y = 135x^2 - 245x + 1180$.

27. a. Substitute the values for x and y into the quadratic form.

$224 = a(1)^2 + b(1) + c$

$a + b + c = 224$

$176 = a(3)^2 + b(3) + c$

$9a + 3b + c = 176$

$104 = a(4)^2 + b(4) + c$

$16a + 4b + c = 104$

Multiply the first equation by –1 and add to both the second and the third equations to obtain 2 new equations with 2 variables.

$-a - b - c = -224$

$9a + 3b + c = 176$

$8a + 2b = -48$

$-a - b - c = -224$

$16a + 4b + c = 104$

$15a + 3b = -120$

Use the two new equations to solve for a and b. Multiply the first equation by –3 and the second equation by 2 and add the results together. Solve for a. Substitute that value in $8a + 2b = -48$ and solve for b.

$-24a - 6b = 144$

$30a + 6b = -240$

$6a = -96$

$a = -16$

$8(-16) + 2b = -48$

$-128 + 2b = -48$

$2b = 80$

$b = 40$

Substitute –16 for a and 40 for b into the equation $a + b + c = 224$ and solve for c.

$-16 + 40 + c = 224$

$c = 200$

The equation is $y = -16x^2 + 40x + 200$.

b. $-16(5)^2 + 40(5) + 200 = 0$
The ball hit the ground after 5 seconds.

29. $x + y + z = 256$

$x - y = 4$

$y - z = 36$

Multiply the second equation by _1 and add to the first equation.

$x + y + z = 256$

$-x + y = -4$

$2y + z = 252$

Add this new equation to equation to the third equation and solve for y.

$2y + z = 252$

$y - z = 36$

$3y = 288$

$y = 96$

Substitute 96 for y in the equation $x - y = 4$ and solve for x. Substitute 96 for y into the equation $y - z = 36$ and solve for z.

$x - 96 = 4$

$x = 100$

$96 - z = 36$

$z = -60$

$z = 60$

Andrew Carnegie's fortune is worth $100 billion in today's money. Cornelius Vanderbilt's fortune is worth $96 billion and Bill Gates is worth $60 billion.

31. x = number of $8 tickets sold
y = number of $10 tickets sold
z = number of $12 tickets sold
From the given conditions we have the following system of equations.

$x + y + z = 400$

$8x + 10y + 12z = 3700$

$x + y = 7z$ or $x + y - 7z = 0$

Eliminate z from Equations 1 and 2 multiplying Equation 1 by –12 and adding the resulting equation to Equation 2.

$-12x - 12y - 12z = -4800$

$\underline{8x + 10y + 12z = 3700}$

$\qquad -4x - 2y = -1100 \qquad$ Equation 4

Eliminate z from Equations 1 and 3 by multiplying Equation 1 by 7 and adding the resulting equation to Equation 3.

$7x + 7y + 7z = 2800$

$\underline{x + y - 7z = 0}$

$\qquad 8x + 8y = 2800 \qquad$ Equation 5

Solve Equations 4 and 5 for x and y by multiplying Equation 4 by 2 and adding the resulting equation to Equation 5.

$-8x - 4y = -2200$

$\underline{8x + 8y = 2800}$

$\qquad 4y = 600$

$\qquad y = 150$

Substitute 150 for y in Equation 5 and solve for x.

$8x + 8(150) = 2800$

$\qquad 8x = 2800 - 1200$

$\qquad 8x = 1600$

$\qquad x = 200$

Substitute 200 for x and 150 for y in Equation 1 and solve for z.

$200 + 150 + z = 400$

$\qquad 350 + z = 400$

$\qquad z = 50$

The number of \$8 tickets sold was 200.
The number of \$10 tickets sold was 150.
The number of \$12 tickets sold was 50.

33. x = amount of money invested at 10%
y = amount of money invested at 12%
z = amount of money invested at 15%

$\qquad x + y + z = 6700$

$0.08x + 0.10y + 0.12z = 716$

$\qquad\qquad z = x + y + 300$

Arrange Equation 3 so that variable terms appear on the left and constants appear on the right.

$-x - y + z = 300 \qquad$ Equation 4

Eliminate x and y from Equations 1 and 4 by adding Equations 1 and 4.

$x + y + z = 6700$

$\underline{-x - y + z = 300}$

$\qquad 2z = 7000$

$\qquad z = 3500$

Substitute 3500 for z in Equation 1 and Equation 2 and simplify.

$x + y + 3500 = 6700$

$\qquad x + y = 3200 \qquad$ Equation 5

$0.08x + 0.10y + 0.12(3500) = 716$

$\qquad 0.08x + 0.10y + 420 = 716$

$\qquad\qquad 0.08x + 10y = 296 \qquad$ Equation 6

Solve Equations 5 and 6 for x and y by multiplying Equation 5 by -0.10 and adding the resulting equation to Equation 6.

$-0.10x - 0.10y = -320$

$\underline{0.08x + 0.10y = 296}$

$\qquad -0.02x = 24$

$\qquad x = 1200$

Substitute 1200 for x and 3,500 for z in Equation 1 and solve for y.

$1200 + y + 3500 = 6700$

$\qquad y + 4700 = 6700$

$\qquad y = 2000$

The person invested \$1200 at 8%, \$2000 at 10%, and \$3500 at 12%.

35. $x + y + z = 180$

$2x - 5 + z = 180$

$\qquad 2x + z = 185$

$2x + 5 + y = 180$

$\qquad 2x + y = 175$

Multiply the second equation by -1 and add to the first equation. Use the new equation and the third equation to solve for x and z.

$$-2x - z = -185$$
$$x + y + z = 180$$
$$-x + y = -5$$

Multiply the new equation by -1.

$$x - y = 5$$
$$2x + y = 175$$
$$3x = 180$$
$$x = 60$$

$$60 - y = 5$$
$$-y = -55$$
$$y = 55$$

Substitute 60 for x and 55 for y in the first equation and solve for z.

$$60 + 55 + z = 180$$
$$z = 65$$

37.–39. Answers may vary.

41. Exercise 21 $y = 2x^2 - x + 3$

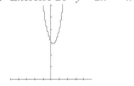

Exercise 23 $y = 2x^2 + x - 5$

43. Answers may vary.

Section 5.3

Check Point Exercises

1. $\dfrac{5x - 1}{(x - 3)(x + 4)} = \dfrac{A}{x - 3} + \dfrac{B}{x + 4}$

Multiply both sides of the equation by the least common denominator $(x - 3)(x + 4)$ and divide out common factors.

$$5x - 1 = A(x + 4) + B(x - 3)$$
$$5x - 1 = Ax + 4A + Bx - 3B$$
$$5x - 1 = (A + B)x + 4A - 3B$$

Equate coefficients of like powers of x and equate constant terms.

$$A + B = 5$$
$$4A - 3B = -1$$

Solving the above system for A and B we find

$A = 2$ and $B = 3$.

$$\dfrac{5x - 1}{(x - 3)(x + 4)} = \dfrac{2}{x - 3} + \dfrac{3}{x + 4}$$

2. $\dfrac{x + 2}{x(x - 1)^2} = \dfrac{A}{x} + \dfrac{B}{x - 1} + \dfrac{C}{(x - 1)^2}$

Multiply both sides of the equation by the least common denominator $x(x - 1)^2$ and divide out common factors.

$$x + 2 = A(x - 1)^2 + Bx(x - 1) + Cx$$
$$x + 2 = A\left(x^2 - 2x + 1\right) + Bx^2 - Bx + Cx$$
$$x + 2 = Ax^2 - 2Ax + A + Bx^2 - Bx + Cx$$
$$x + 2 = Ax^2 + Bx^2 - 2Ax - Bx + Cx + A$$
$$x + 2 = (A + B)x^2 + (-2A - B + C)x + A$$

Equate coefficients of like powers of x and equate constant terms.

$$A + B = 0$$
$$-2A - B + C = 1$$
$$A = 2$$

Since $A = 2$, we find that $B = -2$ and $C = 3$ by substitution.

$$\dfrac{x + 2}{x(x - 1)^2} = \dfrac{2}{x} - \dfrac{2}{x - 1} + \dfrac{3}{(x - 1)^2}$$

278

3. $\dfrac{8x^2 + 12x - 20}{(x+3)(x^2 + x + 2)} = \dfrac{A}{x+3} + \dfrac{Bx + C}{x^2 + x + 2}$

Multiply both sides of the equation by the least common denominator $(x+3)(x^2 + x + 2)$ and divide out common factors.

$8x^2 + 12x - 20 = A(x^2 + x + 2) + (Bx + C)(x + 3)$

$8x^2 + 12x - 20 = Ax^2 + Ax + 2A + Bx^2 + 3Bx + Cx + 3C$

$8x^2 + 12x - 20 = Ax^2 + Bx^2 + Ax + 3Bx + Cx + 2A + 3C$

$8x^2 + 12x - 20 = (A + B)x^2 + (A + 3B + C)x + 2A + 3C$

Equate coefficients of like powers of x and equate constant terms.

$\qquad A + B = 8$

$A + 3B + C = 12$

$\qquad 2A + 3C = -20$

Solving the above system for A, B, and C we find $A = 2$, $B = 6$, and $C = -8$.

$\dfrac{8x^2 + 12x - 20}{(x+3)(x^2 + x + 2)} = \dfrac{2}{x+3} + \dfrac{6x - 8}{x^2 + x + 2}$

4. $\dfrac{2x^3 + x + 3}{\left(x^2 + 1\right)^2} = \dfrac{Ax + B}{x^2 + 1} + \dfrac{Cx + D}{\left(x^2 + 1\right)^2}$

Multiply both sides of the equation by the common denominator $\left(x^2 + 1\right)^2$ and divide out common factors.

$2x^3 + x + 3 = (Ax + B)(x^2 + 1) + Cx + D$

$2x^3 + x + 3 = Ax^3 + Bx^2 + Ax + B + Cx + D$

$2x^3 + x + 3 = Ax^3 + Bx^2 + Ax + Cx + B + D$

$2x^3 + x + 3 = Ax^3 + Bx^2 + (A + C)x + B + D$

Equate coefficients of like powers of x and equate constant terms.

$\qquad A = 2$

$\qquad B = 0$

$A + C = 1$

$B + D = 3$

Since $A = 2$ and $B = 0$ we find that $C = -1$ and $D = 3$ by substitution.

$\dfrac{2x^3 + x + 3}{\left(x^2 + 1\right)^2} = \dfrac{2x}{x^2 + 1} + \dfrac{-x + 3}{\left(x^2 + 1\right)^2} = \dfrac{2x}{x^2 + 1} - \dfrac{x - 3}{\left(x^2 + 1\right)^2}$

Exercise Set 5.3

1. $\dfrac{11x-10}{(x-2)(x+1)} = \dfrac{A}{x-2} + \dfrac{B}{x+1}$

3. $\dfrac{6x^2-14x-27}{(x+2)(x-3)^2} = \dfrac{A}{x+2} + \dfrac{B}{x-3} + \dfrac{C}{(x-3)^2}$

5. $\dfrac{5x^2-6x+7}{(x-1)(x^2+1)} = \dfrac{A}{x-1} + \dfrac{Bx+C}{x^2+1}$

7. $\dfrac{x^3+x^2}{(x^2+4)^2} = \dfrac{Ax+B}{x^2+4} + \dfrac{Cx+D}{(x^2+4)^2}$

9. $\dfrac{x}{(x-3)(x-2)} = \dfrac{A}{x-3} + \dfrac{B}{x-2}$

Multiply both sides of the equation by the least common denominator $(x-3)(x-2)$ and divide out common factors.

$x = A(x-2) + B(x-3)$

$x = Ax - 2A + Bx - 3B$

$x = Ax + Bx - 2A - 3B$

$x = (A+B)x - (2A+3B)$

Equate coefficients of like powers of x, and equate constant terms.

$\quad A+B=1$

$2A+3B=0$

Solving the above system for A and B, we find $A = 3$ and $B = -2$.

$\dfrac{x}{(x-3)(x-2)} = \dfrac{3}{x-3} - \dfrac{2}{x-2}$

11. $\dfrac{3x+50}{(x-9)(x+2)} = \dfrac{A}{x-9} + \dfrac{B}{x+2}$

Multiply both sides of the equation by the least common denominator $(x-9)(x+2)$ and divide out common factors.

$3x+50 = A(x+2) + B(x-9)$

$3x+50 = Ax + 2A + Bx - 9B$

$3x+50 = Ax + Bx + 2A - 9B$

$3x+50 = (A+B)x + (2A-9B)$

Equate coefficients of like powers of x, and equate constant terms.

$\quad A+B=3$

$2A-9B=50$

Solving the above system for A and B, we find $A = 7$ and $B = -4$.

$\dfrac{3x+50}{(x-9)(x+2)} = \dfrac{7}{x-9} - \dfrac{4}{x+2}$

13. $\dfrac{7x-4}{x^2-x-12} = \dfrac{7x-4}{(x-4)(x+3)} = \dfrac{A}{x-4} + \dfrac{B}{x+3}$

Multiply both sides of the last equation by the least common denominator $(x-4)(x-3)$ and divide out common factors.

$7x-4 = A(x+3) + B(x-4)$

$7x-4 = Ax + 3A + Bx - 4B$

$7x-4 = Ax + Bx + 3A - 4B$

$7x-4 = (A+B)x + (3A-4B)$

Equate coefficients of like powers of x, and equate constant terms.

$\quad A+B=7$

$3A-4B=-4$

Solving the above system for A and B, we

find $A = \dfrac{24}{7}$ and $B = \dfrac{25}{7}$.

$$\frac{7x-4}{x^2-x-12} = \frac{24}{7(x-4)} + \frac{25}{7(x+3)}$$

15. $\dfrac{4}{(2x+1)(x-3)} = \dfrac{A}{2x+1} + \dfrac{B}{x-3}$

Multiply both sides of the equation by the least common denominator $(2x + 1)(x - 3)$ and divide out common factors.

$4 = A(x-3) + B(2x+1)$

$4 = Ax - A3 + B2x + B$

$4 = (A+2B)x + (-3A+B)$

Equate coefficients of like powers of x and equate the constant terms. Solve for A and B.

$$\frac{4}{(2x+1)(x-3)} = \frac{-8}{7(2x+1)} + \frac{4}{7(x-3)}$$

$A + 2B = 0$
$-3A + B = 4$

$3A + 6B = 0$
$-3A + B = 4$
$7B = 4$
$B = \dfrac{4}{7}$

$A + 2B = 0$
$6A - 2B = -8$
$7A = -8$
$A = -\dfrac{8}{7}$

17. $\dfrac{4x^2 + 13x - 9}{x(x-1)(x+3)} = \dfrac{A}{x} + \dfrac{B}{x-3} + \dfrac{C}{x+3}$

Multiply both sides of the equation by the least common denominator $x(x-1)(x+3)$ and divide out common factors.

$4x^2 + 13x - 9 = A(x-1)(x+3) + Bx(x+3) + Cx(x-1)$

$4x^2 + 13x - 9 = A(x^2 + 2x - 3) + Bx^2 + 3Bx + Cx^2 - Cx$

$4x^2 + 13x - 9 = Ax^2 + 2Ax - 3A + Bx^2 + 3Bx + Cx^2 - Cx$

$4x^2 + 13x - 9 = Ax^2 + Bx^2 + Cx^2 + 2Ax + 3Bx - Cx - 3A$

$4x^2 + 13x - 9 = (A + B + C)x^2 + (2A + 3B - C)x - 3A$

Equate coefficients of like powers of x, and equate constant terms.

$A + B + C = 4$

$2A + 3B - C = 13$

$-3A = -9$

Solving the above system for A, B, and C, we find $A = 3$ and $B = 2$, and $C = -1$.

$\dfrac{4x^2 + 13x - 9}{x(x-1)(x+3)} = \dfrac{3}{x} + \dfrac{2}{x-1} - \dfrac{1}{x+3}$

19. $\dfrac{4x^2 - 7x - 3}{x^3 - x} = \dfrac{4x^2 - 7x - 3}{x(x+1)(x-1)} = \dfrac{A}{x} + \dfrac{B}{x+1} + \dfrac{C}{x-1}$

Multiply both sides of the last equation by the least common denominator $x(x+1)(x-1)$ and divide out common factors.

$4x^2 - 7x - 3 = A(x+1)(x-1) + Bx(x-1) + Cx(x+1)$

$4x^2 - 7x - 3 = A(x^2 - 1) + Bx^2 - Bx + Cx^2 + Cx$

$4x^2 - 7x - 3 = Ax^2 - A + Bx^2 - Bx + Cx^2 + Cx$

$4x^2 - 7x - 3 = Ax^2 + Bx^2 + Cx^2 - Bx + Cx - A$

$4x^2 - 7x - 3 = (A + B + C)x^2 + (-B + C)x - A$

Equate coefficients of like powers of x, and equate constant terms.

$A + B + C = 4$

$-B + C = -7$

$-A = -3$

Solving the above system for A, B, and C, we find $A = 3$ and $B = 4$, and $C = -3$.

$\dfrac{4x^2 - 7x - 3}{x^3 - x} = \dfrac{3}{x} + \dfrac{4}{x+1} - \dfrac{3}{x-1}$

21. $\dfrac{6x-11}{(x-1)^2} = \dfrac{A}{x-1} + \dfrac{B}{(x-1)^2}$

Multiply both sides of the equation by the least common denominator $(x-1)^2$ and divide out common factors.

$6x - 11 = A(x-1) + B$

$6x - 11 = Ax - A + B$

Equate coefficients of like powers of x, and equate constant terms.

$\quad A = 6$

$-A + B = -11$

Since $A = 6$, we find that $B = -5$ by substitution. $\dfrac{6x-11}{(x-1)^2} = \dfrac{6}{x-1} - \dfrac{5}{(x-1)^2}$

23. $\dfrac{x^2-6x+3}{(x-2)^3} = \dfrac{A}{x-2} + \dfrac{B}{(x-2)^2} + \dfrac{C}{(x-2)^3}$

Multiply both sides of the equation by the least common denominator $(x-2)^3$ and divide out common factors.

$x^2 - 6x + 3 = A(x-2)^2 + B(x-2) + C$

$x^2 - 6x + 3 = A(x^2 - 4x + 4) + Bx - 2B + C$

$x^2 - 6x + 3 = Ax^2 - 4Ax + 4A + Bx - 2B + C$

$x^2 - 6x + 3 = Ax^2 - 4Ax + Bx + 4A - 2B + C$

$x^2 - 6x + 3 = Ax^2 + (-4A + B)x + 4A - 2B + C$

Equate coefficients of like powers of x, and equate constant terms.

$\quad\quad A = 1$

$\quad -4A + B = -6$

$4A - 2B + C = 3$

Since $A = 1$, we find that $B = -2$ and $C = -5$ by substitution. $\dfrac{x^2-6x+3}{(x-2)^3} = \dfrac{1}{x-2} - \dfrac{2}{(x-2)^2} - \dfrac{5}{(x-2)^3}$

25. $\dfrac{x^2+2x+7}{x(x-1)^2} = \dfrac{A}{x} + \dfrac{B}{x-1} + \dfrac{C}{(x-1)^2}$

Multiply both sides of the equation by the least common denominator $x(x-1)^2$ and divide out common factors.

$x^2 + 2x + 7 = A(x-1)^2 + Bx(x-1) + Cx$

$x^2 + 2x + 7 = A(x^2 - 2x + 1) + Bx^2 - Bx + Cx$

$x^2 + 2x + 7 = Ax^2 - 2Ax + A + Bx^2 - Bx + Cx$

$x^2 + 2x + 7 = Ax^2 + Bx^2 - 2Ax - Bx + Cx + A$

$x^2 + 2x + 7 = (A+B)x^2 + (-2A - B + C)x + A$

$$A + B = 1$$
$$-2A - B + C = 2$$
$$A = 7$$

Since $A = 7$, we find that $B = -6$ and $C = 10$ by substitution. $\dfrac{x^2 + 2x + 7}{x(x-1)^2} = \dfrac{7}{x} - \dfrac{6}{x-1} + \dfrac{10}{(x-1)^2}$

27. $\dfrac{x^2}{(x+1)(x-1)^2} = \dfrac{A}{x+1} + \dfrac{B}{x-1} + \dfrac{C}{(x-1)^2}$

Multiply both sides of the equation by the least common denominator $(x+1)(x-1)^2$ and divide out common factors.

$$x^2 = A(x-1)^2 + B(x+1)(x-1) + C(x+1)$$
$$x^2 = x^2 A - 2xA + A + Bx^2 - B + Cx + C$$
$$x^2 = (A+B)x^2 + (-2A+C)x + (A-B+C)$$

Equate coefficients of like powers of x, and equate constant terms.

$$A + B = 1$$
$$-2A + C = 0$$
$$A - B + C = 0$$

Solving the above system for A, B, and C, we find $A = \dfrac{1}{4}$, $B = \dfrac{3}{4}$, and $C = \dfrac{1}{2}$.

$$\dfrac{x^2}{(x+1)(x-1)^2} = \dfrac{1}{4(x+1)} + \dfrac{3}{4(x-1)} + \dfrac{1}{2(x-1)^2}$$

29. $\dfrac{5x^2 - 6x + 7}{(x-1)(x^2+1)} = \dfrac{A}{x-1} + \dfrac{Bx+C}{x^2+1}$

Multiply both sides of the equation by the least common denominator $(x-1)(x^2+1)$ and divide out common factors.

$$5x^2 - 6x + 7 = A(x^2+1) + (Bx+C)(x-1)$$
$$5x^2 - 6x + 7 = Ax^2 + A + Bx^2 - Bx + Cx - C$$
$$5x^2 - 6x + 7 = Ax^2 + Bx^2 - Bx + Cx + A - C$$
$$5x^2 - 6x + 7 = (A+B)x^2 + (-B+C)x + A - C$$

Equate coefficients of like powers of x, and equate constant terms.

$$A + B = 5$$
$$-B + C = -6$$
$$A - C = 7$$

Solving the above system for A, B, and C, we find $A = 3$, $B = 2$, and $C = -4$.

$$\dfrac{5x^2 - 6x + 7}{(x-1)(x^2+1)} = \dfrac{3}{x-1} + \dfrac{2x-4}{x^2+1}$$

284

31. $\dfrac{5x^2 + 6x + 3}{(x+1)(x^2 + 2x + 2)} = \dfrac{A}{x+1} + \dfrac{Bx + C}{x^2 + 2x + 2}$

Multiply both sides of the equation by the least common denominator $(x + 1)(x^2 + 2x + 2)$ and divide out common factors.

$5x^2 + 6x + 3 = A(x^2 + 2x + 2) + (Bx + C)(x + 1)$

$5x^2 + 6x + 3 = Ax^2 + 2Ax + 2A + Bx^2 + Bx + Cx + C$

$5x^2 + 6x + 3 = Ax^2 + Bx^2 + 2Ax + Bx + Cx + 2A + C$

$5x^2 + 6x + 3 = (A + B)x^2 + (2A + B + C)x + 2A + C$

Equate coefficients of like powers of x, and equate constant terms.

$\quad A + B = 5$

$2A + B + C = 6$

$\quad 2A + C = 3$

Solving the above system for A, B, and C, we find $A = 2$, $B = 3$, and $C = -1$.

$\dfrac{5x^2 + 6x + 3}{(x+1)(x^2 + 2x + 2)} = \dfrac{2}{x+1} + \dfrac{3x - 1}{x^2 + 2x + 2}$

33. $\dfrac{x + 4}{x^2(x^2 + 4)} = \dfrac{A}{x} + \dfrac{B}{x^2} + \dfrac{Cx + D}{x^2 + 4}$

Multiply both sides of the equation by the least common denominator $x^2(x^2 + 4)$ and divide out common factors.

$x + 4 = Ax(x^2 + 4) + B(x^2 + 4) + (Cx + D)x^2$

$x + 4 = Ax^3 + 4Ax + Bx^2 + 4B + Cx^3 + Dx^2$

$x + 4 = (A + C)x^3 + (B + D)x^2 + 4Ax + 4B$

Equate coefficients of like powers of x, and equate constant terms

$A + C = 0$

$B + D = 0$

$4A = 1$

$4B = 4$

Solving the above system for A, B, and C, we find $A = \dfrac{1}{4}$, $B = 1$, $C = -\dfrac{1}{4}$, and $D = -1$.

$$\frac{x+4}{x^2(x^2+4)} = \frac{1}{4x} + \frac{1}{x^2} + \frac{-1x-4}{4\left(x^2+2\right)}$$

35. $\dfrac{6x^2-x+1}{x^3+x^2+x+1} = \dfrac{6x^2-x+1}{(x+1)(x^2+1)} = \dfrac{A}{x+1} + \dfrac{Bx+C}{x^2+1}$

Multiply both sides of the last equation by the least common denominator $(x+1)(x^2+1)$ and divide out common factors.

$6x^2 - x + 1 = A(x^2+1) + (Bx+C)(x+1)$

$6x^2 - x + 1 = Ax^2 + A + Bx^2 + Bx + Cx + C$

$6x^2 - x + 1 = Ax^2 + Bx^2 + Bx + Cx + A + C$

$6x^2 - x + 1 = (A+B)x^2 + (B+C)x + A + C$

Equate coefficients of like powers of x, and equate constant terms.

$A + B = 6$

$B + C = -1$

$A + C = 1$

Solving the above system for A, B, and C, we find $A = 4$, $B = 2$, and $C = -3$.

$$\frac{6x^2-x+1}{x^3+x^2+x+1} = \frac{4}{x+1} + \frac{2x-3}{x^2+1}$$

37. $\dfrac{x^3+x^2+2}{\left(x^2+2\right)^2} = \dfrac{Ax+B}{x^2+2} + \dfrac{Cx+D}{\left(x^2+2\right)^2}$

Multiply both sides of the last equation by the least common denominator $(x^2+2)^2$ and divide out common factors.

$x^3 + x^2 + 2 = \left(Ax+B\right)\left(x^2+2\right) + Cx + D$

$x^3 + x^2 + 2 = Ax^3 + Bx^2 + 2Ax + 2B + Cx + D$

$x^3 + x^2 + 2 = Ax^3 + Bx^2 + 2Ax + Cx + 2B + D$

$x^3 + x^2 + 2 = Ax^3 + Bx^2 + \left(2A+C\right)x + \left(2B+D\right)$

Equate coefficients of like powers of x, and equate constant terms.

$A = 1$

$B = 1$

$2A + C = 0$

$2B + D = 2$

Since $A = 1$ and $B = 1$, we find that $C = -2$ and $D = 0$ by substitution.

$$\frac{x^3+x^2+2}{\left(x^2+2\right)^2} = \frac{x+1}{x^2+2} - \frac{2x}{\left(x^2+2\right)^2}$$

39. $\dfrac{x^3 - 4x^2 + 9x - 5}{(x^2 - 2x + 3)^2} = \dfrac{Ax + B}{x^2 - 2x + 3} + \dfrac{Cx + D}{(x^2 - 2x + 3)^2}$

Multiply both sides of the equation by the least common denominator $(x^2 - 2x + 3)^2$ and divide out common factors.

$x^3 - 4x^2 + 9x - 5 = (Ax + B)(x^2 - 2x + 3) + Cx + D$

$x^3 - 4x^2 + 9x - 5 = Ax^3 - 2Ax^2 + 3Ax + Bx^2 - 2Bx + 3B + Cx + D$

$x^3 - 4x^2 + 9x - 5 = Ax^3 - 2Ax^2 + Bx^2 + 3Ax - 2Bx + Cx + 3B + D$

$x^3 - 4x^2 + 9x - 5 = Ax^3 + (-2A + B)x^2 + (3A - 2B + C)x + 3B + D$

Equate coefficients of like powers of x, and equate constant terms.

$A = 1$

$-2A + B = -4$

$3A - 2B + C = 9$

$3B + D = -5$

Since $A = 1$, we find that $B = -2$, $C = 2$, and $D = 1$ by substitution.

$\dfrac{x^3 - 4x^2 + 9x - 5}{(x^2 - 2x + 3)^2} = \dfrac{x - 2}{x^2 - 2x + 3} + \dfrac{2x + 1}{(x^2 - 2x + 3)^2}$

41. $\dfrac{4x^2 + 3x + 14}{x^3 - 8} = \dfrac{4x^2 + 3x + 14}{(x - 2)(x^2 + 2x + 4)} = \dfrac{A}{x - 2} + \dfrac{Bx + C}{x^2 + 2x + 4}$

Multiply both sides of the last equation by the least common denominator $(x - 2)(x^2 + 2x + 4)$ and divide out common factors.

$4x^2 + 3x + 14 = A(x^2 + 2x + 4) + (Bx + C)(x - 2)$

$4x^2 + 3x + 14 = A^2 + 2Ax + 4A + Bx^2 - 2Bx + Cx - 2C$

$4x^2 + 3x + 14 = Ax^2 + Bx^2 + 2Ax - 2Bx + Cx + 4A - 2C$

$4x^2 + 3x + 14 = (A + B)x^2 + (2A - 2B + C)x + (4A - 2C)$

Equate coefficients of like powers of x, and equate constant terms.

$A + B = 4$

$2A - 2B + C = 3$

$4A - 2C = 14$

Solving the above system for A, B, and C, we find $A = 3$, $B = 1$, and $C = -1$.

$\dfrac{4x^2 + 3x + 4}{x^3 - 8} = \dfrac{3}{x - 2} + \dfrac{x - 1}{x^2 + 2x + 4}$

43. $\dfrac{1}{x(x + 1)} = \dfrac{A}{x} + \dfrac{B}{x + 1}$

Multiply both sides of the equation by the least common denominator $x(x + 1)$ and divide out common factors.

$$1 = A(x + 1) + Bx$$
$$1 = Ax + A + Bx$$
$$1 = Ax + Bx + A$$
$$1 = (A + B)x + A$$

Equate coefficients of like powers of x, and equate constant terms.

$$A + B = 0$$
$$A = 1$$

Since $A = 1$ we find that $B = -1$ by substitution.

$$\frac{1}{x(x+1)} = \frac{1}{x} - \frac{1}{x+1}$$

$$\frac{1}{1\cdot 2} + \frac{1}{2\cdot 3} + \frac{1}{3\cdot 4} + \cdots \frac{1}{99\cdot 100} = \left(\frac{1}{1} - \frac{1}{2}\right) + \left(\frac{1}{2} - \frac{1}{3}\right) + \left(\frac{1}{3} - \frac{1}{4}\right) + \cdots \left(\frac{1}{99} - \frac{1}{100}\right)$$

$$= \frac{1}{1} - \frac{1}{100}$$

$$= \frac{99}{100}$$

45.–49. Answers may vary.

47. Exercise 9

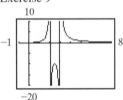

Exercise 11

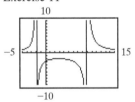

Exercise 13

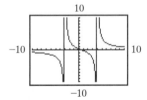

Exercise 15

Exercise 17

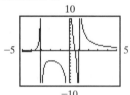

Exercise 19

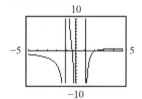

53. When the denominator of a rational expression contains a power of a cubic factor, set up a partial fraction decomposition with quadratic numerators. $(Ax^2 + Bx + C, Dx^2 + Ex + F$ etc.)

55.

$$\frac{4x^2 + 5x - 9}{x^3 - 6x - 9} = \frac{4x^2 + 5x - 9}{(x-3)(x^2 + 3x + 3)} = \frac{A}{x-3} + \frac{Bx + C}{x^2 + 3x + 3}$$

Multiply both sides of the last equation by the common denominator $(x-3)(x^2 + 3x + 3)$ and divide out common factors.

$$4x^2 + 5x - 9 = A(x^2 + 3x + 3) + (Bx + C)(x - 3)$$

$$4x^2 + 5x - 9 = Ax^2 + 3Ax + 3A + Bx^2 - 3Bx + Cx - 3C$$

$$4x^2 + 5x - 9 = Ax^2 + Bx^2 + 3Ax - 3Bx + Cx + 3A - 3C$$

$$4x^2 + 5x - 9 = (A + B)x^2 + (3A - 3B + C)x + 3A - 3C$$

Equate coefficients of like powers of x and equate constant terms.

$$A + B = 4$$
$$3A - 3B + C = 5$$
$$3A - 3C = -9$$

Solving the above system for A, B, and C, we find $A = 2$, and $B = 2$, and $C = 5$.

$$\frac{4x^2 + 5x - 9}{x^3 - 6x - 9} = \frac{2}{x-3} + \frac{2x + 5}{x^2 + 3x + 3}$$

Section 5.4

Check Point Exercises

1. $x^2 = y - 1$

$4x - y = -1$

Solve the first equation for y.

$y = x^2 + 1$

Substitute the expression $x^2 + 1$ for y in the second equation and solve for x.

$4x - (x^2 + 1) = -1$

$4x - x^2 - 1 = -1$

$x^2 - 4x = 0$

$x(x - 4) = 0$

$x = 0$ or $x - 4 = 0$

$x = 4$

If $x = 0$, $y = (0)^2 + 1 = 1$.

If $x = 4$, $y = (4)^2 + 1 = 17$.

The solution set is $\{(0, 1), (4, 17)\}$.

2. $x + 2y = 0$

$(x - 1)^2 + (y - 1)^2 = 5$

Solve the first equation for x.

$x = -2y$

Substitute the expression $-2y$ for x in the second equation and solve for y.

$(-2y - 1)^2 + (y - 1)^2 = 5$

$4y^2 + 4y + 1 + y^2 - 2y + 1 = 5$

$5y^2 + 2y - 3 = 0$

$(5y - 3)(y + 1) = 0$

$5y - 3 = 0$ or $y + 1 = 0$

$y = \dfrac{3}{5}$ or $y = -1$

If $y = \dfrac{3}{5}$, $x = -2\left(\dfrac{3}{5}\right) = -\dfrac{6}{5}$.

If $y = -1$, $x = -2(-1) = 2$.

The solution set is $\left\{\left(-\dfrac{6}{5}, \dfrac{3}{5}\right), (2, -1)\right\}$.

3. $3x^2 + 2y^2 = 35$

$4x^2 + 3y^2 = 48$

Eliminate the y^2-term by multiplying the first equation by –3 and the second equation by 2. Add the resulting equations.

$-9x^2 - 6y = -105$

$\underline{8x^2 + 6y^2 = 96}$

$-x^2 = -9$

$x^2 = 9$

$x = \pm 3$

If $x = 3$,

$3(3)^2 + 2y^2 = 35$

$y^2 = 4$

$y = \pm 2$

If $x = -3$,

$3(-3)^2 + 2y^2 = 35$

$y^2 = 4$

$y = \pm 2$

The solution set is $\{(3,2),(3,-2),(-3,2),(-3,-2)\}$.

4. $y = x^2 + 5$

$x^2 + y^2 = 25$

Arrange the first equation so that variable terms appear on the left, and constants appear on the right. Add the resulting equations to eliminate the x^2-terms and solve for y.

$-x^2 + y = 5$

$\underline{x^2 + y^2 = 25}$

$y^2 + y = 30$

$y^2 + y - 30 = 0$

$(y + 6)(y - 5) = 0$

$y + 6 = 0$ or $y - 5 = 0$

$y = -6$ or $y = 5$

If $y = -6$,

$$x^2 + (-6)^2 = 25$$
$$x^2 = -11$$
no real solution
If $y = 5$,
$$x^2 + (5)^2 = 25$$
$$x^2 = 0$$
$$x = 0$$
The solution set is $\{(0, 5)\}$.

5. $2x + 2y = 20$
$$xy = 21$$
Solve the second equation for x.
$$x = \frac{21}{7}$$
Substitute the expression $\frac{21}{y}$ for x in the
first equation and solve for y.
$$2\left(\frac{21}{y}\right) + 2y = 20$$
$$\frac{42}{y} + 2y = 20$$
$$y^2 - 10y + 21 = 0$$
$$(y - 7)(y - 3) = 0$$
$$y - 7 = 0 \quad \text{or} \quad y - 3 = 0$$
$$y = 7 \quad \text{or} \quad y = 3$$
If $y = 7$, $x = \dfrac{21}{7} = 3$.
If $y = 3$, $x = \dfrac{21}{3} = 7$.
The dimensions are 7 feet by 3 feet.

Exercise Set 5.4

1. $x + y = 2$
$$y = x^2 - 4$$
Solve the first equation for y. $y = 2 - x$.
Substitute the expression $2 - x$ for y in the
second equation and solve for x.

$$2 - x = x^2 - 4$$
$$x^2 + x - 6 = 0$$
$$(x + 3)(x - 2) = 0$$
$$x + 3 = 0 \quad \text{or} \quad x - 2 = 0$$
$$x = -3 \quad \text{or} \quad x = 2$$
If $x = -3$, $y = 2 - (-3) = 5$.
If $x = 2$, $y = 2 - 2 = 0$.
The solution set is $\{(-3, 5), (2, 0)\}$.

3. $x + y = 2$
$$y = x^2 - 4x + 4$$
Substitute the expression $x^2 - 4x + 4$ for y
in the first equation and solve for x.
$$x + x^2 - 4x + 4 = 2$$
$$x^2 - 3x + 2 = 0$$
$$(x - 1)(x - 2) = 0$$
$$x - 1 = 0 \qquad x - 2 = 0$$
$$x = 1 \qquad x = 2$$
Substitute $x = 1$ and then $x = 2$ into the
equation $x + y = 2$ and solve for each value
of y.
$$1 + y = 2 \qquad\qquad 2 + y = 2$$
$$y = 1 \qquad\qquad\quad y = 0$$
The solution set is $\{(1, 1), (2, 0)\}$.

5. $y = x^2 - 4x - 10$
$$y = -x^2 - 2x + 14$$
Substitute the expression $x^2 - 4x - 10$ for y
in the second equation and solve for x.
$$x^2 - 4x - 10 = -x^2 - 2x + 14$$
$$2x^2 - 2x - 24 = 0$$
$$x^2 - x - 12 = 0$$
$$(x - 4)(x + 3) = 0$$
$$x - 4 = 0 \quad \text{or} \quad x + 3 = 0$$
$$x = 4 \qquad \text{or} \qquad x = -3$$

If $x = 4$, $y = (4)^2 - 4(4) - 10 = -10$.

If $x = -3$, $y = (-3)^2 - 4(-3) - 10 = 11$.

The solution set is $\{(4, -10), (-3, 11)\}$.

7. $x^2 + y^2 = 25$

$x - y = 1$

Solve the second equation for y. $y = x - 1$

Substitute the expression $x - 1$ for y in the first equation and solve for x.

$$x^2 + (x - 1)^2 = 25$$

$$x^2 + x^2 - 2x + 1 = 25$$

$$2x^2 - 2x - 24 = 0$$

$$x^2 - x - 12 = 0$$

$$(x - 4)(x + 3) = 0$$

$$x - 4 = 0 \quad \text{or} \quad x + 3 = 0$$

$$x = 4 \quad \text{or} \quad x = -3$$

If $x = 4, y = 4 - 1 = 3$.

If $x = -3, y = -3 - 1 = -4$.

The solution set is $\{(4, 3), (-3, -4)\}$.

9. $xy = 6$

$2x - y = 1$

Solve the first equation for y.

$$y = \frac{6}{x}$$

Substitute the expression $\frac{6}{x}$ for y in the second equation and solve for x.

$$2x - \frac{6}{x} = 1$$

$$2x^2 - 6 = x$$

$$2x^2 - x - 6 = 0$$

$$(2x + 3)(x - 2) = 0$$

$$2x + 3 = 0 \quad \text{or} \quad x - 2 = 0$$

$$x = -\frac{3}{2} \quad \text{or} \quad x = 2$$

If $x = -\frac{3}{2}$, $y = \frac{6}{-\frac{3}{2}} = -4$.

If $x = 2$, $y = \frac{6}{2} = 3$.

The solution set is $\left\{\left(-\frac{3}{2}, -4\right), (2, 3)\right\}$.

11. $y^2 = x^2 - 9$

$2y = x - 3$

Solve the second equation for y.

$$y = \frac{x - 3}{2}$$

Substitute the expression $\frac{x - 3}{2}$ for y in the first equation and solve for x.

$$\left(\frac{x - 3}{2}\right)^2 = x^2 - 9$$

$$\frac{x^2 - 6x + 9}{4} = x^2 - 9$$

$$x^2 - 6x + 9 = 4x^2 - 36$$

$$3x^2 + 6x - 45 = 0$$

$$x^2 + 2x - 15 = 0$$

$$(x + 5)(x - 3) = 0$$

$$x + 5 = 0 \quad \text{or} \quad x - 3 = 0$$

$$x = -5 \quad \text{or} \quad x = 3$$

If $x = -5, y = \frac{-5 - 3}{2} = -4$.

If $x = 3, y = \frac{3 - 3}{2} = 0$.

The solution set is $\{(-5, -4), (3, 0)\}$.

13. $xy = 3$

$x^2 + y^2 = 10$

Solve the second equation for y.

$$y = \frac{3}{x}$$

Substitute the expression $\dfrac{3}{x}$ for y in the second equation and solve for x.

$$x^2 + \left(\frac{3}{x}\right)^2 = 10$$

$$x^2 + \frac{9}{x^2} - 10 = 0$$

$$x^4 - 10x^2 + 9 = 0$$

$$\left(x^2 - 9\right)\left(x^2 - 1\right) = 0$$

$$(x-3)(x+3)(x-1)(x+1) = 0$$

$x - 3 = 0$ or $x + 3 = 0$ or $x - 1 = 0$ or $x + 1 = 0$

$\quad x = 3$ or $\quad x = -3$ or $\quad x = 1$ or $\quad x = -1$

If $x = 3, y = \dfrac{3}{3} = 1.$

If $x = -3, y = \dfrac{3}{-3} = -1.$

If $x = 1, y = \dfrac{3}{1} = 3.$

If $x = -1, y = \dfrac{3}{-1} = -3.$

The solution set is

$$\left\{ (3,1), (-3,-1), (1,3), (-1,-3) \right\}.$$

15. $\qquad x + y = 1$

$x^2 + xy - y^2 = -5$

Solve the first equation for y. $y = 1 - x$

Substitute the expression $1 - x$ for y in the second equation and solve for x.

$$x^2 + x(1-x) - (1-x)^2 = -5$$

$$x^2 + x - x^2 - \left(1 - 2x + x^2\right) = -5$$

$$x - 1 + 2x - x^2 = -5$$

$$x^2 - 3x - 4 = 0$$

$$(x-4)(x+1) = 0$$

$x - 4 = 0$ or $x + 1 = 0$

$\quad x = 4$ or $\quad x = -1$

If $x = 4, y = 1 - 4 = -3.$

If $x = -1, y = 1 - (-1) = 2.$

The solution set is $\left\{ (4,-3), (-1,2) \right\}.$

17. $x + y = 1$

$$(x-1)^2 + (y+2)^2 = 10$$

Solve the first equation for y.

$y = 1 - x$

Substitute the expression $1 - x$ for y in the second equation and solve for x.

$$(x-1)^2 + (1 - x + 2)^2 = 10$$

$$(x-1)^2 + (3 - x)^2 = 10$$

$$x^2 - 2x + 1 + 9 - 6x + x^2 - 10 = 0$$

$$2x^2 - 8x = 0$$

$$x^2 - 4x = 0$$

$$x(x-4) = 0$$

$x = 0$ or $x - 4 = 0$

$\qquad\qquad x = 4$

If $x = 0, y = 1 - 0 = 1.$

If $x = 4, y = 1 - 4 = -3.$

The solution set is $\left\{ (0,1), (4,-3) \right\}.$

19. Eliminate the y^2 –terms by adding the equations.

$$x^2 + y^2 = 13$$
$$\underline{x^2 - y^2 = 5}$$
$$2x^2 = 18$$
$$x^2 = 9$$
$$x = \pm 3$$

If $x = 3,$

$$(3)^2 + y^2 = 13$$
$$y^2 = 4$$
$$y = \pm 2$$

If $x = -3,$

$$(-3)^2 + y^2 = 13$$
$$y^2 = 4$$
$$y = \pm 2$$

The solution set is {(3, 2), (3, − 2), (−3, 2), (−3, −2)}.

21. $x^2 - 4y^2 = -7$

$$3x^2 + y^2 = 31$$

Eliminate the x^2–terms by multiplying the first equation by –3 and adding the resulting equations.

$$-3x^2 + 12y^2 = 21$$
$$\underline{3x^2 + y^2 = 31}$$
$$13y^2 = 52$$
$$y^2 = 4$$
$$y = \pm 2$$

If $y = 2$,
$$x^2 - 4(2)^2 = -7$$
$$x^2 = 9$$
$$x = \pm 3$$

If $y = -2$,
$$x^2 - 4(-2)^2 = -7$$
$$x^2 = 9$$
$$x = \pm 3$$

The solution set is
$$\left\{ (3,2), (3,-2), (-3,2), (-3,-2) \right\}.$$

23. Arrange the equations so that variable terms appear on the left and constants appear on the right.

$$3x^2 + 4y^2 = 16$$
$$2x^2 - 3y^2 = 5$$

Eliminate the y^2–terms by multiplying the first equation by 3 and the second equation by 4. Add the resulting equations.

$$9x^2 + 12y^2 = 48$$
$$\underline{8x^2 - 12y^2 = 20}$$
$$17x^2 = 68$$
$$x^2 = 4$$
$$x = \pm 2$$

If $x = 2$,
$$3(2)^2 + 4y^2 = 16$$
$$y^2 = 1$$
$$y = \pm 1$$

If $x = -2$,
$$3(-2)^2 + 4y^2 = 16$$
$$y = \pm 1$$

The solution set is
{(2, 1), (2, –1), (–2, 1), (–2, –1)}.

25. $x^2 + y^2 = 25$

$$(x-8)^2 + y^2 = 41$$

Expand the second equation and eliminate x^2 and y^2–terms by multiplying the first equation by –1 and adding the resulting equations.

$$x^2 - 16x + 64 + y^2 = 41$$
$$\underline{-x^2 - y^2 = -25}$$
$$-16x + 64 = 16$$
$$-16x = -48$$
$$x = 3$$

If $x = 3$,
$$(3)^2 + y^2 = 25$$
$$y^2 = 16$$
$$y = \pm 4$$

The solution set is $\left\{ (3,4), (3,-4) \right\}.$

27. $y^2 - x = 4$
$$x^2 + y^2 = 4$$

Eliminate the y^2–terms by multiplying the first equation by –1 and adding the resulting equations.

$x - y^2 = -4$

$\underline{x^2 + y^2 = 4}$

$x^2 + x = 0$

$x(x+1) = 0$

$x = 0 \quad \text{or} \quad x + 1 = 0$

$\qquad\qquad\qquad x = -1$

If $x = 0$,

$y^2 = 4$

$y = \pm 2$

If $x = -1$,

$y^2 - (-1) = 4$

$\quad y^2 = 3$

$\quad y = \pm\sqrt{3}$

The solution set is

$\left\{ (0,2), (0,-2), \left(-1, \sqrt{3}\right), \left(-1, -\sqrt{3}\right) \right\}$.

29. The addition method is used here to solve the system.

$3x^2 + 4y^2 = 16$

$2x^2 - 3y^2 = 5$

Eliminate the y^2-terms by multiplying the first equation by 3 and the second equation by 4. Add the resulting equations.

$9x^2 + 12y^2 = 48$

$\underline{8x^2 - 12y^2 = 20}$

$17x^2 = 68$

$\quad x^2 = 4$

$\quad\quad x = \pm 2$

If $x = 2$,

$3(2)^2 + 4y^2 = 16$

$\quad\quad y^2 = 1$

$\quad\quad y = \pm 1$

If $x = -2$,

$3(-2)^2 + 4y^2 = 16$

$\quad\quad y = \pm 1$

The solution set is
$\{(2, 1), (2, -1), (-2, 1), (-2, -1)\}$.

31. The substitution method is used here to solve the system.

$2x^2 + y^2 = 18$

$\quad\quad xy = 4$

Solve the second equation for y.

$y = \dfrac{4}{x}$

Substitute the expression $\dfrac{4}{x}$ for y in the first equation and solve for x.

$2x^2 + \left(\dfrac{4}{x}\right)^2 = 18$

$2x^2 + \dfrac{16}{x^2} = 18$

$2x^4 + 16 = 18x^2$

$x^4 - 9x^2 + 8 = 0$

$\left(x^2 - 8\right)\left(x^2 - 1\right) = 0$

$x^2 - 8 = 0 \quad \text{or} \quad x^2 - 1 = 0$

$x^2 = 8 \quad\quad \text{or} \quad\quad x^2 = 1$

$x = \pm 2\sqrt{2} \quad \text{or} \quad\quad x = \pm 1$

If $x = 2\sqrt{2}$, $y = \dfrac{4}{2\sqrt{2}} = \sqrt{2}$.

If $x = -2\sqrt{2}$, $y = \dfrac{4}{-2\sqrt{2}} = -\sqrt{2}$.

If $x = 1$, $y = \dfrac{4}{1} = 4$.

If $x = -1$, $y = \dfrac{4}{-1} = -4$.

The solution set is

$\left\{ \left(2\sqrt{2}, \sqrt{2}\right), \left(-2\sqrt{2}, -\sqrt{2}\right), (1, 4), (-1, -4) \right\}$
.

33. The substitution method is used here to solve the system.

$x^2 + 4y^2 = 20$

$x + 2y = 6$

Solve the second equation for x.

$x = 6 - 2y$

Substitute the expression $6 - 2y$ for x in the first equation and solve for y.

$$(6 - 2y)^2 + 4y^2 = 20$$

$$36 - 24y + 4y^2 + 4y^2 - 20 = 0$$

$$8y^2 - 24y + 16 = 0$$

$$y^2 - 3y + 2 = 0$$

$$(y - 2)(y - 1) = 0$$

$y - 2 = 0$ or $y - 1 = 0$

$y = 2$ or $y = 1$

If $y = 2, x = 6 - 2(2) = 2.$

If $y = 1, x = 6 - 2(1) = 4.$

The solution set is $\{(2,2),(4,1)\}.$

35. Eliminate y by adding the equations.

$x^3 + y = 0$

$\underline{x^2 - y = 0}$

$x^3 + x^2 = 0$

$x^2(x + 1) = 0$

$x^2 = 0$ or $x + 1 = 0$

$x = 0$ or $x = -1$

If $x = 0,$

$(0)^3 + y = 0$

$y = 0$

If $x = -1,$

$(-1)^3 + y = 0$

$y = 1$

The solution set is $\{(0,0),(-1,1)\}.$

37. The substitution method is used here to solve the system.

$x^2 + (y - 2)^2 = 4$

$x^2 - 2y = 0$

Solve the second equation for x^2.

$x^2 = 2y$

Substitute the expression $2y$ for x^2 in the first equation and solve for y.

$$2y + (y - 2)^2 = 4$$

$$2y + y^2 - 4y + 4 = 4$$

$$y^2 - 2y = 0$$

$$y(y - 2) = 0$$

$y = 0$ or $y - 2 = 0$

$y = 2$

If $y = 0,$

$x^2 = 2(0)$

$x^2 = 0$

$x = 0$

If $y = 2,$

$x^2 = 2(2)$

$x^2 = 4$

$x = \pm 2$

The solution set is $\{(0, 0), (-2, 2), (2, 2)\}.$

39. The substitution method is used here to solve the system.

$y = (x + 3)^2$

$x + 2y = -2$

Solve the first equation for x.

$x = -2y - 2$

Substitute the expression $-2y-2$ for x in the first equation and solve for y.

$$y = (-2y - 2 + 3)^2 = (-2y + 1)^2$$

$$y = 4y^2 - 4y + 1$$

$$4y^2 - 5y + 1 = 0$$

$$(4y - 1)(y - 1) = 0$$

$4y - 1 = 0$ or $y - 1 = 0$

$y = \dfrac{1}{4}$ or $y = 1$

If $y = \dfrac{1}{4}$, $x = -2\left(\dfrac{1}{4}\right) - 2 = -\dfrac{5}{2}$.

If $y = 1$, $x = -2(1) - 2 = -4$.

The solution set is $\left\{(-4, 1), \left(-\dfrac{5}{2}, \dfrac{1}{4}\right)\right\}$.

41. The substitution method is used here to solve the system.

$x^2 + y^2 + 3y = 22$

$2x + y = -1$

Solve the second equation for y.

$y = -2x - 1$

Substitute the expression $-2x-1$ for y in the first equation and solve for x.

$x^2 + \left(-2x - 1\right)^2 + 3\left(-2x - 1\right) - 22 = 0$

$x^2 + 4x^2 + 4x + 1 - 6x - 3 - 22 = 0$

$5x^2 - 2x - 24 = 0$

$(5x - 12)(x + 2) = 0$

$5x - 12 = 0$ or $x + 2 = 0$

$x = \dfrac{12}{5}$ or $x = -2$

If $x = \dfrac{12}{5}$, $y = -2\left(\dfrac{12}{5}\right) - 1 = -\dfrac{29}{5}$.

If $x = -2$, $y = -2(-2) - 1 = 3$.

The solution set is $\left\{\left(\dfrac{12}{5}, -\dfrac{29}{5}\right), (-2, 3)\right\}$.

43. The substitution method is used here to solve the system.

$x + y = 10$

$xy = 24$

Solve the first equation for y.

$y = 10 - x$

Substitute the expression $10 - x$ for y in the second equation and solve for x.

$x\left(10 - x\right) = 24$

$10x - x^2 = 24$

$x^2 - 10x + 24 = 0$

$\left(x - 4\right)\left(x - 6\right) = 0$

$x - 4 = 0$ or $x - 6 = 0$

$x = 4$ or $x = 6$

If $x = 4$, $y = 10 - 4 = 6$.

If $x = 6$, $y = 10 - 6 = 4$.

The numbers are 4 and 6.

45. Eliminate the y^2–terms by adding the equations.

$x^2 - y^2 = 3$

$\underline{2x^2 + y^2 = 9}$

$3x^2 = 12$

$x^2 = 4$

$x = \pm 2$

If $x = 2$,

$2(2)^2 + y^2 = 9$

$y^2 = 1$

$y = \pm 1$

If $x = -2$,

$2(-2)^2 + y^2 = 9$

$y^2 = 1$

$y = \pm 1$

The numbers are 2 and 1, 2 and -1, -2 and 1, or -2 and -1.

47. $16x^2 + 4y^2 = 64$

$y = x^2 - 4$

Substitute the expression $x^2 - 4$ for y in the first equation and solve for x.

$16x^2 + 4\left(x^2 - 4\right)^2 = 64$

$$16x^2 + 4\left(x^4 - 8x^2 + 16\right) = 64$$
$$16x^2 + 4x^4 - 32x^2 + 64 = 64$$
$$4x^4 - 16x^2 = 0$$
$$x^4 - 4x^2 = 0$$
$$x^2\left(x^2 - 4\right) = 0$$
$$x^2 = 0 \quad \text{or} \quad x^2 - 4 = 0$$
$$x = 0 \quad \text{or} \quad x^2 = 4$$
$$x = \pm 2$$

If $x = 0$, $y = (0)^2 - 4 = -4$.

If $x = 2$, $y = (2)^2 - 4 = 0$.

If $x = -2$, $y = (-2)^2 - 4 = 0$.

It is possible for the comet to intersect the orbiting body at $(0, -4)$, $(-2, 0)$, $(2, 0)$.

49. $2L + 2W = 36$

$LW = 77$

Divide each term in the first equation by 2 and solve L.

$L + W = 18$

$L = 18 - W$

Substitute the expression $18 - W$ for L in the second equation and solve for W.

$$(18 - W)W = 77$$
$$18W - W^2 = 77$$
$$W^2 - 18W + 77 = 0$$
$$(W - 11)(W - 7) = 0$$
$$W - 11 = 0 \quad \text{or} \quad W - 7 = 0$$
$$W = 11 \quad \text{or} \quad W = 7$$

If $W = 11$, $L = 18 - 11 = 7$.

If $W = 7$, $L = 18 - 7 = 11$.

The dimensions are 11 feet by 7 feet.

51. $L^2 + W^2 = 10^2 = 100$

$LW = 48$

Solve the second equation for L. $L = \dfrac{48}{W}$

Substitute the expression $\dfrac{48}{W}$ for L in the

first equation and solve for W.

$$\left(\frac{48}{W}\right)^2 + W^2 = 100$$
$$\frac{2304}{W^2} + W^2 - 100 = 0$$
$$2304 + W^4 - 100W^2 = 0$$
$$W^4 - 100W^2 + 2304 = 0$$
$$\left(W^2 - 36\right)\left(W^2 - 64\right) = 0$$
$$W^2 - 36 = 0 \quad \text{or} \quad W^2 - 64 = 0$$
$$W^2 = 36 \quad \text{or} \quad W^2 = 64$$
$$W = \pm 6 \quad \text{or} \quad W = \pm 8$$

The width cannot be –6 or –8 inches.

If $W = 6$,

$$L = \frac{48}{6} = 8$$

If $W = 8$,

$$L = \frac{48}{8} = 6$$

The dimensions are 8 inches by 6 inches.

53. $x^2 - y^2 = 21$

$4x + 2y = 24$

Divide each term in the second equation by 2 and solve for y.

$2x + y = 12$

$y = 12 - 2x$

Substitute the expression $12 - 2x$ for y in the first equation and solve for x.

$$x^2 - (12 - 2x)^2 = 21$$
$$x^2 - \left(144 - 48x + 4x^2\right) = 21$$
$$3x^2 - 48x + 165 = 0$$
$$x^2 - 16x + 55 = 0$$
$$(x - 5)(x - 11) = 0$$
$$x - 5 = 0 \quad \text{or} \quad x - 11 = 0$$
$$x = 5 \quad \text{or} \quad x = 11$$

If $x = 11$, $y = 12 - 2(11) = -10$.

If $x = 5$, $y = 12 - 2(5) = 2$.

The dimensions of the floor are 5 meters by

5 meters and the dimensions of the square that will accomodate the pool are 2 meters by 2 meters.

55.–57. Answers may vary.

59. Exercise 1

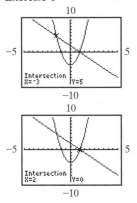

Exercise 3

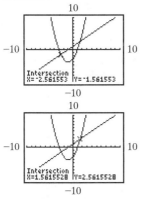

Exercise 5

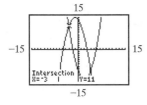

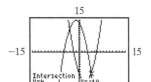

Exercise 7

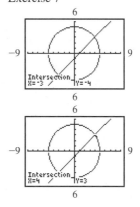

Exercise 9

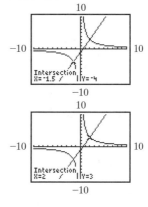

61. a. False; a circle and a line will have at most 2 intersection points.

b. True; a parabola can intersect a circle in 4 points.

c. False; It is possible for two circles to not intersect.

d. False; A circle can intersect a parabola at one point. See Check Point 4 for an example.

(b) is true.

63. By the Pythagorean Theorem:

$a^2 + b^2 = 10^2 = 100$

$a^2 + (b+9)^2 = 17^2$

Expand the second equation.

$a^2 + b^2 + 18b + 81 = 289$

Eliminate the a^2 and b^2–terms by multiplying the first equation by -1 and adding the resulting equations.

$$a^2 + b^2 + 18b = 208$$
$$\underline{-a^2 - b^2 = -100}$$
$$18b = 108$$
$$b = 6$$

$$a^2 + (6)^2 = 100$$
$$a^2 = 64$$
$$a = 8$$

65. $\log x^2 = y + 3$

$\log x = y - 1$

$10^{y+3} = x^2$

$10^{y-1} = x$

Substitute the expression 10^{y-1} for x in the equation $10^{y+3} = x^2$ and solve for y.

$$10^{y+3} = \left(10^{y-1}\right)^2$$
$$10^{y+3} = 10^{2y-2}$$
$$y + 3 = 2y - 2$$
$$y = 5$$

$$x = 10^{5-1} = 10,000$$

The solution set is $\{(10,000, 5)\}$.

Section 5.5

Check Point Exercises

1. $2x - 4y < 8$

Graph $2x - 4y = 8$ as a dashed line using its x-intercept $(4, 0)$, and its y-intercept $(0, -2)$.

Test $(0, 0)$:

$2(0) - 4(0) < 8$?

$0 < 8$ true

Shade the half-plane containing $(0, 0)$.

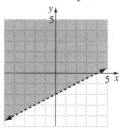

2. $y \geq \dfrac{1}{2}x$

Graph $y = \dfrac{1}{2}x$ as a solid line by using its slope, $\dfrac{1}{2}$, and its y-intercept $(0, 0)$.

Test $(1, 1)$:

$1 \geq \dfrac{1}{2}(1)$?

$1 \geq \dfrac{1}{2}$ true

Shade the half plane containing $(1, 1)$.

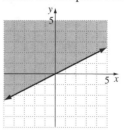

3. $x^2 + y^2 \geq 16$

Graph $x^2 + y^2 = 16$ as a solid circle with

radius 4 and center (0, 0).

Test (0, 0):

$$(0)^2 + (0)^2 \geq 16?$$

$$0 \geq 16 \text{ false}$$

Shade the half plane not containing (0, 0).

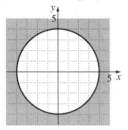

4. $x + 2y > 4$

   $2x - 3y \leq -6$

   Begin by graphing $x + 2y = 4$ as a dashed line by using its *x*-intercept, (4, 0), and its *y*-intercept (0, 2). Since (0, 0) makes the

   inequality $x + 2y > 4$ false, shade the half-plane not containing (0, 0). Graph $2x - 3y = -6$ as a solid line by graphing its *x*-intercept, (–3, 0), and its *y*-intercept (0, 2). Since (0, 0) makes the inequality $2x - 3y \leq -6$ false, shade the half-plane not containing (0, 0). The solution set of the system is the intersection of the above half-planes, and is indicated as the shaded region in the following graph.

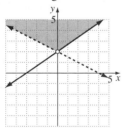

5. $y \geq x^2 - 4$

   $x + y \leq 2$

   Begin by graphing $y = x^2 - 4$ as a solid parabola with vertex (0, –4) and *x*-intercepts (–2, 0) and (2, 0). Since (0, 0) makes the inequality $y \geq x^2 - 4$ true, shade the half-plane containing (0, 0). Graph $x + y = 2$ as a solid line by using its *x*-intercept, (2, 0), and its *y*-intercept (0, 2). Since (0, 0) makes the inequality $x + y \leq 2$ true, shade the half-plane containing (0, 0). The solution set of the system is the intersection of the above half-planes, and is indicated as the shaded region in the following graph.

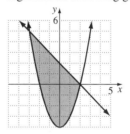

6. $x + y < 2$

   $-2 \leq x < 1$

   $y > -3$

   Begin by graphing $x + y = 2$ as a dashed line by using its *x*-intercept, (2, 0), and its *y*-intercept (0, 2). Since (0, 0) makes the inequality $x + y < 2$ true, shade the half-plane containing (0, 0). Graph $x = -2$ as a solid vertical line and $x = 1$ as a dashed vertical line. Since (0, 0) makes the inequality $-2 \leq x < 1$ true, shade the region between the two vertical lines. Graph $y = -3$ as a dashed horizontal line. Since (0, 0) makes the inequality $y > -3$ true, shade the half-plane containing (0, 0). The solution set of the system is the intersection of the above half-planes, and is indicated as the shaded region in the following graph.

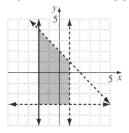

7. Answers may vary.

Exercise Set 5.5

1. $x + 2y \le 8$

Graph $x + 2y = 8$ as a solid line using its
x-intercept, $(8, 0)$, and its y-intercept, $(0, 4)$.
Test $(0, 0)$:
$0 + 2(0) \le 8$?
$0 \le 8$ true
Shade the half-plane containing $(0, 0)$.

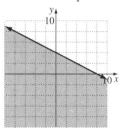

3. $x - 2y > 10$

Graph $x - 2y = 10$ as a dashed line using its
x-intercept, $(10, 0)$, and its y-intercept,
$(0, -5)$.
Test $(0, 0)$:
$0 - 2(0) > 10$?
$\quad 0 > 10$ false

Shade the half-plane not containing $(0, 0)$.

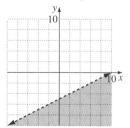

5. $y \le \dfrac{1}{3}x$

Graph $y = \dfrac{1}{3}x$ as a solid line using its slope,

$\dfrac{1}{3}$, and its y-intercept $(0, 0)$.
Test $(1, 1)$:

$1 \le \dfrac{1}{3}(1)$?

$1 \le \dfrac{1}{3}$ false

Shade the half-plane not containing $(1, 1)$.

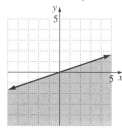

7. $y > 2x - 1$

Graph $y = 2x - 1$ as a dashed line using its

x-intercept, $\left(\dfrac{1}{2}, 0\right)$ and its y-intercept,

$(0, -1)$.
Test $(0,0)$:
$0 > 2(0) - 1$?
$0 > -1$ true

Shade the half-plane containing (0, 0).

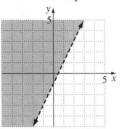

9. $x \leq 1$

Graph $x = 1$ as a solid vertical line.

Test (0, 0):

$0 \leq 1$ true

Shade the half-plane containing (0, 0).

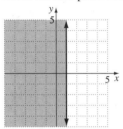

11. $y > 1$

Graph $y = 1$ as a dashed horizontal line.

Test (0, 0):

$0 > 1$ false

Shade the half-plane not containing (0, 0).

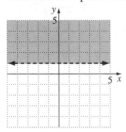

13. $x^2 + y^2 \leq 1$

Graph $x^2 + y^2 = 1$ as a solid circle with

radius 1 and center (0, 0).

Test (0, 0):

$(0)^2 + (0)^2 \leq 1?$

$0 \leq 1$ true

Shade the half-plane containing (0, 0).

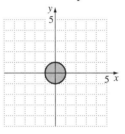

15. $x^2 + y^2 > 25$

Graph $x^2 + y^2 = 25$ as a dashed circle with

radius 5 and center (0, 0).

Test (0, 0):

$(0)^2 + (0)^2 > 25?$

$0 > 25$ false

Shade the half-plane not containing (0, 0).

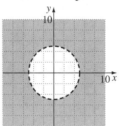

17. $y < x^2 - 1$

Graph $y = x^2 - 1$ as a dashed parabola with vertex $(0, -1)$ and x-intercepts $(1, 0)$ and $(-1, 0)$.

Test $(0, 0)$:

$0 < (0)^2 - 1$?

$0 < -1$ false

Shade the half-plane not containing $(0, 0)$.

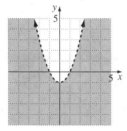

19. $y \geq x^2 - 9$

Graph $y = x^2 - 9$ as a solid parabola with vertex $(0, -9)$ and x-intercepts $(3, 0)$ and $(-3, 0)$.

Test $(0, 0)$:

$0 \geq (0)^2 - 9$?

$0 \geq -9$ true

Shade the half-plane containing $(0, 0)$.

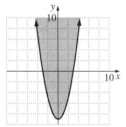

21. $y > 2^x$

Graph $y = 2^x$ as a dashed exponental function with base 2 that passes through the point $(0, 1)$.

Test $(0, 0)$:

$0 > 2^0$?

$0 > 1$ false

Shade the half-plane not containing $(0, 0)$.

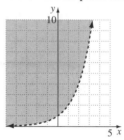

23. $3x + 6y \leq 6$

$2x + y \leq 8$

Begin by graphing $3x + 6y = 6$ as a solid line using its x-intercept, $(2, 0)$, and its y-intercept, $(0, 1)$. Since $(0, 0)$ makes the inequality $3x + 6y \leq 6$ true, shade the half-plane containing $(0, 0)$. Graph $2x + y = 8$ as a solid line using its x-intercept, $(4, 0)$, and its y-intercept, $(0, 8)$. Since $(0, 0)$ makes the inequality $2x + y \leq 8$ true, shade the half-plane containing $(0, 0)$. The solution set of the system is the intersection of the above shaded half-planes, and is shown as the shaded region in the following graph.

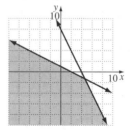

25. $2x - 5y \le 10$

$3x - 2y > 6$

Begin by graphing $2x - 5y = 10$ as a solid line using its x-intercept, $(5, 0)$, and its y-intercept, $(0, -2)$. Since $(0, 0)$ makes the inequality $2x - 5y \le 10$ true, shade the half-plane containing $(0, 0)$. Graph $3x - 2y = 6$ as a dashed line using its x-intercept, $(2, 0)$, and its y-intercept, $(0, -3)$. Since $(0, 0)$ makes the inequality $3x - 2y > 6$ false, shade the half-plane containing $(0, 0)$. The solution set of the system is the intersection of the above shaded half-planes, and is shown as the shaded region in the following graph.

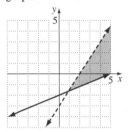

27. $y > 2x - 3$

$y < -x + 6$

Begin by graphing $y = 2x - 3$ as a dashed line using its slope, 2, and its y-intercept, $(0, -3)$. Since $(0, 0)$ makes the inequality $y > 2x - 3$ true, shade the half-plane containing $(0, 0)$. Graph $y = -x + 6$ as a dashed line using its slope, -1, and its y-intercept, $(0, 6)$. Since $(0, 0)$ makes the inequality $y < -x + 6$ true, shade the half-plane containing $(0, 0)$. The solution set of the system is the intersection of the above shaded half-planes, and is shown as the

shaded region in the following graph.

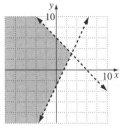

29. $x + 2y \le 4$

$y \ge x - 3$

Begin by graphing $x + 2y = 4$ as a solid line using its x-intercept, $(4, 0)$, and its y-intercept, $(0, 2)$. Since $(0, 0)$ makes the inequality $x + 2y \le 4$ true, shade the half-plane containing $(0, 0)$. Graph $y = x - 3$ as a solid line using its slope, 1, and its y-intercept, $(0, -3)$. Since $(0, 0)$ makes the inequality $y \ge x - 3$ true, shade the half-plane containing $(0, 0)$. The solution set of the system is the intersection of the above shaded half-planes, and is shown as the shaded region in the following graph.

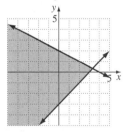

31. $x \le 2$

$y \ge -1$

Begin by graphing $x = 2$ as a solid vertical line . Since $(0, 0)$ makes the inequality $x \le 2$ true, shade the half-plane containing $(0, 0)$. Graph $y = 1$ as a solid horizontal line. Since $(0, 0)$ makes the inequality $y \ge -1$ true, shade the half-plane containing $(0, 0)$. The solution set of the system is the intersection of the above shaded half-planes, and is shown as the shaded region in the following graph.

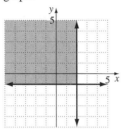

33. $-2 \le x < 5$

Graph $x = -2$ as a solid vertical line and $x = 5$ as a dashed vertical line. Since $(0, 0)$ makes the inequality $-2 \le x < 5$ true, shade the region between the two lines.

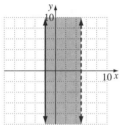

35. $x - y \le 1$

$x \ge 2$

Begin by graphing $x - y = 1$ as a solid line using its x-intercept, $(1, 0)$, and its y-intercept $(0, -1)$. Since $(0, 0)$ makes the inequality $x - y \le 1$ true, shade the half-plane containing $(0, 0)$. Graph $x = 2$ as a solid horizontal line. Since $(0, 0)$ makes the inequality $x \ge 2$ false, shade the half-plane not containing $(0, 0)$. The solution set of the system is the intersection of the above shaded half-planes, and is shown as the

shaded region in the following graph.

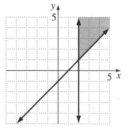

37. $x + y > 4$

$x + y < -1$

Begin by graphing $x + y = 4$ as a dashed line using its x-intercept, $(4, 0)$, and its y-intercept $(0, 4)$. Since $(0, 0)$ makes the inequality $x + y > 4$ false, shade the half-plane not containing $(0, 0)$. Graph $x + y = -1$ as a dashed line using its x-intercept, $(-1, 0)$, and its y-intercept,

$(0, -1)$. Since $(0, 0)$ makes the inequality $x + y < -1$ false, shade the half-plane not containing $(0, 0)$. The solution set of the system is the intersection of the above half-planes. Since these half-planes do not intersect the system has no solution.

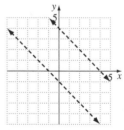

39. $x + y > 4$

$x + y > -1$

Begin by graphing $x + y = 4$ as a dashed line using its x-intercept, $(4, 0)$, and its y-intercept, $(0, 4)$. Since $(0, 0)$ makes the inequality $x + y > 4$ false, shade the half-plane not containing $(0, 0)$. Graph $x + y = -1$ as a dashed line using its x-intercept, $(-1, 0)$, and its y-intercept,

$(0, -1)$. Since $(0, 0)$ makes the inequality $x + y > -1$ true, shade the half-plane containing $(0, 0)$. The solution set of the system is the intersection of the above half-planes, and is shown as the shaded region in the following graph.

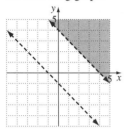

41. $y \geq x^2 - 1$

$x - y \geq -1$

Begin by graphing $y = x^2 - 1$ as a solid parabola with vertex $(0, -1)$ and x-intercepts, $(-1, 0)$, and $(1, 0)$. Since $(0, 0)$ makes the inequality $y \geq x^2 - 1$ true, shade the half-plane containing $(0, 0)$. Graph $x - y = -1$ as a solid line using its x-intercept, $(-1, 0)$, and its y-intercept, $(0, 1)$. Since $(0, 0)$ makes the inequality $x - y \geq -1$ true, shade the half-plane containing $(0, 0)$. The solution set of the system is the intersection of the above half-planes, and is shown as the shaded region in the following graph.

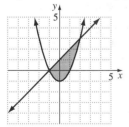

43. $x^2 + y^2 \leq 16$

$x + y > 2$

Begin by graphing $x^2 + y^2 = 16$ as a solid circle with radius 4 and center, $(0, 0)$. Since

$(0, 0)$ makes the inequality $x^2 + y^2 \leq 16$ true, shade the half-plane containing $(0, 0)$. Graph $x + y = 2$ as a dashed line using its x-intercept, $(2, 0)$, and its y-intercept, $(0, 2)$. Since $(0, 0)$ makes the inequality $x + y > 2$ false, shade the half-plane not containing $(0, 0)$. The solution set of the system is the intersection of the above half-planes, and is shown as the shaded region in the following graph.

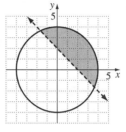

45. $x^2 + y^2 > 1$

$x^2 + y^2 < 4$

Begin by graphing $x^2 + y^2 = 1$ as a dashed circle with radius 1 and center, $(0, 0)$. Since $(0, 0)$ makes the inequality $x^2 + y^2 > 1$ false, shade the half-plane not containing $(0, 0)$. Graph $x^2 + y^2 = 4$ as a dashed circle with radius 2 and center $(0, 0)$. Since $(0, 0)$ makes the inequality $x^2 + y^2 < 4$ true, shade the half-plane containing $(0, 0)$. The solution set of the system is the intersection of the above half-planes, and is shown as the shaded region in the following graph.

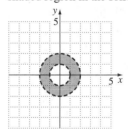

47. $x - y \le 2$

$x \ge -2$

$y \le 3$

Begin by graphing $x - y = 2$ as a solid line using its x-intercept, $(2, 0)$, and its y-intercept, $(0, -2)$. Since $(0, 0)$ makes the inequality $x - y \le 2$ true, shade the half-plane containing $(0, 0)$. Graph $x = -2$ as a solid vertical line. Since $(0, 0)$ makes the inequality $x \ge -2$ true, shade the half-plane containing $(0, 0)$. Graph $y = 3$ as a solid horizontal line. Since $(0, 0)$ makes the inequality $y \le 3$ true, shade the half-plane containing $(0, 0)$. The solution set of the system is the intersection of the above half-planes, and is shown as the shaded region in the following graph.

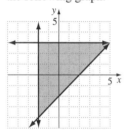

49. $x \ge 0$

$y \ge 0$

$2x + 5y \le 10$

$3x + 4y \le 12$

Since $x \ge 0$ and $y \ge 0$ the solution to the system lies in the first quadrant. Graph $2x + 5y = 10$ as a solid line using its x-intercept, $(5, 0)$, and its y-intercept, $(0, 2)$. Since $(0, 0)$ makes the inequality $2x + 5y \le 10$ true, shade the half-plane containing $(0, 0)$. Graph $3x + 4y = 12$ as a solid line by using its x-intercept, $(4, 0)$, and its y-intercept, $(0, 3)$. Since $(0, 0)$ makes the inequality $3x + 4y \le 12$ true, shade the half-plane containing $(0, 0)$. The solution set of the system is the intersection of the above

half-planes which lies in the first quadrant, and is shown as the shaded region in the following graph.

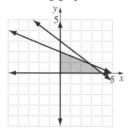

51. $3x + y \le 6$

$2x - y \le -1$

$x \ge -2$

$y \le 4$

Begin by graphing $3x + y = 6$ as a solid line using its x-intercept, $(2, 0)$, and its y-intercept, $(0, 6)$. Since $(0, 0)$ makes the inequality $3x + y \le 6$ true, shade the half-plane containing $(0, 0)$. Graph $2x - y = -1$ as a solid line using its x-intercept,

$\left(-\dfrac{1}{2}, 0\right)$, and its y-intercept, $(0, 1)$. Since

$(0, 0)$ makes the inequality $2x - y \le -1$ false, shade the half-plane not containing $(0, 0)$. Graph $x = -2$ as a solid vertical line. Since $(0, 0)$ makes the inequality $x \ge -2$ true, shade the half-plane containing $(0, 0)$. Graph $y = 4$ as a solid horizontal line. Since $(0, 0)$ makes the inequality $y \le 4$ true, shade the half-plane containing $(0, 0)$. The solution set of the system is the intersection of the above half-planes, and is shown as the shaded region in the following graph.

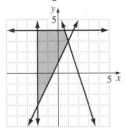

53. $5T - 7P \le 70$ Check the point (50, 30)

$5(50) - 7(30)$

$250 - 210$

$40 \le 70$

55. a. $50x + 150y > 2000$

b. Graph $50x + 150y$ as a dashed line using its *x*-intercept, (40, 0), and its *y*-intercept,

$$\left(0, \frac{40}{3}\right).$$

Test (0, 0):

$50(0) + 150(0) > 2000$?

$$0 > 2000 \text{ false}$$

Shade the half-plane not containing (0, 0).

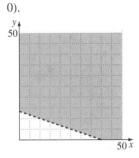

c. Ordered pairs may vary.

57. x = amount invested at high risk.

y = amount invested at high risk.

$x + y \le 15,000$

$x \ge 2000$

$y \ge 3x$

$x \ge 0$

$y \ge 0$

Since $x \ge 0$ and $y \ge 0$ the solution set to the system lies in the first quadrant. Graph $x + y = 15,000$ as a solid line using its *x*-intercept, (15,000, 0), and its *y*-intercept, (0, 15,000). Since (0, 0) makes the inequality $x + y \le 15,000$ true, shade the half-plane containing (0, 0). Graph $y = 3x$ as a solid line by using its slope, 3, and its *y*-intercept, (0, 0). Since (1, 1) makes the inequality $y \ge 3x$ false, shade the half-plane not containing (0, 0). Graph $x = 2000$ as a solid vertical line. Since (0, 0) makes the inequality $x \ge 2000$ false, shade the half-

plane not containing (0, 0). The solution set of the system is the intersection of the above half-planes, and is shown as the shaded region in the following graph.

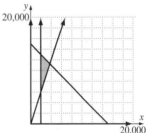

59. Answers may vary.

61. a. $BMI = \dfrac{703 \cdot 100}{50^2} = 28.1$

b. Overweight

63.–67. Answers may vary.

69. $y \geq \dfrac{2}{3}x - 2$

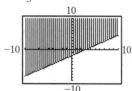

71. $y \geq \dfrac{1}{2}x^2 - 2$

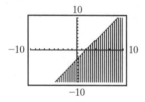

73. $3x - 2y \geq 6$

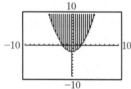

75- 79. Answers may vary.

Section 5.6

Check Point Exercises

1. The total profit is 25 times the number of bookshelves, x, plus 55 times the number of desks.
    $z = 25x + 55y$

2. $x + y \leq 80$

3. Let x represent the number of bookshelves and y represent the number of desks.
    between 30 and 80 bookselves: $30 \leq x \leq 80$
    at least 10 and no more than 30 desks:
    $10 \leq y \leq 30$

objective function: $z = 25x + 55y$
constraints: $x + y \leq 80$
$30 \leq x \leq 80$
$10 \leq y \leq 30$

4. We must maximize $z = 25x + 55y$ subject to the constraints
    $x + y \leq 80$
    $30 \leq x \leq 80$
    $10 \leq y \leq 30$
    Because x(the number of bookshelves) and y(the number of desks) must be nonnegative, graph the system of inequalitites in quadrant I and its boundary only. To graph the inequality $x + y \leq 80$, graph the equation $x + y = 80$ as a solid line with x-intercept $(80, 0)$ and y-intercept $(0, 80)$. The test point $(0, 0)$ satisfies the inequality so shade the region containing $(0, 0)$. To graph the inequality $30 \leq x \leq 80$, graph the equations $x = 30$ and $x = 80$ as solid vertical lines and shade the region between these lines. To graph the inequality $10 \leq y \leq 30$, graph the equations $y = 10$ and $y = 30$ as solid horizontal lines and shade the region between these lines. The system of inequalities representing the constraints is shown where all shaded regions overlap.

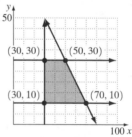

The lines $x = 30$ and $y = 10$ intersect at $(30, 10)$.
The lines $x = 30$ and $y = 10$ intersect at $(30, 30)$.
Use the substitution method to find where $x + y = 80$ and $y = 10$ intersect.

$$x + y = 80$$
$$x + 10 = 80$$
$$x = 70$$

So the intersection point is (70, 10).
Use the substitution method to find where
$x + y = 80$ and $y = 30$ intersect.

$$x + y = 80$$
$$x + 30 = 80$$
$$x = 50$$

So the intersection point is (50, 30).
Evaluate the objective function
$z = 25x + 55y$ at the four corner points of
the region found above.

(30, 10): $25(30) + 55(10) = 1300$

(30, 30): $25(30) + 55(30) = 2400$

(50, 30): $25(50) + 55(30) = 2900$

(70, 10): $25(70) + 55(10) = 2300$

The maximum value of z is 2900 and this
occurs when $x = 50$ and $y = 30$. This means
50 bookshelves and 30 desks should be
manufactured per day. The maximum profit
is $2900.

5. objective function: $z = 3x + 5y$
   constraints: $x \geq 0,\ y \geq 0$
   $$x + y \geq 1$$
   $$x + y \leq 6$$

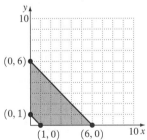

Evaluate the objective function at the four
vertices of the region shown:

(1, 0): $3(1) + 5(0) = 3$

(0, 1): $3(0) + 5(1) = 5$

(0, 6): $3(0) + 5(6) = 30$

(6, 0): $3(6) + 5(0) = 18$

The maximum value of z is 30 and this
occurs when $x = 0$ and $y = 6$.

Exercise Set 5.6

1. $z = 5x + 6y$
   (1, 2): $5(1) + 6(2) = 5 + 12 = 17$
   (2, 10): $5(2) + 6(10) = 10 + 60 = 70$
   (7, 5): $5(7) + 6(5) = 35 + 30 = 65$
   (8, 3): $5(8) + 6(3) = 40 + 18 = 58$
   The maximum value is $z = 70$; the minimum
   value is $z = 17$.

3. $z = 40x + 50y$
   (0, 0): $40(0) + 50(0) = 0 + 0 = 0$
   (0, 8): $40(0) + 50(8) = 0 + 400 = 400$
   (4, 9): $40(4) + 50(9) = 160 + 450 = 610$
   (8, 0): $40(8) + 50(0) = 320 + 0 = 320$
   The maximum value is $z = 610$; the
   minimum value is $z = 0$.

5. $z = 3x + 2y$
   $$x \geq 0, y \geq 0$$
   $$2x + y \leq 8$$
   $$x + y \geq 4$$

   a.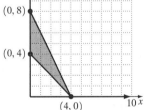

   b. (0, 8): $z = 3(0) + 2(8) = 16$
      (0, 4): $z = 3(0) + 2(4) = 8$
      (4, 0): $z = 3(4) + 2(0) = 12$

   c. The maximum value is 16 at $x = 0$ and y
      $= 8$.

at $x = 0$ and $y = 4$ and at $x = \dfrac{6}{7}$

and $y = \dfrac{24}{7}$.

7. $z = 4x + y$
$x \geq 0, y \geq 0$
$2x + 3y \leq 12$
$x + y \geq 3$

a.

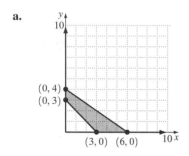

b. $(0, 4)$: $z = 4(0) + 4 = 4$
$(0, 3)$: $z = 4(0) + 3 = 3$
$(3, 0)$: $z = 4(3) + 0 = 12$
$(6, 0)$: $z = 4(6) + 0 = 24$

c. The maximum value is 24 at $x = 6$ and $y = 0$.

9. $z = 3x - 2y$
$1 \leq x \leq 5$
$y \geq 2$
$x - y \geq -3$

a.

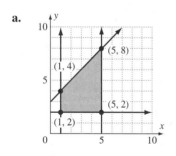

b. $(1, 2)$: $z = 3(1) - 2(2) = -1$
$(1, 4)$: $z = 3(1) - 2(4) = -5$
$(5, 8)$: $z = 3(5) - 2(8) = -1$
$(5, 2)$: $z = 3(5) - 2(2) = 11$

c. Maximum value is 11 at $x = 5$ and $y = 2$.

11. $z = 4x + 2y$
$x \geq 0, y \geq 0$
$2x + 3y \leq 12$
$3x + 2y \leq 12$
$x + y \geq 2$

a.

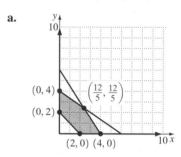

b. $(0, 4)$: $z = 4(0) + 2(4) = 8$
$(0, 2)$: $z = 4(0) + 2(2) = 4$
$(2, 0)$: $z = 4(2) + 2(0) = 8$
$(4, 0)$: $z = 4(4) + 2(0) = 16$
$\left(\dfrac{12}{5}, \dfrac{12}{5} \right)$: $z = 4\left(\dfrac{12}{5} \right) + 2\left(\dfrac{12}{5} \right)$

$= \dfrac{48}{5} + \dfrac{24}{5} = \dfrac{72}{5}$

c. The maximum value is 16 at $x = 4$ and $y = 0$.

13. $z = 10x + 12y$
$x \geq 0, y \geq 0$
$x + y \leq 7$
$2x + y \leq 10$
$2x + 3y \leq 18$

a.

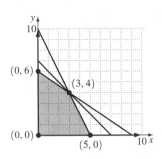

b. $(0, 6)$: $z = 10(0) + 12(6) = 72$
$(0, 0)$: $z = 10(0) + 12(0) = 0$
$(5, 0)$: $z = 10(5) + 12(0) = 50$
$(3, 4)$: $z = 10(3) + 12(4) =$
$\qquad = 30 + 48 = 78$

c. The maximum value is 78 at $x = 3$ and $y = 4$.

15. a. $z = 125x + 200y$

b. $x \le 450$
$y \le 200$
$600x + 900y \le 360{,}000$

c. Simplify the third inequality by dividing by 300 to get $2x + 3y \le 1200$.

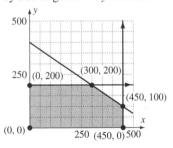

d. $(0, 0)$: $125(0) + 200(0) = 0 + 0 = 0$
$(0, 200)$: $125(0) + 200(200)$
$\qquad = 0 + 40{,}000 = 40{,}000$
$(300, 200)$: $125(300) + 200(200)$
$\qquad = 37{,}500 + 40{,}000 = 77{,}500$
$(450, 100)$: $125(450) + 200(100)$
$\qquad = 56{,}250 + 20{,}000 = 76{,}250$

$(450, 0)$: $125(450) + 200(0)$
$\qquad = 56{,}250 + 0 = 56{,}250$

e. The television manufacturer will make the greatest profit by manufacturing <u>300</u> console televisions each month and <u>200</u> wide-screen televisions each month. The maximum monthly profit is <u>$77,500</u>.

17. Let x = number of model A bicycles and y = number of model B bicycles.
The constraints are
$5x + 4y \le 200$
$2x + 3y \le 108$
Graph these inequalities in the first quadrant, since x and y cannot be negative.

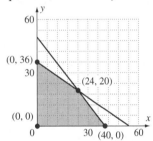

The quantity to be maximized is the profit, which is $25x + 15y$.
$(0, 0)$: $25(0) + 15(0) = 0 + 0 = 0$
$(0, 36)$: $25(0) + 15(36) = 0 + 540 = 540$
$(24, 20)$: $25(24) + 15(20) = 600 + 300 = 900$
$(40, 0)$: $25(40) + 15(0) = 1000 + 0 = 1000$
40 model A bicycles and no model B bicycles should be produced.

19. Let x = the number of cartons of food and y = the number of cartons of clothing.
The constraints are:
$20x + 10y \le 8{,}000$ or $2x + y \le 8000$
$50x + 20y \le 19{,}000$ or $5x + 2y \le 1900$
Graph these inequalities in the first quadrant, since x and y cannot be negative.

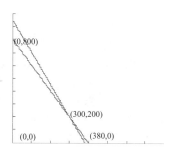

The quantity to be maximized is the number of people helped, which is $12x + 5y$.

(0, 0): $12(0) + 5(0) = 0 + 0 = 0$

(0, 800): $12(0) + 5(800) = 0 + 4000 = 4000$

(300, 200): $12(300) + 5(200) = 4600$

(380, 0): $12(380) + 5(0) = 4500$

300 cartons of food and 200 cartons of clothing should be shipped. This will help 4600 people.

21. Let x = number of students attending and y = number of parents attending.

The constraints are

$x + y \leq 150$

$\quad 2x \geq y$

or

$\quad x + y \leq 150$

$2x - y \geq 0$

Graph these inequalities in the first quadrant, since x and y cannot be negative.

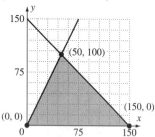

The quantity to be maximized is the amount of money raised, which is $x + 2y$.

(0, 0): $0 + 2(0) = 0 + 0 = 0$

(50, 100): $50 + 2(100) = 50 + 200 = 250$

(150, 0): $150 + 2(0) = 150 + 0 = 150$

50 students and 100 parents should attend.

23. Let x = number of Boeing 727s, y = number of Falcon 20s.

Maximize $z = x + y$ with the following constraints:

$1400x + 500y \leq 35,000$ or $14x + 5y \leq 350$

$42,000x + 6000y \geq 672,000$ or

$7x + y \geq 112$

$x \leq 20$

$x \geq 0, y \geq 0$

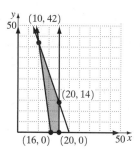

$\left(16, 0\right): z = 16$

$\left(20, 0\right): z = 20$

$\left(20, 14\right): z = 34$

$\left(10, 42\right): z = 52$

Federal Express should have purchased 10 Boeing 727s and 42 Falcon 20s.

25.–27. Answers may vary.

29. $z = 6x + 8y$

$\quad x \geq 0, y \geq 0$

$\quad x + 2y \leq 6$ or $y \leq -0.5x + 3$

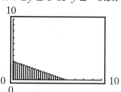

(6, 0): $6(6) + 8(0) = 36$

(0, 3): $6(0) + 8(3) = 24$

Maximum value is 36.

31. $z = 9x + 14y$

$x \geq 0, y \geq 0$

$2x + y \leq 10$ or $y \leq -2x + 10$

$2x + 3y \leq 18$ or $y \leq -\dfrac{2}{3}x + 6$

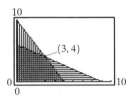

$(3, 4)$: $9(3) + 14(4) = 83$

$(5, 0)$: $9(5) + 14(0) = 45$

$(0, 6)$: $9(0) + 14(6) = 84$

Maximum value is 84.

33. Let x = amount invested in stocks and y = amount invested in bonds.

The constraints are:

$x + y \leq 10,000$

$y \geq 3000$

$x \geq 2000$

$y \geq x$

Graph these inequalities in the first quadrant, since x and y cannot be negative.

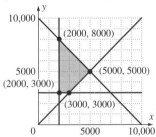

The quantity to be maximized is the return on the investment, which is $0.12x + 0.08y$.

$(2000, 3000)$:

$0.12(2000) + 0.08(3000) = 240 + 240 = 480$

$(2000, 8000)$:

$0.12(2000) + 0.08(8000) = 240 + 640 = 880$

$(5000, 5000)$:

$0.12(5000) + 0.08(5000) = 600 + 400 = 1000$

$(3000, 3000)$:

$0.12(3000) + 0.08(3000) = 360 + 240 = 600$

The greatest return occurs when \$5000 is invested in stocks and \$5000 is invested in bonds.

Review Exercises

1. $y = 4x + 1$
    $3x + 2y = 13$
    Substitute $4x + 1$ for y in the second equation:
    $3x + 2(4x + 1) = 13$
    $3x + 8x + 2 = 13$
    $11x = 11$
    $x = 1$
    $y = 4(1) + 1 = 5$
    The solution set is $\{(1, 5)\}$.

2. $x + 4y = 14$
    $2x - y = 1$
    Multiply the second equation by 4 and add to the first equation.
    $\quad x + 4y = 14$
    $\underline{\;8x - 4y = 4\;}$
    $\quad\quad 9x = 18$
    $\quad\quad x = 2$
    $2(2) - y = 1$
    $\quad -y = -3$
    $\quad\quad y = 3$
    The solution set is $\{(2, 3)\}$.

3. $5x + 3y = 1$
    $3x + 4y = -6$
    Multiply the first equation by 4 and the second equation by –3.
    Then add.
    $\quad 20x + 12y = 4$
    $\underline{-9x - 12y = 18}$
    $\quad\quad 11x = 22$
    $\quad\quad\quad x = 2$
    $5(2) + 3y = 1$
    $\quad\quad 3y = -9$
    $\quad\quad\; y = -3$
    The solution set is $\{(2, -3)\}$.

4. $2y - 6x = 7$
    $3x - y = 9$
    The second equation can be written as
    $y = 3x - 9$.

    Substitute:
    $2(3x - 9) - 6x = 7$
    $6x - 18 - 6x = 7$
    $\quad\quad\quad -18 = 7$
    Since this is false, the system has no solution.
    The solution set is the empty set, $\varnothing$.

5. $4x - 8y = 16$
    $3x - 6y = 12$
    Divide the first equation by 4 and the second equation by 3.
    $x - 2y = 4$
    $x - 2y = 4$
    Since these equations are identical, the system
    ihas an infinite number of solutions.
    The solution set is $\left\{(x, y) \mid 4x - 8y = 16\right\}$ or
    $\left\{(x, y) \mid 3x - 6y = 12\right\}$.

6. **a.** $C = 60{,}000 + 200x$

    b. $R = 450x$

    c. $450x = 60000 + 200x$
    $\quad 250x = 60000$
    $\quad\quad x = 240$
    $450(240) = 108{,}000$
    The company must make 240 desks at a cost of \$108,000 to break even.

7.
$$N = -60p + 100$$
$$N = 4p + 200$$
$$-60p + 1000 = 4p + 200$$
$$800 = 64p$$
$$p = 12.5$$
$$N = 4(12.5) + 200 = 250$$
250 copies can be supplied and sold for $12.50 each.

8. $12 = 10(x - y)$
$x + y = 3.1 + 7.3$
Rearrange the equations so the letters are in line.
$10x - 10x = 12$
$x + y = 10.4$
Solve the system.
$$10x - 10y = 12$$
$$-10x - 10y = -104$$
$$-20y = -92$$
$$y = 4.6$$

$$x + 4.6 = 10.4$$
$$x = 5.8$$
5.8 million pounds of potato chips and 4.6 million pounds of tortilla chips

9. Let x = the cost of the hotel
     y = the cost of the car
$3x + 2y = 360$
$4x + 3y = 500$
Solve the system.
$$12x + 8y = 1440$$
$$-12x - 9y = -1500$$
$$-y = -60$$
$$y = 60$$

$$3x + 2(60) = 360$$
$$3x = 240$$
$$x = 80$$
The room costs $80 a day and the car rents for $60 a day.

10. x = number of apples
    y = number of avocados
$100x + 350y = 1000$
$24x + 14y = 100$
$$100x + 350y = 1000$$
$$-600x - 350y = -2500$$
$$-500x = -1500$$
$$x = 3$$
$$100(3) + 350y = 1000$$
$$350y = 700$$
$$y = 2$$
3 apples and 2 avocados supply 1000 calories and 100 grams of carbohydrates.

11. $2x - y + z = 1$ (1)
    $3x - 3y + 4z = 5$ (2)
    $4x - 2y + 3z = 4$ (3)
Eliminate y from (1) and (2) by multiplying (1) by -3 and adding the result to (2).
$$-6x + 3y - 3z = -3$$
$$3x - 3y + 4z = 5$$
$$-3x + z = 2 \quad (4)$$
Eliminate y from (1) and (3) by multiplying (1) by -2 and adding the result to (3).
$$-4x + 2y - 2z = -2$$
$$4x - 2y + 3z = 4$$
$$z = 2$$
Substituting $z = 2$ into (4), we get:
$$-3x + 2 = 2$$
$$-3x = 0$$
$$x = 0$$
Substituting $x = 0$ and $z = 2$ into (1), we have:
$$2(0) - y + 2 = 1$$
$$-y = -1$$
$$y = 1$$
The solution set is $\{(0, 1, 2)\}$.

12. $x + 2y - z = 5$ (1)
    $2x - y + 3z = 0$ (2)

$2y + z = 1$ (3)

Eliminate x from (1) and (2) by multiplying (1) by -2 and adding the result to (2).

$-2x - 4y + 2z = -10$

$\underline{2x - y + 3z = 0}$

$-5y + 5z = -10$

$\quad\quad y - z = 2$ (4)

Adding (3) and (4), we get:

$2y + z = 1$

$\underline{y - z = 2}$

$\quad 3y = 3$

$\quad\quad y = 1$

Substituting $y = 1$ into (3), we have:

$2(1) + z = 1$

$z = -1$

Substituting $y = 1$ and $z = -1$ into (1), we obtain:

$x + 2(1) - (-1) = 5$

$\quad x + 3 = 5$

$\quad\quad x = 2$

The solution set is $\{(2, 1, -1)\}$.

13. $y = ax^2 + bx + c$

$(1, 4): 4 = a + b + c$ (1)

$(3, 20): 20 = 9a + 3b + c$ (2)

$(-2, 25): 25 = 4a - 2b + c$ (3)

Multiply (1) by -1 and add to (2).

$20 = 9a + 3b + c$

$\underline{-4 = -a - b - c}$

$16 = 8a + 2b$

$\quad 8 = 4a + b$

$\quad 8 = 4a + b$ (4)

Multiply (1) by -1 and add to (3).

$25 = 4a - 2b + c$

$\underline{-4 = -a - b - c}$

$21 = 3a - 3b$

$\quad 7 = a - b$ (5)

Add (4) and (5).

$8 = 4a + b$

$\underline{7 = a - b}$

$15 = 5a$

$\quad a = 3$

$\quad\quad 8 = 4(3) + b$

$\quad\quad b = -4$

$3 - 4 + c = 4$

$\quad c = 5$

Hence, the quadratic function is

$y = 3x^2 - 4x + 5$.

14. **a.** $(0, 3.5)$ $(15, 5)$ $(29, 4.1)$

b. Put the value for each point into the equation $y = ax^2 + bx + c$.

$3.5 = a(0)^2 + b(0) + c$

$3.5 = c$

$5 = a(15)^2 + b(15) + c$

$5 = 225a + 15b + c$

$4.1 = a(29)^2 + b(29) + c$

$4.1 = 841a + 29b + c$

15. $x + y + z = 50$ (1)

$\quad x = y + 4$ (2)

$\quad x = 2z + 2$ (3)

Rewrite the equations with the letters in line and solve the system.

$$x + y + z = 50$$
$$x - y = 4$$
$$x - 2z = 2$$

$$x + y + z = 50$$
$$x - y = 4$$
$$2x + z = 54$$

$$2x + z = 54$$
$$-2x + 4z = -4$$
$$5z = 50$$
$$z = 10$$

$$2x + 10 = 54$$
$$2x = 44$$
$$x = 22$$

$$22 + y + 10 = 50$$
$$y = 18$$

22 languages in the United States, 18 languages in Colombia, and 10 languages in India have become extinct.

16. $\dfrac{x}{(x-3)(x+2)} = \dfrac{A}{x-3} + \dfrac{B}{x+2}$

$x = A(x+2) + B(x-3)$
$\quad = (A+B)x + (2A-3B)$
$\quad A + B = 1$

$2A - 3B = 0$
Multiply first equation by 3, then add to second equation.

$$3A + 3B = 3$$
$$\underline{2A - 3B = 0}$$
$$5A = 3$$

$A = \dfrac{3}{5}$, $B = \dfrac{2}{5}$

$$\dfrac{x}{(x-3)(x+2)} = \dfrac{3}{5(x-3)} + \dfrac{2}{5(x+2)}$$

17. $\dfrac{11x-2}{x^2-x-12} = \dfrac{11x-2}{(x-4)(x+3)} = \dfrac{A}{x-4} + \dfrac{B}{x+3}$

$11x - 2 = A(x+3) + B(x-4)$
$\quad\quad = Ax + 3A + Bx - 4B$
$\quad\quad = (A+B)x + (3A - 4B)$

$A + B = 11$
$3A - 4B = -2$
Multiply first equation by 4, then add to second equation.

$$3A - 4B = -2$$
$$\underline{4A + 4B = 44}$$
$$7A = 42$$

$A = 6$, $B = 5$

$$\dfrac{11x-2}{x^2-x-12} = \dfrac{6}{x-4} + \dfrac{5}{x+3}$$

18.

$$\dfrac{4x^2-3x-4}{x^3+x^2-2x} = \dfrac{4x^2-3x-4}{x(x+2)(x-1)}$$

$$= \dfrac{A}{x} + \dfrac{B}{x+2} + \dfrac{C}{x-1}$$

$4x^2 - 3x - 4 = A(x+2)(x-1) + Bx(x-1) + Cx(x+2)$
$\quad\quad = A(x^2+x-2) + Bx^2 - Bx + Cx^2 + 2Cx$
$\quad\quad = Ax^2 + Ax - 2A + Bx^2 - Bx + Cx^2 + 2Cx$
$\quad\quad = (A+B+C)x^2 + (A-B+2C)x - 2A$

$A + B + C = 4$
$A - B + 2C = -3$
$-2A = -4$
$A = 2$

$B + C = 2$
$\underline{-B + 2C = -5}$
$3C = -3$
$C = -1$

$B - 1 = 2$
$B = 3$

$$\dfrac{4x^2-3x-4}{x^3+x^2-2x} = \dfrac{2}{x} + \dfrac{3}{x+2} - \dfrac{1}{x-1}$$

19. $\dfrac{2x+1}{(x-2)^2} = \dfrac{A}{x-2} + \dfrac{B}{(x-2)^2}$

$2x+1 = A(x-2) + B = Ax - 2A + B$

$A = 2$
$-2A + B = 1$

$-2(2) + B = 1$

$B = 5$

$\dfrac{2x+1}{(x-2)^2} = \dfrac{2}{x-2} + \dfrac{5}{(x-2)^2}$

20. $\dfrac{2x-6}{(x-1)(x-2)^2} = \dfrac{A}{x-1} + \dfrac{B}{x-2} + \dfrac{C}{(x-2)^2}$

$2x-6 = A(x-2)^2 + B(x-1)(x-2) + C(x-1)$

$\quad = A(x^2 - 4x + 4) + B(x^2 - 3x + 2) + C(x-1)$

$\quad = Ax^2 - 4Ax + 4A + Bx^2 - 3Bx + 2B + Cx - C$

$\quad = (A+B)x^2 + (-4A - 3B + C)x + (4A + 2B - C)$

$A + B = 0$

$-4A - 3B + C = 2$

$\underline{4A + 2B - C = -6}$

$-B = -4$

$B = 4$

$A = -4$

$4(-4) + 2(4) - C = -6$

$-16 + 8 - C = -6$

$-C - 8 = -6$

$-C = 2$

$C = -2$

$\dfrac{2x-6}{(x-1)(x-2)^2} = -\dfrac{4}{x-1} + \dfrac{4}{x-2} - \dfrac{2}{(x-2)^2}$

21. $\dfrac{3x}{(x-2)(x^2+1)} = \dfrac{A}{x-2} + \dfrac{Bx+C}{x^2+1}$

$3x = A(x^2+1) + (Bx+C)(x-2)$

$\quad = Ax^2 + A + Bx^2 - 2Bx + Cx - 2C$

$\quad = (A+B)x^2 + (-2B+C)x - (2C - A)$

$A + B = 0$

$-2B + C = 3$

$2C - A = 0$

$A = 2C$

$B + 2C = 0$

$\underline{4B - 2C = -6}$

$5B = -6$

$B = -\dfrac{6}{5}$

$A = \dfrac{6}{5}$

$C = \dfrac{6}{10} = \dfrac{3}{5}$

$\dfrac{3x}{(x-2)(x^2+1)} = \dfrac{6}{5(x-2)} + \dfrac{-6x+3}{5(x^2+1)}$

22. $\dfrac{7x^2 - 7x + 23}{(x-3)(x^2+4)} = \dfrac{A}{x-3} + \dfrac{Bx+C}{x^2+4}$

$7x^2 - 7x + 23 = A(x^2+4) + (Bx+C)(x-3)$

$\quad = Ax^2 + 4A + Bx^2 - 3Bx + Cx - 3C$

$\quad = (A+B)x^2 + (-3B+C)x + (4A - 3C)$

$A + B = 7$

$-3B + C = -7$

$4A - 3C = 23$

$3A + 3B = 21$

$\underline{-3B + C = -7}$

$3A + C = 14$

$9A + 3C = 42$

$\underline{4A - 3C = 23}$

$13A = 65$

$A = 5$

320

$$5 + B = 7$$

$$B = 7 - 5 = 2$$

$$-3(2) + C = -7$$

$$C = -7 + 6 = -1$$

$$\frac{7x^2 - 7x + 23}{(x-3)(x^2+4)} = \frac{5}{(x-3)} + \frac{2x-1}{(x^2+4)}$$

23.
$$\frac{x^3}{(x^2+4)^2} = \frac{Ax+B}{x^2+4} + \frac{Cx+D}{(x^2+4)^2}$$

$$x^3 = (Ax+B)(x^2+4) + Cx + D$$

$$= Ax^3 + 4Ax + Bx^2 + 4B + Cx + D$$

$$= Ax^3 + Bx^2 + (4A+C)x + (4B+D)$$

$$A = 1$$

$$B = 0$$

$$4A + C = 0$$

$$4B + D = 0$$

$$C = -4$$

$$0 + D = 0, D = 0$$

$$\frac{x^2}{(x^2+4)^2} = \frac{x}{x^2+4} - \frac{4x}{(x^2+4)^2}$$

24.

$$\frac{4x^3 + 5x^2 + 7x - 1}{(x^2+x+1)^2} = \frac{Ax+B}{x^2+x+1} + \frac{Cx+D}{(x^2+x+1)^2}$$

$$4x^3 + 5x^2 + 7x - 1$$

$$= (Ax+B)(x^2+x+1) + Cx + D$$

$$= Ax^3 + Ax^2 + Ax + Bx^2 + Bx + B + Cx + D$$

$$= Ax^3 + (A+B)x^2 (A+B+C)x + (B+D)$$

$$A = 4$$

$$A + B = 5$$

$$A + B + C = 7$$

$$B + D = -1$$

$$4 + B = 5, B = 1$$

$$4 + 1 + C = 7, C = 2$$

$$1 + D = -1, D = -2$$

$$\frac{4x^3 + 5x^2 + 7x - 1}{(x^2+x+1)^2} = \frac{4x+1}{x^2+x+1} + \frac{2x-2}{(x^2+x+1)^2}$$

25.
$$5y = x^2 - 1$$

$$x - y = 1$$

$$y = x - 1$$

$$5(x-1) = x^2 - 1$$

$$5x - 5 = x^2 - 1$$

$$x^2 - 5x + 4 = 0$$

$$(x-4)(x-1) = 0$$

$$x = 4, 1$$

If $x = 4, y = 4 - 1 = 3$.

If $x = 1, y = 1 - 1 = 0$.

The solution set is $\{(4,3),(1,0)\}$.

26.
$$y = x^2 + 2x + 1$$

$$x + y = 1$$

$$y = 1 - x$$

$$1 - x = x^2 + 2x + 1$$

$$x^2 + 3x = 0$$

$$x(x+3) = 0$$

$$x = 0, -3$$

If $x = 0, y = 1 - 0 = 1$.

If $x = -3, y = 1 - (-3) = 4$.

The solution set is $\{(0,1),(-3,4)\}$.

27. $x^2 + y^2 = 2$
                    $x + y = 0$

                          $x = -y$

              $(-y)^2 + y^2 = 2$

                      $2y^2 = 2$

                        $y^2 = 1$

                        $y = 1, -1$

If $y = 1, x = -1$.

If $y = -1, x = 1$.

The solution set is $\{(1, -1), (-1, 1)\}$.

28. $2x^2 + y^2 = 24$

           $x^2 + y^2 = 15$

          $2x^2 + y^2 = 24$

          $\underline{-x^2 - y^2 = -15}$

                    $x^2 = 9$

                  $x = 3, -3$

If $x = 3, 3^2 + y^2 = 15, y^2 = 6$ and $y = \pm\sqrt{6}$.

If $x = -3, y = \pm\sqrt{6}$.

The solution set is

$\left\{\left(3, \sqrt{6}\right), \left(3, -\sqrt{6}\right), \left(-3, \sqrt{6}\right), \left(-3, -\sqrt{6}\right)\right\}$.

29. $xy - 4 = 0$
             $y - x = 0$

                    $y = x$

                  $xy = 4$

                  $x^2 = 4$

                $x = 2, -2$

If $x = 2, y = 2$.

If $x = -2, y = -2$.

The solution set is $\{(2, 2), (-2, -2)\}$.

30. $y^2 = 4x$
          $x - 2y + 3 = 0$

                  $x = \dfrac{y^2}{4}$

$\dfrac{y^2}{4} - 2y + 3 = 0$

$y^2 - 8y + 12 = 0$

$(y - 6)(y - 2) = 0$

                    $y = 6, 2$

If $y = 6, x = \dfrac{36}{4} = 9$.

If $y = 2, x = \dfrac{4}{4} = 1$.

The solution set is $\{(9, 6), (1, 2)\}$.

31. $x^2 + y^2 = 10$

                    $y = x + 2$

              $x^2 + (x + 2)^2 = 10$

        $x^2 + x^2 + 4x + 4 - 10 = 0$

                $2x^2 + 4x - 6 = 0$

                  $x^2 + 2x - 3 = 0$

                $(x + 3)(x - 1) = 0$

                              $x = -3, 1$

If $x = -3, y = -3 + 2 = -1$.

If $x = 1, y = 1 + 2 = 3$.

The solution set is $\{(-3, -1), (1, 3)\}$.

32. $xy = 1$

              $y = 2x + 1$

                $x(2x + 1) = 1$

              $2x^2 + x - 1 = 0$

            $(2x - 1)(x + 1) = 0$

                        $x = \dfrac{1}{2}, -1$

If $x = \dfrac{1}{2}, y = 2\left(\dfrac{1}{2}\right) + 1 = 2$.

If $x = -1, y = 2(-1) + 1 = -1$.

The solution set is $\left\{\left(\dfrac{1}{2}, 2\right), (-1, -1)\right\}$.

33.
$$x + y + 1 = 0$$
$$x^2 + y^2 + 6y - x = -5$$
$$x = -y - 1$$
$$(-y-1)^2 + y^2 + 6y - (-y-1) + 5 = 0$$
$$y^2 + 2y + 1 + y^2 + 6y + y + 1 + 5 = 0$$
$$2y^2 + 9y + 7 = 0$$
$$(2y + 7)(y + 1) = 0$$
$$y = -\frac{7}{2}, -1$$

If $y = -\frac{7}{2}, x = \frac{7}{2} - 1 = \frac{5}{2}$.

If $y = -1, x = 1 - 1 = 0$.

The solution set is $\left\{ \left(\frac{5}{2}, -\frac{7}{2} \right), (0, -1) \right\}$.

34. $x^2 + y^2 = 13$
$$x^2 - y = 7$$
$$x^2 + y^2 = 13$$
$$\underline{-x^2 + y = -7}$$
$$y^2 + y = 6$$
$$y^2 + y - 6 = 0$$
$$(y + 3)(y - 2) = 0$$
$$y = -3, 2$$

If $y = -3, x^2 + 3 = 7$

$x^2 = 4, x = 2, -2$

If $y = 2, x^2 - 2 = 7, x^2 = 9, x = 3, -3$.

The solution set is
$\{(2, -3), (-2, -3), (3, 2), (-3, 2)\}$.

35. $2x^2 + 3y^2 = 21$
$$3x^2 - 4y^2 = 23$$
$$8x^2 + 12y^2 = 84$$
$$\underline{9x^2 - 12y^2 = 69}$$
$$17x^2 = 153$$
$$x^2 = \frac{153}{17} = 9$$
$$x = 3, -3$$

If $x = 3, 2(3)^2 + 3y^2 = 21$.

$3y^2 = 21 - 18 = 3$

$y^2 = 1, y = 1, -1$

If $x = -3, y = 1, -1$.

The solution set is
$\{(3, 1), (3, -1), (-3, 1), (-3, -1)\}$.

36. $2L + 2W = 26$
$$LW = 40$$
$$L = \frac{40}{W}$$
$$2\left(\frac{40}{W} \right) + 2W = 26$$
$$\frac{80}{W} + 2W = 26$$
$$80 + 2W^2 = 26W$$
$$2W^2 - 26W + 80 = 0$$
$$W^2 - 13W + 40 = 0$$
$$(W - 8)(W - 5) = 0$$
$$W = 8, 5$$

If $W = 5, L = \frac{40}{5} = 8$

The dimensions are 8 m by 5 m.

37.
$$xy = 6$$
$$y = \frac{6}{x}$$
$$2x + y = 8$$
$$2x + \frac{6}{x} = 8$$
$$2x^2 + 6 = 8x$$
$$2x^2 - 8x + 6 = 0$$
$$x^2 - 4x + 3 = 0$$
$$(x - 1)(x - 3) = 0$$
$$x = 1, 3$$

If $x = 1, y = 6$.

If $x = 3, y = 2$.

The solution set is $\{(1, 6), (3, 2)\}$.

38. $x^2 + y^2 = 2900$

$4x + 2y = 240$

$2x + y = 120$

$y = 120 - 2x$

$x^2 + (120 - 2x)^2 = 2900$

$x^2 + 14,400 - 480x + 4x^2 - 2900 = 0$

$5x^2 - 480x + 11,500 = 0$

$x^2 - 96x + 2300 = 0$

$(x - 46)(x - 50) = 0$

$x = 46, 50$

If $x = 46, y = 120 - 2(46) = 28$.

If $x = 50, y = 120 - 2(50) = 20$.

$x = 46$ ft and $y = 28$ ft or $x = 50$ ft and $y = 20$ ft

39. $3x - 4y > 12$

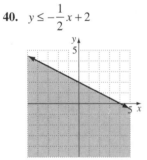

40. $y \le -\dfrac{1}{2}x + 2$

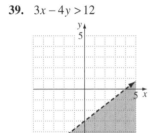

41. $x < -2$

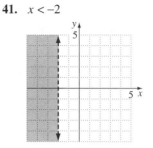

42. $y \ge 3$

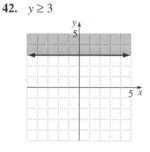

43. $x^2 + y^2 > 4$

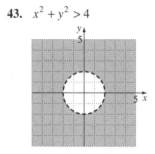

44. $y \le x^2 - 1$

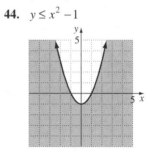

45. $y \le 2^x$

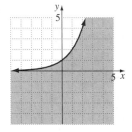

46. $3x + 2y \ge 6$

$2x + y \ge 6$

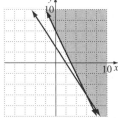

47. $2x - y \ge 4$

$x + 2y < 2$

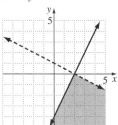

48. $y < x$

$y \le 2$

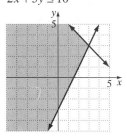

49. $y \le x$

$2x + 5y \le 10$

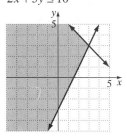

50. $0 \le x \le 3$

$y > 2$

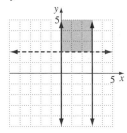

51. $2x + y < 4$

$2x + y > 6$

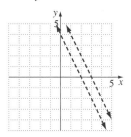

No solution

325

52. $x^2 + y^2 \le 16$

$x + y < 2$

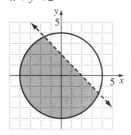

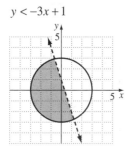

53. $x^2 + y^2 \le 9$

$y < -3x + 1$

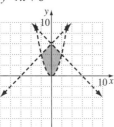

54. $y > x^2$

$x + y < 6$

$y < x + 6$

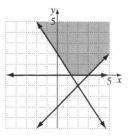

55. $y \ge 0$

$3x + 2y \ge 4$

$x - y \le 3$

56. $z = 2x + 3y$

$(2,2): z = 2(2) + 3(2) = 10$

$(4,0): z = 2(4) + 3(0) = 8$

$\left(\frac{1}{2}, \frac{1}{2}\right): z = 2\left(\frac{1}{2}\right) + 3\left(\frac{1}{2}\right) = \frac{5}{2}$

$(1,0): z = 2(1) + 3(0) = 2$

The maximum value is 10 and the minimum value is 2.

57. $z = 2x + 3y$

$x \ge 0, y \ge 0$

$x + y \le 8$

$3x + 2y \ge 6$

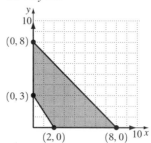

$(0,8): z = 2(0) + 3(8) = 24$

$(8,0): z = 2(8) + 3(0) = 16$

$(0,3): z = 2(0) + 3(3) = 9$

$(2,0): z = 2(2) + 3(0) = 6$

Maximum value is 24.

58. $z = x + 4y$

$0 \le x \le 5$

$0 \le y \le 7$

$x + y \ge 3$

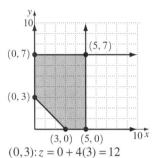

$(0, 3): z = 0 + 4(3) = 12$

$(3, 0): z = 3 + 4(0) = 3$

$(0, 7): z = 0 + 4(7) = 28$

$(5, 0): z = 5 + 4(0) = 5$

$(5, 7): z = 5 + 4(7) = 33$

Maximum value is 33.

59. $z = 5x + 6y$

$x \geq 0,\ y \geq 0,\ y \leq x$

$2x + y \leq 12$

$2x + 3y > 6$

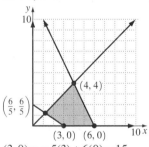

$(3, 0): z = 5(3) + 6(0) = 15$

$(6, 0): z = 5(6) + 6(0) = 30$

$\left(\dfrac{6}{5}, \dfrac{6}{5}\right): z = 5\left(\dfrac{6}{5}\right) + 6\left(\dfrac{6}{5}\right) = \dfrac{66}{5} = 13.2$

$(4, 4): 5(4) + 6(4) = 44$

The maximum value is 44.

60. a. $z = 500x + 350y$

b. $x + y \leq 200$

$x \geq 10$

$y \geq 80$

c.

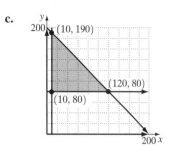

d.

Vertex	Objective Function
	$z = 500x + 350y$
(10, 80)	$z = 500(10) + 350(80)$ $= 33,000$
(10, 190)	$z = 500(10) + 350(190)$ $= 71,500$
(120, 80)	$z = 500(120) + 350(80)$ $= 88,000$

e. The company will make the greatest profit by producing 120 units of writing paper and 80 units of newsprint each day. The maximum daily profit is $88,000.

61. Let x = number of model A tents produced and

y = number of model B tents produced.

The constraints are:

$0.9x + 1.8y \leq 864$

$0.8x + 1.2y \leq 672$

$x \geq 0$

$y \geq 0$

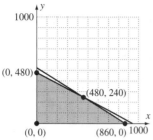

The vertices of the region are (0, 0), (0, 480), (480, 240), and (840, 0).

The objective is to maximize $25x + 40y$.

(0, 0): $25(0) + 40(0) = 0 + 0 = 0$

(0, 480): $25(0) + 40(480) = 0 + 19,200 = 19,200$

(480, 240): $25(480) + 40(240) = 12,000 + 9600$

$$= 21,600$$

(840, 0): $25(840) + 40(0) = 21,000 + 0 = 21,000$

The manufacturer should make 480 of model A and 240 of model B.

Chapter 5 Test

1. $x = y + 4$

$3x + 7y = -18$

Substitute $y + 4$ for x into second equation.

$3(y + 4) + 7y = -18$

$3y + 12 + 7y = -18$

$$10y = -30$$

$$y = -3$$

$$x = -3 + 4 = 1$$

The solution set to the system is $\{(1, -3)\}$.

2. $2x + 5y = -2$

$3x - 4y = 20$

Multiply the first equation by 3 and the second equation by -2 and add the result.

$6 + 15y = -6$

$\underline{-6x + 8y = -40}$

$\quad\quad 23y = -46$

$\quad\quad\quad y = -2$

Substitute $y = -2$ into the first equation:

$2x + 5(-2) = -2$

$\quad 2x - 10 = -2$

$\quad\quad\quad 2x = 8$

$\quad\quad\quad\quad x = 4$

The solution to the system is $\{(4, -2)\}$.

3. $\quad x + y + z = 6$ $\quad$ (1)

$\quad 3x + 4y - 7z = 1$ $\quad$ (2)

$\quad 2x - y + 3z = 5$ $\quad$ (3)

Eliminate x by multiplying (1) by -3 and adding the result to (2) and by multiplying (1) by -2 and adding the result to (3).

$-3x - 3y - 3z = -18$

$\underline{3x + 4y - 7z = 1}$

$\quad\quad y - 10z = -17 \,(4)$

$-2x - 2y - 2z = -12$

$\underline{2x - y + 3z = 5}$

$\quad\quad -3y + z = -7 \quad (5)$

Multiply (4) by 3 and add the result to (5) to eliminate y.

$3y - 30z = -51$

$\underline{-3y + z = -7}$

$\quad -29z = -58$

$\quad\quad\quad z = 2$

Substitute $z = 2$ into (5).

$-3y + 2 = -7$

$\quad -3y = -9$

$\quad\quad\quad y = 3$

Substitute $z = 2$ and $y = 3$ into (1).

$x + 3 + 2 = 6$

$\quad\quad\quad x = 1$

The solution to the system is $\{(1, 3, 2)\}$.

4. $x^2 + y^2 = 25$

$x + y = 1$

$y = 1 - x$

Substitute $1 - x$ for y in the first equation.

$$x^2 + (1-x)^2 = 25$$

$$x^2 + 1 - 2x + x^2 = 25$$

$$2x^2 - 2x - 24 = 0$$

$$x^2 - x - 12 = 0$$

$$(x-4)(x+3) = 0$$

$$x = 4, -3$$

If $x = 4, y = 1 - 4 = -3$.

If $x = -3, y = 1 - (-3) = 4$.

The solution set is $\{(4,-3),(-3,4)\}$.

5. $2x^2 - 5y^2 = -2$

$3x^2 + 2y^2 = 35$

Multiply first equation by 2 and the second equation by 5. Then add.

$$4x^2 - 10y^2 = -4$$

$$\underline{15x^2 + 10y^2 = 175}$$

$$19x^2 = 171$$

$$x^2 = 9$$

$$x = 3, -3$$

If $x = 3, 2(3)^2 - 5y^2 = -2$.

$$18 - 5y^2 = -2$$

$$-5y^2 = -20$$

$$y^2 = 4$$

$$y = 2, -2$$

If $x = -3, y = -2$.

The solution to the system is
$\{(3, 2),(3, -2),(-3, 2),(-3, -2)\}$.

6. $\dfrac{x}{(x+1)(x^2+9)} = \dfrac{A}{x+1} + \dfrac{Bx+C}{x^2+9}$

$x = A(x^2 + 9) + (Bx + C)(x+1)$

$\quad = Ax^2 + 9A + Bx^2 + Bx + Cx + C$

$\quad = (A+B)x^2 + (B+C)x + (9A+C)$

$A + B = 0 \rightarrow A = -B$

$$B + C = 1$$

$$9A + C = 0$$

$$-9B + C = 0$$

$$9B - C = 0$$

$$\underline{B + C = 1}$$

$$10B = 1$$

$$B = \frac{1}{10}$$

$$A = -\frac{1}{10}$$

$$\frac{1}{10} + C = 1, \quad C = \frac{9}{10}$$

$$\frac{x}{(x+1)(x^2+9)} = \frac{-1}{10(x+1)} + \frac{x+9}{10(x^2+9)}$$

7. $x - 2y < 8$

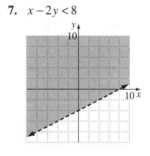

8. $x \geq 0, y \geq 0$

$3x + y \leq 9$

$2x + 3y \geq 6$

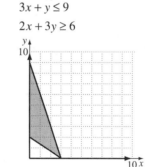

9. $x^2 + y^2 > 1$

$x^2 + y^2 < 4$

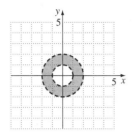

10. $y \leq 1 - x^2$

$x^2 + y^2 \leq 9$

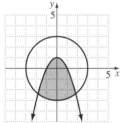

11. $z = 3x + 5y$
$x \geq 0, y \geq 0$

$x + y \leq 6$

$x \geq 2$

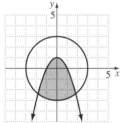

$(2, 0): z = 3(2) + 5(0) = 6$

$(6, 0): z = 3(6) + 5(0) = 18$

$(2, 4): z = 3(2) + 5(4) = 26$

Maximum value is 26.

12. $x =$ mg of cholesterol in one ounce of shrimp
$y =$ mg of cholesterol in one ounce of scallops
$3x + 2y = 156$
$5x + 3y = 255$
Multiply the first equation by -3 and

multiply the second equation by 2.
Add the resulting equations together.
$-9x - 6y = -468$

$\underline{10x + 6y = 510}$

$x = 42$

$3(42) + 2y = 156$

$126 + 2y = 156$

$2y = 30$

$y = 15$

$3(42) + 2y = 156$

$126 + 2y = 156$

$2y = 30$

$y = 15$

Shrimp: 42 mg of cholesterol per ounce
Scallops: 15 mg of cholesterol per ounce

13.　a. $C = 360,000 + 850x$

b. $R = 1150x$

c. $1150x = 360000 + 850x$

$300x = 360000$

$x = 1200$

$1150(1200) = 1,380,000$

1200 computers need to be sold to make
$1,380,00 for the company to break even.

14. $y = ax^2 + bx + c$
$(-1, -2): -2 = a - b + c$
$(2, 1): 1 = 4a + 2b + c$
$(-2, 1): 1 = 4a - 2b + c$
$4a + 2b + c = 1$

$\underline{-4a + 2b - c = -1}$

$4b = 0$

$b = 0$

$a + c = -2$

$4a + c = 1$

$\underline{-a - c = 2}$

$3a = 3$

$a = 1$

$a + c = -2$

$c = -3$

The quadratic function is $y = x^2 - 3$.

15. $2x + y = 39$

$xy = 180$

$y = 39 - 2x$

$x(39 - 2x) = 180$

$39x - 2x^2 = 180$

$2x^2 - 39x + 180 = 0$

$(2x - 15)(x - 12) = 0$

$$x = \frac{15}{2}, 12$$

If $x = \frac{15}{2}, \frac{15}{2} y = 180$ and $y = 24$.

If $x = 12, 12y = 180$ and $y = 15$.

The dimensions are 7.5 ft by 24 ft
or 12 ft by 15 ft

16. Let x = regular, y = deluxe.

objective function: $z = 200x + 250y$

constraints: $x \geq 50, y \geq 75$

$$x + y \leq 150$$

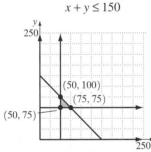

$(50, 75): z = 200(50) + 250(75) = 28,750$

$(50, 100): z = 200(50) + 250(100) = 35,000$

$(75, 75): z = 200(75) + 250(75) = 33,750$

For a maximum profit of $35,000 a week,
the company should manufacture 50 regular
and 100 deluxe jet skis.

Cumulative Review Exercises (Chapters 1–5)

1. $\sqrt{x^2 - 3x} = 2x - 6$

$x^2 - 3x = 4x^2 - 24x + 36$

$3x^2 - 21x + 36 = 0$

$x^2 - 7x + 12 = 0$

$(x - 3)(x - 4) = 0$

$x = 3, 4$

The solution set is $\{3, 4\}$.

2. $4x^2 = 8x - 7$

$4x^2 - 8x + 7 = 0$

$$x = \frac{8 \pm \sqrt{64 - 112}}{8} = \frac{8 \pm \sqrt{-48}}{8}$$

$$= \frac{8 \pm 4\sqrt{3}i}{8} = \frac{2 \pm \sqrt{3}i}{2}$$

The solution set is $\left\{ \frac{2 + i\sqrt{3}}{2}, \frac{2 - i\sqrt{3}}{2} \right\}$.

3. $\left| \frac{x}{3} + 2 \right| < 4$

$-4 < \frac{x}{3} + 2 < 4$

$-6 < \frac{x}{3} < 2$

$-18 < x < 6$

The solution is

$\{x \mid -18 < x < 6\}$ or $(-18, 6)$.

4. $\frac{x + 5}{x - 1} > 2$

$\frac{x + 5}{x - 1} - 2 > 0$

$\frac{x + 5 - 2(x - 1)}{x - 1} > 0$

$\frac{x + 5 - 2x + 2}{x - 1} > 0$

$\frac{-x + 7}{x - 1} > 0$

$\dfrac{-x+7}{x-1} = 0$ when $x = 7$ and is undefined
when
$x = 1$.
Test $x = 0$:
$\dfrac{0+5}{0-1} > 2$?
$\dfrac{5}{-1} > 2$?
$-5 \not> 2$
Test $x = 2$:
$\dfrac{2+5}{2-1} > 2$?
$\dfrac{7}{1} > 2$?
$7 > 2$
Test $x = 8$:
$\dfrac{8+5}{8-1} > 2$?
$\dfrac{13}{7} > 2$?
$\dfrac{13}{7} \not> \dfrac{14}{7}$
The solution is $\left\{x \mid 1 < x < 7\right\}$ or $(1, 7)$.

5. $2x^3 + x^2 - 13x + 6 = 0$

$f(x) = 2x^3 + x^2 - 13x + 6$ has 2 sign
changes: 2 or 0 positive real roots.

$f(-x) = -2x^3 + x^2 + 13x + 6$ has 1 sign
change: 1 negative real root.

p: ±1, ±2, ±3, ±6

q: ±1, ±2

$\dfrac{p}{q}$: $\pm 1, \pm\dfrac{1}{2}, \pm 2, \pm 3, \pm\dfrac{3}{2}, \pm 6$

$$
\begin{array}{r|rrrr}
-3 & 2 & 1 & -13 & 6 \\
   &   & -6 & 15 & -6 \\
\hline
   & 2 & -5 & 2 & 0
\end{array}
$$

$2x^3 + x^2 - 13x + 6 = (x+3)(2x^2 - 5x + 2)$
$\qquad\qquad\qquad\quad = (x+3)(2x-1)(x-2)$

$x = -3$, $x = \dfrac{1}{2}$, $x = 2$

The solution set is $\left\{-3, \frac{1}{2}, 2\right\}$.

6. $6x - 3(5x + 2) = 4(1 - x)$
$\quad 6x - 15x - 6 = 4 - 4x$
$\qquad\quad -9x - 6 = 4 - 4x$
$\qquad\qquad\quad -5x = 10$
$\qquad\qquad\qquad x = -2$
The solution set is $\{-2\}$.

7. $\log(x+3) + \log x = 1$
$\quad \log x(x+3) = 1$
$\qquad\quad x(x+3) = 10$
$\qquad\quad x^2 + 3x - 10 = 0$
$\qquad\quad (x+5)(x-2) = 0$
$\qquad\qquad\qquad x = -5$ or $x = 2$
$\qquad\qquad\qquad x = -5$ is extraneous.
$\qquad\qquad\qquad x = 2$
The solution set is $\{2\}$.

8. $3^{x+2} = 11$
$\quad \log_3 3^{x+2} = \log_3 11$
$\qquad\quad x + 2 = \log_3 11$
$\qquad\qquad x = -2 + \log_3 11$
$\qquad\qquad x = -2 + \dfrac{\log 11}{\log 3} \approx 0.18$
The solution set is $\left\{-2 + \log_3 11\right\}$.

9. $f(x) = (x+2)^2 - 4$
vertex: $(-2, -4)$
y-intercept:
$\quad f(0) = (0+2)^2 - 4 = 0$
x-intercepts:

$$(x+2)^2 - 4 = 0$$
$$x^2 + 4x + 4 - 4 = 0$$
$$x^2 + 4x = 0$$
$$x(x+4) = 0$$
$$x = 0, x - 4$$

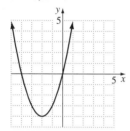

10. $2x - 3y \le 6$

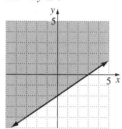

11. $y = 3^{x-2}$

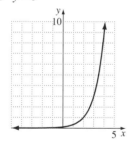

12. $f(x) = \dfrac{x^2 - x - 6}{x+1}$

vertical asymptote: $x = -1$
horizontal asymptote: $m > n$, none
x-intercepts:
$$x^2 - x - 6 = 0$$
$$(x-3)(x+2) = 0$$
$$x = 3, x = -2$$

y-intercept:
$$f(0) = \frac{0^2 - 0 - 6}{0 + 1} = -6$$

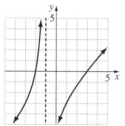

13. $\log_2(8x^5) = \log_2 8 + \log_2 x^5$
$$= 3 + 5\log_2 x$$

14. $A = Pe^{rt}$
$$18{,}000 = 6000e^{10r}$$
$$3 = e^{10r}$$
$$\ln 3 = \ln e^{10r}$$
$$\ln 3 = 10r$$
$$r = \frac{\ln 3}{10} \approx 0.1099$$
$$10.99\%$$

15. $f(x) = 7x - 3$
$$x = 7y - 3$$
$$x + 3 = 7y$$
$$y = \frac{1}{7}x + \frac{3}{7}$$
$$f^{-1}(x) = \frac{1}{7}x + \frac{3}{7}$$

16. $f(x) = 7x - 3, g(x) = 3x - 7$
$$g(f(x)) = 3(7x - 3) - 7 = 21x - 9 - 7 = 21x - 16$$

17. Answers may vary.

18. $3x - y = -2$
$2x^2 - y = 0$
Solve the first equation for y.
$y = 3x + 2$
Substitute the expression $3x + 2$ for y in the

second equation and solve for x.

$$2x^2 - (3x + 2) = 0$$

$$2x^2 - 3x - 2 = 0$$

$$x = \frac{3 \pm \sqrt{9 + 16}}{4} = \frac{3 \pm 5}{4}$$

$$x = \frac{3 + 5}{4} = 2 \quad \text{or} \quad x = \frac{3 - 5}{4} = -\frac{1}{2}$$

If $x = 2, y = 3(2) + 2 = 8$.

If $x = -\frac{1}{2}, y = 3\left(-\frac{1}{2}\right) + 2 = \frac{1}{2}$.

The solution set is $\left\{(2, 8), \left(-\frac{1}{2}, \frac{1}{2}\right)\right\}$.

19.
$$L = 2W + 1$$
$$LW = 36$$

$$W(2W + 1) = 36$$

$$2W^2 + W - 36 = 0$$

$$(2W + 9)(W - 4) = 0$$

$$W = -\frac{9}{2} \text{ or } 4$$

Length cannot be negative. If $W = 4$, $4L = 36$,

$L = 9$. The dimensions are 4 m by 9 m.

20. $f(x) = 0.1x^2 - 3x + 22$

$$f(90) = 0.1(90)^2 - 3(90) + 22$$

$$= 810 - 270 + 22$$

$$= 562$$

A plane with an initial landing speed of 90 feet per second needs 562 feet to land. There is a problem since 550 feet is not enough.

Chapter 6

Section 6.1

Check Point Exercises

1. $\begin{bmatrix} 1 & -1 & 1 & | & 8 \\ 0 & 1 & -12 & | & -15 \\ 0 & 0 & 1 & | & 1 \end{bmatrix} \rightarrow \begin{array}{l} 1x - 1y + 1z = 8 \\ 0x + 1y - 12z = -15 \\ 0x + 0y + 1z = 1 \end{array}$

$x - y + z = 8$
$y - 12z = -15$
$z = 1$

Solve for y by back-substitution.
$y - 12(1) = -15$
$y - 12 = -15$
$y = -3$

Use back substitution for x.
$x - (-3) + 1 = 8$
$x + 4 = 8$
$x = 4$

The solution set for the system is $\{(4, -3, 1)\}$.

2. a. The notation $R_1 \leftrightarrow R_2$ means to interchange the elements in row 1 and row 2. This results in the row-equivalent matrix

$\begin{bmatrix} 1 & 6 & -3 & | & 7 \\ 4 & 12 & -20 & | & 8 \\ -3 & -2 & 1 & | & -9 \end{bmatrix}$.

b. The notation $\frac{1}{4}R_1$ means to multiply each element in row 1 by $\frac{1}{4}$. This results in the row-equivalent matrix

$\begin{bmatrix} \frac{1}{4}(4) & \frac{1}{4}(12) & \frac{1}{4}(-20) & | & \frac{1}{4}(8) \\ 1 & 6 & -3 & | & 7 \\ -3 & -2 & 1 & | & -9 \end{bmatrix} = \begin{bmatrix} 1 & 3 & -5 & | & 2 \\ 1 & 6 & -3 & | & 7 \\ -3 & -2 & 1 & | & -9 \end{bmatrix}$

c. The notation $3R_2 + R_3$ means to add 3 times the elements in row 2 to the corresponding elements in row 3. Replace the elements in row 3 by these sums. First, we find 3 times the elements in row 2: $3(1) = 3, 3(6) = 18, 3(-3) = -9, 3(7) = 21$. Now we add these products to the corresponding elements in row 3. This results in the row equivalent matrix

$$\begin{bmatrix} 4 & 12 & -20 & 8 \\ 1 & 6 & -3 & 7 \\ -3+3=0 & -2+18=16 & 1-9=-8 & -9+21=12 \end{bmatrix} = \begin{bmatrix} 4 & 12 & -20 & 8 \\ 1 & 6 & -3 & 7 \\ 0 & 16 & -8 & 12 \end{bmatrix}.$$

3. $\begin{aligned} 2x + y + 2z &= 18 \\ x - y + 2z &= 9 \\ x + 2y - z &= 6 \end{aligned} \rightarrow \begin{bmatrix} 2 & 1 & 2 & 18 \\ 1 & -1 & 2 & 9 \\ 1 & 2 & -1 & 6 \end{bmatrix}$

Interchange row 1 with row 2 to get 1 in the top position of the first column.

$$\begin{bmatrix} 1 & -1 & 2 & 9 \\ 2 & 1 & 2 & 18 \\ 1 & 2 & -1 & 6 \end{bmatrix}$$

Multiply the first row by –2 and add these products to row 2.

$$\begin{bmatrix} 1 & -1 & 2 & 9 \\ 2+-2=0 & 1+2=3 & 2+-4=-2 & -18+18=0 \\ 1 & 2 & -1 & 6 \end{bmatrix} = \begin{bmatrix} 1 & -1 & 2 & 9 \\ 0 & 3 & -2 & 0 \\ 1 & 2 & -1 & 6 \end{bmatrix}$$

Next, multiply the top row by –1 and add these products to row 3.

$$\begin{bmatrix} 1 & -1 & 2 & 9 \\ 0 & 3 & -2 & 0 \\ 1+-1=0 & 2+1=3 & -1-2=-3 & 6-9=-3 \end{bmatrix} = \begin{bmatrix} 1 & -1 & 2 & 9 \\ 0 & 3 & -2 & 0 \\ 0 & 3 & -3 & -3 \end{bmatrix}$$

Next, to obtain a 1 in the second row, second column, multiply 3 by its reciprocal, $\frac{1}{3}$. Therefore, we

multiply all the numbers in the second row by $\frac{1}{3}$ to get

$$\begin{bmatrix} 1 & -1 & 2 & 9 \\ 0 & 1 & -\frac{2}{3} & 0 \\ 0 & 3 & -3 & -3 \end{bmatrix}.$$

Next, to obtain a 0 in the third row, second column, multiply the second row by –3 and add the products to row three. The resulting matrix is

$$\begin{bmatrix} 1 & -1 & 2 & 9 \\ 0 & 1 & -\frac{2}{3} & 0 \\ 0 & 0 & -1 & -3 \end{bmatrix}.$$

To get 1 in the third row, third column, multiply –1 by its reciprocal, –1. Multiply all numbers in the third row by –1 to obtain the resulting matrix

$$\begin{bmatrix} 1 & -1 & 2 & 9 \\ 0 & 1 & -\frac{2}{3} & 0 \\ 0 & 0 & 1 & 3 \end{bmatrix}.$$

The system represented by this matrix is:

$$x - y + 2z = 9$$

$$y - \frac{2}{3}z = 0$$

$$z = 3$$

Use back substitution to find y and x.

$$y - \frac{2}{3}(3) = 0 \qquad\qquad x - 2 + 6 = 9$$

$$y - 2 = 0 \qquad\qquad x + 4 = 9$$

$$y = 2 \qquad\qquad x = 5$$

The solution set for the original system is $\{(5, 2, 3)\}$.

4. $w - 3x - 2y + z = -3$
        $2w - 7x - y + 2z = 1$

     $3w - 7x - 3y + 3z = -5$

     $5w + x + 4y - 2z = 18$

The augmented matrix is

$$\begin{bmatrix} 1 & -3 & -2 & 1 & | & -3 \\ 2 & -7 & -1 & 2 & | & 1 \\ 3 & -7 & -3 & 3 & | & -5 \\ 5 & 1 & 4 & -2 & | & 18 \end{bmatrix}.$$

Multiply the top row by –2 and add the products to the second row. Multiply the top row by –3 and add the pro-ducts to the third row. Multiply the top row by –5 and add the products to the fourth row. The resulting matrix is

$$\begin{bmatrix} 1 & -3 & -2 & 1 & | & -3 \\ 0 & -1 & 3 & 0 & | & 7 \\ 0 & 2 & 3 & 0 & | & 4 \\ 0 & 16 & 14 & -7 & | & 33 \end{bmatrix}.$$

Next, multiply the second row by –1 to obtain a 1 in the second row, second column.

$$\begin{bmatrix} 1 & -3 & -2 & 1 & | & -3 \\ 0 & 1 & -3 & 0 & | & -7 \\ 0 & 2 & 3 & 0 & | & 4 \\ 0 & 16 & 14 & -7 & | & 33 \end{bmatrix}$$

Next, multiply the second row by –2 and add the products to the third row. Multiply the second row by –16 and add the products to the fourth row. The resulting matrix is

$$\begin{bmatrix} 1 & -3 & -2 & 1 & | & -3 \\ 0 & 1 & -3 & 0 & | & -7 \\ 0 & 0 & 9 & 0 & | & 18 \\ 0 & 0 & 62 & -7 & | & 145 \end{bmatrix}.$$

Next, multiply the third row by $\frac{1}{9}$ to obtain a 1 in the third row, third column. The resulting matrix is

$$\begin{bmatrix} 1 & -3 & -2 & 1 & | & -3 \\ 0 & 1 & -3 & 0 & | & -7 \\ 0 & 0 & 1 & 0 & | & 2 \\ 0 & 0 & 62 & -7 & | & 145 \end{bmatrix}.$$

Multiply the third row by –62 and add the products to the fourth row to obtain the resulting matrix

$$\begin{bmatrix} 1 & -3 & -2 & 1 & | & -3 \\ 0 & 1 & -3 & 0 & | & -7 \\ 0 & 0 & 1 & 0 & | & 2 \\ 0 & 0 & 0 & -7 & | & 21 \end{bmatrix}.$$

Multiply the fourth row by $-\frac{1}{7}$, the reciprocal of –7. The resulting matrix is

$$\begin{bmatrix} 1 & -3 & -2 & 1 & | & -3 \\ 0 & 1 & -3 & 0 & | & -7 \\ 0 & 0 & 1 & 0 & | & 2 \\ 0 & 0 & 0 & 1 & | & -3 \end{bmatrix}.$$

The system of linear equations corresponding to the resulting matrix is

$$w - 3x - 2y + z = -3$$
$$x - 3y = -7$$
$$y = 2$$
$$z = -3$$

Using back-substitution solve for x and w.
$$x - 3(2) = -7$$
$$x = -1$$

$$w - 3(-1) - 2(2) - 3 = -3$$
$$w - 4 = -3$$
$$w = 1$$

The solution set is $\{(1, -1, 2, -3)\}$.

5. The matrix obtained in 3 will be the starting
point.

$$\begin{bmatrix} 1 & -1 & 2 & | & 9 \\ 0 & 1 & -\frac{2}{3} & | & 0 \\ 0 & 0 & 1 & | & 3 \end{bmatrix}$$

Next, multiply the third row by $\dfrac{2}{3}$ and add
the products to the second row. Multiply
the third row by 2 and add the products to
the first row. The resulting matrix is

$$\begin{bmatrix} 1 & -1 & 0 & 3 \\ 0 & 1 & 0 & 2 \\ 0 & 0 & 1 & 3 \end{bmatrix}.$$

Add the second row to the first row and
replace the first row.

$$\begin{bmatrix} 1 & 0 & 0 & 5 \\ 0 & 1 & 0 & 2 \\ 0 & 0 & 1 & 3 \end{bmatrix}$$

This matrix corresponds to $x = 5$, $y = 2$ and
$z = 3$. The solution set is $\{(5, 2, 3)\}$.

Exercise Set 6.1

1. $\begin{bmatrix} 2 & 1 & 2 & | & 2 \\ 3 & -5 & -1 & | & 4 \\ 1 & -2 & -3 & | & -6 \end{bmatrix}$

3. $\begin{bmatrix} 1 & -1 & 1 & | & 8 \\ 0 & 1 & -12 & | & -15 \\ 0 & 0 & 1 & | & 1 \end{bmatrix}$

5. $\begin{bmatrix} 5 & -2 & -3 & | & 0 \\ 1 & 1 & 0 & | & 5 \\ 2 & 0 & -3 & | & 4 \end{bmatrix}$

7. $\begin{bmatrix} 2 & 5 & -3 & 1 & | & 2 \\ 0 & 3 & 1 & 0 & | & 4 \\ 1 & -1 & 5 & 0 & | & 9 \\ 5 & -5 & -2 & 0 & | & 1 \end{bmatrix}$

9. $5x + 3z = -11$
$\quad y - 4z = 12$
$\quad 7x + 2y = 3$

11. $w + x + 4y + z = 3$
$\quad -w + x - y = 7$
$\quad 12w + 5z = 11$
$\quad 12y + 4z = 5$

13. $\quad x - 4z = 5$
$\quad y - 12z = 13$
$$z = -\frac{1}{2}$$
$$y - 12\left(-\frac{1}{2}\right) = 13$$
$$y + 6 = 13$$
$$y = 7$$
$$x - 4\left(-\frac{1}{2}\right) = 5$$
$$x + 2 = 5$$
$$x = 3$$

The solution set is $\left\{\left(3, 7, -\dfrac{1}{2}\right)\right\}$.

15. $\begin{bmatrix} 1 & \frac{1}{2} & 1 & | & \frac{11}{2} \\ 0 & 1 & \frac{3}{2} & | & 7 \\ 0 & 0 & 1 & | & 4 \end{bmatrix}$

$$x + \frac{1}{2}y + z = \frac{11}{2}$$

$$y + \frac{3}{2}z = 7$$

$$z = 4$$

$$y + \frac{3}{2}(4) = 7$$

$$y + 6 = 7$$

$$y = 1$$

$$x + \frac{1}{2}(1) + 4 = \frac{11}{2}$$

$$x + \frac{9}{2} = \frac{11}{2}$$

$$x = \frac{11}{2} - \frac{9}{2}$$

$$x = 1$$

The solution set is $\{(1, 1, 4)\}$.

17. $\begin{bmatrix} 1 & -1 & 1 & 1 & | & 3 \\ 0 & 1 & -2 & -1 & | & 0 \\ 0 & 0 & 1 & 6 & | & 17 \\ 0 & 0 & 0 & 1 & | & 3 \end{bmatrix}$

$$w - x + y + z = 3$$

$$x - 2y - z = 0$$

$$y + 6z = 17$$

$$z = 3$$

$$y + 6(3) = 17$$

$$y + 18 = 17$$

$$y = -1$$

$$x - 2(-1) - 3 = 0$$

$$x - 1 = 0$$

$$x = 1$$

$$w - 1 + (-1) + 3 = 3$$

$$w + 1 = 3$$

$$w = 2$$

The solution set is $\{(2, 1, -1, 3)\}$.

19. $\begin{bmatrix} 2\left(\frac{1}{2}\right) & -6\left(\frac{1}{2}\right) & 4\left(\frac{1}{2}\right) & | & 10\left(\frac{1}{2}\right) \\ 1 & 5 & -5 & | & 0 \\ 3 & 0 & 4 & | & 7 \end{bmatrix} \begin{matrix} \frac{1}{2}R_1 \\ \\ \\ \end{matrix}$

$\begin{bmatrix} 1 & -3 & 2 & | & 5 \\ 1 & 5 & -5 & | & 0 \\ 3 & 0 & 4 & | & 7 \end{bmatrix}$

21. $\begin{bmatrix} 1 & -3 & 2 & 0 \\ -3(1)+3 & -3(-3)+1 & -3(2)+-1 & -3(0)+7 \\ 2 & -2 & 1 & 3 \end{bmatrix} -3R_1 + R_2$

$\begin{bmatrix} 1 & -3 & 2 & 0 \\ 0 & 10 & -7 & 7 \\ 2 & -2 & 1 & 3 \end{bmatrix}$

23. $\begin{bmatrix} 1 & -1 & 1 & 1 & 3 \\ 0 & 1 & -2 & -1 & 0 \\ 2 & 0 & 3 & 4 & 11 \\ 5 & 1 & 2 & 4 & 6 \end{bmatrix} \begin{matrix} \\ -2R_1 + R_3 \\ -5R_1 + R_4 \end{matrix}$

$\begin{bmatrix} 1 & -1 & 1 & 1 & 3 \\ 0 & 1 & -2 & -1 & 0 \\ -2(1)+2 & -2(-1)+0 & -2(1)+3 & -2(1)+4 & -2(3)+11 \\ -5(1)+5 & -5(-1)+1 & -5(1)+2 & -5(1)+4 & -5(3)+6 \end{bmatrix} = \begin{bmatrix} 1 & -1 & 1 & 1 & 3 \\ 0 & 1 & -2 & -1 & 0 \\ 0 & 2 & 1 & 2 & 5 \\ 0 & 6 & -3 & -1 & -9 \end{bmatrix}$

25. $\begin{bmatrix} 1 & -1 & 1 & 8 \\ 2 & 3 & -1 & -2 \\ 3 & -2 & -9 & 9 \end{bmatrix}$

$\begin{bmatrix} 1 & -1 & 1 & 8 \\ -2(1)+2 & -2(-1)+3 & -2(1)-1 & -2(8)-2 \\ -3(1)+3 & -3(-1)-2 & -3(1)-9 & -3(8)+9 \end{bmatrix}$

$\begin{bmatrix} 1 & -1 & 1 & 8 \\ 0 & 5 & -3 & -18 \\ 0 & 1 & -12 & -15 \end{bmatrix}$

$$\begin{bmatrix} 1 & -1 & 1 & | & 8 \\ 0\left(\frac{1}{5}\right) & 1\left(\frac{1}{5}\right) & -3\left(\frac{1}{5}\right) & | & -18\left(\frac{1}{5}\right) \\ 0 & 1 & -12 & | & -15 \end{bmatrix}$$

$$\begin{bmatrix} 1 & -1 & 1 & | & 8 \\ 0 & 1 & -\frac{3}{5} & | & -\frac{18}{5} \\ 0 & 1 & -12 & | & -15 \end{bmatrix}$$

27. $\quad x + y - z = -2$
$\quad\quad 2x - y + z = 5$
$\quad\quad -x + 2y + 2z = 1$

$$\begin{bmatrix} 1 & 1 & -1 & | & -2 \\ 2 & -1 & 1 & | & 5 \\ -1 & 2 & 2 & | & 1 \end{bmatrix} -2R_1 + R_2$$

$$\begin{bmatrix} 1 & 1 & -1 & | & -2 \\ 0 & -3 & 3 & | & 9 \\ -1 & 2 & 2 & | & 1 \end{bmatrix} 1R_1 + R_3$$

$$\begin{bmatrix} 1 & 1 & -1 & | & -2 \\ 0 & -3 & 3 & | & 9 \\ 0 & 3 & 1 & | & -1 \end{bmatrix} -\frac{1}{3}R_2$$

$$\begin{bmatrix} 1 & 1 & -1 & | & -2 \\ 0 & 1 & -1 & | & -3 \\ 0 & 3 & 1 & | & -1 \end{bmatrix} -3R_2 + R_3$$

$$= \begin{bmatrix} 1 & 1 & -1 & | & -2 \\ 0 & 1 & -1 & | & -3 \\ 0 & 0 & 4 & | & 8 \end{bmatrix}$$

$4z = 8$
$z = 2$
$y - z = -3$
$y - 2 = -3$
$\quad\quad y = -1$
$x + y - z = -2$
$x - 1 - 2 = -2$
$\quad x - 3 = -2$
$\quad\quad x = 1$

The solution set is $\{(1, -1, 2)\}$.

29. $\quad x + 3y = 0$
$\quad\quad x + y + z = 1$
$\quad\quad 3x - y - z = 11$

$$\begin{bmatrix} 1 & 3 & 0 & | & 0 \\ 1 & 1 & 1 & | & 1 \\ 3 & -1 & -1 & | & 11 \end{bmatrix} -1R_1 + R_2$$

$$\begin{bmatrix} 1 & 3 & 0 & | & 0 \\ 0 & -2 & 1 & | & 1 \\ 3 & -1 & -1 & | & 11 \end{bmatrix} -3R_1 + R_3$$

$$\begin{bmatrix} 1 & 3 & 0 & | & 0 \\ 0 & -2 & 1 & | & 1 \\ 0 & -10 & -1 & | & 11 \end{bmatrix} -\frac{1}{2}R_2$$

$$\begin{bmatrix} 1 & 3 & 0 & | & 0 \\ 0 & 1 & -\frac{1}{2} & | & -\frac{1}{2} \\ 0 & -10 & -1 & | & 11 \end{bmatrix} 10R_2 + R_3$$

$$\begin{bmatrix} 1 & 3 & 0 & | & 0 \\ 0 & 1 & -\frac{1}{2} & | & -\frac{1}{2} \\ 0 & 0 & -6 & | & 6 \end{bmatrix} -\frac{1}{6}R_3$$

$$\begin{bmatrix} 1 & 3 & 0 & | & 0 \\ 0 & 1 & -\frac{1}{2} & | & -\frac{1}{2} \\ 0 & 0 & 1 & | & -1 \end{bmatrix}$$

$z = -1$
$$y - \frac{1}{2}z = -\frac{1}{2}$$
$$y - \frac{1}{2}(-1) = -\frac{1}{2}$$
$$y + \frac{1}{2} = -\frac{1}{2}$$
$$y = -1$$

Interchange row one and row two.

$x + 3y = 0$
$x + 3(-1) = 0$
$\quad\quad x = 3$

The solution set is $\{(3, -1, -1)\}$.

31. $\quad 2x - y - z = 4$
$\quad\quad x + y - 5z = -4$
$\quad\quad x - 2y = 4$

$$\begin{bmatrix} 2 & -1 & -1 & 4 \\ 1 & 1 & -5 & -4 \\ 1 & -2 & 0 & 4 \end{bmatrix}$$

Interchange rows one and two.

$$\begin{bmatrix} 1 & 1 & -5 & -4 \\ 2 & -1 & -1 & 4 \\ 1 & -2 & 0 & 4 \end{bmatrix}$$

Replace row two with $-2R_1 + R_2$.
Replace row three with $-R_1 + R_3$.

$$\begin{bmatrix} 1 & 1 & -5 & -4 \\ 0 & -3 & 9 & 12 \\ 0 & -3 & 5 & 8 \end{bmatrix}$$

Replace row two with $-\dfrac{1}{3}R_2$.

$$\begin{bmatrix} 1 & 1 & -5 & -4 \\ 0 & 1 & -3 & -4 \\ 0 & -3 & 5 & 8 \end{bmatrix}$$

Replace row three with $3R_2 + R_3$.

$$\begin{bmatrix} 1 & 1 & -5 & -4 \\ 0 & 1 & -3 & -4 \\ 0 & 0 & -4 & -4 \end{bmatrix}$$

Replace row three with $-\dfrac{1}{4}R_3$.

$$\begin{bmatrix} 1 & 1 & -5 & -4 \\ 0 & 1 & -3 & -4 \\ 0 & 0 & 1 & 1 \end{bmatrix}$$

$z = 1$
$\quad y - 3z = -4$
$\quad y - 3(1) = -4$
$\qquad\qquad y = -1$
$\quad x + y - 5z = -4$
$\quad x - 1 - 5(1) = -4$
$\qquad\quad x - 6 = -4$
$\qquad\qquad x = 2$

The solution set is $\{(2, -1, 1)\}$.

33. $x + y + z = 4$
$\quad x - y - z = 0$
$\quad x - y + z = 2$

$$\begin{bmatrix} 1 & 1 & 1 & 4 \\ 1 & -1 & -1 & 0 \\ 1 & -1 & 1 & 2 \end{bmatrix}$$

Replace row two with $-R_1 + R_2$.
Replace row three with $-R_1 + R_3$.

$$\begin{bmatrix} 1 & 1 & 1 & 4 \\ 0 & -2 & -2 & -4 \\ 0 & -2 & 0 & -2 \end{bmatrix}$$

Replace row two with $-\dfrac{1}{2}R_2$.

$$\begin{bmatrix} 1 & 1 & 1 & 4 \\ 0 & 1 & 1 & 2 \\ 0 & -2 & 0 & -2 \end{bmatrix}$$

Replace row 3 with $2R_2 + R_3$.

$$\begin{bmatrix} 1 & 1 & 1 & 4 \\ 0 & 1 & 1 & 2 \\ 0 & 0 & 2 & 2 \end{bmatrix}$$

Replace row 3 with $\dfrac{1}{2}R_3$.

$$\begin{bmatrix} 1 & 1 & 1 & 4 \\ 0 & 1 & 1 & 2 \\ 0 & 0 & 1 & 1 \end{bmatrix}$$

$z = 1$
$y + 1 = 2$
$\quad y = 1$
$x + 1 + 1 = 4$
$\qquad x = 2$

The solution set is $\{(2, 1, 1)\}$.

35. Write the equations in standard form.
$\quad x + 2y - z = -1$
$\quad\quad x - y + z = 4$
$\quad x + y - 3z = -2$

$$\begin{bmatrix} 1 & 2 & -1 & -1 \\ 1 & -1 & 1 & 4 \\ 1 & 1 & -3 & -2 \end{bmatrix}$$

Replace row two with $-R_1 + R_2$.
Replace row three with $-R_1 + R_3$.

$$\begin{bmatrix} 1 & 2 & -1 & -1 \\ 0 & -3 & 2 & 5 \\ 0 & -1 & -2 & -1 \end{bmatrix}$$

Replace row two with $-R_3$.
Replace row three with R_2.

$$\begin{bmatrix} 1 & 2 & -1 & -1 \\ 0 & 1 & 2 & 1 \\ 0 & -3 & 2 & 5 \end{bmatrix}$$

Replace row 3 with $3R_2 + R_3$.

$$\begin{bmatrix} 1 & 2 & -1 & -1 \\ 0 & 1 & 2 & 1 \\ 0 & 0 & 8 & 8 \end{bmatrix}$$

Replace row 3 with $\dfrac{1}{8}R_3$.

$$\begin{bmatrix} 1 & 2 & -1 & -1 \\ 0 & 1 & 2 & 1 \\ 0 & 0 & 1 & 1 \end{bmatrix}$$

$z = 1$
$y + 2(1) = 1$
$\qquad y = -1$
$x + 2(-1) - 1 = -1$
$\qquad x = 2$
The solution set is $\{(2, -1, 1)\}$.

37. $3a - b - 4c = 3$
$2a - b + 2c = -8$

$a + 2b - 3c = 9$
Interchange equations 1 and 3.

$$\begin{bmatrix} 1 & 2 & -3 & 9 \\ 2 & -1 & 2 & -8 \\ 3 & -1 & -4 & 3 \end{bmatrix}$$

Replace row two with $-2R_1 + R_2$.
Replace row three with $-3R_1 + R_3$.

$$\begin{bmatrix} 1 & 2 & -3 & 9 \\ 0 & -5 & 8 & -26 \\ 0 & -7 & 5 & -24 \end{bmatrix}$$

Replace row two with $-\dfrac{1}{5}R_2$.

$$\begin{bmatrix} 1 & 2 & -3 & 9 \\ 0 & 1 & -\dfrac{8}{5} & \dfrac{26}{5} \\ 0 & -7 & 5 & -24 \end{bmatrix}$$

Replace row three with $7R_2 + R_3$.

$$\begin{bmatrix} 1 & 2 & -3 & 9 \\ 0 & 1 & -\dfrac{8}{5} & \dfrac{26}{5} \\ 0 & 0 & -\dfrac{31}{5} & \dfrac{62}{5} \end{bmatrix}$$

Replace row 3 with $-\dfrac{5}{31}R_3$.

$$\begin{bmatrix} 1 & 2 & -3 & 9 \\ 0 & 1 & -\dfrac{8}{5} & \dfrac{26}{5} \\ 0 & 0 & 1 & -2 \end{bmatrix}$$

$z = -2$
$$y - \frac{8}{5}(-2) = \frac{26}{5}$$
$$y + \frac{16}{5} = \frac{26}{5}$$
$$y = 2$$
$x + 2(2) - 3(-2) = 9$
$\qquad x + 4 + 6 = 9$
$\qquad\qquad x = -1$
The solution set is $\{(-1, 2, -2)\}$.

39. $2x + 2y + 7z = -1$
$\quad 2x + y + 2z = 2$
$\quad 4x + 6y + z = 15$

$$\begin{bmatrix} 2 & 2 & 7 & | & -1 \\ 2 & 1 & 2 & | & 2 \\ 4 & 6 & 1 & | & 15 \end{bmatrix} \frac{1}{2}R_1$$

$$\begin{bmatrix} 1 & 1 & \frac{7}{2} & | & -\frac{1}{2} \\ 2 & 1 & 2 & | & 2 \\ 4 & 6 & 1 & | & 15 \end{bmatrix} -2R_1 + R_2$$

$$\begin{bmatrix} 1 & 1 & \frac{7}{2} & | & -\frac{1}{2} \\ 0 & -1 & -5 & | & 3 \\ 4 & 6 & 1 & | & 15 \end{bmatrix} -4R_1 + R_3$$

$$\begin{bmatrix} 1 & 1 & \frac{7}{2} & -\frac{1}{2} \\ 0 & -1 & -5 & 3 \\ 0 & 2 & -13 & 17 \end{bmatrix} -1R_2$$

$$\begin{bmatrix} 1 & 1 & \frac{7}{2} & -\frac{1}{2} \\ 0 & 1 & 5 & -3 \\ 0 & 2 & -13 & 17 \end{bmatrix} -2R_2 + R_3$$

$$\begin{bmatrix} 1 & 1 & \frac{7}{2} & -\frac{1}{2} \\ 0 & 1 & 5 & -3 \\ 0 & 0 & -23 & 23 \end{bmatrix} -\frac{1}{23}R_3$$

$$\begin{bmatrix} 1 & 1 & \frac{7}{2} & -\frac{1}{2} \\ 0 & 1 & 5 & -3 \\ 0 & 0 & 1 & -1 \end{bmatrix}$$

$$z = -1$$
$$y + 5z = -3$$
$$y + 5(-1) = -3$$
$$y - 5 = -3$$
$$y = 2$$
$$x + y + \frac{7}{2}z = -\frac{1}{2}$$
$$x + 2 + \frac{7}{2}(-1) = -\frac{1}{2}$$
$$x - \frac{3}{2} = -\frac{1}{2}$$
$$x = 1$$

The solution set is $\{(1, 2, -1)\}$.

41.
$$w + x + y + z = 4$$
$$2w + x - 2y - z = 0$$
$$w - 2x - y - 2z = -2$$
$$3w + 2x + y + 3z = 4$$

$$\begin{bmatrix} 1 & 1 & 1 & 1 & 4 \\ 2 & 1 & -2 & -1 & 0 \\ 1 & -2 & -1 & -2 & -2 \\ 3 & 2 & 1 & 3 & 4 \end{bmatrix} -2R_1 + R_2$$

$$\begin{bmatrix} 1 & 1 & 1 & 1 & 4 \\ 0 & -1 & -4 & -3 & -8 \\ 1 & -2 & -1 & -2 & -2 \\ 3 & 2 & 1 & 3 & 4 \end{bmatrix} -1R_1 + R_3$$

$$\begin{bmatrix} 1 & 1 & 1 & 1 & 4 \\ 0 & -1 & -4 & -3 & -8 \\ 0 & -3 & -2 & -3 & -6 \\ 3 & 2 & 1 & 3 & 4 \end{bmatrix} -3R_1 + R_4$$

$$\begin{bmatrix} 1 & 1 & 1 & 1 & 4 \\ 0 & -1 & -4 & -3 & -8 \\ 0 & -3 & -2 & -3 & -6 \\ 0 & -1 & -2 & 0 & -8 \end{bmatrix} -1R_2$$

$$\begin{bmatrix} 1 & 1 & 1 & 1 & 4 \\ 0 & 1 & 4 & 3 & 8 \\ 0 & -3 & -2 & -3 & -6 \\ 0 & -1 & -2 & 0 & -8 \end{bmatrix} 3R_2 + R_3$$

$$\begin{bmatrix} 1 & 1 & 1 & 1 & 4 \\ 0 & 1 & 4 & 3 & 8 \\ 0 & 0 & 10 & 6 & 18 \\ 0 & -1 & -2 & 0 & -8 \end{bmatrix} 1R_2 + R_4$$

$$\begin{bmatrix} 1 & 1 & 1 & 1 & 4 \\ 0 & 1 & 4 & 3 & 8 \\ 0 & 0 & 10 & 6 & 18 \\ 0 & 0 & 2 & 3 & 0 \end{bmatrix} \frac{1}{10}R_3$$

$$\begin{bmatrix} 1 & 1 & 1 & 1 & 4 \\ 0 & 1 & 4 & 3 & 8 \\ 0 & 0 & 1 & \frac{3}{5} & \frac{9}{5} \\ 0 & 0 & 2 & 3 & 0 \end{bmatrix} -2R_3 + R_4$$

$$\begin{bmatrix} 1 & 1 & 1 & 1 & 4 \\ 0 & 1 & 4 & 3 & 8 \\ 0 & 0 & 1 & \frac{3}{5} & \frac{9}{5} \\ 0 & 0 & 0 & \frac{9}{5} & -\frac{18}{5} \end{bmatrix} \frac{5}{9}R_4$$

$$\begin{bmatrix} 1 & 1 & 1 & 1 & 4 \\ 0 & 1 & 4 & 3 & 8 \\ 0 & 0 & 1 & \frac{3}{5} & \frac{9}{5} \\ 0 & 0 & 0 & 1 & -2 \end{bmatrix}$$

344

$z = -2$

$$y + \frac{3}{5}z = \frac{9}{5}$$

$$y + \frac{3}{5}(-2) = \frac{9}{5}$$

$$y - \frac{6}{5} = \frac{9}{5}$$

$$y = 3$$

$$x + 4y + 3z = 8$$

$$x + 4(3) + 3(-2) = 8$$

$$x + 6 = 8$$

$$x = 2$$

$$w + x + y + z = 4$$

$$w + 2 + 3 - 2 = 4$$

$$w + 3 = 4$$

$$w = 1$$

The solution set is $\{(1, 2, 3, -2)\}$.

43. $\quad 3w - 4x + y + z = 9$

$\qquad w + x - y - z = 0$

$\qquad 2w + x + 4y - 2z = 3$

$\qquad -w + 2x + y - 3z = 3$

$$\left[\begin{array}{cccc|c} 3 & -4 & 1 & 1 & 9 \\ 1 & 1 & -1 & -1 & 0 \\ 2 & 1 & 4 & -2 & 3 \\ -1 & 2 & 1 & -3 & 3 \end{array}\right] R_1 \leftrightarrow R_2$$

$$\left[\begin{array}{cccc|c} 1 & 1 & -1 & -1 & 0 \\ 3 & -4 & 1 & 1 & 9 \\ 2 & 1 & 4 & -2 & 3 \\ -1 & 2 & 1 & -3 & 3 \end{array}\right] -3R_1 + R_2$$

$$\left[\begin{array}{cccc|c} 1 & 1 & -1 & -1 & 0 \\ 0 & -7 & 4 & 4 & 9 \\ 2 & 1 & 4 & -2 & 3 \\ -1 & 2 & 1 & -3 & 3 \end{array}\right] -2R_1 + R_3$$

$$\left[\begin{array}{cccc|c} 1 & 1 & -1 & -1 & 0 \\ 0 & -7 & 4 & 4 & 9 \\ 0 & -1 & 6 & 0 & 3 \\ -1 & 2 & 1 & -3 & 3 \end{array}\right] 1R_1 + R_4$$

$$\left[\begin{array}{cccc|c} 1 & 1 & -1 & -1 & 0 \\ 0 & -7 & 4 & 4 & 9 \\ 0 & -1 & 6 & 0 & 3 \\ 0 & 3 & 0 & -4 & 3 \end{array}\right] R_2 \leftrightarrow R_3$$

$$\left[\begin{array}{cccc|c} 1 & 1 & -1 & -1 & 0 \\ 0 & -1 & 6 & 0 & 3 \\ 0 & -7 & 4 & 4 & 9 \\ 0 & 3 & 0 & -4 & 3 \end{array}\right] -R_2$$

$$\left[\begin{array}{cccc|c} 1 & 1 & -1 & -1 & 0 \\ 0 & 1 & -6 & 0 & -3 \\ 0 & -7 & 4 & 4 & 9 \\ 0 & 3 & 0 & -4 & 3 \end{array}\right] 7R_2 + R_3$$

$$\left[\begin{array}{cccc|c} 1 & 1 & -1 & -1 & 0 \\ 0 & 1 & -6 & 0 & -3 \\ 0 & 0 & -38 & 4 & -12 \\ 0 & 3 & 0 & -4 & 3 \end{array}\right] -3R_2 + R_4$$

$$\left[\begin{array}{cccc|c} 1 & 1 & -1 & -1 & 0 \\ 0 & 1 & -6 & 0 & -3 \\ 0 & 0 & -38 & 4 & -12 \\ 0 & 0 & 18 & -4 & 12 \end{array}\right] -\frac{1}{38}R_3$$

$$\left[\begin{array}{cccc|c} 1 & 1 & -1 & -1 & 0 \\ 0 & 1 & -6 & 0 & -3 \\ 0 & 0 & 1 & -\frac{2}{19} & \frac{6}{19} \\ 0 & 0 & 18 & -4 & 12 \end{array}\right] -18R_3 + R_4$$

$$\left[\begin{array}{cccc|c} 1 & 1 & -1 & -1 & 0 \\ 0 & 1 & -6 & 0 & -3 \\ 0 & 0 & 1 & -\frac{2}{19} & \frac{6}{19} \\ 0 & 0 & 0 & -\frac{40}{19} & \frac{120}{19} \end{array}\right] -\frac{19}{40}R_4$$

$$\left[\begin{array}{cccc|c} 1 & 1 & -1 & -1 & 0 \\ 0 & 1 & -6 & 0 & -3 \\ 0 & 0 & 1 & -\frac{2}{19} & \frac{6}{19} \\ 0 & 0 & 0 & 1 & -3 \end{array}\right]$$

$z = -3$

$$y - \frac{2}{19}z = \frac{6}{19}$$

$$y - \frac{2}{19}(-3) = \frac{6}{19}$$

$$y + \frac{6}{19} = \frac{6}{19}$$

$$y = 0$$

$$x - 6y = -3$$

$$x - 6(0) = -3$$

$$x = -3$$

$$w + x - y - z = 0$$

$$w - 3 + 0 + 3 = 0$$

$$w = 0$$

The solution set is $\{(0, -3, 0, -3)\}$.

45. a.
$$3965 = a(1)^2 + b(1) + c$$

$$5625 = a(5)^2 + b(5) + c$$

$$7250 = a(10)^2 + b(10) + c$$

Write the equations in standard form.
$$a + b + c = 3965$$

$$25a + 5b + c = 5625$$

$$100a + 10b + c = 7250$$

$$\begin{bmatrix} 1 & 1 & 1 & 3965 \\ 25 & 5 & 1 & 5625 \\ 100 & 10 & 1 & 7250 \end{bmatrix}$$

Replace row two with $-25R_1 + R_2$.
Replace row three with $-100R_1 + R_3$.

$$\begin{bmatrix} 1 & 1 & 1 & 3965 \\ 0 & -20 & -24 & -93500 \\ 0 & -90 & -99 & -389250 \end{bmatrix}$$

Replace row three with $-9R_2 + 2R_3$.

$$\begin{bmatrix} 1 & 1 & 1 & 3965 \\ 0 & -20 & -24 & -93500 \\ 0 & 0 & 18 & 63000 \end{bmatrix}$$

Divide row 3 by 18.

$$\begin{bmatrix} 1 & 1 & 1 & 3965 \\ 0 & -20 & -24 & -93500 \\ 0 & 0 & 1 & 3500 \end{bmatrix}$$

$$c = 3500$$

$$-20b - 24c = -93500$$

$$-20b - 24(3500) = -93500$$

$$-20b - 84000 = -93500$$

$$-20b = -9500$$

$$b = 475$$

$$a + b + c = 3965$$

$$a + 475 + 3500 = 3965$$

$$a = -10$$

$$P(x) = -10x^2 + 475x + 3500$$

b. $P(12) = -10(12)^2 + 475(12) + 3500$

$$P(12) = 7760$$

$(12, 7760)$

After the program is in effect for 12 years, there will be 7760 alligators.

47. Let $x =$ those who said yes
Let $y =$ those who said no
Let $z =$ those who are not sure

$$x + y + z = 100$$

$$y = x + z + 22$$

$$2x = y + 7$$

Write the equations in standard form.
$$x + y + z = 100$$

$$-x + y - z = 22$$

$$2x - y = 7$$

$$\begin{bmatrix} 1 & 1 & 1 & 100 \\ -1 & 1 & -1 & 22 \\ 2 & -1 & 0 & 7 \end{bmatrix}$$

Replace row two with $R_1 + R_2$.
Replace row three with $-2R_1 + R_3$.

$$\begin{bmatrix} 1 & 1 & 1 & 100 \\ 0 & 2 & 0 & 122 \\ 0 & -3 & -2 & -193 \end{bmatrix}$$

Replace row two with $\frac{1}{2}R_2$.

$$\begin{bmatrix} 1 & 1 & 1 & 100 \\ 0 & 1 & 0 & 61 \\ 0 & -3 & -2 & -193 \end{bmatrix}$$

Replace row three with $3R_2 + R_3$.

$$\begin{bmatrix} 1 & 1 & 1 & 100 \\ 0 & 1 & 0 & 61 \\ 0 & 0 & -2 & -10 \end{bmatrix}$$

Replace row three with $-\dfrac{1}{2}R_3$.

$$\begin{bmatrix} 1 & 1 & 1 & 100 \\ 0 & 1 & 0 & 61 \\ 0 & 0 & 1 & 5 \end{bmatrix}$$

$z = 5$

$y = 61$

$x + y + z = 100$

$x + 61 + 5 = 100$

$x = 34$

34% of single women said yes, 61% said no, 5% did not know.

49. Let $x =$ Food A

Let $y =$ Food B

Let $z =$ Food C

$$40x + 200y + 400z = 660$$
$$5x + 2y + 4z = 25$$
$$30x + 10y + 300z = 425$$
$$2x + 10y + 20z = 33$$
$$5x + 2y + 4z = 25$$
$$6x + 2y + 60z = 85$$

$$\begin{bmatrix} 2 & 10 & 20 & | & 33 \\ 5 & 2 & 4 & | & 25 \\ 6 & 2 & 60 & | & 85 \end{bmatrix} \frac{1}{2}R_1$$

$$\begin{bmatrix} 1 & 5 & 10 & | & \frac{33}{2} \\ 5 & 2 & 4 & | & 25 \\ 6 & 2 & 60 & | & 85 \end{bmatrix} -5R_1 + R_2$$

$$\begin{bmatrix} 1 & 5 & 10 & | & \frac{33}{2} \\ 0 & -23 & -46 & | & -\frac{115}{2} \\ 6 & 2 & 60 & | & 85 \end{bmatrix} -6R_1 + R_3$$

$$\begin{bmatrix} 1 & 5 & 10 & | & \frac{33}{2} \\ 0 & -23 & -46 & | & -\frac{115}{2} \\ 0 & -28 & 0 & | & -14 \end{bmatrix} -\frac{1}{23}R_2$$

$$\begin{bmatrix} 1 & 5 & 10 & | & \frac{33}{2} \\ 0 & 1 & 2 & | & \frac{5}{2} \\ 0 & -28 & 0 & | & -14 \end{bmatrix} 28R_2 + R_3$$

$$\begin{bmatrix} 1 & 5 & 10 & | & \frac{33}{2} \\ 0 & 1 & 2 & | & \frac{5}{2} \\ 0 & 0 & 56 & | & 56 \end{bmatrix} \frac{1}{56}R_3$$

$$\begin{bmatrix} 1 & 5 & 10 & | & \frac{33}{2} \\ 0 & 1 & 2 & | & \frac{5}{2} \\ 0 & 0 & 1 & | & 1 \end{bmatrix}$$

$z = 1$

$y + 2z = \dfrac{5}{2}$

$y + 2 = \dfrac{5}{2}$

$2y + 4 = 5$

$2y = 1$

$y = \dfrac{1}{2}$

$x + 5y + 10z = \dfrac{33}{2}$

$x + \dfrac{5}{2} + 10 = \dfrac{33}{2}$

$2x + 5 + 20 = 33$

$2x + 25 = 33$

$2x = 8$

$x = 4$

4 ounces of Food A

$\dfrac{1}{2}$ ounce of Food B

1 ounce of Food C

51.–59. Answers may vary.

61. $y = ax^3 + bx^2 + cx + d$

$-3 = a(0)^3 + b(0)^2 + c(0) + d$

$-3 = d$

$5 = a + b + c + d$

$-7 = a(-1)^3 + b(-1)^2 + c(-1) + d$

$-7 = -a + b - c + d$

$-13 = a(-2)^3 + b(-2)^2 + c(-2) + d$

$-13 = -8a + 4b - 2c + d$

$a + b + c + d = 5$

$-a + b - c + d = -7$

$-8a + 4b - 2c + d = -13$

$d = -3$

$$\left[\begin{array}{cccc|c} 1 & 1 & 1 & 1 & 5 \\ -1 & 1 & -1 & 1 & -7 \\ -8 & 4 & -2 & 1 & -13 \\ 0 & 0 & 0 & 1 & -3 \end{array}\right] \begin{array}{l} \\ R_1 + R_2 \\ 8R_1 + R_3 \\ \end{array}$$

$$\left[\begin{array}{cccc|c} 1 & 1 & 1 & 1 & 5 \\ 0 & 2 & 0 & 2 & -2 \\ 0 & 12 & 6 & 9 & 27 \\ 0 & 0 & 0 & 1 & -3 \end{array}\right] \begin{array}{l} \\ \\ \frac{1}{2}R_2 \\ \end{array}$$

$$\left[\begin{array}{cccc|c} 1 & 1 & 1 & 1 & 5 \\ 0 & 1 & 0 & 1 & -1 \\ 0 & 12 & 6 & 9 & 27 \\ 0 & 0 & 0 & 1 & -3 \end{array}\right] \begin{array}{l} \\ -1R_2 + R_1 \\ -12R_2 + R_3 \\ \end{array}$$

$$\left[\begin{array}{cccc|c} 1 & 0 & 1 & 0 & 6 \\ 0 & 1 & 0 & 1 & -1 \\ 0 & 0 & 6 & -3 & 39 \\ 0 & 0 & 0 & 1 & -3 \end{array}\right] \begin{array}{l} \\ \frac{1}{6}R_3 \\ -R_4 + R_2 \\ \end{array}$$

$$\left[\begin{array}{cccc|c} 1 & 0 & 1 & 0 & 6 \\ 0 & 1 & 0 & 0 & 2 \\ 0 & 0 & 1 & \frac{-1}{2} & \frac{13}{2} \\ 0 & 0 & 0 & 1 & -3 \end{array}\right] \begin{array}{l} \frac{1}{2}R_4 + R_3 \\ \\ \\ \end{array}$$

$$\left[\begin{array}{cccc|c} 1 & 0 & 1 & 0 & 6 \\ 0 & 1 & 0 & 0 & 2 \\ 0 & 0 & 1 & 0 & 5 \\ 0 & 0 & 0 & 1 & -3 \end{array}\right] \begin{array}{l} \\ -R_3 + R_1 \\ \\ \end{array}$$

$$\left[\begin{array}{cccc|c} 1 & 0 & 0 & 0 & 1 \\ 0 & 1 & 0 & 0 & 2 \\ 0 & 0 & 1 & 0 & 5 \\ 0 & 0 & 0 & 1 & -3 \end{array}\right]$$

$a = 1$

$b = 2$

$c = 5$

$d = -3$

$y = x^3 + 2x^2 + 5x - 3$

Section 6.2

Check Point Exercises

1. $\begin{aligned} x - 2y - z &= 5 \\ 2x - 3y - z &= 0 \\ 3x - 4y - z &= 1 \end{aligned} \rightarrow \left[\begin{array}{ccc|c} 1 & -2 & -1 & -5 \\ 2 & -3 & -1 & 0 \\ 3 & -4 & -1 & 1 \end{array}\right]$

$$\left[\begin{array}{ccc|c} 1 & -2 & -1 & -5 \\ 2 & -3 & -1 & 0 \\ 3 & -4 & -1 & 1 \end{array}\right] \begin{array}{l} \\ -2R_1 + R_2 \\ -3R_1 + R_3 \end{array}$$

$$\left[\begin{array}{ccc|c} 1 & -2 & -1 & -5 \\ 0 & 1 & 1 & 10 \\ 0 & 2 & 2 & 16 \end{array}\right] \begin{array}{l} \\ -2R_2 + R_3 \\ \end{array}$$

$$\left[\begin{array}{ccc|c} 1 & -2 & -1 & -5 \\ 0 & 1 & -1 & -10 \\ 0 & 0 & 0 & -4 \end{array}\right]$$

$0x + 0y + 0z = -4$ This equation can never be a true statement. Consequently, the system has no solution. The solution set is $\varnothing$, the empty set.

2. $\begin{aligned} x - 2y - z &= 5 \\ 2x - 5y + 3z &= 16 \\ x - 3y + 4z &= 1 \end{aligned} \rightarrow \left[\begin{array}{ccc|c} 1 & -2 & -1 & 5 \\ 2 & -5 & 3 & 6 \\ 1 & -3 & 4 & 1 \end{array}\right]$

$$\left[\begin{array}{ccc|c} 1 & -2 & -1 & 5 \\ 2 & -5 & 3 & 6 \\ 1 & -3 & 4 & 1 \end{array}\right] \begin{array}{l} \\ -2R_1 + R_2 \\ -1R_1 + R_3 \end{array}$$

$$\left[\begin{array}{ccc|c} 1 & -2 & -1 & 5 \\ 0 & -1 & 5 & -4 \\ 0 & -1 & 5 & -4 \end{array}\right] \begin{array}{l} \\ -1R_2 \\ \end{array}$$

$$\left[\begin{array}{ccc|c} 1 & -2 & -1 & 5 \\ 0 & 1 & -5 & 4 \\ 0 & -1 & 5 & -4 \end{array}\right] \begin{array}{l} \\ 1R_2 + R_3 \\ \end{array}$$

$$\begin{bmatrix} 1 & -2 & -1 & | & 5 \\ 0 & 1 & -5 & | & 4 \\ 0 & 0 & 0 & | & 0 \end{bmatrix}$$

$0x + 0y + 0z = 0$ or $0 = 0$

This equation, $0x + 0y + 0z = 0$ is *dependent* on the other two equations. Thus, it can be dropped from the system which can now be expressed in the form

$$\begin{bmatrix} 1 & -2 & -1 & | & 5 \\ 0 & 1 & -5 & | & 4 \end{bmatrix}$$

The original system is equivalent to the system

$x - 2y - z = 5$

$y - 5z = 4$

Solve for x and y in terms of z

$y = 5z + 4$

Use back-substitution for y in the previous equation.

$x - 2(5z + 4) - z = 5$

$x - 10z - 8 - z = 5$

$x = 11z + 13$

Finally, letting $z = t$ (or any letter of your choice), the solutions to the system are all of the form $x = 11t + 13$, $y = 5t + 4$, $z = t$, where t is a real number. The solution set of the system with dependent equations can be written as $\{(11t + 13, 5t + 4, t)\}$.

3. $\begin{aligned} x + 2y + 3z &= 70 \\ x + y + z &= 60 \end{aligned} \rightarrow \begin{bmatrix} 1 & 2 & 3 & | & 70 \\ 1 & 1 & 1 & | & 60 \end{bmatrix}$

$$\begin{bmatrix} 1 & 2 & 3 & | & 70 \\ 1 & 1 & 1 & | & 60 \end{bmatrix} -1R_1 + R_2$$

$$\begin{bmatrix} 1 & 2 & 3 & | & 70 \\ 0 & -1 & -2 & | & -10 \end{bmatrix} -1R_2$$

$$\begin{bmatrix} 1 & 2 & 3 & | & 70 \\ 0 & 1 & 2 & | & 10 \end{bmatrix} \rightarrow \begin{aligned} x + 2y + 3z &= 70 \\ y + 2z &= 10 \end{aligned}$$

Express x and y in terms of z using back-substitution.

$y = -2z + 10$

$x + 2(-2z + 10) + 3z = 70$

$x - 4z + 20 + 3z = 70$

$x = z + 50$

With $z = t$, the ordered solution (x, y, z) enables us to express the system's solution set as $\{(t + 50, -2t + 10, t)\}$.

4. a. I_1: $10 + 5 = 15$ cars enter I_1, and $w + z$ cars leave I_1, then $w + z = 15$.

I_2: $20 + 10 = 30$ cars enter I_2 and $w + x$ cars leave I_2, then $w + x = 30$.

I_3: $15 + 30 = 45$ cars enter I_3 and $x + y$ cars leave I_3, then $x + y = 45$.

I_4: $10 + 20 = 30$ cars enter I_4 and $y + z$ cars leave I_4, then $y + z = 30$.

The system of equations that describes this situation is given by

$w + z = 15$

$w + x = 30$

$x + y = 45$

$y + z = 30$

b. $$\begin{bmatrix} 1 & 0 & 0 & 1 & | & 15 \\ 1 & 1 & 0 & 0 & | & 30 \\ 0 & 1 & 1 & 0 & | & 45 \\ 0 & 0 & 1 & 1 & | & 30 \end{bmatrix} -1R_1 + R_2$$

$$\begin{bmatrix} 1 & 0 & 0 & 1 & | & 15 \\ 0 & 1 & 0 & -1 & | & 15 \\ 0 & 1 & 1 & 0 & | & 45 \\ 0 & 0 & 1 & 1 & | & 30 \end{bmatrix} -1R_2 + R_3$$

$$\begin{bmatrix} 1 & 0 & 0 & 1 & | & 15 \\ 0 & 1 & 0 & -1 & | & 15 \\ 0 & 0 & 1 & 1 & | & 30 \\ 0 & 0 & 1 & 1 & | & 30 \end{bmatrix} -1R_3 + R_4$$

$$\begin{bmatrix} 1 & 0 & 0 & 1 & | & 15 \\ 0 & 1 & 0 & -1 & | & 15 \\ 0 & 0 & 1 & 1 & | & 30 \\ 0 & 0 & 0 & 0 & | & 0 \end{bmatrix}$$

$x + w = 15$

$y - w = 15$

$z + w = 30$

The last row of the matrix shows that the system has dependent equations and infinitely many solutions.

Let z be any real number.

Express w, x and y in terms of z

$w = 15 - z$

$x = 15 + z$

$y = 30 - z$

With $w = t$, the ordered solution (w, x, y, z) enables us to express the system's solution set

as $\{(-t + 15, t + 15, -t + 30, t)\}$

Exercise Set 6.2

1. $\begin{bmatrix} 5 & 12 & 1 & | & 10 \\ 2 & 5 & 2 & | & -1 \\ 1 & 2 & -3 & | & 5 \end{bmatrix} R_1 \leftrightarrow R_3$

$\begin{bmatrix} 1 & 2 & -3 & | & 5 \\ 2 & 5 & 2 & | & -1 \\ 5 & 12 & 1 & | & 10 \end{bmatrix} \begin{matrix} \\ -2R_1 + R_2 \\ -5R_1 + R_3 \end{matrix}$

$\begin{bmatrix} 1 & 2 & -3 & | & 5 \\ 0 & 1 & 8 & | & -11 \\ 0 & 2 & 16 & | & -15 \end{bmatrix} -2R_2 + R_3$

$\begin{bmatrix} 1 & 2 & 3 & | & 5 \\ 0 & 1 & 8 & | & -11 \\ 0 & 0 & 0 & | & 7 \end{bmatrix}$

From the last row, we see that the system has no solution. The solution set is $\varnothing$, the empty set.

3. $\begin{bmatrix} 5 & 8 & -6 & | & 14 \\ 3 & 4 & -2 & | & 8 \\ 1 & 2 & -2 & | & 3 \end{bmatrix} R_1 \leftrightarrow R_3$

$\begin{bmatrix} 1 & 2 & -2 & | & 3 \\ 3 & 4 & -2 & | & 8 \\ 5 & 8 & -6 & | & 14 \end{bmatrix} \begin{matrix} \\ -3R_1 + R_2 \\ -5R_1 + R_3 \end{matrix}$

$\begin{bmatrix} 1 & 2 & -2 & | & 3 \\ 0 & -2 & 4 & | & -1 \\ 0 & -2 & 4 & | & -1 \end{bmatrix} -1R_2 + R_3$

$\begin{bmatrix} 1 & 2 & -2 & | & 3 \\ 0 & -2 & 4 & | & -1 \\ 0 & 0 & 0 & | & 0 \end{bmatrix} -\dfrac{1}{2}R_2$

$\begin{bmatrix} 1 & 2 & -2 & | & 3 \\ 0 & 1 & -2 & | & \frac{1}{2} \\ 0 & 0 & 0 & | & 0 \end{bmatrix}$

$x + 2y - 2z = 3$

The system $\quad y - 2z = \dfrac{1}{2} \quad$ has no unique

solution. Express x and y in terms of z

$y = 2z + \dfrac{1}{2}$

$x + 2\left(2z + \dfrac{1}{2}\right) - 2z = 3$

$x + 4z + 1 - 2z = 3$

$x + 2z + 1 = 3$

$x = -2z + 2$

With $z = t$, the complete solution to the

system is $\left\{\left(-2t + 2,\ 2t + \dfrac{1}{2},\ t\right)\right\}$.

5. $\begin{bmatrix} 3 & 4 & 2 & | & 3 \\ 4 & -2 & -8 & | & -4 \\ 1 & 1 & -1 & | & 3 \end{bmatrix} R_1 \leftrightarrow R_3$

$\begin{bmatrix} 1 & 1 & -1 & | & 3 \\ 4 & -2 & -8 & | & -4 \\ 3 & 4 & 2 & | & 3 \end{bmatrix} \begin{matrix} \\ -4R_1 + R_2 \\ -3R_1 + R_3 \end{matrix}$

$$\begin{bmatrix} 1 & 1 & -1 & | & 3 \\ 0 & -6 & -4 & | & -16 \\ 0 & 1 & 5 & | & -6 \end{bmatrix} R_2 \leftrightarrow R_3$$

$$\begin{bmatrix} 1 & 1 & -1 & | & 3 \\ 0 & 1 & 5 & | & -6 \\ 0 & -6 & -4 & | & -16 \end{bmatrix} 6R_2 + R_3$$

$$\begin{bmatrix} 1 & 1 & 1 & | & 3 \\ 0 & 1 & 5 & | & -6 \\ 0 & 0 & 26 & | & -52 \end{bmatrix} \frac{1}{26}R_3$$

$$\begin{bmatrix} 1 & 1 & -1 & | & 3 \\ 0 & 1 & 5 & | & -6 \\ 0 & 0 & 1 & | & -2 \end{bmatrix}$$

This corresponds to the system

$x + y - z = 3$
$\quad y + 5z = -6$
$\qquad z = -2$

Use back-substitution to find the values of x and y:

$y + 5(-2) = -6$
$\quad y - 10 = -6$
$\qquad y = 4$
$x + 4 + 2 = 3$
$\quad x + 6 = 3$
$\qquad x = -3$

The solution to the system is $\{(-3, 4, -2)\}$.

7. $\begin{bmatrix} 8 & 5 & 11 & | & 30 \\ -1 & -4 & 2 & | & 3 \\ 2 & -1 & 5 & | & 12 \end{bmatrix} R_1 \leftrightarrow R_2$

$$\begin{bmatrix} -1 & -4 & 2 & | & 3 \\ 8 & 5 & 11 & | & 30 \\ 2 & -1 & 5 & | & 12 \end{bmatrix} -1R_1$$

$$\begin{bmatrix} 1 & 4 & -2 & | & -3 \\ 8 & 5 & 11 & | & 30 \\ 2 & -1 & 5 & | & 12 \end{bmatrix} \begin{matrix} -8R_1 + R_2 \\ -2R_1 + R_3 \end{matrix}$$

$$\begin{bmatrix} 1 & 4 & -2 & | & -3 \\ 0 & -27 & 27 & | & 54 \\ 0 & -9 & 9 & | & 18 \end{bmatrix} -\frac{1}{27}R_2$$

$$\begin{bmatrix} 1 & 4 & -2 & | & -3 \\ 0 & 1 & -1 & | & -2 \\ 0 & -9 & 9 & | & 18 \end{bmatrix} 9R_2 + R_3$$

$$\begin{bmatrix} 1 & 4 & -2 & | & -3 \\ 0 & 1 & -1 & | & -2 \\ 0 & 0 & 0 & | & 0 \end{bmatrix}$$

The system $\begin{aligned} x + 4y - 2z &= -3 \\ y - z &= -2 \end{aligned}$ has no unique solution. Express x and y in terms of z.

$y = -2 + z$
$x + 4(-2 + z) - 2z = -3$
$x - 8 + 4z - 2z = -3$
$x - 8 + 2z = -3$
$x = 5 - 2z$

With $z = t$, the complete solution to the system is $\{(5 - 2t, -2 + t, t)\}$.

9. $\begin{bmatrix} 1 & -2 & -1 & -3 & | & -9 \\ 1 & 1 & -1 & 0 & | & 0 \\ 3 & 4 & 0 & 1 & | & 6 \\ 0 & 2 & -2 & 1 & | & 3 \end{bmatrix} \begin{matrix} -1R_1 + R_2 \\ -3R_1 + R_3 \end{matrix}$

$$\begin{bmatrix} 1 & -2 & -1 & -3 & | & -9 \\ 0 & 3 & 0 & 3 & | & 9 \\ 0 & 10 & 3 & 10 & | & 33 \\ 0 & 2 & -2 & 1 & | & 3 \end{bmatrix} \frac{1}{3}R_2$$

$$\begin{bmatrix} 1 & -2 & -1 & -3 & | & -9 \\ 0 & 1 & 0 & 1 & | & 3 \\ 0 & 10 & 3 & 10 & | & 33 \\ 0 & 2 & -2 & 1 & | & 3 \end{bmatrix} \begin{matrix} -10R_2 + R_3 \\ -2R_2 + R_4 \end{matrix}$$

$$\begin{bmatrix} 1 & -2 & -1 & -3 & | & -9 \\ 0 & 1 & 0 & 1 & | & 3 \\ 0 & 0 & 3 & 0 & | & 3 \\ 0 & 0 & -2 & -1 & | & -3 \end{bmatrix} \frac{1}{3}R_3$$

$$\begin{bmatrix} 1 & -2 & -1 & -3 & | & -9 \\ 0 & 1 & 0 & 1 & | & 3 \\ 0 & 0 & 1 & 0 & | & 1 \\ 0 & 0 & -2 & -1 & | & -3 \end{bmatrix} 2R_3 + R_4$$

$$\begin{bmatrix} 1 & -2 & -1 & -3 & | & -9 \\ 0 & 1 & 0 & 1 & | & 3 \\ 0 & 0 & 1 & 0 & | & 1 \\ 0 & 0 & 0 & -1 & | & -1 \end{bmatrix} -1R_4$$

$$\begin{bmatrix} 1 & -2 & -1 & -3 & | & -9 \\ 0 & 1 & 0 & 1 & | & 3 \\ 0 & 0 & 1 & 0 & | & 1 \\ 0 & 0 & 0 & 1 & | & 1 \end{bmatrix}$$

This corresponds to the system

$$w - 2x - y - 3z = -9$$
$$x + z = 3$$
$$y = 1$$
$$z = 1$$

Use back-substitution to find the values of w and x:

$$x + 1 = 3$$
$$x = 2$$
$$w - 2(2) - 1 - 3(1) = -9$$
$$w - 4 - 1 - 3 = -9$$
$$w - 8 = -9$$
$$w = -1$$

The solution to the system is $\{(-1, 2, 1, 1)\}$.

11.
$$\begin{bmatrix} 2 & 1 & -1 & 0 & | & 3 \\ 1 & -3 & 2 & 0 & | & -4 \\ 3 & 1 & -3 & 1 & | & 1 \\ 1 & 2 & -4 & -1 & | & -2 \end{bmatrix} R_1 \leftrightarrow R_2$$

$$\begin{bmatrix} 1 & -3 & 2 & 0 & | & -4 \\ 2 & 1 & -1 & 0 & | & 3 \\ 3 & 1 & -3 & 1 & | & 1 \\ 1 & 2 & -4 & -1 & | & -2 \end{bmatrix} \begin{matrix} -2R_1 + R_2 \\ -3R_1 + R_3 \\ -1R_1 + R_4 \end{matrix}$$

$$\begin{bmatrix} 1 & -3 & 2 & 0 & | & -4 \\ 0 & 7 & -5 & 0 & | & 11 \\ 0 & 10 & -9 & 1 & | & 13 \\ 0 & 5 & -6 & -1 & | & 2 \end{bmatrix} \frac{1}{7}R_2$$

$$\begin{bmatrix} 1 & -3 & 2 & 0 & | & -4 \\ 0 & 1 & -\frac{5}{7} & 0 & | & \frac{11}{7} \\ 0 & 10 & -9 & 1 & | & 13 \\ 0 & 5 & -6 & -1 & | & 2 \end{bmatrix} \begin{matrix} -10R_2 + R_3 \\ -5R_2 + R_4 \end{matrix}$$

$$\begin{bmatrix} 1 & -3 & 2 & 0 & | & -4 \\ 0 & 1 & -\frac{5}{7} & 0 & | & \frac{11}{7} \\ 0 & 0 & -\frac{13}{7} & 1 & | & -\frac{19}{7} \\ 0 & 0 & -\frac{17}{7} & -1 & | & -\frac{41}{7} \end{bmatrix} -\frac{7}{13}R_3$$

$$\begin{bmatrix} 1 & -3 & 2 & 0 & | & -4 \\ 0 & 1 & -\frac{5}{7} & 0 & | & \frac{11}{7} \\ 0 & 0 & 1 & -\frac{7}{13} & | & \frac{19}{13} \\ 0 & 0 & -\frac{17}{7} & -1 & | & -\frac{41}{7} \end{bmatrix} \frac{17}{7}R_3 + R_4$$

$$\begin{bmatrix} 1 & -3 & 2 & 0 & | & -4 \\ 0 & 1 & -\frac{5}{7} & 0 & | & \frac{11}{7} \\ 0 & 0 & 1 & -\frac{7}{13} & | & \frac{19}{13} \\ 0 & 0 & 0 & -\frac{30}{13} & | & -\frac{30}{13} \end{bmatrix} -\frac{13}{30}R_4$$

$$\begin{bmatrix} 1 & -3 & 2 & 0 & | & -4 \\ 0 & 1 & -\frac{5}{7} & 0 & | & \frac{11}{7} \\ 0 & 0 & 1 & -\frac{7}{13} & | & \frac{19}{13} \\ 0 & 0 & 0 & 1 & | & 1 \end{bmatrix}$$

This corresponds to the system

$$w - 3x + 2y = -4$$
$$x - \frac{5}{7}y = \frac{11}{7}$$
$$y - \frac{7}{13}z = \frac{19}{13}$$
$$z = 1$$

Use back-substitution to find the values of w, x, and y:

$$y - \frac{7}{13}z = \frac{19}{13}$$
$$y - \frac{7}{13}(1) = \frac{19}{13}$$
$$y = 2$$
$$x - \frac{5}{7}(2) = \frac{11}{7}$$
$$x - \frac{10}{7} = \frac{11}{7}$$
$$x = 3$$
$$w - 3(3) + 2(2) = -4$$
$$w - 9 + 4 = -4$$

$$w - 5 = -4$$
$$w = 1$$

The solution to the system is $\{(1, 3, 2, 1)\}$.

13. $\begin{bmatrix} 1 & -3 & 1 & -4 & | & 4 \\ -2 & 1 & 2 & 0 & | & -2 \\ 3 & -2 & 1 & -6 & | & 2 \\ -1 & 3 & 2 & -1 & | & -6 \end{bmatrix} \begin{matrix} 2R_1 + R_2 \\ -3R_1 + R_3 \\ R_1 + R_4 \end{matrix}$

$\begin{bmatrix} 1 & -3 & 1 & -4 & | & 4 \\ 0 & -5 & 4 & -8 & | & 6 \\ 0 & 7 & -2 & 6 & | & -10 \\ 0 & 0 & 3 & -5 & | & -2 \end{bmatrix} -\frac{1}{5}R_2$

$\begin{bmatrix} 1 & -3 & 1 & -4 & | & 4 \\ 0 & 1 & -\frac{4}{5} & \frac{8}{5} & | & -\frac{6}{5} \\ 0 & 7 & -2 & 6 & | & -10 \\ 0 & 0 & 3 & -5 & | & -2 \end{bmatrix} -7R_2 + R_3$

$\begin{bmatrix} 1 & -3 & 1 & -4 & | & 4 \\ 0 & 1 & -\frac{4}{5} & \frac{8}{5} & | & -\frac{6}{5} \\ 0 & 0 & \frac{18}{5} & -\frac{26}{5} & | & -\frac{8}{5} \\ 0 & 0 & 3 & -5 & | & -2 \end{bmatrix} \frac{5}{18}R_3$

$\begin{bmatrix} 1 & -3 & 1 & -4 & | & 4 \\ 0 & 1 & -\frac{4}{5} & \frac{8}{5} & | & -\frac{6}{5} \\ 0 & 0 & 1 & -\frac{13}{9} & | & -\frac{4}{9} \\ 0 & 0 & 3 & -5 & | & -2 \end{bmatrix} -3R_3 + R_4$

$\begin{bmatrix} 1 & -3 & 1 & -4 & | & 4 \\ 0 & 1 & -\frac{4}{5} & \frac{8}{5} & | & -\frac{6}{5} \\ 0 & 0 & 1 & -\frac{13}{9} & | & -\frac{4}{9} \\ 0 & 0 & 0 & -\frac{2}{3} & | & -\frac{2}{3} \end{bmatrix} -\frac{3}{2}R_4$

$\begin{bmatrix} 1 & -3 & 1 & -4 & | & 4 \\ 0 & 1 & -\frac{4}{5} & \frac{8}{5} & | & -\frac{6}{5} \\ 0 & 0 & 1 & -\frac{13}{9} & | & -\frac{4}{9} \\ 0 & 0 & 0 & 1 & | & 1 \end{bmatrix}$

This corresponds to the system

$$w - 3x + y - 4z = 4$$
$$x - \frac{4}{5}y + \frac{8}{5}z = -\frac{6}{5}$$
$$y - \frac{13}{9}z = -\frac{4}{9}$$
$$z = 1$$

Use back-substitution to find the values of w, z, and y:

$$y - \frac{13}{9}(1) = -\frac{4}{9}$$
$$y = 1$$
$$x - \frac{4}{5}(1) + \frac{8}{5}(1) = -\frac{6}{5}$$
$$x + \frac{4}{5} = -\frac{6}{5}$$
$$x = -2$$
$$w - 3(-2) + 1 - 4 = 4$$
$$w + 6 - 3 = 4$$
$$w = 1$$

The solution to the system is $\{(1, -2, 1, 1)\}$.

15. $\begin{bmatrix} 2 & 1 & -1 & | & 2 \\ 3 & 3 & -2 & | & 3 \end{bmatrix} \frac{1}{2}R_1$

$\begin{bmatrix} 1 & \frac{1}{2} & -\frac{1}{2} & | & 1 \\ 3 & 3 & -2 & | & 3 \end{bmatrix} -3R_1 + R_2$

$\begin{bmatrix} 1 & \frac{1}{2} & -\frac{1}{2} & | & 1 \\ 0 & \frac{3}{2} & -\frac{1}{2} & | & 0 \end{bmatrix} \frac{2}{3}R_2$

$\begin{bmatrix} 1 & \frac{1}{2} & -\frac{1}{2} & | & 1 \\ 0 & 1 & -\frac{1}{3} & | & 0 \end{bmatrix}$

The system $x + \frac{1}{2}y - \frac{1}{2}z = 1$ has no unique

$$y - \frac{1}{3}z = 0$$

solution. Express x and y in terms of z

$$y = \frac{1}{3}z$$

$$x + \frac{1}{2}\left(\frac{1}{3}z\right) - \frac{1}{2}z = 1$$

$$x + \frac{1}{6}z - \frac{1}{2}z = 1$$

$$x - \frac{1}{3}z = 1$$

$$x = 1 + \frac{1}{3}z$$

With $z = t$, the complete solution to the system is $\left\{\left(1 + \frac{1}{3}t, \frac{1}{3}t, t\right)\right\}$.

17. The system $\begin{aligned} x + 2y + 3z &= 5 \\ y - 5z &= 0 \end{aligned}$ has no unique solution. Express x and y in terms of z

$y = 5z$

$x + 2(5z) + 3z = 5$

$x + 10z + 3z = 5$

$x = -13z + 5$

With $z = t$, the complete solution to the system is $\{(-13t + 5, 5t, t)\}$.

19. $\begin{bmatrix} 1 & 1 & -2 & | & 2 \\ 3 & -1 & -6 & | & -7 \end{bmatrix} -3R_1 + R_2$

$\begin{bmatrix} 1 & 1 & -2 & | & 2 \\ 0 & -4 & 0 & | & -13 \end{bmatrix} -\frac{1}{4}R_2$

$\begin{bmatrix} 1 & 1 & -2 & | & 2 \\ 0 & 1 & 0 & | & \frac{13}{4} \end{bmatrix}$

$x + y - 2z = 2$

The system $\quad y = \dfrac{13}{4}\quad$ has no unique

solution. Express x in terms of z

$$x + \frac{13}{4} - 2z = 2$$

$$x = 2z - \frac{5}{4}$$

With $z = t$, the complete solution to the system is $\left\{\left(2t - \frac{5}{4}, \frac{13}{4}, t\right)\right\}$.

21. $\begin{bmatrix} 1 & 1 & -1 & 1 & | & -2 \\ 2 & -1 & 2 & -1 & | & 7 \\ -1 & 2 & 1 & 2 & | & -1 \end{bmatrix} \begin{matrix} -2R_1 + R_2 \\ 1R_1 + R_3 \end{matrix}$

$\begin{bmatrix} 1 & 1 & -1 & 1 & | & -2 \\ 0 & -3 & 4 & -3 & | & 11 \\ 0 & 3 & 0 & 3 & | & -3 \end{bmatrix} R_2 \leftrightarrow R_3$

$\begin{bmatrix} 1 & 1 & -1 & 1 & | & -2 \\ 0 & 3 & 0 & 3 & | & -3 \\ 0 & -3 & 4 & -3 & | & 11 \end{bmatrix} \frac{1}{3}R_2$

$\begin{bmatrix} 1 & 1 & -1 & 1 & | & -2 \\ 0 & 1 & 0 & 1 & | & -1 \\ 0 & -3 & 4 & -3 & | & 11 \end{bmatrix} 3R_2 + R_3$

$\begin{bmatrix} 1 & 1 & -1 & 1 & | & -2 \\ 0 & 1 & 0 & 1 & | & -1 \\ 0 & 0 & 4 & 0 & | & 8 \end{bmatrix} \frac{1}{4}R_3$

$\begin{bmatrix} 1 & 1 & -1 & 1 & | & -2 \\ 0 & 1 & 0 & 1 & | & -1 \\ 0 & 0 & 1 & 0 & | & 2 \end{bmatrix}$

The system $\begin{aligned} x + y - z + w &= -2 \\ y + w &= -1 \\ z &= 2 \end{aligned}$ has no

unique solution. Express x and y in terms of w:

$y = -w - 1$

$x + (-w - 1) - 2 + w = -2$

$x - w + 1 - 2 + w = -2$

$x = 1$

With $w = t$, the complete solution to the system is $\{(1, -t - 1, 2, t)\}$.

23. $\begin{bmatrix} 1 & 2 & 3 & -1 & | & 7 \\ 0 & 2 & -3 & 1 & | & 4 \\ 1 & -4 & 1 & 0 & | & 3 \end{bmatrix} -1R_1 + R_3$

$\begin{bmatrix} 1 & 2 & 3 & -1 & | & 7 \\ 0 & 2 & -3 & 1 & | & 4 \\ 0 & -6 & -2 & 1 & | & -4 \end{bmatrix} \frac{1}{2}R_2$

$$\begin{bmatrix} 1 & 2 & 3 & -1 & | & 7 \\ 0 & 1 & -\frac{3}{2} & \frac{1}{2} & | & 2 \\ 0 & -6 & -2 & 1 & | & -4 \end{bmatrix} 6R_2 + R_3$$

$$\begin{bmatrix} 1 & 2 & 3 & -1 & | & 7 \\ 0 & 1 & -\frac{3}{2} & \frac{1}{2} & | & 2 \\ 0 & 0 & -11 & 4 & | & 8 \end{bmatrix} -\frac{1}{11} R_3$$

$$\begin{bmatrix} 1 & 2 & 3 & -1 & | & 7 \\ 0 & 1 & -\frac{3}{2} & \frac{1}{2} & | & 2 \\ 0 & 0 & 1 & -\frac{4}{11} & | & -\frac{8}{11} \end{bmatrix}$$

The system has no unique solution. Express w, x, and y in terms of w:

$$y = \frac{4}{11}z - \frac{8}{11}$$

$$x - \frac{3}{2}\left(\frac{4}{11}z - \frac{8}{11}\right) + \frac{1}{2}z = 2$$

$$x - \frac{6}{11}z + \frac{12}{11} + \frac{1}{2}z = 2$$

$$y - \frac{1}{22}z + \frac{12}{11} = 2$$

$$y = \frac{1}{22}z + \frac{10}{11}$$

$$x + 2\left(\frac{1}{22}z + \frac{10}{11}\right) + 3\left(\frac{4}{11}z - \frac{8}{11}\right) - z = 7$$

$$x + \frac{1}{11}z + \frac{20}{11} + \frac{12}{11}z - \frac{24}{11} - z = 7$$

$$x + \frac{2}{11}z - \frac{4}{11} = 7$$

$$x = -\frac{2}{11}z + \frac{81}{11}$$

With $z = t$, the complete solution to the system is

$$\left\{\left(-\frac{2}{11}t + \frac{81}{11}, \frac{1}{22}t + \frac{10}{11}, \frac{4}{11}t - \frac{8}{11}, t\right)\right\}.$$

25. $z + 12 = x + 6$

27. $x - y = 4$

$x - z = 6$

$y - z = 2$

$$\begin{bmatrix} 1 & -1 & 0 & | & 4 \\ 1 & 0 & -1 & | & 6 \\ 0 & 1 & -1 & | & 2 \end{bmatrix} -1R_1 + R_2$$

$$\begin{bmatrix} 1 & -1 & 0 & | & 4 \\ 0 & -1 & 1 & | & -2 \\ 0 & 1 & -1 & | & 2 \end{bmatrix} -1R_2$$

$$\begin{bmatrix} 1 & -1 & 0 & | & 4 \\ 0 & 1 & -1 & | & 2 \\ 0 & 1 & -1 & | & 2 \end{bmatrix} \begin{matrix} -1R_2 + R_3 \\ 1R_2 + R_1 \end{matrix}$$

$$\begin{bmatrix} 1 & 0 & -1 & | & 6 \\ 0 & 1 & -1 & | & 2 \\ 0 & 0 & 0 & | & 0 \end{bmatrix}$$

The system has no unique solution. Express x and y in terms of z

$x - z = 6$

$y - z = 2$

$x = z + 6$

$y = z + 2$

With $z = t$, the complete solution to the system is $\{(t + 6, t + 2, t)\}$.

29. a. From left to right along Palm Drive, then along Sunset Drive, we get the equations

$$w + z = 200 + 180 = 380;$$
$$w + x = 400 + 200 = 600;$$
$$z + 70 = y + 20 \text{ or } y - z = 50;$$
$$y + 200 = x + 30 \text{ or } x - y = 170.$$

The system is

$w + z = 380$

$w + x = 600$

$y - z = 50$

$x - y = 170$

b.
$$\left[\begin{array}{cccc|c} 1 & 0 & 0 & 1 & 380 \\ 0 & 1 & 0 & -1 & 220 \\ 0 & 0 & 1 & -1 & 50 \\ 0 & 1 & -1 & 0 & 170 \end{array}\right] -1R_2 + R_4$$

$$\left[\begin{array}{cccc|c} 1 & 0 & 0 & 1 & 380 \\ 0 & 1 & 0 & -1 & 220 \\ 0 & 0 & 1 & -1 & 50 \\ 0 & 0 & -1 & 1 & -50 \end{array}\right] 1R_3 + R_4$$

$$\left[\begin{array}{cccc|c} 1 & 0 & 0 & 1 & 380 \\ 0 & 1 & 0 & -1 & 220 \\ 0 & 0 & 1 & -1 & 50 \\ 0 & 0 & 0 & 0 & 0 \end{array}\right]$$

The system has no unique solution.
Express x and y and z in terms of z:
$w = 380 - z$

$x = 220 + z$

$y = 50 + z$

With $z = t$, the complete solution to the system is $\{(380 - t, 220 + t, 50 + t, t)\}$.

c. Letting $w = 50$, the solution is $x = 330$, $y = 270$, $z = 100$, $w = 50$.

31. Let x = the amount of Food 1,
y = the amount of Food 2, and
z = the amount of Food 3, in ounces.
The amount of vitamin A is $20x + 30y + 10z$; the amount of iron is $20x + 10y + 10z$; the amount of calcium is $10x + 10y + 30z$.

a. Not having Food 1 means that all x terms are left out. The vitamin A requirement can then be represented by $30y + 10z = 220$; the iron requirement is $10y + 10z = 180$; the calcium requirement is $10y + 30z = 340$. The corresponding system is
$30y + 10z = 220$
$10y + 10z = 180$
$10y + 30z = 340$.

Dividing all of the numbers by 10, the matrix for this system is

$$\left[\begin{array}{cc|c} 3 & 1 & 22 \\ 1 & 1 & 18 \\ 1 & 3 & 34 \end{array}\right] R_1 \leftrightarrow R_2$$

$$\left[\begin{array}{cc|c} 1 & 1 & 18 \\ 3 & 1 & 22 \\ 1 & 3 & 34 \end{array}\right] \begin{array}{l} -3R_1 + R_2 \\ -1R_1 + R_3 \end{array}$$

$$\left[\begin{array}{cc|c} 1 & 1 & 18 \\ 0 & -2 & -32 \\ 0 & 2 & 16 \end{array}\right] 1R_2 + R_3$$

$$\left[\begin{array}{cc|c} 1 & 1 & 18 \\ 0 & -2 & -32 \\ 0 & 0 & -16 \end{array}\right].$$

From the last row, we see that the system has no solution, so there is no way to satisfy these dietary requirements with no Food 1 available.

b. With Food 1 available, and dropping the vitamin A requirement, the system is
$20x + 10y + 10z = 180$
$10x + 10y + 30z = 340$.
Dividing all of the numbers by 10, the matrix for this system is

$$\left[\begin{array}{ccc|c} 2 & 1 & 1 & 18 \\ 1 & 1 & 3 & 34 \end{array}\right] R_1 \leftrightarrow R_2$$

$$\left[\begin{array}{ccc|c} 1 & 1 & 3 & 34 \\ 2 & 1 & 1 & 18 \end{array}\right] -2R_1 + R_2$$

$$\left[\begin{array}{ccc|c} 1 & 1 & 3 & 34 \\ 0 & -1 & -5 & -50 \end{array}\right] -1R_2$$

$$\left[\begin{array}{ccc|c} 1 & 1 & 3 & 34 \\ 0 & 1 & 5 & 50 \end{array}\right].$$

The system $\begin{array}{l} x + y + 3z = 34 \\ y + 5z = 50 \end{array}$ has no unique solution. Express x and y in terms of z:
$y = -5z + 50$
$x + (-5z + 50) + 3z = 34$

$$x - 2z + 50 = 34$$
$$x = 2z - 16$$

Now we can choose a value for z, i.e., an amount of Food 3, and find the corresponding values of x and y. Note that negative amounts of food are not realistic, so $z \geq 0$, $y = -5z + 50 \geq 0$, and $x = 2z - 16 \geq 0$. These conditions are equivalent to $8 \leq z \leq 10$.

Using $z = 8$ and $z = 10$, two possibilities are 0 ounces of Food 1, 10 ounces of Food 2, and 8 ounces of Food 3 or 4 ounces of Food 1, 0 ounces of Food 2, and 10 ounces of Food 3. (Other answers are possible.)

33.–35. Answers may vary.

37. $\begin{bmatrix} 1 & 3 & 1 & | & a^2 \\ 2 & 5 & 2a & | & 0 \\ 1 & 1 & a^2 & | & -9 \end{bmatrix} \begin{matrix} \\ -2R_1 + R_2 \\ -1R_1 + R_3 \end{matrix}$

$\begin{bmatrix} 1 & 3 & 1 & | & a^2 \\ 0 & -1 & 2a-2 & | & -2a^2 \\ 0 & -2 & a^2-1 & | & -9-a^2 \end{bmatrix} -1R_2$

$\begin{bmatrix} 1 & 3 & 1 & | & a^2 \\ 0 & 1 & 2-2a & | & 2a^2 \\ 0 & -2 & a^2-1 & | & -9-a^2 \end{bmatrix} 2R_2 + R_3$

$\begin{bmatrix} 1 & 3 & 1 & | & a^2 \\ 0 & 1 & 2-2a & | & 2a^2 \\ 0 & 0 & a^2-4a+3 & | & -9+3a^2 \end{bmatrix}$

The system will be inconsistent when $a^2 - 4a + 3 = 0$ but $-9 + 3a^2 \neq 0$.
$a^2 - 4a + 3 = (a-1)(a-3) = 0$ when $a = 1$ or $a = 3$. $-9 + 3a^2 = 0$ when $a = \pm\sqrt{3}$.
Thus, the system is inconsistent when $a = 1$ or $a = 3$.

Section 6.3

Check Point Exercises

1. a. The matrix $A = \begin{bmatrix} 5 & -2 \\ -3 & \pi \\ 1 & 6 \end{bmatrix}$ has 3 rows and 2 columns, so it is of order 3×2.

b. The element a_{12} is in the first row and second column. Thus, $a_{12} = -2$. The element a_{31} is in the third row and first column. Thus, $a_{31} = 1$.

2. a. $\begin{bmatrix} -4 & 3 \\ 7 & -6 \end{bmatrix} + \begin{bmatrix} 6 & -3 \\ 2 & -4 \end{bmatrix}$
$= \begin{bmatrix} -4+6 & 3+(-3) \\ 7+2 & -6+(-4) \end{bmatrix} = \begin{bmatrix} 2 & 0 \\ 9 & -10 \end{bmatrix}$

b. $\begin{bmatrix} 5 & 4 \\ -3 & 7 \\ 0 & 1 \end{bmatrix} - \begin{bmatrix} -4 & 8 \\ 6 & 0 \\ -5 & 3 \end{bmatrix}$
$= \begin{bmatrix} 5-(-4) & 4-8 \\ -3-6 & 7-0 \\ 0-(-5) & 1-3 \end{bmatrix}$
$= \begin{bmatrix} 9 & -4 \\ -9 & 7 \\ 5 & -2 \end{bmatrix}$

3. a. $-6B = -6\begin{bmatrix} -1 & -2 \\ 8 & 5 \end{bmatrix}$
$= \begin{bmatrix} -6(-1) & -6(-2) \\ -6(8) & -6(5) \end{bmatrix}$
$= \begin{bmatrix} -6 & 12 \\ -48 & -30 \end{bmatrix}$

b.

$$3A + 2B = \begin{bmatrix} -4 & 1 \\ 3 & 0 \end{bmatrix} + 2\begin{bmatrix} -1 & -2 \\ 8 & 5 \end{bmatrix}$$

$$= \begin{bmatrix} 3(-4) & 3(1) \\ 3(3) & 3(0) \end{bmatrix} + \begin{bmatrix} 2(-1) & 2(-2) \\ 2(8) & 2(5) \end{bmatrix}$$

$$= \begin{bmatrix} -12 & 3 \\ 9 & 0 \end{bmatrix} + \begin{bmatrix} -2 & -4 \\ 16 & 10 \end{bmatrix}$$

$$= \begin{bmatrix} -12 + (-2) & 3 + (-4) \\ 9 + 16 & 0 + 10 \end{bmatrix}$$

$$= \begin{bmatrix} -14 & -1 \\ 25 & 10 \end{bmatrix}$$

4. $3X + A = B$

$3X = B - A$

$X = \dfrac{1}{3}(B - A)$

$X = \dfrac{1}{3}\left(\begin{bmatrix} -10 & 1 \\ -9 & 17 \end{bmatrix} - \begin{bmatrix} 2 & -8 \\ 0 & 4 \end{bmatrix} \right)$

$X = \dfrac{1}{3}\begin{bmatrix} -12 & 9 \\ -9 & 13 \end{bmatrix}$

$X = \begin{bmatrix} -4 & 3 \\ -3 & \dfrac{13}{3} \end{bmatrix}$

5. Given $A = \begin{bmatrix} 1 & 3 \\ 2 & 5 \end{bmatrix}$ and $B = \begin{bmatrix} 4 & 6 \\ 1 & 0 \end{bmatrix}$,

$$AB = \begin{bmatrix} 1 & 3 \\ 2 & 5 \end{bmatrix} \cdot \begin{bmatrix} 4 & 6 \\ 1 & 0 \end{bmatrix} = \begin{bmatrix} 1(4) + 3(1) & 1(6) + 3(0) \\ 2(4) + 5(1) & 2(6) + 5(0) \end{bmatrix}$$

$$= \begin{bmatrix} 7 & 6 \\ 13 & 12 \end{bmatrix}$$

6. If $A = \begin{bmatrix} 2 & 0 & 4 \end{bmatrix}$ and $B = \begin{bmatrix} 1 \\ 3 \\ 7 \end{bmatrix}$, then

$$AB = \begin{bmatrix} 2 & 0 & 4 \end{bmatrix}\begin{bmatrix} 1 \\ 3 \\ 7 \end{bmatrix}$$

$$= \begin{bmatrix} 2(1) + 0(3) + 4(7) \end{bmatrix}$$

$$= \begin{bmatrix} 2 + 0 + 28 \end{bmatrix}$$

$$= \begin{bmatrix} 30 \end{bmatrix}$$

and $BA = \begin{bmatrix} 1 \\ 3 \\ 7 \end{bmatrix}\begin{bmatrix} 2 & 0 & 4 \end{bmatrix} = \begin{bmatrix} 1(2) & 1(0) & 1(4) \\ 3(2) & 3(0) & 3(4) \\ 7(2) & 7(0) & 7(4) \end{bmatrix} = \begin{bmatrix} 2 & 0 \\ 6 & 0 \\ 14 & 0 \end{bmatrix}$

7. a.

$$\begin{bmatrix} 1 & 3 \\ 0 & 2 \end{bmatrix}\begin{bmatrix} 2 & 3 & -1 & 6 \\ 0 & 5 & 4 & 1 \end{bmatrix}$$

$$= \begin{bmatrix} 1(2) + 3(0) & 1(3) + 3(5) & 1(-1) + 3(4) & 1(6) + 3(1) \\ 0(2) + 2(0) & 0(3) + 2(5) & 0(-1) + 2(4) & 0(6) + 2(1) \end{bmatrix}$$

$$= \begin{bmatrix} 2 & 18 & 11 & 9 \\ 0 & 10 & 8 & 2 \end{bmatrix}$$

b. $\begin{bmatrix} 2 & 3 & -1 & 6 \\ 0 & 5 & 4 & 1 \end{bmatrix}\begin{bmatrix} 1 & 3 \\ 0 & 2 \end{bmatrix}$

The number of columns in the first matrix does not equal the number of rows in the second matrix. Thus, the product of these two matrices is undefined.

8. Because the *L* is dark gray and the background is light gray, a digital photograph of Figure 9.7 can be represented by the matrix

$$\begin{bmatrix} 2 & 1 & 1 \\ 2 & 1 & 1 \\ 2 & 2 & 1 \end{bmatrix}$$

We can make the *L* light gray by decreasing

each 2 in the above matrix to 1. We can make the background black by increasing each 1 in the matrix to 3. This is accomplished using the following matrix addition.

$$\begin{bmatrix} 2 & 1 & 1 \\ 2 & 1 & 1 \\ 2 & 2 & 1 \end{bmatrix} + \begin{bmatrix} -1 & 2 & 2 \\ -1 & 2 & 2 \\ -1 & -1 & 2 \end{bmatrix} = \begin{bmatrix} 1 & 3 & 3 \\ 1 & 3 & 3 \\ 1 & 1 & 3 \end{bmatrix}$$

9. The gas station's total sales is represented in the first column of the product matrix

$$\begin{bmatrix} 1322 & 234.80 \\ 1252 & 223.60 \\ 1457 & 259.40 \end{bmatrix}.$$

The gas station's total sales for Monday, Tuesday, and Wednesday is 1322 + 1252 + 1457 or $4031.

Exercise Set 6.3

1. a. 2 x 3

   b. a_{32} does not exist (A only has 2 rows).
      $a_{23} = -1$

3. a. 3 χ 4

   b. $a_{32} = \dfrac{1}{2}$; $a_{23} = -6$

5. $\begin{bmatrix} x \\ 4 \end{bmatrix} = \begin{bmatrix} 6 \\ y \end{bmatrix}$
     $x = 6$
     $y = 4$

7. $\begin{bmatrix} x & 2y \\ z & 9 \end{bmatrix} = \begin{bmatrix} 4 & 12 \\ 3 & 9 \end{bmatrix}$
     $x = 4$
     $2y = 12$
     $y = 6$
     $z = 3$

9. a. $A + B = \begin{bmatrix} 4+5 & 1+9 \\ 3+0 & 2+7 \end{bmatrix} = \begin{bmatrix} 9 & 10 \\ 3 & 9 \end{bmatrix}$

   b. $A - B = \begin{bmatrix} 4-5 & 1-9 \\ 3-0 & 2-7 \end{bmatrix} = \begin{bmatrix} -1 & -8 \\ 3 & -5 \end{bmatrix}$

   c. $-4A = \begin{bmatrix} -16 & -4 \\ -12 & -8 \end{bmatrix}$

   d.

$$3A + 2B = \begin{bmatrix} 12+10 & 3+18 \\ 9+0 & 6+14 \end{bmatrix} = \begin{bmatrix} 22 & 21 \\ 9 & 20 \end{bmatrix}$$

11. a. $A + B = \begin{bmatrix} 1+2 & 3+(-1) \\ 3+3 & 4+(-2) \\ 5+0 & 6+1 \end{bmatrix} = \begin{bmatrix} 3 & 2 \\ 6 & 2 \\ 5 & 7 \end{bmatrix}$

   b. $A - B = \begin{bmatrix} 1-2 & 3-(-1) \\ 3-3 & 4-(-2) \\ 5-0 & 6-1 \end{bmatrix} = \begin{bmatrix} -1 & 4 \\ 0 & 6 \\ 5 & 5 \end{bmatrix}$

   c. $-4A = \begin{bmatrix} -4 & -12 \\ -12 & -16 \\ -20 & -24 \end{bmatrix}$

   d. $3A + 2B = \begin{bmatrix} 3+4 & 9-2 \\ 9+6 & 12-4 \\ 15+0 & 18+2 \end{bmatrix} = \begin{bmatrix} 7 & 7 \\ 15 & 8 \\ 15 & 20 \end{bmatrix}$

13. a. $A + B = \begin{bmatrix} 2+(-5) \\ -4+3 \\ 1+(-1) \end{bmatrix} = \begin{bmatrix} -3 \\ -1 \\ 0 \end{bmatrix}$

   b. $A - B = \begin{bmatrix} 2-(-5) \\ -4-3 \\ 1-(-1) \end{bmatrix} = \begin{bmatrix} 7 \\ -7 \\ 2 \end{bmatrix}$

c. $-4A = \begin{bmatrix} -8 \\ 16 \\ -4 \end{bmatrix}$

d. $3A + 2B = \begin{bmatrix} 6-10 \\ -12+6 \\ 3-2 \end{bmatrix} = \begin{bmatrix} -4 \\ -6 \\ 1 \end{bmatrix}$

15. a.

$A + B = \begin{bmatrix} 2+6 & -10+10 & -2+(-2) \\ 14+0 & 12+(-12) & 10+(-4) \\ 4+(-5) & -2+2 & 2+(-2) \end{bmatrix}$

$= \begin{bmatrix} 8 & 0 & -4 \\ 14 & 0 & 6 \\ -1 & 0 & 0 \end{bmatrix}$

b.

$A - B = \begin{bmatrix} 2-6 & -10-10 & -2-(-2) \\ 14-0 & 12-(-12) & 10-(-4) \\ 4-(-5) & -2-2 & 2-(-2) \end{bmatrix}$

$= \begin{bmatrix} -4 & -20 & 0 \\ 14 & 24 & 14 \\ 9 & -4 & 4 \end{bmatrix}$

c. $-4A = \begin{bmatrix} -8 & 40 & 8 \\ -56 & -48 & -40 \\ -16 & 8 & -8 \end{bmatrix}$

d.

$3A + 2B = \begin{bmatrix} 6+12 & -30+20 & -6-4 \\ 42+0 & 36-24 & 30-8 \\ 12-10 & -6+4 & 6-4 \end{bmatrix}$

$= \begin{bmatrix} 18 & -10 & -10 \\ 42 & 12 & 22 \\ 2 & -2 & 2 \end{bmatrix}$

17. $X - A = B$

$\qquad X = A + B$

$\qquad X = \begin{bmatrix} -3 & -7 \\ 2 & -9 \\ 5 & 0 \end{bmatrix} + \begin{bmatrix} -5 & -1 \\ 0 & 0 \\ 3 & -4 \end{bmatrix}$

$\qquad X = \begin{bmatrix} -8 & -8 \\ 2 & -9 \\ 8 & -4 \end{bmatrix}$

19. $2X + A = B$

$$2X = B - A$$

$$X = \frac{1}{2}(B - A)$$

$$X = \frac{1}{2}\left(\begin{bmatrix} -5 & -1 \\ 0 & 0 \\ 3 & -4 \end{bmatrix} - \begin{bmatrix} -3 & -7 \\ 2 & -9 \\ 5 & 0 \end{bmatrix}\right)$$

$$X = \frac{1}{2}\begin{bmatrix} -2 & 6 \\ -2 & 9 \\ -2 & -4 \end{bmatrix}$$

$$X = \begin{bmatrix} -1 & 3 \\ -1 & \dfrac{9}{2} \\ -1 & -2 \end{bmatrix}$$

21. $3X + 2A = B$

$\quad\ 3X = B - 2A$

$$X = \frac{1}{3}(B - 2A)$$

$$X = \frac{1}{3}\left(\begin{bmatrix} -5 & -1 \\ 0 & 0 \\ 3 & -4 \end{bmatrix} - 2\begin{bmatrix} -3 & -7 \\ 2 & -9 \\ 5 & 0 \end{bmatrix}\right)$$

$$X = \frac{1}{3}\begin{bmatrix} 1 & 13 \\ -4 & 18 \\ -7 & -4 \end{bmatrix}$$

$$X = \begin{bmatrix} \dfrac{1}{3} & \dfrac{13}{3} \\ -\dfrac{4}{3} & 6 \\ -\dfrac{7}{3} & -\dfrac{4}{3} \end{bmatrix}$$

23. $\qquad\qquad\qquad B - X = 4A$

$\qquad\qquad\qquad\ B - 4A = X$

$$\begin{bmatrix} -5 & -1 \\ 0 & 0 \\ 3 & -4 \end{bmatrix} - 4\begin{bmatrix} -3 & -7 \\ 2 & -9 \\ 5 & 0 \end{bmatrix} = X$$

$$\begin{bmatrix} -5 & -1 \\ 0 & 0 \\ 3 & -4 \end{bmatrix} + \begin{bmatrix} 12 & 28 \\ -8 & 36 \\ -20 & 0 \end{bmatrix} = X$$

$$\begin{bmatrix} 7 & 27 \\ -8 & 36 \\ -17 & -4 \end{bmatrix} = X$$

25.

$$4A + 3B = -2X$$

$$-\frac{1}{2}(4A + 3B) = X$$

$$-\frac{1}{2}\left(4\begin{bmatrix} -3 & -7 \\ 2 & -9 \\ 5 & 0 \end{bmatrix} + 3\begin{bmatrix} -5 & -1 \\ 0 & 0 \\ 3 & -4 \end{bmatrix}\right) = X$$

$$-\frac{1}{2}\left(\begin{bmatrix} -12 & -28 \\ 8 & -36 \\ 20 & 0 \end{bmatrix} + \begin{bmatrix} -15 & -3 \\ 0 & 0 \\ 9 & -12 \end{bmatrix}\right) = X$$

$$-\frac{1}{2}\begin{bmatrix} -27 & -31 \\ 8 & -36 \\ 29 & -12 \end{bmatrix} = X$$

$$\begin{bmatrix} \dfrac{27}{2} & \dfrac{31}{2} \\ -4 & 18 \\ -\dfrac{29}{2} & 6 \end{bmatrix} = X$$

27. a.

$$AB = \begin{bmatrix} 1 & 3 \\ 5 & 3 \end{bmatrix}\begin{bmatrix} 3 & -2 \\ -1 & 6 \end{bmatrix}$$

$$= \begin{bmatrix} (1)(3) + (3)(-1) & (1)(-2) + (3)(6) \\ (5)(3) + (3)(-1) & (5)(-2) + (3)(6) \end{bmatrix}$$

$$= \begin{bmatrix} 3 - 3 & -2 + 18 \\ 15 - 3 & -10 + 18 \end{bmatrix}$$

$$= \begin{bmatrix} 0 & 16 \\ 12 & 8 \end{bmatrix}$$

b.

$$BA = \begin{bmatrix} 3 & -2 \\ -1 & 6 \end{bmatrix}\begin{bmatrix} 1 & 3 \\ 5 & 3 \end{bmatrix}$$

$$= \begin{bmatrix} (3)(1) + (-2)(5) & (3)(3) + (-2)(3) \\ (-1)(1) + (6)(5) & (-1)(3) + (6)(3) \end{bmatrix}$$

$$= \begin{bmatrix} 3 - 10 & 9 - 6 \\ -1 + 30 & -3 + 18 \end{bmatrix}$$

$$= \begin{bmatrix} -7 & 3 \\ 29 & 15 \end{bmatrix}$$

29. a.

$$AB = \begin{bmatrix} 1 & 2 & 3 & 4 \end{bmatrix}\begin{bmatrix} 1 \\ 2 \\ 3 \\ 4 \end{bmatrix}$$

$$= [(1)(1) + (2)(2) + (3)(3) + (4)(4)]$$

$$= [1 + 4 + 9 + 16] = [30]$$

b.

$$BA = \begin{bmatrix} 1 \\ 2 \\ 3 \\ 4 \end{bmatrix}\begin{bmatrix} 1 & 2 & 3 & 4 \end{bmatrix}$$

$$= \begin{bmatrix} (1)(1) & (1)(2) & (1)(3) & (1)(4) \\ (2)(1) & (2)(2) & (2)(3) & (2)(4) \\ (3)(1) & (3)(2) & (3)(3) & (3)(4) \\ (4)(1) & (4)(2) & (4)(3) & (4)(4) \end{bmatrix}$$

$$= \begin{bmatrix} 1 & 2 & 3 & 4 \\ 2 & 4 & 6 & 8 \\ 3 & 6 & 9 & 12 \\ 4 & 8 & 12 & 16 \end{bmatrix}$$

31. a.
$$AB = \begin{bmatrix} 1 & -1 & 4 \\ 4 & -1 & 3 \\ 2 & 0 & -2 \end{bmatrix} \begin{bmatrix} 1 & 1 & 0 \\ 1 & 2 & 4 \\ 1 & -1 & 3 \end{bmatrix}$$

$$= \begin{bmatrix} (1)(1)+(-1)(1)+(4)(1) & (1)(1)+(-1)(2)+(4)(-1) & (1)(0)+(-1)(4)+(4)(3) \\ (4)(1)+(-1)(1)+(3)(1) & (4)(1)+(-1)(2)+(3)(-1) & (4)(0)+(-1)(4)+(3)(3) \\ (2)(1)+(0)(1)+(-2)(1) & (2)(1)+(0)(2)+(-2)(-1) & (2)(0)+(0)(4)+(-2)(3) \end{bmatrix}$$

$$= \begin{bmatrix} 1-1+4 & 1-2-4 & 0-4+12 \\ 4-1+3 & 4-2-3 & 0-4+9 \\ 2+0-2 & 2+0+2 & 0+0-6 \end{bmatrix}$$

$$= \begin{bmatrix} 4 & -5 & 8 \\ 6 & -1 & 5 \\ 0 & 4 & -6 \end{bmatrix}$$

b.
$$BA = \begin{bmatrix} 1 & 1 & 0 \\ 1 & 2 & 4 \\ 1 & -1 & 3 \end{bmatrix} \begin{bmatrix} 1 & -1 & 4 \\ 4 & -1 & 3 \\ 2 & 0 & -2 \end{bmatrix}$$

$$= \begin{bmatrix} (1)(1)+(1)(4)+(0)(2) & (1)(-1)+(1)(-1)+(0)(0) & (1)(4)+(1)(3)+(0)(-2) \\ (1)(1)+(2)(4)+(4)(2) & (1)(-1)+(2)(-1)+(4)(0) & (1)(4)+(2)(3)+(4)(-2) \\ (1)(1)+(-1)(4)+(3)(2) & (1)(-1)+(-1)(-1)+(3)(0) & (1)(4)+(-1)(3)+(3)(-2) \end{bmatrix}$$

$$= \begin{bmatrix} 1+4+0 & -1-1+0 & 4+3+0 \\ 1+8+8 & -1-2+0 & 4+6-8 \\ 1-4+6 & -1+1+0 & 4-3-6 \end{bmatrix}$$

$$= \begin{bmatrix} 5 & -2 & 7 \\ 17 & -3 & 2 \\ 3 & 0 & -5 \end{bmatrix}$$

33. a.
$$AB = \begin{bmatrix} 4 & 2 \\ 6 & 1 \\ 3 & 5 \end{bmatrix} \begin{bmatrix} 2 & 3 & 4 \\ -1 & -2 & 0 \end{bmatrix}$$

$$= \begin{bmatrix} (4)(2)+(2)(-1) & (4)(3)+(2)(-2) & (4)(4)+(2)(0) \\ (6)(2)+(1)(-1) & (6)(3)+(1)(-2) & (6)(4)+(1)(0) \\ (3)(2)+(5)(-1) & (3)(3)+(5)(-2) & (3)(4)+(5)(0) \end{bmatrix}$$

$$= \begin{bmatrix} 8-2 & 12-4 & 16+0 \\ 12-1 & 18-2 & 24+0 \\ 6-5 & 9-10 & 12+0 \end{bmatrix}$$

$$= \begin{bmatrix} 6 & 8 & 16 \\ 11 & 16 & 24 \\ 1 & -1 & 12 \end{bmatrix}$$

b. $BA = \begin{bmatrix} 2 & 3 & 4 \\ -1 & -2 & 0 \end{bmatrix} \begin{bmatrix} 4 & 2 \\ 6 & 1 \\ 3 & 5 \end{bmatrix} = \begin{bmatrix} (2)(4)+(3)(6)+(4)(3) & (2)(2)+(3)(1)+(4)(5) \\ (-1)(4)+(-2)(6)+(0)(3) & (-1)(2)+(-2)(1)+(0)(5) \end{bmatrix}$

$$= \begin{bmatrix} 8+18+12 & 4+3+20 \\ -4-12+0 & -2-2+0 \end{bmatrix}$$

$$= \begin{bmatrix} 38 & 27 \\ -16 & -4 \end{bmatrix}$$

35. a. $AB = \begin{bmatrix} 2 & -3 & 1 & -1 \\ 1 & 1 & -2 & 1 \end{bmatrix} \begin{bmatrix} 1 & 2 \\ -1 & 1 \\ 5 & 4 \\ 10 & 5 \end{bmatrix}$

$$= \begin{bmatrix} (2)(1)+(-3)(-1)+(1)(5)+(-1)(10) & (2)(2)+(-3)(1)+(1)(4)+(-1)(5) \\ (1)(1)+(1)(-1)+(-2)(5)+(1)(10) & (1)(2)+(1)(1)+(-2)(4)+(1)(5) \end{bmatrix}$$

$$= \begin{bmatrix} 2+3+5-10 & 4-3+4-5 \\ 1-1-10+10 & 2+1-8+5 \end{bmatrix}$$

$$= \begin{bmatrix} 0 & 0 \\ 0 & 0 \end{bmatrix}$$

b. $BA = \begin{bmatrix} 1 & 2 \\ -1 & 1 \\ 5 & 4 \\ 10 & 5 \end{bmatrix} \begin{bmatrix} 2 & -3 & 1 & -1 \\ 1 & 1 & -2 & 1 \end{bmatrix}$

$= \begin{bmatrix} (1)(2)+(2)(1) & (1)(-3)+(2)(1) & (1)(1)+(2)(-2) & (1)(-1)+(2)(1) \\ (-1)(2)+(1)(1) & (-1)(-3)+(1)(1) & (-1)(1)+(1)(-2) & (-1)(-1)+(1)(1) \\ (5)(2)+(4)(1) & (5)(-3)+(4)(1) & (5)(1)+(4)(-2) & (5)(-1)+(4)(1) \\ (10)(2)+(5)(1) & (10)(-3)+(5)(1) & (10)(1)+(5)(-2) & (10)(-1)+(5)(1) \end{bmatrix}$

$= \begin{bmatrix} 2+2 & -3+2 & 1-4 & -1+2 \\ -2+1 & 3+1 & -1-2 & 1+1 \\ 10+4 & -15+4 & 5-8 & -5+4 \\ 20+5 & -30+5 & 10-10 & -10+5 \end{bmatrix}$

$= \begin{bmatrix} 4 & -1 & -3 & 1 \\ -1 & 4 & -3 & 2 \\ 14 & -11 & -3 & -1 \\ 25 & -25 & 0 & -5 \end{bmatrix}$

37.

$$4B - 3C = \begin{bmatrix} 20 & 4 \\ -8 & -8 \end{bmatrix} - \begin{bmatrix} 3 & -3 \\ -3 & 3 \end{bmatrix}$$

$$= \begin{bmatrix} 20-3 & 4-(-3) \\ -8-(-3) & -8-3 \end{bmatrix} = \begin{bmatrix} 17 & 7 \\ -5 & -11 \end{bmatrix}$$

39.

$$BC + CB = \begin{bmatrix} 5-1 & -5+1 \\ -2+2 & 2-2 \end{bmatrix} + \begin{bmatrix} 5+2 & 1+2 \\ -5-2 & -1-2 \end{bmatrix}$$

$$= \begin{bmatrix} 4 & -4 \\ 0 & 0 \end{bmatrix} + \begin{bmatrix} 7 & 3 \\ -7 & -3 \end{bmatrix} = \begin{bmatrix} 11 & -1 \\ -7 & -3 \end{bmatrix}$$

41. $A - C$ is not defined because A is 3 x 2 and C is 2 x 2.

43.

$$A(BC) = \begin{bmatrix} 4 & 0 \\ -3 & 5 \\ 0 & 1 \end{bmatrix} \begin{bmatrix} 5-1 & -5+1 \\ -2+2 & 2-2 \end{bmatrix}$$

$$= \begin{bmatrix} 4 & 0 \\ -3 & 5 \\ 0 & 1 \end{bmatrix} \begin{bmatrix} 4 & -4 \\ 0 & 0 \end{bmatrix}$$

$$= \begin{bmatrix} 16+0 & -16+0 \\ -12+0 & 12+0 \\ 0+0 & 0+0 \end{bmatrix} = \begin{bmatrix} 16 & -16 \\ -12 & 12 \\ 0 & 0 \end{bmatrix}$$

45.

a. $\begin{bmatrix} 1 & 3 & 1 \\ 3 & 3 & 3 \\ 1 & 3 & 1 \end{bmatrix}$

b. $\begin{bmatrix} 1 & 3 & 1 \\ 3 & 3 & 3 \\ 1 & 3 & 1 \end{bmatrix} + \begin{bmatrix} -1 & -1 & -1 \\ -1 & -1 & -1 \\ -1 & -1 & -1 \end{bmatrix} = \begin{bmatrix} 0 & 2 & 0 \\ 2 & 2 & 2 \\ 0 & 2 & 0 \end{bmatrix}$

c. $\begin{bmatrix} 1 & 3 & 1 \\ 3 & 3 & 3 \\ 1 & 3 & 1 \end{bmatrix} + \begin{bmatrix} 1 & -2 & 1 \\ -2 & -2 & -2 \\ 1 & -2 & 1 \end{bmatrix} = \begin{bmatrix} 2 & 1 & 2 \\ 1 & 1 & 1 \\ 2 & 1 & 2 \end{bmatrix}$

47. a. $AB = \begin{bmatrix} -1 & 0 \\ 0 & 1 \end{bmatrix} \cdot \begin{bmatrix} 0 & 3 & 3 & 1 & 1 & 0 \\ 0 & 0 & 1 & 1 & 5 & 5 \end{bmatrix}$

$$= \begin{bmatrix} 0 & -3 & -3 & -1 & -1 & 0 \\ 0 & 0 & 1 & 1 & 5 & 5 \end{bmatrix}$$

b.

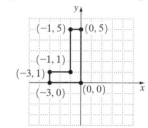

Rotated L about the *y*-axis.

49. a. $A = \begin{bmatrix} 26 & 19 \\ 12 & 11 \end{bmatrix}$

b. $B = \begin{bmatrix} 31 & 26 \\ 17 & 16 \end{bmatrix}$

c. $B - A = \begin{bmatrix} 31 & 26 \\ 17 & 16 \end{bmatrix} - \begin{bmatrix} 26 & 19 \\ 12 & 11 \end{bmatrix}$

$$= \begin{bmatrix} 5 & 7 \\ 5 & 5 \end{bmatrix}$$

$B - A$ represents the difference in the number of graduates between 2000 and 1900.

51. a. System 1: The midterm and final both count for 50% of the course grade. System 2: The midterm counts for 30% of the course grade and the final counts for 70%

b. $AB = \begin{bmatrix} 84 & 87.2 \\ 79 & 81 \\ 90 & 88.4 \\ 73 & 68.6 \\ 69 & 73.4 \end{bmatrix}$

System 1 grades are listed first
(if different).
Student 1: B; Student 2: C or B;
Student 3: A or B; Student 4: C or D;
Student 5: D or C

53.–65. Answers may vary.

Section 6.4

Check Point Exercises

1. We must show that: $AB = I_2 = \begin{bmatrix} 1 & 0 \\ 0 & 1 \end{bmatrix}$, and

   $BA = I_2 = \begin{bmatrix} 1 & 0 \\ 0 & 1 \end{bmatrix}$.

   $AB = \begin{bmatrix} 2 & 1 \\ 1 & 1 \end{bmatrix}\begin{bmatrix} 1 & -1 \\ -1 & 2 \end{bmatrix}$

   $= \begin{bmatrix} 2(1)+1(-1) & 2(-1)+1(2) \\ 1(1)+1(-1) & 1(-1)+1(2) \end{bmatrix}$

   $= \begin{bmatrix} 1 & 0 \\ 0 & 1 \end{bmatrix}$

   $BA = \begin{bmatrix} 1 & -1 \\ -1 & 2 \end{bmatrix}\begin{bmatrix} 2 & 1 \\ 1 & 1 \end{bmatrix}$

   $= \begin{bmatrix} 1(2)+-1(1) & 1(1)+-1(1) \\ -1(2)+2(1) & -1(1)+2(1) \end{bmatrix}$

   $= \begin{bmatrix} 1 & 0 \\ 0 & 1 \end{bmatrix}$

   Both products (*AB* and *BA*) give the multiplicative identity matrix, I_2. Thus, *B* is the mulpilicative inverse of *A*.

2. Let us denote the multiplicative inverse of *A* by $A^{-1} = \begin{bmatrix} w & x \\ y & z \end{bmatrix}$. Because *A* is a 2×2 matrix, we use the equation $AA^{-1} = I_2$ to find values for *w*, *x*, *y* and *z*

   $\begin{bmatrix} 5 & 7 \\ 2 & 3 \end{bmatrix}\begin{bmatrix} w & x \\ y & z \end{bmatrix} = \begin{bmatrix} 1 & 0 \\ 0 & 1 \end{bmatrix}$

   $\begin{bmatrix} 5w+7y & 5x+7z \\ 2w+3y & 2x+3z \end{bmatrix} = \begin{bmatrix} 1 & 0 \\ 0 & 1 \end{bmatrix}$

   $5w+7y = 1 \qquad 5x+7z = 0$

   $2w+3y = 0 \qquad 2x+3z = 1$

   Each of these systems can be solved using the addition method.
   Multiply by –2:
   $5w+7y = 1 \rightarrow -10w-14y = -2$
   Multiply by 5:
   $2w+3y = 0 \rightarrow \quad 10w+15y = 0$
   Use back substitution: $w = 3$, $y = -2$
   Multiply by –2:
   $5x+7z = 0 \rightarrow -10x-14z = 0$
   Multiply by 5:
   $2x+3z = 1 \rightarrow 10x+15z = 5$
   Use back substitution: $x = -7$, $z = 5$
   Using these values, we have

   $A^{-1} = \begin{bmatrix} 3 & -7 \\ -2 & 5 \end{bmatrix}$.

3. $A^{-1} = \dfrac{1}{ad-bc}\begin{bmatrix} d & -b \\ -c & a \end{bmatrix}$

   $= \dfrac{1}{3(1)-(-2)(-1)}\begin{bmatrix} 1 & -(-2) \\ -(-1) & 3 \end{bmatrix}$

   $= \dfrac{1}{3-2}\begin{bmatrix} 1 & 2 \\ 1 & 3 \end{bmatrix}$

   $= \dfrac{1}{1}\begin{bmatrix} 1 & 2 \\ 1 & 3 \end{bmatrix}$

   $= \begin{bmatrix} 1 & 2 \\ 1 & 3 \end{bmatrix}$

4. The augmented matrix $\left[A \mid I_3 \right]$ is

$$\begin{bmatrix} 1 & 0 & 2 & | & 1 & 0 & 0 \\ -1 & 2 & 3 & | & 0 & 1 & 0 \\ 1 & -1 & 0 & | & 0 & 0 & 1 \end{bmatrix}.$$

Perform row transformations on $\left[A \mid I_3 \right]$ to obtain a matrix of the form $\left[I_3 \mid B \right]$.

$$\begin{bmatrix} 1 & 0 & 2 & | & 1 & 0 & 0 \\ -1 & 2 & 3 & | & 0 & 1 & 0 \\ 1 & -1 & 0 & | & 0 & 0 & 1 \end{bmatrix} \quad 1R_1 / R_2$$

$$= \begin{bmatrix} 1 & 0 & 2 & | & 1 & 0 & 0 \\ 0 & 2 & 5 & | & 1 & 1 & 0 \\ 1 & -1 & 0 & | & 0 & 0 & 1 \end{bmatrix} -1R_3$$

$$= \begin{bmatrix} 1 & 0 & 2 & | & 1 & 0 & 0 \\ 0 & 2 & 5 & | & 1 & 1 & 0 \\ -1 & 1 & 0 & | & 0 & 0 & -1 \end{bmatrix} R_1 + R_3$$

$$= \begin{bmatrix} 1 & 0 & 2 & | & 1 & 0 & 0 \\ 0 & 2 & 5 & | & 1 & 1 & 0 \\ 0 & 1 & 2 & | & 1 & 0 & -1 \end{bmatrix} \tfrac{1}{2} R_2$$

$$= \begin{bmatrix} 1 & 0 & 2 & | & 1 & 0 & 0 \\ 0 & 1 & \tfrac{5}{2} & | & \tfrac{1}{2} & \tfrac{1}{2} & 0 \\ 0 & 1 & 2 & | & 1 & 0 & -1 \end{bmatrix} -1R_2 + R_3$$

$$= \begin{bmatrix} 1 & 0 & 2 & | & 1 & 0 & 0 \\ 0 & 1 & \tfrac{5}{2} & | & \tfrac{1}{2} & \tfrac{1}{2} & 0 \\ 0 & 0 & -\tfrac{1}{2} & | & \tfrac{1}{2} & -\tfrac{1}{2} & -1 \end{bmatrix} -2R_3$$

$$= \begin{bmatrix} 1 & 0 & 2 & | & 1 & 0 & 0 \\ 0 & 1 & \tfrac{5}{2} & | & \tfrac{1}{2} & \tfrac{1}{2} & 0 \\ 0 & 0 & 1 & | & -1 & 1 & 2 \end{bmatrix} \begin{array}{l} -2R_3 + R_1 \\ -\tfrac{5}{2} R_3 + R_2 \end{array}$$

$$= \begin{bmatrix} 1 & 0 & 0 & | & 3 & -2 & -4 \\ 0 & 1 & 0 & | & 3 & -2 & -5 \\ 0 & 0 & 1 & | & 1 & 1 & 2 \end{bmatrix}$$

Thus, the multiplicative inverse of A is

$$A^{-1} = \begin{bmatrix} 3 & -2 & -4 \\ 3 & -2 & -5 \\ -1 & 1 & 2 \end{bmatrix}.$$

5. The linear system can be written as $AX = B$.

$$\begin{bmatrix} 1 & 0 & 2 \\ -1 & 2 & 3 \\ 1 & -1 & 0 \end{bmatrix} \begin{bmatrix} x \\ y \\ z \end{bmatrix} = \begin{bmatrix} 6 \\ -5 \\ 6 \end{bmatrix}.$$

$$X = A^{-1}B = \begin{bmatrix} 3 & -2 & -4 \\ 3 & -2 & -5 \\ -1 & 1 & 2 \end{bmatrix} \begin{bmatrix} 6 \\ -5 \\ 6 \end{bmatrix}$$

$$= \begin{bmatrix} 3(6) + -2(-5) + -4(6) \\ 3(6) + -2(-5) + -5(6) \\ -1(6) + 1(-5) + 2(6) \end{bmatrix}$$

$$= \begin{bmatrix} 18 + 10 - 24 \\ 18 + 10 - 30 \\ -6 - 5 + 12 \end{bmatrix} = \begin{bmatrix} 4 \\ -2 \\ 1 \end{bmatrix}$$

Thus, $x = 4$, $y = -2$, and $z = 1$. The solution set is $\{(4, -2, 1)\}$.

6. The numerical representation of the word BASE is 2, 1, 19, 5. The 2×2 matrix formed is $\begin{bmatrix} 2 & 19 \\ 1 & 5 \end{bmatrix}$.

$$\begin{bmatrix} -2 & -3 \\ 3 & 4 \end{bmatrix} \begin{bmatrix} 2 & 19 \\ 1 & 5 \end{bmatrix}$$

$$= \begin{bmatrix} -2(2) + -3(1) & -2(19) + -3(5) \\ 3(2) + 4(1) & 3(19) + 4(5) \end{bmatrix}$$

$$= \begin{bmatrix} -4 - 3 & -38 - 15 \\ 6 + 4 & 57 + 20 \end{bmatrix} = \begin{bmatrix} -7 & -53 \\ 10 & 77 \end{bmatrix}$$

The encoded message is $-7, 10, -53, 77$.

7. Use the multiplicative inverse of the coding matrix. It is $\begin{bmatrix} 4 & 3 \\ -3 & -2 \end{bmatrix}$.

$$\begin{bmatrix} 4 & 3 \\ -3 & -2 \end{bmatrix} \begin{bmatrix} -7 & -53 \\ 10 & 77 \end{bmatrix}$$

$$= \begin{bmatrix} 4(-7) + 3(10) & 4(-53) + 3(77) \\ -3(-7) + -2(10) & -3(-53) + -2(77) \end{bmatrix}$$

$$= \begin{bmatrix} -28 + 30 & -212 + 231 \\ 21 - 20 & 159 - 154 \end{bmatrix} = \begin{bmatrix} 2 & 19 \\ 1 & 5 \end{bmatrix}$$

The numbers are 2, 1, 19, and 5. Using letters, the decoded message is BASE.

Exercise Set 6.4

1. $A = \begin{bmatrix} 4 & -3 \\ -5 & 4 \end{bmatrix}$ $B = \begin{bmatrix} 4 & 3 \\ 5 & 4 \end{bmatrix}$

$AB = \begin{bmatrix} 16-15 & 12-12 \\ -20+20 & -15+16 \end{bmatrix} = \begin{bmatrix} 1 & 0 \\ 0 & 1 \end{bmatrix}$

$BA = \begin{bmatrix} 16-15 & -12+12 \\ 20-20 & -15+16 \end{bmatrix} = \begin{bmatrix} 1 & 0 \\ 0 & 1 \end{bmatrix}$

Since $AB = I_2$ $BA = I_2$, $B = A^{-1}$.

3. $AB = \begin{bmatrix} 8+0 & -16+0 \\ -2+0 & 4+3 \end{bmatrix} = \begin{bmatrix} 8 & -16 \\ -2 & 7 \end{bmatrix}$

$BA = \begin{bmatrix} 8+4 & 0+12 \\ 0+1 & 0+3 \end{bmatrix} = \begin{bmatrix} 12 & 12 \\ 1 & 3 \end{bmatrix}$

If B is the multiplicative inverse of A, both products (AB and BA) will be the multiplicative identity matrix, I_2.
Therefore, B is not the multiplicative inverse of A. That is, $B \neq A^{-1}$.

5. $AB = \begin{bmatrix} -2+3 & -4+4 \\ \frac{3}{2}-\frac{3}{2} & 3-2 \end{bmatrix} = \begin{bmatrix} 1 & 0 \\ 0 & 1 \end{bmatrix}$

$BA = \begin{bmatrix} -2+3 & 1-1 \\ -6+6 & 3-2 \end{bmatrix} = \begin{bmatrix} 1 & 0 \\ 0 & 1 \end{bmatrix}$

Since $AB = I_2$ and $BA = I_2$, $B = A^{-1}$.

7. $A = \begin{bmatrix} 0 & 1 & 0 \\ 0 & 0 & 1 \\ 1 & 0 & 0 \end{bmatrix}$ $B = \begin{bmatrix} 0 & 0 & 1 \\ 1 & 0 & 0 \\ 0 & 1 & 0 \end{bmatrix}$

$AB = \begin{bmatrix} 0+1+0 & 0+0+0 & 0+0+0 \\ 0+0+0 & 0+0+1 & 0+0+0 \\ 0+0+0 & 0+0+0 & 1+0+0 \end{bmatrix} = \begin{bmatrix} 1 & 0 & 0 \\ 0 & 1 & 0 \\ 0 & 0 & 1 \end{bmatrix}$

$BA = \begin{bmatrix} 0+0+1 & 0+0+0 & 0+0+0 \\ 0+0+0 & 1+0+0 & 0+0+0 \\ 0+0+0 & 0+0+0 & 0+1+0 \end{bmatrix} = \begin{bmatrix} 1 & 0 & 0 \\ 0 & 1 & 0 \\ 0 & 0 & 1 \end{bmatrix}$

Since $AB = I_3$ and $BA = I_3$, $B = A^{-1}$.

9.

$AB = \begin{bmatrix} \frac{7}{2}-1-\frac{3}{2} & -3+0+3 & \frac{1}{2}+1-\frac{3}{2} \\ \frac{7}{2}-\frac{3}{2}-2 & -3+0+4 & \frac{1}{2}+\frac{3}{2}-2 \\ \frac{7}{2}-2-\frac{3}{2} & -3+0+3 & \frac{1}{2}+2-\frac{3}{2} \end{bmatrix}$

$= \begin{bmatrix} 1 & 0 & 0 \\ 0 & 1 & 0 \\ 0 & 0 & 1 \end{bmatrix}$

$BA = \begin{bmatrix} \frac{7}{2}-3+\frac{1}{2} & 7-9+2 & \frac{21}{2}-12+\frac{3}{2} \\ -\frac{1}{2}+0+\frac{1}{2} & -1+0+2 & -\frac{3}{2}+0+\frac{3}{2} \\ -\frac{1}{2}+1-\frac{1}{2} & -1+3-2 & -\frac{3}{2}+4-\frac{3}{2} \end{bmatrix}$

$= \begin{bmatrix} 1 & 0 & 0 \\ 0 & 1 & 0 \\ 0 & 0 & 1 \end{bmatrix}$

Since $AB = I_3$ and $BA = I_3$, $B = A^{-1}$.

11.

$$AB = \begin{bmatrix} 0+0+0+1 & 0+0-2+2 & 0+0+0+0 & 0+0-2+2 \\ -1+0+0+1 & -2+0+1+2 & 0+0+0+0 & -3+0+1+2 \\ 0+0+0+0 & 0+1-1+0 & 0+1+0+0 & 0+1-1+0 \\ 1+0+0-1 & 2+0+0-2 & 0+0+0+0 & 3+0+0-2 \end{bmatrix}$$

$$= \begin{bmatrix} 1 & 0 & 0 & 0 \\ 0 & 1 & 0 & 0 \\ 0 & 0 & 1 & 0 \\ 0 & 0 & 0 & 1 \end{bmatrix}$$

$$BA = \begin{bmatrix} 0-2+0+3 & 0+0+0+0 & -2+2+0+0 & 1+2+0-3 \\ 0-1+0+1 & 0+0+1+0 & 0+1-1+0 & 0+1+0-1 \\ 0-1+0+1 & 0+0+0+0 & 0+1+0+0 & 0+1+0-1 \\ 0-2+0+2 & 0+0+0+0 & -2+2+0+0 & 1+2+0-2 \end{bmatrix} = \begin{bmatrix} 1 & 0 & 0 & 0 \\ 0 & 1 & 0 & 0 \\ 0 & 0 & 1 & 0 \\ 0 & 0 & 0 & 1 \end{bmatrix}$$

Since $AB = I_4$ and $BA = I_4$, $B = A^{-1}$.

13. $ad - bc = (2)(2) - (3)(-1) = 4 + 3 = 7$

$$A^{-1} = \frac{1}{7}\begin{bmatrix} 2 & -3 \\ 1 & 2 \end{bmatrix} = \begin{bmatrix} \frac{2}{7} & -\frac{3}{7} \\ \frac{1}{7} & \frac{2}{7} \end{bmatrix}$$

$$AA^{-1} = \begin{bmatrix} \frac{4}{7}+\frac{3}{7} & -\frac{6}{7}+\frac{6}{7} \\ -\frac{2}{7}+\frac{2}{7} & \frac{3}{7}+\frac{4}{7} \end{bmatrix} = \begin{bmatrix} 1 & 0 \\ 0 & 1 \end{bmatrix}$$

$$A^{-1}A = \begin{bmatrix} \frac{4}{7}+\frac{3}{7} & \frac{6}{7}-\frac{6}{7} \\ \frac{2}{7}-\frac{2}{7} & \frac{3}{7}+\frac{4}{7} \end{bmatrix} = \begin{bmatrix} 1 & 0 \\ 0 & 1 \end{bmatrix}$$

15. $ad - bc = (3)(2) - (-1)(-4) = 6 - 4 = 2$

$$A^{-1} = \frac{1}{2}\begin{bmatrix} 2 & 1 \\ 4 & 3 \end{bmatrix} = \begin{bmatrix} 1 & \frac{1}{2} \\ 2 & \frac{3}{2} \end{bmatrix}$$

$$AA^{-1} = \begin{bmatrix} 3-2 & \frac{3}{2}-\frac{3}{2} \\ -4+4 & -\frac{4}{2}+\frac{6}{2} \end{bmatrix} = \begin{bmatrix} 1 & 0 \\ 0 & 1 \end{bmatrix}$$

$$A^{-1}A = \begin{bmatrix} 3-\frac{4}{2} & -1+\frac{2}{2} \\ 6-\frac{12}{2} & -2+\frac{6}{2} \end{bmatrix} = \begin{bmatrix} 1 & 0 \\ 0 & 1 \end{bmatrix}$$

17. $ad - bc = (10)(1) - (-2)(-5) = 10 - 10 = 0$

Since division by zero is undefined, A does not have an inverse.

For Problems 19–24, verification that $AA^{-1} = I$ and $A^{-1}A = I$ is left to the student.

19. $\begin{bmatrix} 2 & 0 & 0 & 1 & 0 & 0 \\ 0 & 4 & 0 & 0 & 1 & 0 \\ 0 & 0 & 6 & 0 & 0 & 1 \end{bmatrix}$

Divide row 1 by 2, divide row 2 by 4 and divide row 4 by 6.

$\begin{bmatrix} 1 & 0 & 0 & \frac{1}{2} & 0 & 0 \\ 0 & 1 & 0 & 0 & \frac{1}{4} & 0 \\ 0 & 0 & 1 & 0 & 0 & \frac{1}{6} \end{bmatrix}$

$A^{-1} = \begin{bmatrix} \frac{1}{2} & 0 & 0 \\ 0 & \frac{1}{4} & 0 \\ 0 & 0 & \frac{1}{6} \end{bmatrix}$

21. $\begin{bmatrix} 1 & 2 & -1 & 1 & 0 & 0 \\ -2 & 0 & 1 & 0 & 1 & 0 \\ 1 & -1 & 0 & 0 & 0 & 1 \end{bmatrix}$

Replace row 2 with $2R_1 + R_2$.
Replace row 3 with $R_1 - R_3$.

$\begin{bmatrix} 1 & 2 & -1 & 1 & 0 & 0 \\ 0 & 4 & -1 & 2 & 1 & 0 \\ 0 & 3 & -1 & 1 & 0 & -1 \end{bmatrix}$

Replace row 1 with $R_2 - 2R_1$.
Replace row 3 with $-3R_2 + 4R_3$.

$\begin{bmatrix} -2 & 0 & 1 & 0 & 1 & 0 \\ 0 & 4 & -1 & 2 & 1 & 0 \\ 0 & 0 & -1 & -2 & -3 & -4 \end{bmatrix}$

Replace row 1 with $R_3 + R_1$.
Replace row 2 with $R_2 - R_3$.
Replace row 3 with $-R_3$.

$\begin{bmatrix} -2 & 0 & 0 & -2 & -2 & -4 \\ 0 & 4 & 0 & 4 & 4 & 4 \\ 0 & 0 & 1 & 2 & 3 & 4 \end{bmatrix}$

Divide row 1 by -2 and divide row 2 by 4.

$\begin{bmatrix} 1 & 0 & 0 & 1 & 1 & 2 \\ 0 & 1 & 0 & 1 & 1 & 1 \\ 0 & 0 & 1 & 2 & 3 & 4 \end{bmatrix}$

$A^{-1} = \begin{bmatrix} 1 & 1 & 2 \\ 1 & 1 & 1 \\ 2 & 3 & 4 \end{bmatrix}$

23. $\begin{bmatrix} 2 & 2 & -1 & 1 & 0 & 0 \\ 0 & 3 & -1 & 0 & 1 & 0 \\ -1 & -2 & 1 & 0 & 0 & 1 \end{bmatrix} R_1 \leftrightarrow R_3$

$\begin{bmatrix} -1 & -2 & 1 & 0 & 0 & 1 \\ 0 & 3 & -1 & 0 & 1 & 0 \\ 2 & 2 & -1 & 1 & 0 & 0 \end{bmatrix} -1R_1$

$\begin{bmatrix} 1 & 2 & -1 & 0 & 0 & -1 \\ 0 & 3 & -1 & 0 & 1 & 0 \\ 2 & 2 & -1 & 1 & 0 & 0 \end{bmatrix} -2R_1 + R_3$

$\begin{bmatrix} 1 & 2 & -1 & 0 & 0 & -1 \\ 0 & 3 & -1 & 0 & 1 & 0 \\ 0 & -2 & 1 & 1 & 0 & 2 \end{bmatrix} \frac{1}{3}R_2$

$\begin{bmatrix} 1 & 2 & -1 & 0 & 0 & -1 \\ 0 & 1 & -\frac{1}{3} & 0 & \frac{1}{3} & 0 \\ 0 & -2 & 1 & 1 & 0 & 2 \end{bmatrix} \begin{matrix} -2R_2 + R_1 \\ 2R_2 + R_3 \end{matrix}$

$\begin{bmatrix} 1 & 0 & -\frac{1}{3} & 0 & -\frac{2}{3} & -1 \\ 0 & 1 & -\frac{1}{3} & 0 & \frac{1}{3} & 0 \\ 0 & 0 & \frac{1}{3} & 1 & \frac{2}{3} & 2 \end{bmatrix} \begin{matrix} 1R_3 + R_1 \\ 1R_2 + R_1 \end{matrix}$

$\begin{bmatrix} 1 & 0 & 0 & 1 & 0 & 1 \\ 0 & 1 & 0 & 1 & 1 & 2 \\ 0 & 0 & \frac{1}{3} & 1 & \frac{2}{3} & 2 \end{bmatrix} 3R_3$

$\begin{bmatrix} 1 & 0 & 0 & 1 & 0 & 1 \\ 0 & 1 & 0 & 1 & 1 & 2 \\ 0 & 0 & 1 & 3 & 2 & 6 \end{bmatrix}$

$A^{-1} = \begin{bmatrix} 1 & 0 & 1 \\ 1 & 1 & 2 \\ 3 & 2 & 6 \end{bmatrix}$

25.
$$\left[\begin{array}{ccc|ccc} 5 & 0 & 2 & 1 & 0 & 0 \\ 2 & 2 & 1 & 0 & 1 & 0 \\ -3 & 1 & -1 & 0 & 0 & 1 \end{array}\right] \tfrac{1}{5}R_1$$

$$\left[\begin{array}{ccc|ccc} 1 & 0 & \tfrac{2}{5} & \tfrac{1}{5} & 0 & 0 \\ 2 & 2 & 1 & 0 & 1 & 0 \\ -3 & 1 & -1 & 0 & 0 & 1 \end{array}\right] \begin{array}{l} -2R_1 + R_2 \\ 3R_1 + R_3 \end{array}$$

$$\left[\begin{array}{ccc|ccc} 1 & 0 & \tfrac{2}{5} & \tfrac{1}{5} & 0 & 0 \\ 0 & 2 & \tfrac{1}{5} & -\tfrac{2}{5} & 1 & 0 \\ 0 & 1 & \tfrac{1}{5} & \tfrac{3}{5} & 0 & 1 \end{array}\right] R_2 \leftrightarrow R_3$$

$$\left[\begin{array}{ccc|ccc} 1 & 0 & \tfrac{2}{5} & \tfrac{1}{5} & 0 & 0 \\ 0 & 1 & \tfrac{1}{5} & \tfrac{3}{5} & 0 & 1 \\ 0 & 2 & \tfrac{1}{5} & -\tfrac{2}{5} & 1 & 0 \end{array}\right] -2R_2 + R_3$$

$$\left[\begin{array}{ccc|ccc} 1 & 0 & \tfrac{2}{5} & \tfrac{1}{5} & 0 & 0 \\ 0 & 1 & \tfrac{1}{5} & \tfrac{3}{5} & 0 & 1 \\ 0 & 0 & -\tfrac{1}{5} & -\tfrac{8}{5} & 1 & -2 \end{array}\right] \begin{array}{l} 2R_3 + R_1 \\ 1R_3 + R_2 \end{array}$$

$$\left[\begin{array}{ccc|ccc} 1 & 0 & 0 & -3 & 2 & -4 \\ 0 & 1 & 0 & -1 & 1 & -1 \\ 0 & 0 & -\tfrac{1}{5} & -\tfrac{8}{5} & 1 & -2 \end{array}\right] -5R_3$$

$$\left[\begin{array}{ccc|ccc} 1 & 0 & 0 & -3 & 2 & -4 \\ 0 & 1 & 0 & -1 & 1 & -1 \\ 0 & 0 & 1 & 8 & -5 & 10 \end{array}\right]$$

$$A^{-1} = \left[\begin{array}{ccc} -3 & 2 & -4 \\ -1 & 1 & -1 \\ 8 & -5 & 10 \end{array}\right]$$

27.
$$\left[\begin{array}{cccc|cccc} 1 & 0 & 0 & 0 & 1 & 0 & 0 & 0 \\ 0 & -1 & 0 & 0 & 0 & 1 & 0 & 0 \\ 0 & 0 & 3 & 0 & 0 & 0 & 1 & 0 \\ 1 & 0 & 0 & 1 & 0 & 0 & 0 & 1 \end{array}\right] -1R_1 + R_4$$

$$\left[\begin{array}{cccc|cccc} 1 & 0 & 0 & 0 & 1 & 0 & 0 & 0 \\ 0 & -1 & 0 & 0 & 0 & 1 & 0 & 0 \\ 0 & 0 & 3 & 0 & 0 & 0 & 1 & 0 \\ 0 & 0 & 0 & 1 & -1 & 0 & 0 & 1 \end{array}\right] -1R_2$$

$$\left[\begin{array}{cccc|cccc} 1 & 0 & 0 & 0 & 1 & 0 & 0 & 0 \\ 0 & 1 & 0 & 0 & 0 & -1 & 0 & 0 \\ 0 & 0 & 3 & 0 & 0 & 0 & 1 & 0 \\ 0 & 0 & 0 & 1 & -1 & 0 & 0 & 1 \end{array}\right] \tfrac{1}{3}R_3$$

$$\left[\begin{array}{cccc|cccc} 1 & 0 & 0 & 0 & 1 & 0 & 0 & 0 \\ 0 & 1 & 0 & 0 & 0 & -1 & 0 & 0 \\ 0 & 0 & 1 & 0 & 0 & 0 & \tfrac{1}{3} & 0 \\ 0 & 0 & 0 & 1 & -1 & 0 & 0 & 1 \end{array}\right]$$

$$A^{-1} = \left[\begin{array}{cccc} 1 & 0 & 0 & 0 \\ 0 & -1 & 0 & 0 \\ 0 & 0 & \tfrac{1}{3} & 0 \\ -1 & 0 & 0 & 1 \end{array}\right]$$

29. $\left[\begin{array}{cc} 6 & 5 \\ 5 & 4 \end{array}\right]\left[\begin{array}{c} x \\ y \end{array}\right] = \left[\begin{array}{c} 13 \\ 10 \end{array}\right]$

31. $\left[\begin{array}{ccc} 1 & 3 & 4 \\ 1 & 2 & 3 \\ 1 & 4 & 3 \end{array}\right]\left[\begin{array}{c} x \\ y \\ z \end{array}\right] = \left[\begin{array}{c} -3 \\ -2 \\ -6 \end{array}\right]$

33. $4x - 7y = -3$
$2x - 3y = 1$

35. $2x - z = 6$
$3y = 9$
$x + y = 5$

37. a. $\left[\begin{array}{ccc} 2 & 6 & 6 \\ 2 & 7 & 6 \\ 2 & 7 & 7 \end{array}\right]\left[\begin{array}{c} x \\ y \\ z \end{array}\right] = \left[\begin{array}{c} 8 \\ 10 \\ 9 \end{array}\right]$

b. $\begin{bmatrix} \frac{7}{2} & 0 & -3 \\ -1 & 1 & 0 \\ 0 & -1 & 1 \end{bmatrix}\begin{bmatrix} 8 \\ 10 \\ 9 \end{bmatrix} = \begin{bmatrix} 28+0-27 \\ -8+10+0 \\ 0-10+9 \end{bmatrix} = \begin{bmatrix} 1 \\ 2 \\ -1 \end{bmatrix}$

The solution to the system is $\{(1, 2, -1)\}$.

39. a. $\begin{bmatrix} 1 & -1 & 1 \\ 0 & 2 & -1 \\ 2 & 3 & 0 \end{bmatrix}\begin{bmatrix} x \\ y \\ z \end{bmatrix} = \begin{bmatrix} 8 \\ -7 \\ 1 \end{bmatrix}$

b. $\begin{bmatrix} 3 & 3 & -1 \\ -2 & -2 & 1 \\ -4 & -5 & 2 \end{bmatrix}\begin{bmatrix} 8 \\ -7 \\ 1 \end{bmatrix}$

$= \begin{bmatrix} 24-21-1 \\ -16+14+1 \\ -32+35+2 \end{bmatrix} = \begin{bmatrix} 2 \\ -1 \\ 5 \end{bmatrix}$

The solution to the system is $\{(2, -1, 5)\}$.

41. a. $\begin{bmatrix} 1 & -1 & 2 & 0 \\ 0 & 1 & -1 & 1 \\ -1 & 1 & -1 & 2 \\ 0 & -1 & 1 & -2 \end{bmatrix}\begin{bmatrix} w \\ x \\ y \\ z \end{bmatrix} = \begin{bmatrix} -3 \\ 4 \\ 2 \\ -4 \end{bmatrix}$

b. $\begin{bmatrix} 0 & 0 & -1 & -1 \\ 1 & 4 & 1 & 3 \\ 1 & 2 & 1 & 2 \\ 0 & -1 & 0 & -1 \end{bmatrix}\begin{bmatrix} -3 \\ 4 \\ 2 \\ -4 \end{bmatrix}$

$= \begin{bmatrix} 0+0-2+4 \\ -3+16+2-12 \\ -3+8+2-8 \\ 0-4+0+4 \end{bmatrix} = \begin{bmatrix} 2 \\ 3 \\ -1 \\ 0 \end{bmatrix}$

The solution to the system is $\{(2, 3, -1, 0)\}$.

43. The numerical equivalent of HELP is 8, 5, 12, 16.

$\begin{bmatrix} 4 & -1 \\ -3 & 1 \end{bmatrix}\begin{bmatrix} 8 \\ 5 \end{bmatrix} = \begin{bmatrix} 27 \\ -19 \end{bmatrix},$

$\begin{bmatrix} 4 & -1 \\ -3 & 1 \end{bmatrix}\begin{bmatrix} 12 \\ 16 \end{bmatrix} = \begin{bmatrix} 32 \\ -20 \end{bmatrix}$

The encoded message is 27, −19, 32, −20.

$\begin{bmatrix} 1 & 1 \\ 3 & 4 \end{bmatrix}\begin{bmatrix} 27 \\ -19 \end{bmatrix} = \begin{bmatrix} 8 \\ 5 \end{bmatrix}, \begin{bmatrix} 1 & 1 \\ 3 & 4 \end{bmatrix}\begin{bmatrix} 32 \\ -20 \end{bmatrix} = \begin{bmatrix} 12 \\ 16 \end{bmatrix}$

The decoded message is 8, 5, 12, 16 or HELP.

45. $\begin{bmatrix} 1 & -1 & 0 \\ 3 & 0 & 2 \\ -1 & 0 & -1 \end{bmatrix}\begin{bmatrix} 19 & 4 & 1 \\ 5 & 0 & 19 \\ 14 & 3 & 8 \end{bmatrix}$

$= \begin{bmatrix} 19-5+0 & 4+0+0 & 1-19+0 \\ 57+0+28 & 12+0+6 & 3+0+16 \\ -19+0-14 & -4+0-3 & -1+0-8 \end{bmatrix}$

$= \begin{bmatrix} 14 & 4 & -18 \\ 85 & 18 & 19 \\ -33 & -7 & -9 \end{bmatrix}$

The encoded message is 14, 85, −33, 4, 18, −7, −18, 19, −9.

$\begin{bmatrix} 0 & 1 & 2 \\ -1 & 1 & 2 \\ 0 & -1 & -3 \end{bmatrix}\begin{bmatrix} 14 & 4 & -18 \\ 85 & 18 & 19 \\ -33 & -7 & -9 \end{bmatrix}$

$= \begin{bmatrix} 0+85-66 & 0+18-14 & 0+19-18 \\ -14+85-66 & -4+18-14 & 18+19-18 \\ 0-85+99 & 0-18+21 & 0-19+27 \end{bmatrix}$

$= \begin{bmatrix} 19 & 4 & 1 \\ 5 & 0 & 19 \\ 14 & 3 & 8 \end{bmatrix}$

The decoded message is 19, 5, 14, 4, 0, 3, 1, 19, 8 or SEND_CASH

47.–55. Answers may vary.

57. Enter the matrix $\begin{bmatrix} 3 & -1 \\ -2 & 1 \end{bmatrix}$ as $[A]$,

then use $[A]^{-1}$.

$[A]^{-1} = \begin{bmatrix} 1 & 1 \\ 2 & 3 \end{bmatrix}$

Verify this result by showing that

$[A][A]^{-1} = I_2$ and $[A]^{-1}[A] = I_2$.

59. Enter the matrix $\begin{bmatrix} -2 & 1 & -1 \\ -5 & 2 & -1 \\ 3 & -1 & 1 \end{bmatrix}$

as $[A]$, then use $[A]^{-1}$.

$[A]^{-1} = \begin{bmatrix} 1 & 0 & 1 \\ 2 & 1 & 3 \\ -1 & 1 & 1 \end{bmatrix}$

Verify this result by showing that

$[A][A]^{-1} = I_3$ and $[A]^{-1}[A] = I_3$.

61. Enter the matrix $\begin{bmatrix} 7 & -3 & 0 & 2 \\ -2 & 1 & 0 & -1 \\ 4 & 0 & 1 & -2 \\ -1 & 1 & 0 & -1 \end{bmatrix}$ as $[A]$,

then use $[A]^{-1}$. $[A]^{-1} = \begin{bmatrix} 0 & -1 & 0 & 1 \\ -1 & -5 & 0 & 3 \\ -2 & -4 & 1 & -2 \\ -1 & -4 & 0 & 1 \end{bmatrix}$

Verify this result by showing that

$[A][A]^{-1} = I_4$ and $[A]^{-1}[A] = I_4$.

For Problems 46–50, enter the matrix A as $[A]$ and the matrix B as $[B]$ in your graphing utility, then calculate $[A]^{-1}[B]$ to find X.

63. The system is $AX = B$ where

$A = \begin{bmatrix} 1 & -1 & 1 \\ 4 & 2 & 1 \\ 4 & -2 & 1 \end{bmatrix}$, $X = \begin{bmatrix} x \\ y \\ z \end{bmatrix}$, and $B = \begin{bmatrix} -6 \\ 9 \\ -3 \end{bmatrix}$.

$X = \begin{bmatrix} 2 \\ 3 \\ -5 \end{bmatrix}$, so the solution to the system is

$\{(2, 3, -5)\}$.

65. The system is $AX = B$ where

$A = \begin{bmatrix} 3 & -2 & 1 \\ 4 & -5 & 3 \\ 2 & -1 & 5 \end{bmatrix}$, $X = \begin{bmatrix} x \\ y \\ z \end{bmatrix}$, and $B = \begin{bmatrix} -2 \\ -9 \\ -5 \end{bmatrix}$.

$X = \begin{bmatrix} 1 \\ 2 \\ -1 \end{bmatrix}$ so the solution to the system is

$\{(1, 2, -1)\}$.

67. The system is $AX = B$ where

$A = \begin{bmatrix} 1 & 0 & -3 & 0 & 1 \\ 0 & 1 & 0 & 1 & 0 \\ 0 & 0 & 1 & 0 & 1 \\ 1 & 1 & -1 & 4 & 0 \\ 1 & 1 & 1 & 1 & 1 \end{bmatrix}$, $X = \begin{bmatrix} v \\ w \\ x \\ y \\ z \end{bmatrix}$ and

$B = \begin{bmatrix} -3 \\ -1 \\ 7 \\ -8 \\ 8 \end{bmatrix}$. $X = \begin{bmatrix} 2 \\ 1 \\ 3 \\ -2 \\ 4 \end{bmatrix}$, so the solution to the

system is $\{(2, 1, 3, -2, 4)\}$.

69. Answers may vary.

71. a. False; only square matrices have inverses.

b. False; $\begin{bmatrix} 3 & 6 \\ 2 & 4 \end{bmatrix}$ does not have an inverse since $(3)(4) - (6)(2) = 12 - 12 = 0$ and division by zero is undefined.

c. True; $\begin{bmatrix} 1 & 2 \\ 2 & 3 \end{bmatrix} + \begin{bmatrix} 2 & 4 \\ 0 & 1 \end{bmatrix} = \begin{bmatrix} 3 & 6 \\ 2 & 4 \end{bmatrix}$ and

$\begin{bmatrix} 1 & 2 \\ 2 & 3 \end{bmatrix}^{-1} = \begin{bmatrix} -3 & 2 \\ 2 & -1 \end{bmatrix}$,

$\begin{bmatrix} 2 & 4 \\ 0 & 1 \end{bmatrix}^{-1} = \begin{bmatrix} \frac{1}{2} & -2 \\ 0 & 1 \end{bmatrix}$ while $\begin{bmatrix} 3 & 6 \\ 2 & 4 \end{bmatrix}$

does not have an inverse. [See part (b).]

d. False; to solve the matrix equation for X, multiply the inverse of A and B $(A^{-1}B)$ provided the inverse of A exists.

(c) is true.

73. Answers may vary.

75. Using the statement before problems 9–14, we want to find values for a such that $(1)(4) - (a + 1)(a - 2) = 0$.

$(1)(4) - (a + 1)(a - 2) = 4 - (a^2 - a - 2)$

$\qquad = -a^2 + a + 6$

$0 = -a^2 + a + 6$

$0 = a^2 - a - 6$

$0 = (a - 3)(a + 2)$

$a = 3, -2$

Section 6.5

Check Point Exercises

1. a. $\begin{vmatrix} 10 & 9 \\ 6 & 5 \end{vmatrix} = 10 \cdot 5 - 6 \cdot 9 = 50 - 54 = -4$

b. $\begin{vmatrix} 4 & 3 \\ -5 & -8 \end{vmatrix} = 4 \cdot (-8) - (-5) \cdot (3)$

$\qquad\qquad = -32 + 15 = -17$

2. $5x + 4y = 12$

$3x - 6y = 24$

$$D = \begin{vmatrix} 5 & 4 \\ 3 & -6 \end{vmatrix} = 5 \cdot (-6) - 3 \cdot 4$$

$$= -30 - 12 = -42$$

$$D_x = \begin{vmatrix} 12 & 4 \\ 24 & -6 \end{vmatrix} = 12(-6) - 24(4)$$

$$= -72 - 96 = -168$$

$$D_y = \begin{vmatrix} 5 & 12 \\ 3 & 24 \end{vmatrix} = 5(24) - 3(12)$$

$$= 120 - 36 = 84$$

Thus, $x = \dfrac{D_x}{D} = \dfrac{-168}{-42} = 4$

$$y = \dfrac{D_y}{D} = \dfrac{84}{-42} = -2$$

The solution set is $\{(4, -2)\}$.

3. $\begin{bmatrix} 2 & 1 & 7 \\ -5 & 6 & 0 \\ -4 & 3 & 1 \end{bmatrix}$

The minor for 2 is $\begin{vmatrix} 6 & 0 \\ 3 & 1 \end{vmatrix}$.

The minor for -5 is $\begin{vmatrix} 1 & 7 \\ 3 & 1 \end{vmatrix}$.

The minor for -4 is $\begin{vmatrix} 1 & 7 \\ 6 & 0 \end{vmatrix}$.

$$\begin{bmatrix} 2 & 1 & 7 \\ -5 & 6 & 0 \\ -4 & 3 & 1 \end{bmatrix} = 2\begin{vmatrix} 6 & 0 \\ 3 & 1 \end{vmatrix} - (-5)\begin{vmatrix} 1 & 7 \\ 3 & 1 \end{vmatrix} - 4\begin{vmatrix} 1 & 7 \\ 6 & 0 \end{vmatrix}$$

$$= 2(6 \cdot 1 - 3 \cdot 0) + 5(1 \cdot 1 - 3 \cdot 7) - 4(1 \cdot 0 - 6 \cdot 7)$$

$$= 2(6 - 0) + 5(1 - 21) - 4(0 - 42)$$

$$= 12 - 100 + 168$$

$$= 80$$

4. $\begin{vmatrix} 6 & 4 & 0 \\ -3 & -5 & 3 \\ 1 & 2 & 0 \end{vmatrix} = 0\begin{vmatrix} -3 & -5 \\ 1 & 2 \end{vmatrix} - 3\begin{vmatrix} 6 & 4 \\ 1 & 2 \end{vmatrix} + 0\begin{vmatrix} 6 & 4 \\ -3 & -5 \end{vmatrix}$

$$= 0 - 3(6 \cdot 2 - 1 \cdot 4) + 0$$
$$= -3(12 - 4)$$
$$= -3(8)$$
$$= -24$$

5. $3x - 2y + z = 16$
$2x + 3y - z = -9$
$x + 4y + 3z = 2$

$D = \begin{vmatrix} 3 & -2 & 1 \\ 2 & 3 & -1 \\ 1 & 4 & 3 \end{vmatrix}; \ D_x = \begin{vmatrix} 16 & -2 & 1 \\ -9 & 3 & -1 \\ 2 & 4 & 3 \end{vmatrix}; \ D_y = \begin{vmatrix} 3 & 16 & 1 \\ 2 & -9 & -1 \\ 1 & 2 & 3 \end{vmatrix}; \ D_z = \begin{vmatrix} 3 & -2 & 16 \\ 2 & 3 & -9 \\ 1 & 4 & 2 \end{vmatrix}$

$D = \begin{vmatrix} 3 & -2 & 1 \\ 2 & 3 & -1 \\ 1 & 4 & 3 \end{vmatrix} = 3\begin{vmatrix} 3 & -1 \\ 4 & 3 \end{vmatrix} - 2\begin{vmatrix} -2 & 1 \\ 4 & 3 \end{vmatrix} + 1\begin{vmatrix} -2 & 1 \\ 3 & -1 \end{vmatrix}$

$$= 3[(3) \cdot 3 - 4 \cdot (-1)] - 2[(-2) \cdot 3 - 4 \cdot 1] + 1[(-2) \cdot (-1) - (3) \cdot 1]$$
$$= 3(9 + 4) - 2(-6 - 4) + 1(2 - 3)$$
$$= 39 + 20 - 1$$
$$= 58$$

$D_x = \begin{vmatrix} 16 & -2 & 1 \\ -9 & 3 & -1 \\ 2 & 4 & 3 \end{vmatrix} = 1\begin{vmatrix} -9 & 3 \\ 2 & 4 \end{vmatrix} - (-1)\begin{vmatrix} 16 & -2 \\ 2 & 4 \end{vmatrix} + 3\begin{vmatrix} 16 & -2 \\ -9 & 3 \end{vmatrix}$

$$= 1[(-9) \cdot 4 - 2 \cdot (3)] + 1[16 \cdot 4 - 2(-2)] + 3[16 \cdot (3) - (-9) \cdot (-2)]$$
$$= 1(-36 - 6) + 1(64 + 4) + 3(48 - 18)$$
$$= -42 + 68 + 90$$
$$= 116$$

$D_y = \begin{vmatrix} 3 & 16 & 1 \\ 2 & -9 & -1 \\ 1 & 2 & 3 \end{vmatrix} = 3\begin{vmatrix} -9 & -1 \\ 2 & 3 \end{vmatrix} - 2\begin{vmatrix} 16 & 1 \\ 2 & 3 \end{vmatrix} + 1\begin{vmatrix} 16 & 1 \\ -9 & -1 \end{vmatrix}$

$$= 3[(-9) \cdot 3 - 2 \cdot (-1)] - 2[16 \cdot 3 - 2 \cdot 1] + 1[16(-1) - (-9) \cdot 1]$$
$$= 3(-27 + 2) - 2(48 - 2) + 1(-16 + 9)$$
$$= -75 - 92 - 7$$
$$= -174$$

$$D_z = \begin{vmatrix} 3 & -2 & 16 \\ 2 & 3 & -9 \\ 1 & 4 & 2 \end{vmatrix} = 3\begin{vmatrix} 3 & -9 \\ 4 & 2 \end{vmatrix} - 2\begin{vmatrix} -2 & 16 \\ 4 & 2 \end{vmatrix} + 1\begin{vmatrix} -2 & 16 \\ 3 & -9 \end{vmatrix}$$

$$= 3[(3)2 - 4(-9)] - 2[(-2)2 - 4 \cdot 16] + 1[(-2)(-9) - (3) \cdot 16]$$

$$= 3(6 + 36) - 2(-4 - 64) + 1(18 - 48)$$

$$= 126 + 136 - 30$$

$$= 232$$

$$x = \frac{D_x}{D} = \frac{116}{58} = 2$$

$$y = \frac{D_y}{D} = \frac{-174}{58} = -3$$

$$z = \frac{D_z}{D} = \frac{232}{58} = 4$$

The solution to the system is $\{(2, -3, 4)\}$.

6. $|A| = \begin{vmatrix} 0 & 4 & 0 & -3 \\ -1 & 1 & 5 & 2 \\ 1 & -2 & 0 & 6 \\ 3 & 0 & 0 & 1 \end{vmatrix} = (-1)^{2+3} 5 \begin{vmatrix} 0 & 4 & -3 \\ 1 & -2 & 6 \\ 3 & 0 & 1 \end{vmatrix} = -5 \begin{vmatrix} 0 & 4 & -3 \\ 1 & -2 & 6 \\ 3 & 0 & 1 \end{vmatrix}$

Evaluate the third-order determinant to get $|A| = -5(50) = -250$.

Exercise Set 6.5

1. $\begin{vmatrix} 5 & 7 \\ 2 & 3 \end{vmatrix} = 5 \cdot 3 - 2 \cdot 7 = 15 - 14 = 1$

3. $\begin{vmatrix} -4 & 1 \\ 5 & 6 \end{vmatrix} = (-4)6 - 5 \cdot 1 = -24 - 5 = -29$

5. $\begin{vmatrix} -7 & 14 \\ 2 & -4 \end{vmatrix} = (-7)(-4) - 2(14) = 28 - 28 = 0$

7. $\begin{vmatrix} -5 & -1 \\ -2 & -7 \end{vmatrix} = (-5)(-7) - (-2)(-1) = 35 - 2 = 33$

9. $\begin{vmatrix} \frac{1}{2} & \frac{1}{2} \\ \frac{1}{8} & -\frac{3}{4} \end{vmatrix} = \frac{1}{2}\left(-\frac{3}{4}\right) - \frac{1}{8} \cdot \frac{1}{2} = -\frac{3}{8} - \frac{1}{16} = -\frac{7}{16}$

11. $D = \begin{vmatrix} 1 & 1 \\ 1 & -1 \end{vmatrix} = -1 - 1 = -2$

$D_x = \begin{vmatrix} 7 & 1 \\ 3 & -1 \end{vmatrix} = -7 - 3 = -10$

$D_y = \begin{vmatrix} 1 & 7 \\ 1 & 3 \end{vmatrix} = 3 - 7 = -4$

$x = \dfrac{D_x}{D} = \dfrac{-10}{-2} = 5$

$y = \dfrac{D_y}{D} = \dfrac{-4}{-2} = 2$

The solution set is $\{(5, 2)\}$.

13. $D = \begin{vmatrix} 12 & 3 \\ 2 & -3 \end{vmatrix} = -36 - 6 = -42$

$D_x = \begin{vmatrix} 15 & 3 \\ 13 & -3 \end{vmatrix} = -45 - 39 = -84$

$D_y = \begin{vmatrix} 12 & 15 \\ 2 & 13 \end{vmatrix} = 156 - 30 = 126$

$x = \dfrac{D_x}{D} = \dfrac{-84}{-42} = 2$

$y = \dfrac{D_y}{D} = \dfrac{126}{-42} = -3$

The solution set is $\{(2, -3)\}$.

15. $D = \begin{vmatrix} 4 & -5 \\ 2 & 3 \end{vmatrix} = 12 - (-10) = 22$

$D_x = \begin{vmatrix} 17 & -5 \\ 3 & 3 \end{vmatrix} = 51 - (-15) = 66$

$D_y = \begin{vmatrix} 4 & 17 \\ 2 & 3 \end{vmatrix} = 12 - 34 = -22$

$x = \dfrac{D_x}{D} = \dfrac{66}{22} = 3$

$y = \dfrac{D_y}{D} = \dfrac{-22}{22} = -1$

The solution set is $\{(3, -1)\}$.

17. $D = \begin{vmatrix} 1 & 2 \\ 5 & 10 \end{vmatrix} = 10 - 10 = 0$

$D_x = \begin{vmatrix} 3 & 2 \\ 15 & 10 \end{vmatrix} = 30 - 30 = 0$

$D_y = \begin{vmatrix} 1 & 3 \\ 5 & 15 \end{vmatrix} = 15 - 15 = 0$

Because all 3 determinants equal zero, the system is dependent.

19. $D = \begin{vmatrix} 3 & -4 \\ 2 & 2 \end{vmatrix} = 6 - (-8) = 14$

$D_x = \begin{vmatrix} 4 & -4 \\ 12 & 2 \end{vmatrix} = 8 - (-48) = 56$

$D_y = \begin{vmatrix} 3 & 4 \\ 2 & 12 \end{vmatrix} = 36 - 8 = 28$

$x = \dfrac{D_x}{D} = \dfrac{56}{14} = 4$

$y = \dfrac{D_y}{D} = \dfrac{28}{14} = 2$

The solution set is $\{(4, 2)\}$.

21. $D = \begin{vmatrix} 2 & -3 \\ 5 & 4 \end{vmatrix} = 8 - (-15) = 23$

$D_x = \begin{vmatrix} 2 & -3 \\ 51 & 4 \end{vmatrix} = 8 - (-153) = 161$

$D_y = \begin{vmatrix} 2 & 2 \\ 5 & 51 \end{vmatrix} = 102 - 10 = 92$

$x = \dfrac{D_x}{D} = \dfrac{161}{23} = 7$

$y = \dfrac{D_y}{D} = \dfrac{92}{23} = 4$

The solution set is $\{(7, 4)\}$.

23. $D = \begin{vmatrix} 3 & 3 \\ 2 & 2 \end{vmatrix} = 6 - 6 = 0$

$D_x = \begin{vmatrix} 2 & 3 \\ 3 & 2 \end{vmatrix} = 4 - 9 = -5$

$D_y = \begin{vmatrix} 3 & 2 \\ 2 & 3 \end{vmatrix} = 9 - 4 = 5$

Because $D = 0$ but D_x or $D_y \neq 0$, the system is inconsistent.

$$= -5(12 + 3) = -5(15)$$
$$= -75$$

25. Write the equations in standard form.
$$3x + 4y = 16$$
$$6x + 8y = 32$$

$$D = \begin{bmatrix} 3 & 4 \\ 6 & 8 \end{bmatrix} = 24 - 24 = 0$$

$$D_x = \begin{bmatrix} 16 & 4 \\ 32 & 8 \end{bmatrix} = 128 - 128 = 0$$

$$D_y = \begin{bmatrix} 3 & 16 \\ 6 & 32 \end{bmatrix} = 96 - 69 = 0$$

Since all determinants are zero, the system is dependent.

27.

$$\begin{vmatrix} 3 & 0 & 0 \\ 2 & 1 & -5 \\ -2 & 5 & -1 \end{vmatrix} = 3\begin{vmatrix} 1 & -5 \\ 5 & -1 \end{vmatrix} - 0\begin{vmatrix} 2 & -5 \\ -2 & -1 \end{vmatrix} + 0\begin{vmatrix} 2 & 1 \\ -2 & 5 \end{vmatrix}$$

$$= 3[(1)(-1) - (5)(-5)]$$
$$= 3(-1 + 25) = 3(24)$$
$$= 72$$

29.

$$\begin{vmatrix} 3 & 1 & 0 \\ -3 & 4 & 0 \\ -1 & 3 & -5 \end{vmatrix} = 0\begin{vmatrix} -3 & 4 \\ -1 & 3 \end{vmatrix} - 0\begin{vmatrix} 3 & 1 \\ -1 & 3 \end{vmatrix} + (-5)\begin{vmatrix} 3 & 1 \\ -3 & 4 \end{vmatrix}$$

$$= -5[3 \cdot 4 - (-3)(1)]$$

31. $\begin{vmatrix} 1 & 1 & 1 \\ 2 & 2 & 2 \\ -3 & 4 & -5 \end{vmatrix} - 2R_1 + R_2$

$$\begin{vmatrix} 1 & 1 & 1 \\ 0 & 0 & 0 \\ -3 & 4 & -5 \end{vmatrix} = 0$$

33. $D = \begin{vmatrix} 1 & 1 & 1 \\ 2 & -1 & 1 \\ -1 & 3 & -1 \end{vmatrix}$

$= \begin{vmatrix} -1 & 1 \\ 3 & -1 \end{vmatrix} - \begin{vmatrix} 2 & 1 \\ -1 & -1 \end{vmatrix} + \begin{vmatrix} 2 & -1 \\ -1 & 3 \end{vmatrix}$

$= (1-3) - [-2 - (-1)] + (6-1)$

$= -2 - (-1) + 5 = -2 + 1 + 5 = 4$

$D_x = \begin{vmatrix} 0 & 1 & 1 \\ -1 & -1 & 1 \\ -8 & 3 & -1 \end{vmatrix} = (-1)\begin{vmatrix} -1 & 1 \\ -8 & -1 \end{vmatrix} + \begin{vmatrix} -1 & -1 \\ -8 & 3 \end{vmatrix}$

$= (-1)[1 - (-8)] + (-3 - 8) = (-1)(9) - 11$

$= -20$

$D_y = \begin{vmatrix} 1 & 0 & 1 \\ 2 & -1 & 1 \\ -1 & -8 & -1 \end{vmatrix} = \begin{vmatrix} -1 & 1 \\ -8 & -1 \end{vmatrix} + \begin{vmatrix} 2 & -1 \\ -1 & -8 \end{vmatrix}$

$= 1 - (-8) + (-16 - 1) = 1 + 8 - 17 = -8$

$D_z = \begin{vmatrix} 1 & 1 & 0 \\ 2 & -1 & -1 \\ -1 & 3 & -8 \end{vmatrix} = 1\begin{vmatrix} -1 & -1 \\ 3 & -8 \end{vmatrix} - 1\begin{vmatrix} 2 & -1 \\ -1 & -8 \end{vmatrix}$

$= 8 - (-3) - 1(-16 - 1) = 11 + 17 = 28$

$x = \dfrac{D_x}{D} = \dfrac{-20}{4} = -5$

$y = \dfrac{D_y}{D} = \dfrac{-8}{4} = -2$

$z = \dfrac{D_z}{D} = \dfrac{28}{4} = 7$

The solution to the system is $\{(-5, -2, 7)\}$.

35. $D = \begin{vmatrix} 4 & -5 & -6 \\ 1 & -2 & -5 \\ 2 & -1 & 0 \end{vmatrix} = 2\begin{vmatrix} -5 & -6 \\ -2 & -5 \end{vmatrix} - (-1)\begin{vmatrix} 4 & -6 \\ 1 & -5 \end{vmatrix}$

$= 2(25 - 12) + [-20 - (-6)] = 2(13) + (-14)$

$= 26 - 14 = 12$

$D_x = \begin{vmatrix} -1 & -5 & -6 \\ -12 & -2 & -5 \\ 7 & -1 & 0 \end{vmatrix}$

$= 7\begin{vmatrix} -5 & -6 \\ -2 & -5 \end{vmatrix} - (-1)\begin{vmatrix} -1 & -6 \\ -12 & -5 \end{vmatrix}$

$= 7(25 - 12) + (5 - 72) = 7(13) - 67$

$= 91 - 67 = 24$

$D_y = \begin{vmatrix} 4 & -1 & -6 \\ 1 & -12 & -5 \\ 2 & 7 & 0 \end{vmatrix} = 2\begin{vmatrix} -1 & -6 \\ -12 & -5 \end{vmatrix} - 7\begin{vmatrix} 4 & -6 \\ 1 & -5 \end{vmatrix}$

$= 2(5 - 72) - 7[-20 - (-6)]$

$= 2(-67) - 7(-14) = -134 + 98 = -36$

$D_z = \begin{vmatrix} 4 & -5 & -1 \\ 1 & -2 & -12 \\ 2 & -1 & 7 \end{vmatrix}$

$= 4\begin{vmatrix} -2 & -12 \\ -1 & 7 \end{vmatrix} - (-5)\begin{vmatrix} 1 & -12 \\ 2 & 7 \end{vmatrix} + (-1)\begin{vmatrix} 1 & -2 \\ 2 & -1 \end{vmatrix}$

$= 4(-14 - 12) + 5[7 - (-24)] - [-1 - (-4)]$

$= 4(-26) + 5(31) - (3) = -104 + 155 - 3 = 48$

$x = \dfrac{D_x}{D} = \dfrac{24}{12} = 2,\ y = \dfrac{D_y}{D} = \dfrac{-36}{12} = -3,$

$z = \dfrac{D_z}{D} = \dfrac{48}{12} = 4$

The solution set is $\{(2, -3, 4)\}$.

37. $D = \begin{vmatrix} 1 & 1 & 1 \\ 1 & -2 & 1 \\ 1 & 3 & 2 \end{vmatrix} = 1\begin{vmatrix} -2 & 1 \\ 3 & 2 \end{vmatrix} - 1\begin{vmatrix} 1 & 1 \\ 1 & 2 \end{vmatrix} + 1\begin{vmatrix} 1 & -2 \\ 1 & 3 \end{vmatrix}$

$= -4 - 3 - (2 - 1) + [3 - (-2)]$

$= -7 - 1 + 5 = -3$

$D_x = \begin{vmatrix} 4 & 1 & 1 \\ 7 & -2 & 1 \\ 4 & 3 & 2 \end{vmatrix}$

$$= 4\begin{vmatrix} -2 & 1 \\ 3 & 2 \end{vmatrix} - 1\begin{vmatrix} 7 & 1 \\ 4 & 2 \end{vmatrix} + 1\begin{vmatrix} 7 & -2 \\ 4 & 3 \end{vmatrix}$$

$$= 4(-4 - 3) - (14 - 4) + [21 - (-8)]$$

$$= 4(-7) - 10 + 29 = -28 + 19 = -9$$

$$D_y = \begin{vmatrix} 1 & 4 & 1 \\ 1 & 7 & 1 \\ 1 & 4 & 2 \end{vmatrix} = 1\begin{vmatrix} 7 & 1 \\ 4 & 2 \end{vmatrix} - 1\begin{vmatrix} 4 & 1 \\ 4 & 2 \end{vmatrix} + 1\begin{vmatrix} 4 & 1 \\ 7 & 1 \end{vmatrix}$$

$$= 14 - 4 - (8 - 4) + (4 - 7) = 10 - 4 - 3 = 3$$

$$D_z = \begin{vmatrix} 1 & 1 & 4 \\ 1 & -2 & 7 \\ 1 & 3 & 4 \end{vmatrix}$$

$$= 1\begin{vmatrix} -2 & 7 \\ 3 & 4 \end{vmatrix} - 1\begin{vmatrix} 1 & 4 \\ 3 & 4 \end{vmatrix} + 1\begin{vmatrix} 1 & 4 \\ -2 & 7 \end{vmatrix}$$

$$= -8 - 21 - (4 - 12) + [7 - (-8)]$$

$$= -29 + 8 + 15 = -6$$

$$x = \frac{D_x}{D} = \frac{-9}{-3} = 3, \; y = \frac{D_y}{D} = \frac{3}{-3} = -1,$$

$$z = \frac{D_z}{D} = \frac{-6}{-3} = 2$$

The solution set is $\{3, -1, 2\}$.

$$D_x = \begin{vmatrix} 4 & 0 & 2 \\ 5 & 2 & -1 \\ 13 & 3 & 0 \end{vmatrix} = 4\begin{vmatrix} 2 & -1 \\ 3 & 0 \end{vmatrix} + 2\begin{vmatrix} 5 & 2 \\ 13 & 3 \end{vmatrix}$$

$$= 4[0 - (-3)] + 2(15 - 26)$$

$$= 4(3) + 2(-11) = 12 - 22 = -10$$

$$D_y = \begin{vmatrix} 1 & 4 & 2 \\ 0 & 5 & -1 \\ 2 & 13 & 0 \end{vmatrix} = \begin{vmatrix} 5 & -1 \\ 13 & 0 \end{vmatrix} + 2\begin{vmatrix} 4 & 2 \\ 5 & -1 \end{vmatrix}$$

$$= 0 - (-13) + 2(-4 - 10)$$

$$= 13 + 2(-14) = 13 - 28 = -15$$

$$D_z = \begin{vmatrix} 1 & 0 & 4 \\ 0 & 2 & 5 \\ 2 & 3 & 13 \end{vmatrix} = \begin{vmatrix} 2 & 5 \\ 3 & 13 \end{vmatrix} + 4\begin{vmatrix} 0 & 2 \\ 2 & 3 \end{vmatrix}$$

$$= 26 - 15 + 4(0 - 4) = 11 + 4(-4)$$

$$= 11 - 16 = -5$$

$$x = \frac{D_x}{D} = \frac{-10}{-5} = 2, \; y = \frac{D_y}{D} = \frac{-15}{-5} = 3,$$

$$z = \frac{D_z}{D} = \frac{-5}{-5} = 1$$

The solution set is $\{(2, 3, 1)\}$.

39. $D = \begin{vmatrix} 1 & 0 & 2 \\ 0 & 2 & -1 \\ 2 & 3 & 0 \end{vmatrix} = \begin{vmatrix} 2 & -1 \\ 3 & 0 \end{vmatrix} + 2\begin{vmatrix} 0 & 2 \\ 2 & 3 \end{vmatrix}$

$$= 0 - (-3) + 2(0 - 4) = 3 - 8 = -5$$

41. $\begin{vmatrix} 4 & 2 & 8 & -7 \\ -2 & 0 & 4 & 1 \\ 5 & 0 & 0 & 5 \\ 4 & 0 & 0 & -1 \end{vmatrix} = -2\begin{vmatrix} -2 & 4 & 1 \\ 5 & 0 & 5 \\ 4 & 0 & -1 \end{vmatrix} + 0\begin{vmatrix} 4 & 8 & -7 \\ 5 & 0 & 5 \\ 4 & 0 & -1 \end{vmatrix} - 0\begin{vmatrix} 4 & 8 & -7 \\ -2 & 4 & 1 \\ 4 & 0 & -1 \end{vmatrix} + 0\begin{vmatrix} 4 & 8 & -7 \\ -2 & 4 & 1 \\ 5 & 0 & 5 \end{vmatrix}$

$$= (-2)\left[(-4)\begin{vmatrix} 5 & 5 \\ 4 & -1 \end{vmatrix} + 0\begin{vmatrix} -2 & 1 \\ 4 & -1 \end{vmatrix} - 0\begin{vmatrix} -2 & 1 \\ 5 & 5 \end{vmatrix} \right] = (-2)(-4)[5(-1) - 4 \cdot 5] = 8(-5 - 20) = 8(-25) = -200$$

43. $\begin{vmatrix} -2 & -3 & 3 & 5 \\ 1 & -4 & 0 & 0 \\ 1 & 2 & 2 & -3 \\ 2 & 0 & 1 & 1 \end{vmatrix} = -1\begin{vmatrix} -3 & 3 & 5 \\ 2 & 2 & -3 \\ 0 & 1 & 1 \end{vmatrix} + (-4)\begin{vmatrix} -2 & 3 & 5 \\ 1 & 2 & -3 \\ 2 & 1 & 1 \end{vmatrix} - 0\begin{vmatrix} -2 & -3 & 5 \\ 1 & 2 & -3 \\ 2 & 0 & 1 \end{vmatrix} + 0\begin{vmatrix} -2 & -3 & 3 \\ 1 & 2 & 2 \\ 2 & 0 & 1 \end{vmatrix}$

$$= (-1)\left[0\begin{vmatrix} 3 & 5 \\ 2 & -3 \end{vmatrix} - 1\begin{vmatrix} -3 & 5 \\ 2 & -3 \end{vmatrix} + 1\begin{vmatrix} -3 & 3 \\ 2 & 2 \end{vmatrix} \right] - 4\left[2\begin{vmatrix} 3 & 5 \\ 2 & -3 \end{vmatrix} - 1\begin{vmatrix} -2 & 5 \\ 1 & -3 \end{vmatrix} + 1\begin{vmatrix} -2 & 3 \\ 1 & 2 \end{vmatrix} \right] = (-1)$$

383

$\{(-1)[(-3)(-3) - 2 \cdot 5] + [(-3)(2) - 2 \cdot 3]\} - 4\{2[3(-3) - 2 \cdot 5] - [(-2)(-3) - 1 \cdot 5] + [(-2)(2) - 1 \cdot 3]\}$

$= (-1)[(-1)(9 - 10) + (-6 - 6)] - 4[2(-9 - 10) - (6 - 5) + (-4 - 3)]$

$= (-1)[(-1)(-1) - 12] - 4[2(-19) - 1 - 7]$

$= (-1)(1 - 12) - 4(-38 - 8) = (-1)(-11) - 4(-46) = 11 + 184 = 195$

45. $\text{Area} = \pm\dfrac{1}{2}\begin{vmatrix} 3 & -5 & 1 \\ 2 & 6 & 1 \\ -3 & 5 & 1 \end{vmatrix} = \pm\dfrac{1}{2}\begin{vmatrix} 3 & -5 & 1 \\ -1 & 11 & 0 \\ -6 & 10 & 0 \end{vmatrix} = \pm\dfrac{1}{2}\begin{vmatrix} -1 & 11 \\ -6 & 10 \end{vmatrix} = \pm\dfrac{1}{2}[-10 - (-66)] = \pm\dfrac{1}{2}(56) = 28$

The area is 28 square units.

The slope of the line through $(3, -5)$ and $(-3, 5)$ is $m = \dfrac{5 - (-5)}{-3 - 3} = \dfrac{10}{-6} = -\dfrac{5}{3}$.

The equation of the line is $y - (-5) = -\dfrac{5}{3}(x - 3)$ or $y = -\dfrac{5}{3}x$.

The line perpendicular to $y = -\dfrac{5}{3}x$ through $(2, 6)$ has equation $y - 6 = \dfrac{3}{5}(x - 2)$ or $y = \dfrac{3}{5}x + \dfrac{24}{5}$.

These lines intersect where $-\dfrac{5}{3}x = \dfrac{3}{5}x + \dfrac{24}{5}$.

$-\dfrac{36}{17} = x$ and

$-\dfrac{24}{5} = \dfrac{34}{15}x$ $y = -\dfrac{5}{3}\left(-\dfrac{36}{17}\right) = \dfrac{60}{17}$

Using the side connecting $(3, -5)$ and $(-3, 5)$ as the base, the height is the distance from $(2, 6)$ to $\left(-\dfrac{36}{17}, \dfrac{60}{17}\right)$.

$b = \sqrt{[3 - (-3)]^2 + (-5 - 5)^2}$

$= \sqrt{36 + 100} = \sqrt{136} = 2\sqrt{34}$

$h = \sqrt{\left[2 - \left(-\dfrac{36}{17}\right)\right]^2 + \left(6 - \dfrac{60}{17}\right)^2}$

$= \sqrt{\dfrac{4900}{289} + \dfrac{1764}{289}} = \dfrac{14\sqrt{34}}{17}$

$\dfrac{1}{2}bh = \dfrac{1}{2}\left(2\sqrt{34}\right)\left(\dfrac{14\sqrt{34}}{17}\right) = \dfrac{14(34)}{17}$

$= 14(2) = 28$ square units

47. $\begin{vmatrix} 3 & -1 & 1 \\ 0 & -3 & 1 \\ 12 & 5 & 1 \end{vmatrix} = \begin{vmatrix} 3 & -1 & 1 \\ -3 & -2 & 0 \\ 9 & 6 & 0 \end{vmatrix} = \begin{vmatrix} -3 & -2 \\ 9 & 6 \end{vmatrix}$

$= -18 - (-18) = 0$

Yes, the points are collinear.

49. $\begin{vmatrix} x & y & 1 \\ 3 & -5 & 1 \\ -2 & 6 & 1 \end{vmatrix} = x\begin{vmatrix} -5 & 1 \\ 6 & 1 \end{vmatrix} - y\begin{vmatrix} 3 & 1 \\ -2 & 1 \end{vmatrix} + \begin{vmatrix} 3 & -5 \\ -2 & 6 \end{vmatrix}$

$= x(-5 - 6) - y[3 - (-2)] + (18 - 10)$

$= -11x - 5y + 8$

The equation of the line is $-11x - 5y + 8 = 0$.

The equation of the line in slope-intercept form is $y = -\dfrac{11}{5}x + \dfrac{8}{5}$.

51.–59. Answers may vary.

61. Input the matrix as [*A*], then use det[*A*] to find the determinant.

$$\begin{vmatrix} 8 & 2 & 6 & -1 & 0 \\ 2 & 0 & -3 & 4 & 7 \\ 2 & 1 & -3 & 6 & -5 \\ -1 & 2 & 1 & 5 & -1 \\ 4 & 5 & -2 & 3 & -8 \end{vmatrix} = 13{,}200$$

63. a.

$$\begin{vmatrix} a & a \\ 0 & a \end{vmatrix} = a^2 - 0 = a^2$$

b.

$$\begin{vmatrix} a & a & a \\ 0 & a & a \\ 0 & 0 & a \end{vmatrix} = a \begin{vmatrix} a & a \\ 0 & a \end{vmatrix} - 0 + 0$$

$$= a\left(a^2\right) = a^3$$

c.

$$\begin{vmatrix} a & a & a & a \\ 0 & a & a & a \\ 0 & 0 & a & a \\ 0 & 0 & 0 & a \end{vmatrix} = a \begin{vmatrix} a & a & a \\ 0 & a & a \\ 0 & 0 & a \end{vmatrix} - 0 + 0 - 0$$

$$= a\left(a^3\right) = a^4$$

d. Each determinant has zeros below the main diagonal and *a*'s everywhere else.

e. Each determinant equals *a* raised to the power equal to the order of the determinant.

65. The sign of the value is changed when 2 columns are interchanged in a 2nd order determinant.

67. Evaluate the determinate and write the equation in slope intercept form.

$$\begin{vmatrix} x & y & 1 \\ x_1 & y_1 & 1 \\ x_2 & y_2 & 1 \end{vmatrix} = 0$$

$$x\begin{vmatrix} y_1 & 1 \\ y_2 & 1 \end{vmatrix} - y\begin{vmatrix} x_1 & 1 \\ x_2 & 1 \end{vmatrix} + 1\begin{vmatrix} x_1 & y_1 \\ x_2 & y_2 \end{vmatrix} = 0$$

$$x\left(y_1 - y_2\right) - y\left(x_1 - x_2\right) + x_1 y_2 - x_2 y_1 = 0$$

$$-y\left(x_1 - x_2\right) = -x(y_1 - y_2) + x_2 y_1 - x_1 y_2$$

$$y(x_2 - x_1) = x(y_2 - y_1) + x_2 y_1 - x_1 y_2$$

$$y = \frac{y_2 - y_1}{x_2 - x_1} x + \frac{x_2 y_1 - x_1 y_2}{x_2 - x_1}$$

$$m = \frac{y_2 - y_1}{x_2 - x_1} \qquad b = \frac{x_2 y_1 - x_1 y_2}{x_2 - x_1}$$

Write the slope-point equation of the line the in point slope form.

$$y - y_1 = \frac{y_2 - y_1}{x_2 - x_1}(x - x_1)$$

$$y - y_1 = \frac{y_2 - y_1}{x_2 - x_1} x + \frac{-x_1 y_2 + x_1 y_1}{x_2 - x_1}$$

$$y = \frac{y_2 - y_1}{x_2 - x_1} x + \frac{-x_1 y_2 + x_1 y_1}{x_2 - x_1} + y_1$$

$$y = \frac{y_2 - y_1}{x_2 - x_1} x + \frac{-x_1 y_2 + x_1 y_1}{x_2 - x_1} + \frac{x_2 y_1 - x_1 y_1}{x_2 - x_1}$$

$$y = \frac{y_2 - y_1}{x_2 - x_1} x + \frac{x_2 y_1 - x_1 y_2}{x_2 - x_1}$$

$$m = \frac{y_2 - y_1}{x_2 - x_1} \qquad b = \frac{x_2 y_1 - x_1 y_2}{x_2 - x_1}$$

Since both forms give the same slope and *y*-intercept, the determinant does give the equation of the line.

Chapter 7

Section 7.1

Check Point Exercises

1. $\dfrac{x^2}{36} + \dfrac{y^2}{9} = 1$

$a^2 = 36,\ a = 6$

$b^2 = 9,\ b = 3$

$c^2 = a^2 - b^2 = 36 - 9 = 27$

$c = \sqrt{27} = 3\sqrt{3}$

The foci are located at $(-3\sqrt{3},\ 0)$ and $(3\sqrt{3},\ 0)$.

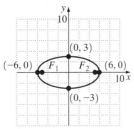

2. $16x^2 + 9y^2 = 144$

$\dfrac{16x^2}{144} + \dfrac{9y^2}{144} = \dfrac{144}{144}$

$\dfrac{x^2}{9} + \dfrac{y^2}{16} = 1$

$a^2 = 16,\ a = 4$

$b^2 = 9,\ b = 3$

$c^2 = a^2 - b^2 = 16 - 9 = 7$

$c = \sqrt{7}$

The foci are located at $(0,\ -\sqrt{7})$ and $(0,\ \sqrt{7})$.

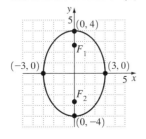

3. $c^2 = 4,\ a^2 = 9$

$b^2 = a^2 - c^2 = 9 - 4 = 5$

$\dfrac{x^2}{9} + \dfrac{y^2}{5} = 1$

4. $\dfrac{(x+1)^2}{9} + \dfrac{(y-2)^2}{4} = 1$

$a^2 = 9,\ a = 3$

$b^2 = 4,\ b = 2$

center at $(-1, 2)$

$c^2 = a^2 - b^2$

$c^2 = 9 - 4$

$c^2 = 5$

$c = \sqrt{5}$

The foci are located at

$(-1 - \sqrt{5},\ 2)$ and $(-1 + \sqrt{5},\ 2)$.

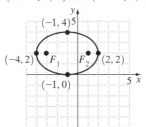

5. $a = 20,\ b = 10$

$\dfrac{x^2}{400} + \dfrac{y^2}{100} = 1$

Let $x = 6$

$$\frac{6^2}{400} + \frac{y^2}{100} = 1$$

$$400\left(\frac{36}{400} + \frac{y^2}{100}\right) = 400(1)$$

$$36 + 4y^2 = 400$$

$$4y^2 = 364$$

$$y^2 = 91$$

$$y = \sqrt{91} \approx 9.54$$

Yes, the truck needs only 9 feet so it will clear.

Exercise Set 7.1

1. $\dfrac{x^2}{16} + \dfrac{y^2}{4} = 1$

   $a^2 = 16, \ a = 4$

   $b^2 = 4, \ b = 2$

   $c^2 = a^2 - b^2 = 16 - 4 = 12$

   $c = \sqrt{12} = 2\sqrt{3}$

   The foci are located at $(-2\sqrt{3}, 0)$ and $(2\sqrt{3}, 0)$.

   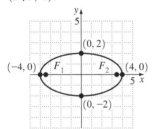

3. $\dfrac{x^2}{9} + \dfrac{y^2}{36} = 1$

   $a^2 = 36, \ a = 6$

   $b^2 = 9, \ b = 3$

   $c^2 = a^2 - b^2 = 36 - 9 = 27$

   $c = \sqrt{27} = 3\sqrt{3}$

   The foci are located at $(0, -3\sqrt{3})$ and

$(0, 3\sqrt{3})$.

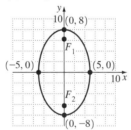

5. $\dfrac{x^2}{25} + \dfrac{y^2}{64} = 1$

   $a^2 = 64, \ a = 8$

   $b^2 = 25, \ b = 5$

   $c^2 = a^2 - b^2 = 64 - 25 = 39$

   $c = \sqrt{39}$

   The foci are located at $(0, -\sqrt{39})$ and $(0, \sqrt{39})$.

7. $\dfrac{x^2}{49} + \dfrac{y^2}{81} = 1$

   $a^2 = 81, \ a = 9$

   $b^2 = 49, \ b = 7$

   $c^2 = a^2 - b^2 = 81 - 49 = 32$

   $c = \sqrt{32} = 4\sqrt{2}$

   The foci are located at $(0, -4\sqrt{2})$ and

$(0,\ 4\sqrt{2})$.

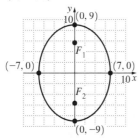

9. $\dfrac{x^2}{\frac{9}{4}} + \dfrac{y^2}{\frac{25}{4}} = 1$

$c^2 = \dfrac{25}{4} - \dfrac{9}{4}$

$c^2 = \dfrac{16}{4}$

$c^2 = 4$

$c = 2$

The foci are located at (0, 2) and (0, -2).

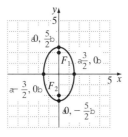

11. $x^2 = 1 - 4y^2$

$x^2 + 4y^2 = 1$

$x^2 + \dfrac{y^2}{\frac{1}{4}} = 1$

$c^2 = 1 - \dfrac{1}{4}$

$c^2 = \dfrac{3}{4}$

$c = \pm\dfrac{\sqrt{3}}{2}$

$c \approx \pm 0.9$

The foci are located at $\left(\dfrac{\sqrt{3}}{2}, 0\right)$ and $\left(-\dfrac{\sqrt{3}}{2}, 0\right)$.

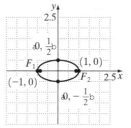

13. $25x^2 + 4y^2 = 100$

$\dfrac{25x^2}{100} + \dfrac{4y^2}{100} = \dfrac{100}{100}$

$\dfrac{x^2}{4} + \dfrac{y^2}{25} = 1$

$a^2 = 25,\ a = 5$

$b^2 = 4,\ b = 2$

$c^2 = a^2 = b^2 = 25 - 4 = 21$

The foci are located at $(0,\ -\sqrt{21})$ and $(0,\ \sqrt{21})$.

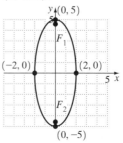

15. $4x^2 + 16y^2 = 64$

$$\frac{x^2}{16} + \frac{y^2}{4} = 1$$

$$a^2 = 16, a = 4$$

$$b^2 = 4, b = 2$$

$$c^2 = 16 - 4$$

$$c^2 = 12$$

$$c = \pm\sqrt{12}$$

$$c = \pm 2\sqrt{3}$$

$$c \approx \pm 3.5$$

The foci are located at $(2\sqrt{3}, 0)$ and $(-2\sqrt{3}, 0)$.

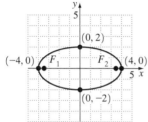

17.
$$7x^2 = 35 - 5y^2$$

$$7x^2 + 5y^2 = 35$$

$$\frac{x^2}{5} + \frac{y^2}{7} = 1$$

$$a^2 = 7, a = \sqrt{7}$$

$$b^2 = 5, b = \sqrt{5}$$

$$c^2 = 7 - 5$$

$$c^2 = 2$$

$$c = \pm\sqrt{2}$$

$$c \approx \pm 1.4$$

The foci are located at $(0, \sqrt{2})$ and $(0, -\sqrt{2})$.

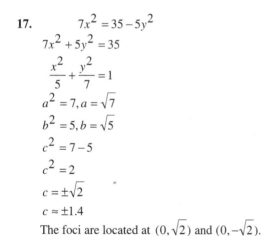

19. $a^2 = 4$, $b^2 = 1$, center at $(0, 0)$

$$\frac{x^2}{4} + \frac{y^2}{1} = 1$$

$$c^2 = a^2 - b^2 = 4 - 1 = 3$$

$$c = \sqrt{3}$$

The foci are at $(-\sqrt{3}, 0)$ and $(\sqrt{3}, 0)$.

21. $a^2 = 4$, $b^2 = 1$,
center: $(0, 0)$

$$\frac{x^2}{1} + \frac{y^2}{4} = 1$$

$$c^2 = a^2 - b^2 = 4 - 1 = 3$$

$$c = \sqrt{3}$$

The foci are at $(0, \sqrt{3})$ and $(0, -\sqrt{3})$.

23. $\dfrac{(x+1)^2}{4} + (y-1)^2 = 1$

$$a^2 = 4, \quad b^2 = 1$$

$$c^2 = 4 - 1$$

$$c^2 = 3$$

$$c = \pm\sqrt{3}$$

The foci are located at

$(-1 + \sqrt{3}, 1)$ and $(-1 - \sqrt{3}, 1)$.

25. $c^2 = 25$, $a^2 = 64$

$$b^2 = a^2 - c^2 = 64 - 25 = 39$$

$$\frac{x^2}{64} + \frac{y^2}{39} = 1$$

27. $c^2 = 16$, $a^2 = 49$

$$b^2 = a^2 - c^2 = 49 - 16 = 33$$

$$\frac{x^2}{33} + \frac{y^2}{49} = 1$$

29. $c^2 = 4$, $b^2 = 9$

$$a^2 = b^2 + c^2 = 9 + 4 = 13$$

$$\frac{x^2}{13} + \frac{y^2}{9} = 1$$

31. $2a = 8$, $a = 4$, $a^2 = 16$

$2b = 4$, $b = 2$, $b^2 = 4$

$$\frac{x^2}{16} + \frac{y^2}{4} = 1$$

33. $2a = 10$, $a = 5$, $a^2 = 25$

$2b = 4$, $b = 2$, $b^2 = 4$

$$\frac{(x+2)^2}{4} + \frac{(y-3)^2}{25} = 1$$

35. length of the major axis = $9 - 3 = 6$

$2a = 6$, $a = 3$ major axis is vertical

length of the minor axis = $9 - 5 = 4$

$2b = 4$, $b = 2$

Center is at $(7, 6)$.

$$\frac{(x-7)^2}{4} + \frac{(y-6)^2}{9} = 1$$

37. $\dfrac{(x-2)^2}{9} + \dfrac{(y-1)^2}{4} = 1$

$a^2 = 9$, $a = 3$

$b^2 = 4$, $b = 2$

center: $(2, 1)$

$c^2 = a^2 - b^2 = 9 - 4 = 5$

$c = \sqrt{5}$

The foci are at $(2 - \sqrt{5}, 1)$ and $(2 + \sqrt{5}, 1)$.

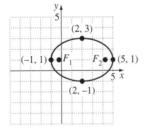

39. $(x+3)^2 + 4(y-2)^2 = 16$

$$\frac{(x+3)^2}{16} + \frac{4(y-2)^2}{16} = \frac{16}{16}$$

$$\frac{(x+3)^2}{16} + \frac{(y-2)^2}{4} = 1$$

$a^2 = 16$, $a = 4$

$b^2 = 4$, $b = 2$

center: $(-3, 2)$

$c^2 = a^2 - b^2 = 16 - 4 = 12$

$c = \sqrt{12} = 2\sqrt{3}$

The foci are at $(-3 - 2\sqrt{3}, 2)$ and $(-3 + 2\sqrt{3}, 2)$.

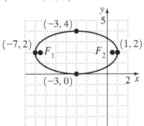

41. $\dfrac{(x-4)^2}{9} + \dfrac{(y+2)^2}{25} = 1$

$a^2 = 25$, $a = 5$

$b^2 = 9$, $b = 3$

center: $(4, -2)$

$c^2 = a^2 - b^2 = 25 - 9 = 16$

$c = 4$

The foci are at $(4, 2)$ and $(4, -6)$.

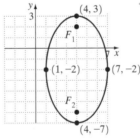

43. $\dfrac{x^2}{25} + \dfrac{(y-2)^2}{36} = 1$

$a^2 = 36,\ a = 6$

$b^2 = 25,\ b = 5$

center: $(0, 2)$

$c^2 = a^2 - b^2 = 36 - 25 = 11$

$c = \sqrt{11}$

The foci are at $(0,\, 2+\sqrt{11})$ and $(0,\, 2-\sqrt{11})$.

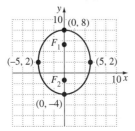

45. $\dfrac{(x+3)^2}{9} + (y-2)^2 = 1$

$a^2 = 9,\ a = 3$

$b^2 = 1,\ b = 1$

center: $(-3, 2)$

$c^2 = a^2 - b^2 = 9 - 1 = 8$

$c = \sqrt{8} = 2\sqrt{2}$

The foci are at $(-3 - 2\sqrt{2},\ 2)$ and $(-3 + 2\sqrt{2},\ 2)$.

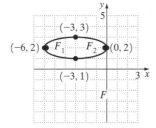

47. $c^2 = 5 - 2$

$c^2 = 3$

$c = \pm\sqrt{3}$

$c \approx \pm 1.7$

The foci are located at $(1, -3+\sqrt{3})$ and $(1, -3-\sqrt{3})$.

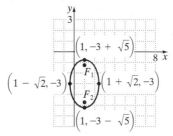

49. $9(x-1)^2 + 4(y+3)^2 = 36$

$\dfrac{9(x-1)^2}{36} + \dfrac{4(y+3)^2}{36} = \dfrac{36}{36}$

$\dfrac{(x-1)^2}{4} + \dfrac{(y+3)^2}{9} = 1$

$a^2 = 9,\ a = 3$

$b^2 = 4,\ b = 2$

center: $(1, -3)$

$c^2 = a^2 - b^2 = 9 - 4 = 5$

$c = \sqrt{5}$

The foci are at $(1,\ -3+\sqrt{5})$ and $(1,\ -3-\sqrt{5})$.

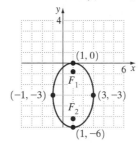

51. $9x^2 + 25y^2 - 36x + 50y - 164 = 0$

$$(9x^2 - 36x) + (25y^2 + 50y) = 164$$

$$9(x^2 - 4x) + 25(y^2 + 2y) = 164$$

$$9(x^2 - 4x + 4) + 25(y^2 + 2y + 1)$$
$$= 164 + 36 + 25$$

$$9(x - 2)^2 + 25(y + 1)^2 = 225$$

$$\frac{9(x-2)^2}{225} + \frac{25(y+1)^2}{225} = \frac{225}{225}$$

$$\frac{(x-2)^2}{25} + \frac{(y+1)^2}{9} = 1$$

center: $(2, -1)$

$a^2 = 25,\ a = 5$

$b^2 = 9,\ b = 3$

$c^2 = a^2 - b^2 = 25 - 9 = 16$

$c = 4$

The foci are at $(-2, -1)$ and $(6, -1)$.

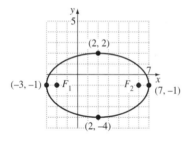

53. $9x^2 + 16y^2 - 18x + 64y - 71 = 0$

$$(9x^2 - 18x) + (16y^2 + 64y) = 71$$

$$9(x^2 - 2x) + 16(y^2 + 4y) = 71$$

$$9(x^2 - 2x + 1) + 16(y^2 + 4y + 4)$$
$$= 71 + 9 + 64$$

$$9(x - 1)^2 + 16(y + 2)^2 = 144$$

$$\frac{9(x-1)^2}{144} + \frac{16(y+2)^2}{144} = \frac{144}{144}$$

$$\frac{(x-1)^2}{16} + \frac{(y+2)^2}{9} = 1$$

center: $(1, -2)$

$a^2 = 16,\ a = 4$

$b^2 = 9,\ b = 3$

$c^2 = a^2 - b^2 = 16 - 9 = 7$

$c = \sqrt{7}$

The foci are at

$(1 - \sqrt{7}, -2)$ and $(1 + \sqrt{7}, -2)$.

55.

$$4x^2 + y^2 + 16x - 6y - 39 = 0$$

$$(4x^2 + 16x) + (y^2 - 6y) = 39$$

$$4(x^2 + 4x) + (y^2 - 6y) = 39$$

$$4(x^2 + 4x + 4) + (y^2 - 6y + 9) = 39 + 16 + 9$$

$$4(x + 2)^2 + (y - 3)^2 = 64$$

$$\frac{4(x+2)^2}{64} + \frac{(y-3)^2}{64} = \frac{64}{64}$$

$$\frac{(x+2)^2}{16} + \frac{(y-3)^2}{64} = 1$$

center: $(-2, 3)$

$a^2 = 64,\ a = 8$

$b^2 = 16,\ b = 4$

$c^2 = a^2 - b^2 = 64 - 16 = 48$

$c = \sqrt{48} = 4\sqrt{3}$

The foci are at $(-2, 3 + 4\sqrt{3})$ and

$\left(-2,\ 3-4\sqrt{3}\right).$

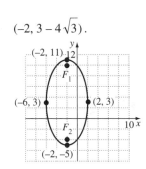

57. $a = 15,\ b = 10$

$$\frac{x^2}{225} + \frac{y^2}{100} = 1$$

Let $x = 4$

$$\frac{4^2}{225} + \frac{y^2}{100} = 1$$

$$900\left(\frac{16}{225} + \frac{y^2}{100}\right) = 900(1)$$

$$64 + 9y^2 = 900$$

$$9y^2 = 836$$

$$y = \sqrt{\frac{836}{9}} \approx 9.64$$

Yes, the truck only needs 7 feet so it will clear.

59. a. $a = 48,\ a^2 = 2304$

$b = 23,\ b^2 = 529$

$$\frac{x^2}{2304} + \frac{y^2}{529} = 1$$

b. $c^2 = a^2 - b^2 = 2304 - 529 = 1775$

$c = \sqrt{1775} \approx 42.13$

He situated his desk about 42 feet from the center of the ellipse, along the major axis.

61.–65. Answers may vary.

67. Exercise 1

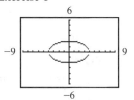

Exercise 3

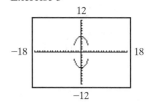

Exercise 5

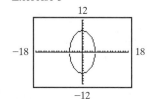

Exercise 7

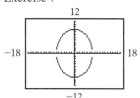

Exercise 9

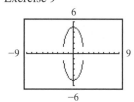

69. Exercise 51

$$25y^2 + 50y + 9x^2 - 36x - 164 = 0$$

$$y = \frac{-50 \pm \sqrt{(50)^2 - 4(25)(9x^2 - 36x - 164)}}{2(25)}$$

$$= \frac{-50 \pm \sqrt{2500 - 900x^2 + 3600x - 16,400}}{50}$$

$$= \frac{-50 \pm \sqrt{-900x^2 + 3600x + 18,900}}{50}$$

$$= \frac{-50 \pm \sqrt{900\left(-x^2 + 2x + 21\right)}}{50}$$

$$= \frac{-50 \pm 30\sqrt{-x^2 + 4x + 21}}{50}$$

$$y = \frac{-5 \pm 3\sqrt{-x^2 + 4x + 21}}{5}$$

71. $a = 6$, $a^2 = 36$

$$\frac{x^2}{b^2} + \frac{y^2}{36} = 1$$

When $x = 2$ and $y = -4$,

$$\frac{2^2}{b^2} + \frac{(-4)^2}{36} = 1$$

$$\frac{4}{b^2} + \frac{16}{36} = 1$$

$$\frac{4}{b^2} = \frac{5}{9}$$

$$36 = 5b^2$$

$$b^2 = \frac{36}{5}$$

$$\frac{x^2}{\frac{36}{5}} + \frac{y^2}{36} = 1$$

73. The large circle has radius 5 with center $(0, 0)$. Its equation is $x^2 + y^2 = 25$. The small circle has radius 3 with center $(0, 0)$. Its equation is $x^2 + y^2 = 9$.

75. $\sqrt{(x+c)^2 + y^2} + \sqrt{(x-c)^2 + y^2} = 2a$

$$\sqrt{(x+c)^2 + y^2} = 2a - \sqrt{(x-c)^2 + y^2}$$

$$(x+c)^2 + y^2 = 4a^2 - 4a\sqrt{(x-c)^2 + y^2} + (x-c)^2 + y^2$$

$$x^2 + 2xc + c^2 = 4a^2 - 4a\sqrt{(x-c)^2 + y^2} + x^2 - 2cx + c^2$$

$$4xc - 4a^2 = -4a\sqrt{(x-c)^2 + y^2}$$

$$xc - a^2 = -a\sqrt{(x-c)^2 + y^2}$$

$$x^2c^2 - 2cx + a^4 = a^2(x^2 - 2cx + c^2 + y^2)$$

$$x^2c^2 - 2a^2cx + a^4 = a^2x^2 - 2a^2cx + a^2c^2 + a^2y^2$$

$$a^4 - a^2c^2 = a^2x^2 - x^2c^2 + a^2y^2$$

$$a^2\left(a^2 - c^2\right) = (a^2 - c^2)x^2 + a^2y^2$$

394

Section 7.2

Check Point Exercises

1. **a.** $a^2 = 25,\ a = 5$

   vertices: (5, 0) and (–5, 0)

   $b^2 = 16$

   $c^2 = a^2 + b^2 = 25 + 16 = 41$

   $c = \sqrt{41}$

   The foci are at

   $(\sqrt{41},\ 0)$ and $(-\sqrt{41},\ 0)$.

   b. $a^2 = 25,\ a = 5$

   vertices: (0, 5) and (0, –5)

   $b^2 = 16$

   $c^2 = a^2 + b^2 = 25 + 16 = 41$

   $c = \sqrt{41}$

   The foci are at

   $(0,\ \sqrt{41})$ and $(0,\ -\sqrt{41})$.

2. $a = 3,\ c = 5$

   $b^2 = c^2 - a^2 = 25 - 9 = 16$

   $\dfrac{y^2}{9} - \dfrac{x^2}{16} = 1$

3. $\dfrac{x^2}{36} - \dfrac{y^2}{9} = 1$

   $a^2 = 36,\ a = 6$

   The vertices are (6, 0) and (-6, 0).

   $b^2 = 9,\ b = 3$

   asymptotes: $y = \pm \dfrac{b}{a} x = \pm \dfrac{3}{6} x = \pm \dfrac{1}{2} x$

   $c^2 = a^2 + b^2 = 36 + 9 = 45$

   $c = \sqrt{45} = 3\sqrt{5}$

   The foci are at $(-3\sqrt{5},\ 0)$ and $(3\sqrt{5},\ 0)$.

   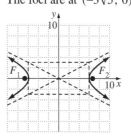

4. $y^2 - 4x^2 = 4$

   $\dfrac{y^2}{4} - \dfrac{4x^2}{4} = \dfrac{4}{4}$

   $\dfrac{y^2}{4} - x^2 = 1$

   $a^2 = 4,\ a = 2$

   The vertices are (0, 2) and (0, –2).

   $b^2 = 1,\ b = 1$

   asymptotes: $y = \pm \dfrac{a}{b} x = \pm 2x$

   $c^2 = a^2 + b^2 = 4 + 1 = 5$

   $c = \sqrt{5}$

The foci are at $(0, \sqrt{5})$ and $(0, -\sqrt{5})$.

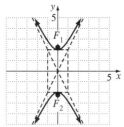

5. $\dfrac{(x-3)^2}{4} - \dfrac{(y-1)^2}{1} = 1$

center at $(3, 1)$

$a^2 = 4, \ a = 2$

$b^2 = 1, \ b = 1$

The vertices are $(1, 1)$ and $(5, 1)$.

asymptotes: $y - 1 = \pm\dfrac{1}{2}(x-3)$

$c^2 = a^2 + b^2 = 4 + 1 = 5$

$c = \sqrt{5}$

The foci are at $(3 - \sqrt{5}, 1)$ and $(3 + \sqrt{5}, 1)$.

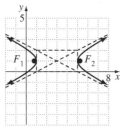

6. $c = 5280$

$2a = 3300, a = 1650$

$b^2 = c^2 - a^2 = 5280^2 - 1650^2 = 25,155,900$

The explosion occurred somewhere at the right branch of the hyperbola given by

$$\frac{x^2}{2,722,500} - \frac{y^2}{25,155,900} = 1.$$

Exercise Set 7.2

1. $a^2 = 4, a = 2$

The vertices are $(2, 0)$ and $(-2, 0)$.

$b^2 = 1$

$c^2 = a^2 + b^2 = 4 + 1 = 5$

$c = \sqrt{5}$

The foci are located at $(\sqrt{5}, 0)$ and $(-\sqrt{5}, 0)$.

graph (b)

3. $a^2 = 4, \ a = 2$

The vertices are $(0, 2)$ and $(0, -2)$.

$b^2 = 1$

$c^2 = a^2 + b^2 = 4 + 1 = 5$

$c = \sqrt{5}$

The foci are located at $(0, \sqrt{5})$ and $(0, -\sqrt{5})$.

graph (a)

5. $a = 1, c = 3$

$b^2 = c^2 - a^2 = 9 - 1 = 8$

$y^2 - \dfrac{x^2}{8} = 1$

7. $a = 3, c = 4$

$b^2 = c^2 - a^2 = 16 - 9 = 7$

$\dfrac{x^2}{9} - \dfrac{y^2}{7} = 1$

9. $2a = 6 - (-6)$

$2a = 12$

$a = 6$

$\dfrac{a}{b} = 2$

$\dfrac{6}{b} = 2$

$6 = 2b$

$3 = b$

Transverse axis is vertical.

$\dfrac{y^2}{36} - \dfrac{x^2}{9} = 1$

11. $a = 2, c = 7 - 4 = 3$

$2^2 + b^2 = 3^2$

$4 + b^2 = 9$

$b^2 = 5$

Transverse axis is horizontal.

$\dfrac{(x-4)^2}{4} - \dfrac{(y+2)^2}{5} = 1$

13. $\dfrac{x^2}{9} - \dfrac{y^2}{25} = 1$

$a^2 = 9, a = 3$

$b^2 = 25, b = 5$

vertices: $(3, 0)$ and $(-3, 0)$

asymptotes: $y = \pm\dfrac{b}{a}x = \pm\dfrac{5}{3}x$

$c^2 = a^2 + b^2 = 9 + 25 = 34$

$c = \sqrt{34}$ on x-axis

The foci are at $(\sqrt{34},\ 0)$ and $(-\sqrt{34},\ 0)$.

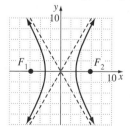

15. $\dfrac{x^2}{100} - \dfrac{y^2}{64} = 1$

$a^2 = 100, a = 10$

$b^2 = 64, b = 8$

vertices: $(10, 0)$ and $(-10, 0)$

asymptotes: $y = \pm\dfrac{b}{a}x = \pm\dfrac{8}{10}x$

or $y = \pm\dfrac{4}{5}x$

$c^2 = a^2 + b^2 = 100 + 64 = 164$

$c = \sqrt{164} = 2\sqrt{41}$ on x-axis

The foci are at $(2\sqrt{41},\ 0)$ and $(-2\sqrt{41},\ 0)$.

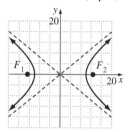

17. $\dfrac{y^2}{16} - \dfrac{x^2}{36} = 1$

$a^2 = 16, a = 4$

$b^2 = 36, b = 6$

vertices: $(0, 4)$ and $(0, -4)$

asymptotes: $y = \pm\dfrac{a}{b}x = \pm\dfrac{4}{6}x$

or $y = \pm\dfrac{2}{3}x$

$c^2 = a^2 + b^2 = 16 + 36 = 52$

$c = \sqrt{52} = 2\sqrt{13}$ on y-axis

The foci are at $(0,\ 2\sqrt{13})$ and $(0,\ -2\sqrt{13})$.

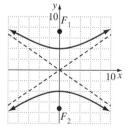

19. $\dfrac{y^2}{\frac{1}{4}} - x^2 = 1$

$a^2 = \dfrac{1}{4}, a = \dfrac{1}{2}$

$b^2 = 1, b = 1$

$c^2 = a^2 + b^2$

$c^2 = \dfrac{1}{4} + 1$

$c^2 = \dfrac{5}{4}$

$c = \pm\dfrac{\sqrt{5}}{2}$

$c \approx \pm 1.1$

The foci are located at

$\left(0, \dfrac{\sqrt{5}}{2}\right)$ and $\left(0, -\dfrac{\sqrt{5}}{2}\right)$.

asymptotes: $y = \pm\dfrac{\frac{1}{2}}{1}x$

$y = \pm\dfrac{1}{2}x$

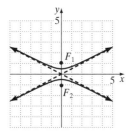

21. $9x^2 - 4y^2 = 36$

$\dfrac{9x^2}{36} - \dfrac{4y^2}{36} = \dfrac{36}{36}$

$\dfrac{x^2}{4} - \dfrac{y^2}{9} = 1$

$a^2 = 4, a = 2$

$b^2 = 9, b = 3$

vertices: $(2, 0)$ and $(-2, 0)$

asymptotes: $y = \pm\dfrac{b}{a}x = \pm\dfrac{3}{2}x$

$c^2 = a^2 + b^2 = 4 + 9 = 13$

$c = \sqrt{13}$ on x-axis

The foci are at $(\sqrt{13}, 0)$ and $(-\sqrt{13}, 0)$.

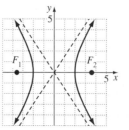

23. $9y^2 - 25x^2 = 225$

$\dfrac{9y^2}{225} - \dfrac{25x^2}{225} = \dfrac{225}{225}$

$\dfrac{y^2}{25} - \dfrac{x^2}{9} = 1$

$a^2 = 25, a = 5$

$b^2 = 9, b = 3$

vertices: $(0, 5)$ and $(0, -5)$

asymptotes: $y = \pm\dfrac{a}{b}x = \pm\dfrac{5}{3}x$

$c^2 = a^2 + b^2 = 25 + 9 = 34$

$c = \sqrt{34}$ on y-axis

The foci are at $(0, \sqrt{34})$ and $(0, -\sqrt{34})$.

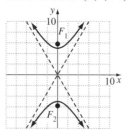

25. $y^2 = x^2 - 2$

$2 = x^2 - y^2$

$1 = \dfrac{x^2}{2} - \dfrac{y^2}{2}$

$a^2 = 2, a = \sqrt{2}$

$b^2 = 2, b = \sqrt{2}$

$c^2 = 2 + 2$

$c^2 = 4$

$c = 2$

The foci are located at $(2,0)$ and $(-2, 0)$.

asymptotes: $y = \pm \dfrac{\sqrt{2}}{\sqrt{2}} x$

$y = \pm x$

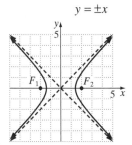

27. $a = 3, b = 5$

$\dfrac{x^2}{9} - \dfrac{y^2}{25} = 1$

29. $a = 2, b = 3$

$\dfrac{y^2}{4} - \dfrac{x^2}{9} = 1$

31. Center $(2, -3)$, $a = 2$, $b = 3$

$\dfrac{(x-2)^2}{4} - \dfrac{(y+3)^2}{9} = 1$

33. $\dfrac{(x+4)^2}{9} - \dfrac{(y+3)^2}{16} = 1$

center: $(-4, -3)$

$a^2 = 9, a = 3$

$b^2 = 16, b = 4$

vertices: $(-7, -3)$ and $(-1, -3)$

asymptotes: $y + 3 = \pm \dfrac{4}{3}(x + 4)$

$c^2 = a^2 + b^2 = 9 + 16 = 25$

$c = \pm 5$ parallel to x-axis

The foci are at $(-9, -3)$ and $(1, -3)$.

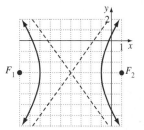

35. $\dfrac{(x+3)^2}{25} - \dfrac{y^2}{16} = 1$

center: $(-3, 0)$

$a^2 = 25, \ a = 5$

$b^2 = 16, \ b = 4$

vertices: $(2, 0)$ and $(-8, 0)$

asymptotes: $y = \pm \dfrac{4}{5}(x + 3)$

$c^2 = a^2 + b^2 = 25 + 16 = 41$

$c = \sqrt{41}$

The foci are at $(-3 + \sqrt{41}, \ 0)$ and $(-3 - \sqrt{41}, \ 0)$.

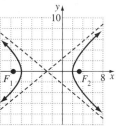

37. $\dfrac{(y+2)^2}{4} - \dfrac{(x-1)^2}{16} = 1$

center: $(1, -2)$

$a^2 = 4, \ a = 2$

$b^2 = 16, \ b = 4$

vertices: $(1, 0)$ and $(1, -4)$

asymptotes: $y + 2 = \pm\dfrac{1}{2}(x - 1)$

$c^2 = a^2 + b^2 = 4 + 16 = 20$

$c = \sqrt{20} = 2\sqrt{5}$ parallel to y-axis

The foci are at $(1, -2 + 2\sqrt{5})$ and

$(1, -2 - 2\sqrt{5})$.

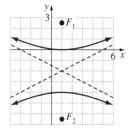

39. $(x - 3)^2 - 4(y + 3)^2 = 4$

$\dfrac{(x-3)^2}{4} - \dfrac{4(y+3)^2}{4} = \dfrac{4}{4}$

$\dfrac{(x-3)^2}{4} - (y+3)^2 = 1$

center: $(3, -3)$

$a^2 = 4,\ a = 2$

$b^2 = 1,\ b = 1$

vertices: $(1, -3)$ and $(5, -3)$

asymptotes: $y + 3 = \pm\dfrac{1}{2}(x - 3)$

$c^2 = a^2 + b^2 = 4 + 1 = 5$

$c = \sqrt{5}$

The foci are at $(3 + \sqrt{5}, -3)$ and

$(3 - \sqrt{5}, -3)$.

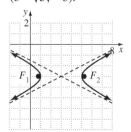

41. $(x - 1)^2 - (y - 2)^2 = 3$

$\dfrac{(x-1)^2}{3} - \dfrac{(y-2)^2}{3} = 1$

center: $(1, 2)$

$a^2 = 3,\ a = \sqrt{3}$

$b^2 = ,\ b = \sqrt{3}$

vertices: $(-1, 2)$ and $(3, 2)$

asymptotes: $y - 2 = \pm(x - 1)$

$c^2 = a^2 + b^2 = 3 + 3 = 6$

$c = \sqrt{6}$ parallel to y-axis

The foci are at $(1 + \sqrt{6}, 2)$ and $(1 - \sqrt{6}, 2)$.

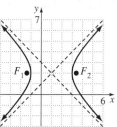

43. $x^2 - y^2 - 2x - 4y - 4 = 0$

$(x^2 - 2x) - (y^2 + 4y) = 4$

$(x^2 - 2x + 1) - (y^2 + 4y + 4) = 4 + 1 - 4$

$(x - 1)^2 - (y + 2)^2 = 1$

center: $(1, -2)$

$a^2 = 1,\ a = 1$

$b^2 = 1,\ b = 1$

$c^2 = a^2 + b^2 = 1 + 1 = 2$

$c = \sqrt{2}$

asymptotes: $y + 2 = \pm(x - 1)$

The foci are at $(1 + \sqrt{2}, -2)$ and

$(1 - \sqrt{2}, -2)$.

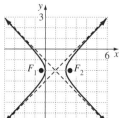

45. $16x^2 - y^2 + 64x - 2y + 67 = 0$

$(16x^2 + 64x) - (y^2 + 2y) = -67$

$16(x^2 + 4x + 4) - (y^2 + 2y + 1)$

$$= -67 + 64 - 1$$

$16(x+2)^2 - (y+1)^2 = -4$

$$\frac{16(x+2)^2}{-4} - \frac{(y+1)^2}{-4} = \frac{-4}{-4}$$

$$\frac{(y+1)^2}{4} - \frac{(x+2)^2}{\frac{1}{4}} = 1$$

center: $(-2, -1)$

$a^2 = 4$, $a = 2$

$b^2 = \dfrac{1}{4}$, $b = \dfrac{1}{2}$

$c^2 = a^2 + b^2 = 4 + \dfrac{1}{4} = \dfrac{17}{4}$

$c = \sqrt{\dfrac{17}{4}} = \sqrt{4.25}$

asymptotes: $(y+1) = \pm \dfrac{2}{\frac{1}{2}}(x+2)$

$y + 1 = \pm 4(x+2)$

The foci are at $\left(-2, -1 + \sqrt{4.25}\right)$ and $\left(-2, -1 - \sqrt{4.25}\right)$.

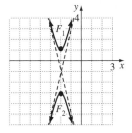

47. $4x^2 - 9y^2 - 16x + 54y - 101 = 0$

$(4x^2 - 16x) - (9y^2 - 54y) = 101$

$4(x^2 - 4x + 4) - 9(y^2 - 6y + 9)$

$$= 101 + 16 - 81$$

$4(x-2)^2 - 9(y-3)^2 = 36$

$$\frac{(x-2)^2}{9} - \frac{(y-3)^2}{4} = 1$$

center: $(2, 3)$

$a^2 = 9$, $a = 3$

$b^2 = 4$, $b = 2$

$c^2 = a^2 + b^2 = 9 + 4 = 13$

$c = \sqrt{13}$

asymptotes: $y - 3 = \pm \dfrac{2}{3}(x-2)$

The foci are at $(2 + \sqrt{13}, 3)$ and $(2 - \sqrt{13}, 3)$.

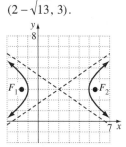

49. $4x^2 - 25y^2 - 32x + 164 = 0$

$(4x^2 - 32x) - 25y^2 = -164$

$4(x^2 - 8x + 16) - 25y^2 = -164 + 64$

$4(x-4)^2 - 25y^2 = -100$

$$\frac{4(x-4)^2}{-100} - \frac{25y^2}{-100} = \frac{-100}{-100}$$

$$\frac{y^2}{4} - \frac{(x-4)^2}{25} = 1$$

center: $(4, 0)$

$a^2 = 4$, $a = 2$

$b^2 = 25$, $b = 5$

$c^2 = a^2 + b^2 = 4 + 25 = 29$

$c = \sqrt{29}$

asymptotes: $y = \pm \dfrac{2}{5}(x-4)$

The foci are at $(4, \sqrt{29})$ and $(4, -\sqrt{29})$.

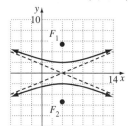

51. $|d_2 - d_1| = 2a = (2 \text{ s})(1100 \text{ ft} / \text{s}) = 2200 \text{ ft}$

$a = 1100 \text{ ft}$

$2c = 5280 \text{ ft}, c = 2640 \text{ ft}$

$b^2 = c^2 - a^2 = (2640)^2 - (1100)^2$

$\qquad = 5,759,600$

$$\frac{x^2}{(1100)^2} - \frac{y^2}{5,759,600} = 1$$

$$\frac{x^2}{1,210,000} - \frac{y^2}{5,759,600} = 1$$

If M_1 is located 2640 feet to the right of the origin on the *x*-axis, the explosion is located on the right branch of the hyperbola given by the equation above.

53. $\qquad 625y^2 - 400x^2 = 250,000$

$$\frac{625y^2}{250,000} - \frac{400x^2}{250,000} = \frac{250,000}{250,000}$$

$$\frac{y^2}{400} - \frac{x^2}{625} = 1$$

$a^2 = 400, a = \sqrt{400} = 20$

$2a = 40$

The houses are 40 yards apart at their closest point.

55.–61. Answers may vary.

65. $\dfrac{x^2}{4} - \dfrac{y^2}{9} = 0$

$y^2 = \dfrac{9}{4}x^2$

$y = \pm\dfrac{3}{2}x$

No; in general, the graph is two intersecting lines.

67. $4x^2 - 6xy + 2y^2 - 3x + 10y - 6 = 0$

$2y^2 + (10 - 6x)y + (4x^2 - 3x - 6) = 0$

$$y = \frac{6x - 10 \pm \sqrt{(10 - 6x)^2 - 8(4x^2 - 3x - 6)}}{4}$$

$$y = \frac{6x - 10 \pm \sqrt{4(x^2 - 24x + 37)}}{4}$$

$$y = \frac{3x - 5 \pm \sqrt{x^2 - 24x + 37}}{2}$$

The *xy*-term rotates the hyperbola. Separation of terms into ones containing only *x* or only *y* would be impossible.

69. a. False; one branch of the hyperbola

$\dfrac{x^2}{a^2} - \dfrac{y^2}{b^2} = 1$ will not pass the vertical

line test, so will not define *y* as a function of *x*.

b. False; none of the points on the asymptotes satisfy the hyperbola's equation, since the hyperbola never touches its asymptotes.

c. True; $y = -\dfrac{2}{3}x$ is one of the asymptotes

of the hyperbola and they will not intersect.

d. False; for example, $\dfrac{x^2}{4} - \dfrac{y^2}{4} = 1$ and

$\dfrac{y^2}{4} - \dfrac{x^2}{4} = 1$ each have asymptotes

$y = \pm x$, but are different hyperbolas.

(c) is true.

71. The center is at the midpoint of the line segment joining the vertices, so it is located at (5, 0). The standard form is:

$$\frac{(y-k)^2}{a^2} - \frac{(x-h)^2}{b^2} = 1$$

$(h, k) = (5, 0)$, and $a = 6$, so $a^2 = 36$.

$$\frac{y^2}{36} - \frac{(x-5)^2}{b^2} = 1.$$

Substitute $x = 0$ and $y = 9$:

$$\frac{9^2}{36} - \frac{(0-5)^2}{b^2} = 1$$

$$-\frac{25}{b^2} = -\frac{5}{4}$$

$$-100 = -5b^2$$

$$b^2 = 20$$

Standard form: $\dfrac{y^2}{36} - \dfrac{(x-5)^2}{20} = 1$

Section 7.3

Check Point Exercises

1. $y^2 = 8x$

$4p = 8, \; p = 2$

foci: $(2, 0)$

directrix: $x = -2$

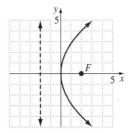

2. $x^2 = -12y$

$4p = -12, \; p = 3$

focus: $(0, -3)$

directrix: $y = 3$

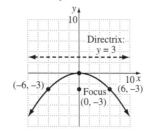

3. $p = 8$

$y^2 = 4 \cdot 8x$

$y^2 = 32x$

4. $(x-2)^2 = 4(y+1)$

$4p = 4, \; p = 1$

vertex: $(2, -1)$

focus: $(2, 0)$

directrix: $y = -2$

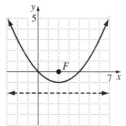

5. $y^2 + 2y + 4x - 7 = 0$

$$y^2 + 2y = -4x + 7$$

$$y^2 + 2y + 1 = -4x + 7 + 1$$

$$(y+1)^2 = -4(x-2)$$

$4p = -4, \; p = -1$

vertex: $(2, -1)$

focus: $(1, -1)$

directix: $x = 3$

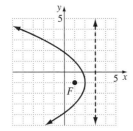

directix: $x = -4$

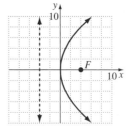

6. $x^2 = 4py$

Let $x = 3$ and $y = 4$.

$3^2 = 4p \cdot 4$

$9 = 16p$

$p = \dfrac{9}{16}$

$x^2 = \dfrac{9}{4}y$

The light should be placed at $\left(0, \dfrac{9}{16}\right)$ or

$\dfrac{9}{16}$ inch above the vertex.

Exercise Set 7.3

1. $y^2 = 4x$

$4p = 4, p = 1$

vertex: $(0, 0)$

focus: $(1, 0)$

directrix: $x = -1$

graph (c)

3. $x^2 = -4y$

$4p = -4, p = -1$

vertex: $(0, 0)$

focus: $(0, -1)$

directrix: $y = 1$

graph (b)

5. $y^2 = 16x$

$4p = 16, p = 4$

vertex: $(0, 0)$

focus: $(4, 0)$

7. $y^2 = -8x$

$4p = -8, p = -2$

vertex: $(0, 0)$

focus: $(-2, 0)$

directrix: $x = 2$

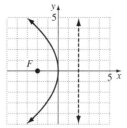

9. $x^2 = 12y$

$4p = 12, p = 3$

vertex: $(0, 0)$

focus: $(0, 3)$

directrix: $y = -3$

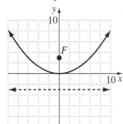

11. $x^2 = -16y$

$4p = -16, p = -4$

vertex: $(0, 0)$

focus: $(0, -4)$

directrix: $y = 4$

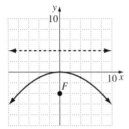

13. $y^2 - 6x = 0$

$\quad y^2 = 6x$

$4p = 6, \ p = \dfrac{6}{4} = \dfrac{3}{2}$

vertex: $(0, 0)$

focus: $\left(\dfrac{3}{2}, 0\right)$

directrix: $x = -\dfrac{3}{2}$

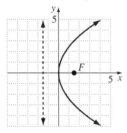

15. $8x^2 + 4y = 0$

$\quad 8x^2 = -4y$

$\quad x^2 = -\dfrac{1}{2}y$

$4p = -\dfrac{1}{2}$

$p = -\dfrac{1}{8}$

focus: $\left(0, -\dfrac{1}{8}\right)$

directrix: $y = \dfrac{1}{8}$

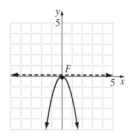

17. $p = 7, \ 4p = 28$

$\quad y^2 = 28x$

19. $p = -5, \ 4p = -20$

$\quad y^2 = -20x$

21. $p = 15, \ 4p = 60$

$\quad x^2 = 60y$

23. $p = -25, \ 4p = -100$

$\quad x^2 = -100y$

25. $p = -5 - (-3) = -2$ Vertex, $(2, -3)$

$\quad (x - 2)^2 = -8(y + 3)$

27. Vertex: $(1, 2) \quad p = 2$

$\quad (y - 2)^2 = 8(x - 1)$

29. Vertex: $(-3, 3), \ p = 1$

$\quad (x + 3)^2 = 4(y - 3)$

31. $(y - 1)^2 = 4(x - 1)$

$\quad 4p = 4, \ p = 1$

vertex: $(1, 1)$

focus: $(2, 1)$

directrix: $x = 0$

graph (c)

33. $(x + 1)^2 = -4(y + 1)$

$\quad 4p = -4, \ p = -1$

vertex: $(-1, -1)$

focus: $(-1, -2)$

directrix: $y = 0$

graph (d)

35. $(x - 2)^2 = 8(y - 1)$
$4p = 8, p = 2$
vertex: $(2, 1)$
focus: $(2, 3)$
directrix: $y = -1$

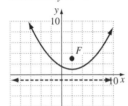

37. $(x + 1)^2 = -8(y + 1)$
$4p = -8, p = -2$
vertex: $(-1, -1)$
focus: $(-1, -3)$
directrix: $y = 1$

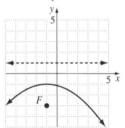

39. $(y + 3)^2 = 12(x + 1)$
$4p = 12, p = 3$
vertex: $(-1, -3)$
focus: $(2, -3)$
directrix: $x = -4$

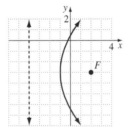

41. $(y + 1)^2 = -8x$
$(y + 1)^2 = -8(x - 0)$

$4p = -8, p = -2$
vertex: $(0, -1)$
focus: $(-2, -1)$
directrix: $x = 2$

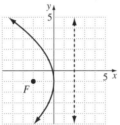

43. $x^2 - 2x - 4y + 9 = 0$
$$x^2 - 2x = 4y - 9$$
$$x^2 - 2x + 1 = 4y - 9 + 1$$
$$(x - 1)^2 = 4y - 8$$
$$(x - 1)^2 = 4(y - 2)$$
$4p = 4, p = 1$
vertex: $(1, 2)$
focus: $(1, 3)$
directrix: $y = 1$

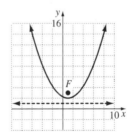

45. $y^2 - 2y + 12x - 35 = 0$
$$y^2 - 2y = -12x + 35$$
$$y^2 - 2y + 1 = -12x + 35 + 1$$
$$(y - 1)^2 = -12x + 36$$
$$(y - 1)^2 = -12(x - 3)$$
$4p = -12, p = -3$
vertex: $(3, 1)$
focus: $(0, 1)$
directrix: $x = 6$

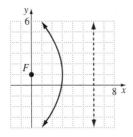

47. $x^2 + 6x - 4y + 1 = 0$

$x^2 + 6x = 4y - 1$

$x^2 + 6x + 9 = 4y - 1 + 9$

$(x + 3)^2 = 4(y + 2)$

$4p = 4, \; p = 1$

vertex: $(-3, -2)$

focus: $(-3, -1)$

directrix: $y = -3$

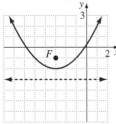

49. $x^2 = 4py$

$2^2 = 4p(1)$

$4 = 4p$

$p = 1$

The light bulb should be placed 1 inch above the vertex

51. $x^2 = 4py$

$6^2 = 4p(2)$

$36 = 8p$

$p = \dfrac{36}{8} = \dfrac{9}{2} = 4.5$

The receiver should be located 4.5 feet from the base of the dish.

53. $x^2 = 4py$

$(640)^2 = 4p(160)$

$p = \dfrac{(640)^2}{640} = 640$

$x = 640 - 200 = 440$

$(440)^2 = 4(640)y$

$y = \dfrac{(440)^2}{4(640)} = 75.625$

The height is 75.6 meters.

55.

$x^2 = 4py$

$\left(\dfrac{200}{2}\right)^2 = 4p(-50)$

$\dfrac{10,000}{-50} = 4p$

$4p = -200$

$x^2 = -200y$

$(30)^2 = -200y$

$y = \dfrac{900}{-200} = -4.5$

(height of bridge) $= 50 - 4.5 = 45.5$ feet.

Yes, the boat will clear the arch.

57.–63. Answers may vary.

65. $y^2 + 2y - 6x + 13 = 0$

$y^2 + 2y + (-6x + 13) = 0$

$$y = \frac{-2 \pm \sqrt{2^2 - 4(-6x + 13)}}{2}$$

$$y = \frac{-2 \pm \sqrt{24x - 48}}{2}$$

$$y = -1 \pm \sqrt{6x - 12}$$

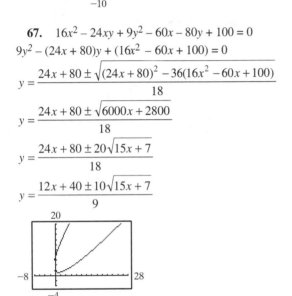

67. $16x^2 - 24xy + 9y^2 - 60x - 80y + 100 = 0$

$9y^2 - (24x + 80)y + (16x^2 - 60x + 100) = 0$

$$y = \frac{24x + 80 \pm \sqrt{(24x + 80)^2 - 36(16x^2 - 60x + 100)}}{18}$$

$$y = \frac{24x + 80 \pm \sqrt{6000x + 2800}}{18}$$

$$y = \frac{24x + 80 \pm 20\sqrt{15x + 7}}{18}$$

$$y = \frac{12x + 40 \pm 10\sqrt{15x + 7}}{9}$$

69. a.   False; it opens to the left.

   b.   True; it opens to the right and has a domain $[3, \infty)$.

   c.   False; any parabola that opens to the right will not be a function of x because at least one x-value will be paired with more than 1 y-value.

   d.   False; the graph is a line.

   (b) is true.

71. $y = 4$ is the directrix and $(-1, 0)$ is the focus. The vertex must be located halfway between them at the point $(-1, 2)$. $p = 2$ and the parabola opens down.

$(x + 1)^2 = 4(2)(y - 2)$

$(x + 1)^2 = 8(y - 2)$

Review Exercises

1. $\dfrac{x^2}{36} + \dfrac{y^2}{25} = 1$

   $a^2 = 36,\ a = 6$

   $b^2 = 25,\ b = 5$

   $c^2 = a^2 - b^2 = 36 - 25 = 11$

   $c = \sqrt{11}$

   The foci are at $(\sqrt{11},\ 0)$ and $(-\sqrt{11},\ 0)$

   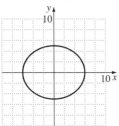

2. $\dfrac{y^2}{25} + \dfrac{x^2}{16} = 1$

   $a^2 = 25,\ a = 5$

   $b^2 = 16,\ b = 4$

   $c^2 = a^2 - b^2$

   $c^2 = 25 - 16$

   $c^2 = 9$

   $c = 3$

   The foci are $(0,\ 3)$ and $(0,\ -3)$.

3. $4x^2 + y^2 = 16$

   $\dfrac{4x^2}{16} + \dfrac{y^2}{16} = \dfrac{16}{16}$

   $\dfrac{x^2}{4} + \dfrac{y^2}{16} = 1$

   $b^2 = 4,\ b = 2$

   $a^2 = 16,\ a = 4$

   $c^2 = a^2 - b^2 = 16 - 4 = 12$

   $c = \sqrt{12} = 2\sqrt{3}$

The foci are at $(0,\ 2\sqrt{3})$ and $(0,\ -2\sqrt{3})$.

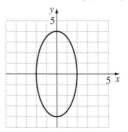

4. $4x^2 + 9y^2 = 36$

   $\dfrac{4x^2}{36} + \dfrac{9y^2}{36} = \dfrac{36}{36}$

   $\dfrac{x^2}{9} + \dfrac{y^2}{4} = 1$

   $a^2 = 9,\ a = 3$

   $b^2 = 4,\ b = 2$

   $c^2 = a^2 - b^2 = 9 - 4 = 5,\ c = \sqrt{5}$

   The foci are at $(\sqrt{5},\ 0)$ and $(-\sqrt{5},\ 0)$.

   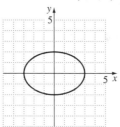

5. $\dfrac{(x-1)^2}{16} + \dfrac{(y+2)^2}{9} = 1$

   $a^2 = 16\ \ a = 4$

   $b^2 = 9\ \ b = 3$

   $c^2 = 16 - 9 = 7,\ c = \sqrt{7}$

   center: $(1,\ -2)$

   The foci are at $(1 + \sqrt{7},\ -2)$ and $(1 - \sqrt{7},\ -2)$.

   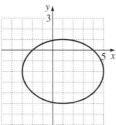

6. $\dfrac{(x+1)^2}{9} + \dfrac{(y-2)^2}{16} = 1$

   $a^2 = 16,\ a = 4$

$b^2 = 9, \ b = 3$

$c^2 = a^2 - b^2 = 16 - 9 = 7, \ c = \sqrt{7}$

center: $(-1, 2)$

The foci are at $(-1, 2 + \sqrt{7})$ and $(-1, 2 - \sqrt{7})$.

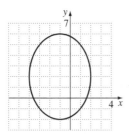

7. $4x^2 + 9y^2 + 24x - 36y + 36 = 0$

   $4x^2 + 24x + 9y^2 - 36y = -36$

   $4(x^2 + 6x + 9) + 9(y^2 - 4y + 4)$

   $= -36 + 36 + 36$

   $= 4(x + 3)^2 + 9(y - 2)^2 = 36$

   $\dfrac{(x+3)^2}{9} + \dfrac{(y-2)^2}{4} = 1$

   $c^2 = a^2 - b^2 = 5, \ c = \sqrt{5}$

   center: $(-3, 2)$

   The foci are at $(-3 + \sqrt{5}, \ 2)$ and $(-3 - \sqrt{5}, \ 2)$.

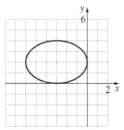

8. $9x^2 + 4y^2 - 18x + 8y - 23 = 0$

   $9x^2 - 18x + 4y^2 + 8y = 23$

   $9(x^2 - 2x + 1) + 4(y^2 + 2y + 1) = 23 + 9 + 4$

   $9(x - 1)^2 + 4(y + 1)^2 = 36$

   $\dfrac{(x-1)^2}{4} + \dfrac{(y+1)^2}{9} = 1$

   $c^2 = a^2 - b^2 = 9 - 4 = 5, \ c = \sqrt{5}$

   center: $(1, -1)$

The foci are at $(1, -1 + \sqrt{5})$ and $(1, -1 - \sqrt{5})$.

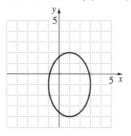

9. $c = 4, c^2 = 16$

    $a = 5, a^2 = 25$

    $b^2 = a^2 - c^2 = 25 - 16 = 9$

    $\dfrac{x^2}{25} + \dfrac{y^2}{9} = 1$

10. $c = 3, c^2 = 9$

    $a = 6, a^2 = 36$

    $b^2 = a^2 - c^2 = 36 - 9 = 27$

    $\dfrac{(x+3)^2}{27} + \dfrac{(y-5)^2}{36} = 1$

11. $2a = 12, a = 6, a^2 = 36$

    $2b = 4, b = 2, b^2 = 4$

    $\dfrac{(x+3)^2}{36} + \dfrac{(y-5)^2}{4} = 1$

12. $2a = 20, a = 10, a^2 = 100$

    $b = 6, b^2 = 36$

    $\dfrac{x^2}{100} + \dfrac{y^2}{36} = 1$

13. $2a = 50, a = 25$

    $b = 15$

    $\dfrac{x^2}{625} + \dfrac{y^2}{225} = 1$

    Let $x = 14$.

    $\dfrac{(14)^2}{625} + \dfrac{y^2}{225} = 1$

    $y^2 = 225\left(1 - \dfrac{196}{625}\right)$

    $y \approx 15(0.8285) \approx 12.4 > 12$

    Yes, the truck can drive under the archway.

14. The hit ball will collide with the other ball.

15. $\dfrac{x^2}{16} - y^2 = 1$

$c^2 = a^2 + b^2 = 16 + 1 = 17, c = \sqrt{17}$

The foci are at $(\sqrt{17}, 0)$ and $(-\sqrt{17}, 0)$.

Asymptotes: $y = \pm \dfrac{1}{4} x$

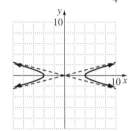

16. $\dfrac{y^2}{16} - x^2 = 1$

$c^2 = a^2 + b^2 = 16 + 1 = 17$

$c = \sqrt{17}$

The foci are at $(0, \sqrt{17})$ and $(0, -\sqrt{17})$.

Asymptotes: $y = \pm 4x$

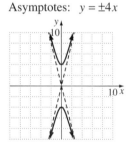

17. $9x^2 - 16y^2 = 144$

$\dfrac{x^2}{16} - \dfrac{y^2}{9} = 1$

$c^2 = a^2 + b^2 = 16 + 9 = 25, c = 5$

The foci are at $(5, 0)$ and $(-5, 0)$.

Asymptotes: $y = \pm \dfrac{3}{4} x$

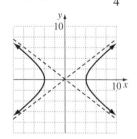

18. $4y^2 - x^2 = 16$

$\dfrac{y^2}{4} - \dfrac{x^2}{16} = 1$

$c^2 = a^2 + b^2 = 4 + 16 = 20$

$c = \sqrt{20} = 2\sqrt{5}$

The foci are at $(0, 2\sqrt{5})$ and $(0, -2\sqrt{5})$.

Asymptotes: $y = \pm \dfrac{1}{2} x$

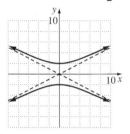

19. $\dfrac{(x-2)^2}{25} - \dfrac{(y+3)^2}{16} = 1$

$c^2 = a^2 + b^2 = 25 + 16 = 41, c = \sqrt{41}$

center: $(2, -3)$

The foci are at

$(2 + \sqrt{41}, -3)$ and $(2 - \sqrt{41}, -3)$.

Asymptotes: $y + 3 = \pm \dfrac{4}{5}(x - 2)$

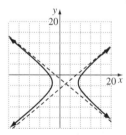

20. $\dfrac{(y+2)^2}{25} - \dfrac{(x-3)^2}{16} = 1$

$c^2 = a^2 + b^2 = 25 + 16 = 41, c = \sqrt{41}$

center: $(3, -2)$

The foci are at

$(3, -2 + \sqrt{41})$ and $(3, -2 - \sqrt{41})$.

Asymptotes: $y + 2 = \pm \dfrac{5}{4}(x - 3)$

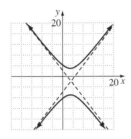

21. $y^2 - 4y - 4x^2 + 8x - 4 = 0$

$(y^2 - 4y + 4) - 4(x^2 - 2x + 1) = 4 + 4 - 4$

$(y - 2)^2 - 4(x - 1)^2 = 4$

$\dfrac{(y-2)^2}{4} - (x-1)^2 = 1$

$c^2 = a^2 + b^2 = 4 + 1 = 5, \ c = \sqrt{5}$

center: $(1, 2)$

The foci are at $(1, 2 + \sqrt{5})$ and $(1, 2 - \sqrt{5})$.

Asymptotes: $y - 2 = \pm 2(x - 1)$

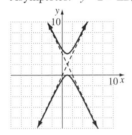

22. $x^2 - y^2 - 2x - 2y - 1 = 0$

$x^2 - 2x - y^2 - 2y = 1$

$(x^2 - 2x + 1) - (y^2 + 2y + 1) = 1 + 1 - 1$

$(x - 1)^2 - (y + 1)^2 = 1$

$c^2 = a^2 + b^2 = 1 + 1 = 2, \ c = \sqrt{2}$

center: $(1, -1)$

The foci are at $(1 + \sqrt{2}, -1)$ and $(1 - \sqrt{2}, -1)$.

Asymptotes: $y + 1 = \pm(x - 1)$

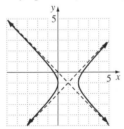

23. $c = 4, c^2 = 16$

$a = 2, a^2 = 4$

$b^2 = c^2 - a^2 = 16 - 4 = 12$

$\dfrac{y^2}{4} - \dfrac{x^2}{12} = 1$

24. $c = 8, c^2 = 64$

$a = 3, a^2 = 9$

$b^2 = c^2 - a^2 = 64 - 9 = 55$

$\dfrac{x^2}{9} - \dfrac{y^2}{55} = 1$

25. If the foci are at $(0, -2)$ and $(0, 2)$, then $c = 2$. If the vertices are at $(0, -3)$ and $(0, 3)$ then $a = 3$. This is not possible since c must be greater than a.

26. foci: $(\pm 100, 0), c = 100$

$|d_1 - d_2| = \left(0.186 \dfrac{\text{mi}}{\mu s}\right)(500 \mu s) = 93 \text{ mi} = 2a$

$a = \dfrac{93}{2}$

$b^2 = c^2 - a^2 = (100)^2 - \left(\dfrac{93}{2}\right)^2 = 7837.75$

$\dfrac{x^2}{\left(\frac{93}{2}\right)^2} - \dfrac{y^2}{7837.75} = 1$

$\dfrac{x^2}{2162.25} - \dfrac{y^2}{7837.75} = 1$

27. $y^2 = 8x$

$4p = 8, p = 2$

vertex: $(0, 0)$

focus: $(2, 0)$

directrix: $x = -2$

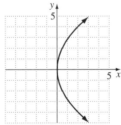

28. $x^2 + 16y = 0$

$\qquad x^2 = -16y$

$4p = -16$

$\ p = -4$

vertex: $(0, 0)$

focus: $(0, -4)$

directrix: $y = 4$

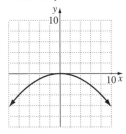

directrix: $y = 2$

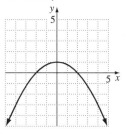

29. $(y-2)^2 = -16x$

$4p = -16$

$p = -4$

vertex: (0, 2)

focus: (−4, 2)

directrix: $x = 4$

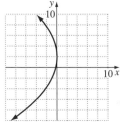

30. $(x-4)^2 = 4(y+1)$

$4p = 4$, $p = 1$

vertex: (4, −1)

focus: (4, 0)

directrix: $y = -2$

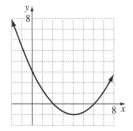

31. $x^2 + 4y = 4$

$x^2 = -4y + 4$

$x^2 = -4(y-1)$

$4p = -4$, $p = -1$

vertex: (0, 1)

focus: (0, 0)

32. $y^2 - 4x - 10y + 21 = 0$

$y^2 - 10y = 4x - 21$

$y^2 - 10y + 25 = 4x - 21 + 25$

$(y-5)^2 = 4(x+1)$

$4p = 4$, $p = 1$

vertex: (−1, 5)

focus: (0, 5)

directrix: $x = -2$

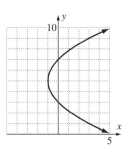

33. $x^2 - 4x - 2y = 0$

$x^2 - 4x = 2y$

$(x^2 - 4x + 4) = 2y + 4$

$(x-2)^2 = 2(y+2)$

$4p = 2$, $p = \dfrac{1}{2}$

vertex: (2, −2)

focus: $\left(2, -\dfrac{3}{2}\right)$

directrix: $y = -\dfrac{5}{2}$

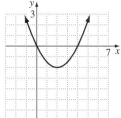

34. $p = 12$
$y^2 = 48x$

35. $p = -11$
$x^2 = -44y$

36. $x^2 = 4py$
$(6)^2 = 4p(3)$
$\quad p = 3$
$\quad x^2 = 12y$
Place the light 3 inches from the vertex at $(0, 3)$.

37. $x^2 = 4py$
$(1750)^2 = 4p(316)$
$4p \approx 9691$
$x^2 = 9691y$
Let $x = 1750 - 1000 = 750$.
$y = \dfrac{x^2}{9691} = \dfrac{(750)^2}{9691} \approx 58$
The height is approximately 58 feet.

38. $x^2 = 4py$
$(150)^2 = 4p(44)$
$22{,}500 = 176p$
$p \approx 128$
The receiver should be placed approximately 128 feet from the base of the dish.

Chapter 7 Test

1. $9x^2 - 4y^2 = 36$
$\dfrac{x^2}{4} - \dfrac{y^2}{9} = 1$
$c^2 = a^2 + b^2 = 4 + 9 = 13, \ c = \sqrt{13}$
hyperbola
Asymptotes: $y = \pm\dfrac{3}{2}x$
The foci are at $\left(\sqrt{13}, 0\right)$ and $\left(-\sqrt{13}, 0\right)$.1

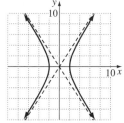

2. $x^2 = -8y$
$4p = -8, \ p = -2$
parabola
vertex: $(0, 0)$
focus: $(0, -2)$
directrix: $y = 2$

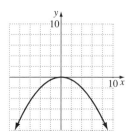

3. $\dfrac{(x+2)^2}{25} + \dfrac{(y-5)^2}{9} = 1$
The center is at $(-2, 5)$.
$c^2 = a^2 - b^2 = 25 - 9 = 16, \ c = 4$
ellipse
The foci are at $(-6, 5)$ and $(2, 5)$.

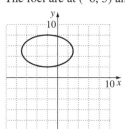

4.

$$4x^2 - y^2 + 8x + 2y + 7 = 0$$
$$\left(4x^2 + 8x\right) - \left(y^2 - 2y\right) = -7$$
$$4\left(x^2 + 2x + 1\right) - \left(y^2 - 2y + 1\right) = -7 + 4 - 1$$
$$4(x+1)^2 - (y-1)^2 = -4$$
$$(y-1)^2 - 4(x+1)^2 = 4$$
$$\dfrac{(y-1)^2}{4} - (x+1)^2 = 1$$
$$c^2 = a^2 + b^2 = 4 + 1 = 5, \ c = \sqrt{5}$$

The center is at $(-1, 1)$. Hyperbola

Asymptotes: $y - 1 = \pm 2(x + 1)$

The foci are at $\left(-1, 1 + \sqrt{5}\right)$ and $\left(-1, 1 - \sqrt{5}\right)$.

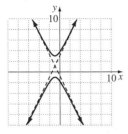

5. $(x + 5)^2 = 8(y - 1)$

$4p = 8$, $p = 2$

parabola

vertex: $(-5, 1)$

focus: $(-5, 3)$

directrix: $y = -1$

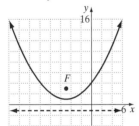

6. $c = 7$, $c^2 = 49$

$a = 10$, $a^2 = 100$

$b^2 = a^2 - c^2 = 100 - 49 = 51$

$\dfrac{x^2}{100} + \dfrac{y^2}{51} = 1$

7. $c = 10$, $c^2 = 100$

$a = 7$, $a^2 = 49$

$b^2 = c^2 - a^2 = 100 - 49 = 51$

$\dfrac{y^2}{49} - \dfrac{x^2}{51} = 1$

8. $p = 50$

$y^2 = 4px$

$y^2 = 200x$

9. $b = 24$, $b^2 = 576$

$2a = 80$, $a = 40$, $a^2 = 1600$

$c^2 = a^2 - b^2 = 1600 - 576 = 1024$

$c = \sqrt{1024} = 32$

The two people should each stand 32 feet from the center of the room, along the major axis.

10. **a.** $x^2 = 4py$

when $x = \pm 3$, $y = 3$

$9 = 4p(3)$

$3 = 4p$

$\dfrac{3}{4} = p$

$x^2 = 3y$

b. focus: $\left(0, \dfrac{3}{4}\right)$

The light is placed $\dfrac{3}{4}$ inch above the vertex.

Cumulative Review Exercises (Chapters 1–7)

1. $2(x - 3) + 5x = 8(x - 1)$

$2x - 6 + 5x = 8x - 8$

$7x - 6 = 8x - 8$

$-x = -2$

$x = 2$

The solution set is $\{2\}$.

2. $-3(2x - 4) > 2(6x - 12)$

$-6x + 12 > 12x - 24$

$-18x > -36$

$x < 2$

The solution set is $\{x \mid x < 2\}$.

3. $x - 5 = \sqrt{x + 7}$

$(x - 5)^2 = x + 7$

$x^2 - 10x + 25 = x + 7$

$x^2 - 11x + 18 = 0$

$(x - 2)(x - 9) = 0$

$x = 2$ or $x = 9$

The solution $x = 2$ is extraneous, so the only solution is $x = 9$.

The solution set is $\{9\}$.

4. $(x - 2)^2 = 20$

$x - 2 = \pm\sqrt{20}$

$x - 2 = \pm 2\sqrt{5}$

$x = 2 \pm 2\sqrt{5}$

The solution set is $\left\{2 + 2\sqrt{5},\, 2 - 2\sqrt{5}\right\}$.

5. $|2x - 1| \geq 7$

$2x - 1 \geq 7$ or $2x - 1 \leq -7$

$2x \geq 8$ $2x \leq -6$

$x \geq 4$ or $x \leq -3$

The solution set is $\{x \mid x \leq -3 \text{ or } x \geq 4\}$

6. $3x^3 + 4x^2 - 7x + 2 = 0$

$p: \pm 1, \pm 2$

$q: \pm 1, \pm 3$

$\dfrac{p}{q}: \pm 1, \pm 2, \pm \dfrac{1}{3}, \pm \dfrac{2}{3}$

Let $f(x) = 3x^3 + 4x^2 - 7x + 2$.

Evaluate f at the possible rational zeros to find

$f\left(\dfrac{2}{3}\right) = 0$.

$$\begin{array}{c|cccc} \dfrac{2}{3} & 3 & 4 & -7 & 2 \\ & & 2 & 4 & -2 \\ \hline & 3 & 6 & -3 & 0 \end{array}$$

$\left(x - \dfrac{2}{3}\right)(3x^2 + 6x - 3) = 0$

$(3x - 2)(x^2 + 2x - 1) = 0$

$x = \dfrac{2}{3}$ or $x = \dfrac{-2 \pm \sqrt{(2)^2 - 4(1)(-1)}}{2}$

$x = \dfrac{-2 \pm \sqrt{8}}{2}$

$x = -1 \pm \sqrt{2}$

The solution set is $\left\{\dfrac{2}{3}, -1 + \sqrt{2}, -1 - \sqrt{2}\right\}$.

7. $\log_2(x + 1) + \log_2(x - 1) = 3$

$\log_2(x^2 - 1) = 3$

$x^2 - 1 = 2^3$

$x^2 = 9$

$x = \pm 3$

$x = -3$ is not a solution of the original equation.
The solution set is $\{3\}$.

8. $3x + 4y = 2$

$2x + 5y = -1$

$\begin{array}{r} 6x + 8y = 4 \\ -6x - 15y = 3 \\ \hline -7y = 7 \end{array}$

$y = -1$

$3x + 4(-1) = 2$

$3x = 6$

$x = 2$

The solution set is $\{(2, -1)\}$.

9. $2x^2 - y^2 = -8$

$x - y = 6$

$x - y = 6$

$x = y + 6$

$x^2 = (y + 6)^2 = y^2 + 12y + 36$

Substitute into first equation.

$2(y^2 + 12y + 36) - y^2 = -8$

$2y^2 + 24y + 72 - y^2 = -8$

$y^2 + 24y + 80 = 0$

$(y + 4)(y + 20) = 0$

$y = -4$ or $y = -20$

$x = 2$ $x = -14$

The solution set is $\{(2, -4), (-14, -20)\}$.

10. Set up the augmented matrix and use
Gauss-Jordan reduction.

$$\left[\begin{array}{ccc|c} 1 & -1 & 1 & 17 \\ -4 & 1 & 5 & -2 \\ 2 & 3 & 1 & 8 \end{array}\right]$$

$$\left[\begin{array}{ccc|c} 1 & -1 & 1 & 17 \\ 0 & -3 & 9 & 66 \\ 0 & 5 & -1 & -26 \end{array}\right] \begin{array}{l} 4R_1 + R_2 \\ -2R_1 + R_3 \end{array}$$

$$\left[\begin{array}{ccc|c} 1 & -1 & 1 & 17 \\ 0 & 1 & -3 & -22 \\ 0 & 5 & -1 & -26 \end{array}\right] -\dfrac{1}{3}R_2$$

$$\left[\begin{array}{ccc|c} 1 & 0 & -2 & -5 \\ 0 & 1 & -3 & -22 \\ 0 & 0 & 14 & 84 \end{array}\right] \begin{array}{l} R_2 + R_1 \\ \\ -5R_2 + R_3 \end{array}$$

$$\left[\begin{array}{ccc|c} 1 & 0 & -2 & -5 \\ 0 & 1 & -3 & -22 \\ 0 & 0 & 1 & 6 \end{array}\right] \dfrac{1}{14}R_3$$

$$\begin{bmatrix} 1 & 0 & 0 & | & 7 \\ 0 & 1 & 0 & | & -4 \\ 0 & 0 & 1 & | & 6 \end{bmatrix} \begin{matrix} 2R_3 + R_1 \\ 3R_3 + R_2 \end{matrix}$$

$x = 7, y = -4, z = 6$

The solution set is $\{(7, -4, 6)\}$.

11. $f(x) = (x-1)^2 - 4$

Parabola with vertex at $(1, -4)$.

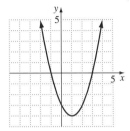

12. $\dfrac{x^2}{9} + \dfrac{y^2}{4} = 1$

Ellipse with center at $(0, 0)$ and vertices at $(3, 0)$ and $(-3, 0)$.

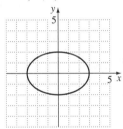

13. $5x + y \le 10 \qquad\qquad y \ge \dfrac{1}{4}x + 2$

$\qquad y \le -5x + 10$

Graph with solid line $y = -5x + 10$ and $y = \dfrac{1}{4}x + 2$. Shade the region which is below the line $y = -5x + 10$ and above the line $y = \dfrac{1}{4}x + 2$. Then dash the solid lines that do not contain the solution set.

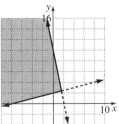

14. a. $p: \pm 1, \pm 3$

$q: \pm 1, \pm 2, \pm 4, \pm 8, \pm 16, \pm 32$

$\dfrac{p}{q}: \pm 1, \pm 3, \pm \dfrac{1}{2}, \pm \dfrac{3}{2}, \pm \dfrac{1}{4}, \pm \dfrac{3}{4}, \pm \dfrac{1}{8},$

$\pm \dfrac{3}{8}, \pm \dfrac{1}{16}, \pm \dfrac{3}{16}, \pm \dfrac{1}{32}, \pm \dfrac{3}{32}$

b. $x = 1$ appears to be a root.

$$\begin{array}{c|cccc} 1 & 32 & -52 & 17 & 3 \\ & & 32 & -20 & -3 \\ \hline & 32 & -20 & -3 & 0 \end{array}$$

$32x^3 - 52x^2 + 17x + 3 = 0$

$(x-1)(32x^2 - 20x - 3) = 0$

$(x-1)(4x-3)(8x+1) = 0$

$x = 1$ or $x = \dfrac{3}{4}$ or $x = -\dfrac{1}{8}$

The solution set is $\left\{ -\dfrac{1}{8}, \dfrac{3}{4}, 1 \right\}$.

15. a. The graph shows that the value is constant in the interval 1980–1990.

b. The graph shows that the value is increasing in the interval 1990–2025.

c. The graph shows that the value is decreasing in the interval 1950–1980.

d. Since the values are approximately 98, a constant function that approximately models the data is $f(x) = 98$.

e. The scale is not uniformly spaced.

16. $f(x) = x^2 - 4, g(x) = x + 2$

$(g \circ f)(x) = g(x^2 - 4) = (x^2 - 4) + 2 = x^2 - 2$

17. $\log_5 \dfrac{x^3 \sqrt{y}}{125} = \log_5 x^3 \sqrt{y} - \log_5 125$

$= \log_5 x^3 + \log_5 \sqrt{y} - 3$

$= 3\log_5 x + \dfrac{1}{2}\log_5 y - 3$

18. $m = \dfrac{y_2 - y_1}{x_2 - x_1} = \dfrac{8 - (-4)}{-5 - 1} = \dfrac{12}{-6} = -2$

$y - y_1 = m(x - x_1)$

$y + 4 = -2(x - 1)$

$y = -2x - 2$

19. Let R = the cost of a rental at Rent-a-Truck and let A = the cost of a rental at Ace Truck Rentals.

$R = 39 + 0.16m$

$A = 25 + 0.24m$

where m is the number of miles.

$39 + 0.16m = 25 + 0.24m$

$\quad\quad\quad 14 = 0.08m$

$\quad\quad\quad\ m = 175$

$R = 39 + 0.16(175) = 67$

The cost will be the same when the number of miles driven is 175 miles. The cost will be \$67.

20. Let x = cost of basic cable,

Let y = cost of movie channel

$\quad x + y = 35$

$x + 2y = 45$

$-x - y = -35$

$\ x + 2y = 45$

$\quad\quad\ y = 10$

$x + 10 = 35$

$\quad\ x = 25$

Basic cable costs \$25 and one movie channel costs \$10.

Chapter 8

Check Point Exercises

1. a. $a_n = 2n + 5$

$a_1 = 2(1) + 5 = 7$

$a_2 = 2(2) + 5 = 9$

$a_3 = 2(3) + 5 = 11$

$a_4 = 2(4) + 5 = 13$

The first four terms are 7, 9, 11, and 13.

b.

$a_n = \dfrac{(-1)^n}{2^n + 1}$

$a_1 = \dfrac{(-1)^1}{2^1 + 1} = = \dfrac{-1}{3} - \dfrac{1}{3}$

$a_2 = \dfrac{(-1)^2}{2^2 + 1} = \dfrac{1}{5}$

$a_3 = \dfrac{(-1)^3}{2^3 + 1} = \dfrac{-1}{9} = -\dfrac{1}{9}$

$a_4 = \dfrac{(-1)^4}{2^4 + 1} = \dfrac{1}{17}$

The first four terms are $-\dfrac{1}{3}, \dfrac{1}{5}, -\dfrac{1}{9},$

and $\dfrac{1}{17}$.

2. $a_1 = 3$ and $a_n = 2a_{n-1} + 5$ for $n \geq 2$

$a_2 = 2a_1 + 5$

$\quad = 2(3) + 5 = 11$

$a_3 = 2a_2 + 5$

$\quad = 2(11) + 5 = 27$

$a_4 = 2a_3 + 5$

$\quad = 2(27) + 5 = 59$

The first four terms are 3, 11, 27, and 59.

3.

$a_n = \dfrac{20}{(n+1)!}$

$a_1 = \dfrac{20}{(1+1)!} = \dfrac{20}{2!} = 10$

$a_2 = \dfrac{20}{(2+1)!} = \dfrac{20}{3!} = \dfrac{20}{6} = \dfrac{10}{3}$

$a_3 = \dfrac{20}{(3+1)!} = \dfrac{20}{4!} = \dfrac{20}{24} = \dfrac{5}{6}$

$a_4 = \dfrac{20}{(4+1)!} = \dfrac{20}{5!} = \dfrac{20}{120} = \dfrac{1}{6}$

The first four terms are $10, \dfrac{10}{3}, \dfrac{5}{6},$ and $\dfrac{1}{6}$.

4. a. $\dfrac{14!}{2!\,12!} = \dfrac{14 \cdot 13 \cdot 12!}{2!\,12!} = \dfrac{14 \cdot 13}{2 \cdot 1} = 91$

b. $\dfrac{n!}{(n-1)!} = \dfrac{n \cdot (n-1)!}{(n-1)!} = n$

5. a. $\displaystyle\sum_{i=1}^{6} 2i^2$

$= 2(1)^2 + 2(2)^2 + 2(3)^2$

$\quad + 2(4)^2 + 2(5)^2 + 2(6)^2$

$= 2 + 8 + 18 + 32 + 50 + 72$

$= 182$

b. $\displaystyle\sum_{k=3}^{5} \left(2^k - 3\right)$

$= \left(2^3 - 3\right) + \left(2^4 - 3\right) + \left(2^5 - 3\right)$

$= (8 - 3) + (16 - 3) + (32 - 3)$

$= 5 + 13 + 29$

$= 47$

c. $\displaystyle\sum_{i=1}^{5} 4 = 4 + 4 + 4 + 4 + 4 = 20$

6. a.   The sum has nine terms, each of the form i^2, starting at $i = 1$ and ending at $i = 9$.

$$1^2 + 2^2 + 3^2 + \cdots + 9^2 = \sum_{i=1}^{9} i^2$$

b.   The sum has n terms, each of the form $\frac{1}{2^{i-1}}$, starting at $i = 1$ and ending at $i = n$.

$$1 + \frac{1}{2} + \frac{1}{4} + \frac{1}{8} + \cdots + \frac{1}{2^{n-1}} = \sum_{i=1}^{n} \frac{1}{2^{i-1}}$$

Exercise Set 8.1

1. $a_n = 3n + 2$

$a_1 = 3(1) + 2 = 5$

$a_2 = 3(2) + 2 = 8$

$a_3 = 3(3) + 2 = 11$

$a_4 = 3(4) + 2 = 14$

The first four terms are 5, 8, 11, and 14.

3. $a_n = 3^n$

$a_1 = 3^1 = 3$

$a_2 = 3^2 = 9$

$a_3 = 3^3 = 27$

$a_4 = 3^4 = 81$

The first four terms are 3, 9, 27, and 81.

5. $a_n = (-3)^n$

$a_1 = (-3)^1 = -3$

$a_2 = (-3)^2 = 9$

$a_3 = (-3)^3 = -27$

$a_4 = (-3)^4 = 81$

The first four terms are -3, 9, -27, and 81.

7. $a_n = (-1)^n (n + 3)$

$a_1 = (-1)^1 (1 + 3) = -4$

$a_2 = (-1)^2 (2 + 3) = 5$

$a_3 = (-1)^3 (3 + 3) = -6$

$a_4 = (-1)^4 (4 + 3) = 7$

The first four terms are -4, 5, -6, and 7.

9. $a_n = \dfrac{2n}{n + 4}$

$a_1 = \dfrac{2(1)}{1 + 4} = \dfrac{2}{5}$

$a_2 = \dfrac{2(2)}{2 + 4} = \dfrac{4}{6} = \dfrac{2}{3}$

$a_3 = \dfrac{2(3)}{3 + 4} = \dfrac{6}{7}$

$a_4 = \dfrac{2(4)}{4 + 4} = \dfrac{8}{8} = 1$

The first four terms are $\frac{2}{5}, \frac{2}{3}, \frac{6}{7}$, and 1.

11. $a_n = \dfrac{(-1)^{n+1}}{2^n - 1}$

$a_1 = \dfrac{(-1)^{1+1}}{2^1 - 1} = \dfrac{1}{1} = 1$ $n = 1$

$a_2 = \dfrac{(-1)^{2+1}}{2^2 - 1} = -\dfrac{1}{3}$

$a_3 = \dfrac{(-1)^{3+1}}{2^3 - 1} = \dfrac{1}{7}$

$a_4 = \dfrac{(-1)^{4+1}}{2^4 - 1} = -\dfrac{1}{15}$

The first four terms are $1, -\frac{1}{3}, \frac{1}{7}$, and $-\frac{1}{15}$.

13. $a_1 = 7$ and $a_n = a_{n-1} + 5$ for $n \geq 2$

$a_2 = a_1 + 5 = 7 + 5 = 12$

$a_3 = a_2 + 5 = 12 + 5 = 17$

$a_4 = a_3 + 5 = 17 + 5 = 22$

The first four terms are 7, 12, 17, and 22.

15. $a_1 = 3$ and $a_n = 4a_{n-1}$ for $n \geq 2$

$a_2 = 4a_1 = 4(3) = 12$

$a_3 = 4a_2 = 4(12) = 48$

$a_4 = 4a_3 = 4(48) = 192$

The first four terms are 3, 12, 48, and 192.

17. $a_1 = 4$ and $a_n = 2a_{n-1} + 3$

$a_2 = 2(4) + 3 = 11$

$a_3 = 2(11) + 3 = 25$

$a_4 = 2(25) + 3 = 53$

The first four terms are 4, 11, 25, and 53.

19. $a_n = \dfrac{n^2}{n!}$

$a_1 = \dfrac{1^2}{1!} = 1$

$a_2 = \dfrac{2^2}{2!} = 2$

$a_3 = \dfrac{3^2}{3!} = \dfrac{9}{6} = \dfrac{3}{2}$

$a_4 = \dfrac{4^2}{4!} = \dfrac{16}{24} = \dfrac{2}{3}$

The first four terms are $1, 2, \frac{3}{2}$, and $\frac{2}{3}$.

21. $a_n = 2(n+1)!$

$a_1 = 2(1+1)! = 2(2) = 4$

$a_2 = 2(2+1)! = 2(6) = 12$

$a_3 = 2(3+1)! = 2(24) = 48$

$a_4 = 2(4+1)! = 2(120) = 240$

The first four terms are 4, 12, 48, and 240.

23. $\dfrac{17!}{15!} = \dfrac{17 \cdot 16 \cdot 15!}{15!} = 17 \cdot 16 = 272$

25. $\dfrac{16!}{2! \cdot 14!} = \dfrac{16 \cdot 15 \cdot 14!}{2! 14!} = \dfrac{16 \cdot 15}{2 \cdot 1} = \dfrac{8 \cdot 15}{1} = 120$

27. $\dfrac{(n+2)!}{n!} = \dfrac{(n+2)(n+1)n!}{n!} = (n+2)(n+1)$

29. $\displaystyle\sum_{i=1}^{6} 5i = 5 \cdot 1 + 5 \cdot 2 + 5 \cdot 3 + 5 \cdot 4 + 5 \cdot 5 + 5 \cdot 6$

$= 5 + 10 + 15 + 20 + 25 + 30$

$= 105$

31. $\displaystyle\sum_{i=1}^{4} 2i^2 = 2 \cdot 1^2 + 2 \cdot 2^2 + 2 \cdot 3^2 + 2 \cdot 4^2$

$= 2 + 8 + 18 + 32$

$= 60$

33.

$\displaystyle\sum_{k=1}^{5} k(k+4) = 1(5) + 2(6) + 3(7) + 4(8) + 5(9)$

$= 5 + 12 + 21 + 32 + 45$

$= 115$

35. $\sum_{i=1}^{4}\left(\dfrac{-1}{2}\right)^i$

$=\left(-\dfrac{1}{2}\right)^1+\left(-\dfrac{1}{2}\right)^2+\left(-\dfrac{1}{2}\right)^3+\left(-\dfrac{1}{2}\right)^4$

$=-\dfrac{1}{2}+\dfrac{1}{4}+-\dfrac{1}{8}+\dfrac{1}{16}$

$=-\dfrac{5}{16}$

37. $\sum_{i=5}^{9}11=11+11+11+11+11=55$

39. $\sum_{i=0}^{4}\dfrac{(-1)^i}{i!}$

$=\dfrac{(-1)^0}{0!}+\dfrac{(-1)^1}{1!}+\dfrac{(-1)^2}{2!}+\dfrac{(-1)^3}{3!}+\dfrac{(-1)^4}{4!}$

$=1-1+\dfrac{1}{2}-\dfrac{1}{6}+\dfrac{1}{24}$

$=\dfrac{9}{24}=\dfrac{3}{8}$

41. $\sum_{i=1}^{5}\dfrac{i!}{(i-1)!}=\dfrac{1!}{0!}+\dfrac{2!}{1!}+\dfrac{3!}{2!}+\dfrac{4!}{3!}+\dfrac{5!}{4!}$

$=1+2+3+4+5=15$

43. $1^2+2^2+3^2+\cdots+15^2=\sum_{i=1}^{15}i^2$

45. $2+2^2+2^3+2^4+\cdots+2^{11}=\sum_{i=1}^{11}2^i$

47. $1+2+3+\cdots+30=\sum_{i=1}^{30}i$

49. $\dfrac{1}{2}+\dfrac{2}{3}+\dfrac{3}{4}+\cdots+\dfrac{14}{14+1}=\sum_{i=1}^{14}\dfrac{i}{i+1}$

51. $4+\dfrac{4^2}{2}+\dfrac{4^3}{3}+\cdots+\dfrac{4^n}{n}=\sum_{i=1}^{n}\dfrac{4^i}{i}$

53. $1+3+5+\cdots+(2n-1)=\sum_{i=1}^{n}(2i-1)$

55. $5+7+9+\cdots+31$

Possible answer: $\sum_{k=1}^{14}(2k+3)$

57. $a+ar+ar^2+\cdots+ar^{12}$

Possible answer: $\sum_{k=0}^{12}ar^k$

59. $a+(a+d)+(a+2d)+\cdots+(a+nd)$

Possible answer: $\sum_{k=0}^{n}(a+kd)$

61. a. $\sum_{i=1}^{10}a_i$

$=333.3+407.5+495.4+662.1+$
$722.9+778.9+753.1+847.0+$
$938.9+942.5=6881.6$
This represents the total number of
CD's sold in the U.S. from 1991 to
2000, in millions.

b. $\dfrac{1}{10}\sum_{i=1}^{10}a_i=\dfrac{1}{10}\left(6881.6\right)=688.16$

This represents the average number of
CD's sold each year from 1991 to 2000,
in millions.

63. a. $\sum_{i=1}^{8}a_i=14.1+14.2+13.7+12.6+10.9$

$+8.7+7.6+6.5=88.3$
From 1993 through 2000, there were 88.3
million Welfare recipients in the US.

b. $\sum_{n=1}^{8}(-1.23n+16.55)$

422

$$= (-1.23 \cdot 1 + 16.55) + (-1.23 \cdot 2 + 16.55)$$
$$+ (-1.23 \cdot 3 + 16.55) + (-1.23 \cdot 4 + 16.55)$$
$$+ (-1.23 \cdot 5 + 16.55) + (-1.23 \cdot 6 + 16.55)$$
$$+ (-1.23 \cdot 7 + 16.55) + (-1.23 \cdot 8 + 16.55)$$
$$= 88.12$$

The model is very close to the actual sum.

65. $a_n = 6000 \left(1 + \dfrac{0.06}{4} \right)^n, n = 1, 2, 3, \cdots$

$a_{20} = 6000 \left(1 + \dfrac{0.06}{4} \right)^{20} \approx 8081.13$

After five years, the balance is \$8081.13.

67.–75. Answers may vary.

77. $\left(\dfrac{300}{20} \right)! = 15! = 1,307,674,368,000$

79. $\dfrac{20!}{(20 - 3)!} = 6840$

81. Answers may vary.

83. $a_n = \left(1 + \dfrac{1}{n} \right)^n$

$a_{10} = \left(1 + \dfrac{1}{10} \right)^{10} \approx 2.5937$

$a_{100} = \left(1 + \dfrac{1}{100} \right)^{100} \approx 2.7048$

$a_{1000} = \left(1 + \dfrac{1}{1000} \right)^{1000} \approx 2.7169$

$a_{10,000} = \left(1 + \dfrac{1}{10,000} \right)^{10,000} \approx 2.7181$

$a_{100,000} = \left(1 + \dfrac{1}{100,000} \right)^{100,000} \approx 2.7183$

As n gets larger, a_n gets closer to $e \approx 2.7183$.

85. $a_n = \dfrac{100}{n}$

As n gets larger, a_n approaches 0.

87. $a_n = \dfrac{3n^4 + n - 1}{5n^4 + 2n^2 + 1}$

As n gets larger, a_n approaches $\dfrac{3}{5}$.

89. $a_n = \begin{cases} \dfrac{a_{n-1}}{2} & \text{if } a_{n-1} \text{ is even.} \\ 3a_n + 5 & \text{if } a_{n-1} \text{ is odd.} \end{cases}$

$a_1 = 9$

Since 9 is odd, $a_2 = 3(9) + 5 = 32$.

Since 32 is even, $a_3 = \dfrac{32}{2} = 16$.

Similarly, $a_4 = \dfrac{16}{2} = 8$, $a_5 = \dfrac{8}{2} = 4$.

The first five terms of the sequence are 9, 32, 16, 8, and 4.

Section 8.2

Check Point Exercises

1. $a_1 = 51.5$

$a_2 = a_1 + 2.18 = 51.5 + 2.18 = 53.68$

$a_3 = a_2 + 2.18 = 53.68 + 2.18 = 55.86$

$a_4 = a_3 + 2.18 = 55.86 + 2.18 = 58.04$

$a_5 = a_4 + 2.18 = 58.04 + 2.18 = 60.22$

The first five terms are 51.5, 53.68, 55.86, 58.04, and 60.22.

2. $a_1 = 6$, $d = -5$

To find the ninth term, a_9, replace n in the formula with 9, a_1 with 6, and d with -5.

$a_n = a_1 + (n - 1)d$

$a_9 = 6 + (9 - 1)(-5)$

$\quad = 6 + 8(-5)$

$\quad = 6 + (-40)$

$\quad = -34$

3. a. $a_n = a_1 + (n - 1)d = 159,000 + (n - 1)9700$

b.

a_1 represents 1995 so a_{15} represents 2010.

$a_{15} = 159000 + (15 - 1)9700 = 294,800$

In 2010, a new one-family house will cost \$294,800.

4. 3, 6, 9, 12, ...

To find the sum of the first 15 terms, S_{15}, replace n in the formuls with 15.

$S_n = \dfrac{n}{2}(a_1 + a_n)$

$S_{15} = \dfrac{15}{2}(a_1 + a_{15})$

Use the formula for the general term of a sequence to find a_{15}. The common difference, d, is 3, and the first term, a_1, is 3.

$a_n = a_1 + (n - 1)d$

$a_{15} = 3 + (15 - 1)(3)$

$\quad = 3 + 14(3)$

$\quad = 3 + 42$

$\quad = 45$

Thus, $S_{15} = \frac{15}{2}(3 + 45) = \frac{15}{2}(48) = 360$.

5. $\displaystyle\sum_{i=1}^{30}(6i - 11) = (6 \cdot 1 - 11) + (6 \cdot 2 - 11) +$

$\qquad\qquad\qquad + (6 \cdot 3 - 11) + \dots + (6 \cdot 30 - 11)$

$\qquad\qquad = -5 + 1 + 7 + \dots + 169$

So the first term, a_1, is -5; the common difference, d, is $1 - (-5) = 6$; the last term, a_{30}, is 169. Substitute $n = 30$, $a_1 = -5$, and $a_{30} = 169$ in the formula $S_n = \frac{n}{2}(a_1 + a_n)$.

$S_{30} = \frac{30}{2}(-5 + 169) = 15(164) = 2460$

Thus, $\displaystyle\sum_{i=1}^{30}(6i - 11) = 2460$

6. Find the sum of the arithmetic sequence whose first term corresponds to costs in 2001 and whose last term corresponds to costs in 2010. Because the model describes costs n years after 2000, $n = 1$ describes the year 2001 and $n = 10$

describes the year 2010.

$a_n = 1800n + 49,730$

$a_1 = 1800 \cdot 1 + 49,730 = 51,530$

$a_{10} = 1800 \cdot 10 + 49,730 = 67,730$

To find the sum of the costs for all 10 years, find the sum of the ten terms of the arithmetic sequence

$51,530, 53,330, \ldots, 67,730$.

There are 10 terms with first term 51,530 and last term 67,730 so $n = 10$,

$a_1 = 51,530$, and $a_{10} = 67,730$.

$S_n = \dfrac{n}{2}(a_1 + a_n)$

$S_{10} = \dfrac{10}{2}(51,530 + 67,730) = 5(119,260)$

$\phantom{S_{10}} = 596,300$

The total cost for the ten-year period is $596,300.

Exercise Set 8.2

1. $a_1 = 200, \ d = 20$

The first six terms are 200, 220, 240, 260, 280, and 300.

3. $a_1 = -7, \ d = 4$

The first six terms are –7, –3, 1, 5, 9, and 13.

5. $a_1 = 300, \ d = -90$

The first six terms are 300, 210, 120, 30, –60, and –150.

7. $a_1 = \dfrac{5}{2}, \ d = -\dfrac{1}{2}$

The first six terms are $\dfrac{5}{2}, 2, \dfrac{3}{2}, 1, \dfrac{1}{2}$, and 0.

9. $a_n = a_{n-1} + 6, \ a_1 = -9$

The first six terms are –9, –3, 3, 9, 15, and 21.

11. $a_n = a_{n-1} - 10, \ a_1 = 30$

The first six terms are 30, 20, 10, 0, –10, and –20.

13. $a_n = a_{n-1} - 0.4, \ a_1 = 1.6$

The first six terms are 1.6, 1.2, 0.8, 0.4, 0, and –0.4.

15. $a_1 = 13, \ d = -4$

$a_n = 13 + (n-1)4$

$a_6 = 13 + 5(4) = 13 + 20 = 33$

17. $a_1 = 7, \ d = 5$

$a_n = 7 + (n-1)2$

$a_{50} = 7 + 49(5) = 252$

19. $a_1 = -40, \ d = 5$

$a_n = -40 + (n-1)5$

$a_{200} = -40 + (199)5 = 955$

21. $a_1 = 35, \ d = -3$

$a_n = 35 - 3(n-1)$

$a_{60} = 35 - 3(59) = -142$

23. 1, 5, 9, 13, …

$d = 5 - 1, \ = 4$

$a_n = 1 + (n-1)4 = 1 + 4n - 4$

$a_n = 4n - 3$

$a_{20} = 4(20) - 3 = 77$

25. 7, 3, –1, –5, …

$d = 3 - 7 = -4$

$a_n = 7 + (n-1)(-4) = 7 - 4n + 4$

$a_n = 11 - 4n$

$a_{20} = 11 - 4(20) = -69$

27. $a_1 = 9, \ d = 2$

$a_n = 9 + (n-1)(2)$

$a_n = 7 + 2n$

$a_{20} = 7 + 2(20) = 47$

29. $a_1 = -20, \ d = -4$

$a_n = -20 + (n-1)(-4)$

$a_n = -20 - 4n + 4$

$a_n = -16 - 4n$

$a_{20} = -16 - 4(20) = -96$

31. $a_n = a_{n-1} + 3, \ a_1 = 4$

$d = 3$

$a_n = 4 + (n-1)(3)$

$a_n = 1 + 3n$

$a_{20} = 1 + 3(20) = 61$

33. $a_n = a_{n-1} - 10, \ a_1 = 30, \ d = -10$

$a_n = 30 - 10(n-1) = 30 - 10n + 10$

$a_n = 40 - 10n$

$a_{20} = 40 - 10(20) = -160$

35. 4, 10, 16, 22, ...

$d = 10 - 4 = 6$

$a_n = 4 + (n-1)(6)$

$a_{20} = 4 + (19)(6) = 118$

$S_{20} = \dfrac{20}{2}(4 + 118) = 1220$

37. −10, −6, −2, 2, ...

$d = -6 - (-10) = -6 + 10 = 4$

$a_n = -10 + (n-1)4$

$a_{50} = -10 + (49)4 = 186$

$S_{50} = \dfrac{50}{2}(-10 + 186) = 4400$

39. $1 + 2 + 3 + 4 + \cdots + 100$

$S_{100} = \dfrac{100}{2}(1 + 100) = 5050$

41. $2 + 4 + 6 + \cdots + 120$

$S_{60} = \dfrac{60}{2}(2 + 120) = 3660$

43. even integers between 21 and 45;

$22 + 24 + 26 + \cdots + 44$

$S_{12} = \dfrac{12}{2}(22 + 44) = 396$

45. $\displaystyle\sum_{i=1}^{17}(5i + 3)$

$= (5+3) + (10+3) + (15+3) + \cdots + (85+3)$

$= 8 + 13 + 18 + \cdots + 88$

$S_{17} = \dfrac{17}{2}(8 + 88) = 816$

47. $\displaystyle\sum_{i=1}^{30}(-3i + 5)$

$= (-3+5) + (-6+5) + (-9+5)$

$\qquad + \cdots + (-90+5)$

$= 2 - 1 - 4 - \cdots - 85$

$S_{30} = \dfrac{30}{2}(2 - 85) = -1245$

49. $\displaystyle\sum_{i=1}^{100} 4i = 4 + 8 + 12 + \cdots + 400$

$S_{100} = \dfrac{100}{2}(4 + 400) = 20,200$

51. a. $a_n = 150 + (n-1)1.7$

b. $2006 - 1970 = 36, \ n = 36$

$a_{36} = 150 + (36 - 1)1.7 = 209.5$

In 2006, the average American will eat 209.5 pounds of vegetables.

53. a. $a_n = 10 + (n-1)0.66$ (Answers may vary)

b. $2006 - 1970 = 36, \ n = 36$

$a_{36} = 10 + (36 - 1)0.66 = 33.1$

In 2006, the average American will eat 33.1 pounds of cheese.

55. Company A:
$$a_n = 24,000 + (n-1)(1600)$$
$$a_{10} = 24,000 + 9(1600) = \$38,400$$
Company B:
$$a_n = 28,000 + (n-1)(1000)$$
$$a_{10} = 28,000 + 9(1000) = \$37,000$$
Company A will pay $1400 more.

57. a. $a_1 = 3.78, \ d = 0.576$
$$a_n = 3.78 + (n-1)(0.576)$$
$$a_n = 3.204 + 0.576n$$

  b. $a_1 = 3.78$
$$a_{41} = 3.204 + 0.576(41) = 26.82$$
$$S_{41} = \frac{41}{2}(3.78 + 26.82) = 627.3$$
The total amount is 627.3 million tons.

59. $a_n = 33,000 + (n-1)(2500)$
$$a_{10} = 33,000 + 9(2500) = 55,500$$
$$S_n = \frac{10}{2}(33,000 + 55,500) = 442,500$$
The total ten year salary is $442,500.

61. $a_n = 30 + (n-1)2$
$$a_{26} = 30 + (25)2 = 80$$
$$S_{26} = \frac{26}{2}(30 + 80) = 1430$$
The theater has 1430 seats.

63.–69. Answers may vary.

71. 21,700, 23,172, 24,644, 26,166, . . . ,
314,628
$$d = 23,172 - 21,700 = 1472$$
$$314,628 = 1472n + 20,228$$
$$1472n = 294,400$$
$$n = 200$$
It is the 200th term.

73. $1 + 3 + 5 + \cdots + (2n-1)$
$$S_n = \frac{n}{2}(1 + 2n - 1)$$
$$= \frac{n}{2}(2n)$$
$$= n^2$$

Section 8.3

Check Point Exercises

1. $a_1 = 12, \ r = \frac{1}{2}$
$$a_2 = 12\left(\frac{1}{2}\right)^1 = 6$$
$$a_3 = 12\left(\frac{1}{2}\right)^2 = \frac{12}{4} = 3$$
$$a_4 = 12\left(\frac{1}{2}\right)^3 = \frac{12}{8} = \frac{3}{2}$$
$$a_5 = 12\left(\frac{1}{2}\right)^4 = \frac{12}{16} = \frac{3}{4}$$
$$a_6 = 12\left(\frac{1}{2}\right)^5 = \frac{12}{32} = \frac{3}{8}$$

The first six terms are
$$12, \ 6, \ 3, \ \frac{3}{2}, \ \frac{3}{4}, \text{and} \ \frac{3}{8}.$$

2. $a_1 = 5, \ r = -3$
$$a_n = 5r^{n-1}$$
$$a_7 = 5(-3)^{7-1} = 5(-3)^6 = 5(729) = 3645$$
The seventh term is 3645.

3. 3, 6, 12, 24, 48, ...

$$r = \frac{6}{3} = 2, \; a_1 = 3$$

$$a_n = 3(2)^{n-1}$$

$$a_8 = 3(2)^{8-1} = 3(2)^7 = 3(128) = 384$$

The eighth term is 384.

4. $a_1 = 2, \; r = \frac{-6}{2} = -3$

$$S_n = \frac{a_1(1-r^r)}{1-r}$$

$$S_9 = \frac{2\left(1-(-3)^9\right)}{1-(-3)} = \frac{2(19,684)}{4} = 9842$$

The sum of the first nine terms is 9842.

5. $\displaystyle\sum_{i=1}^{8} 2 \cdot 3^i$

$$a_1 = 2 \cdot (3)^1 = 6, \; r = 3$$

$$S_n = \frac{a_1(1-r^n)}{1-r}$$

$$S_8 = \frac{6\left(1-3^8\right)}{1-3} = \frac{6(-6560)}{-2} = 19,680$$

Thus, $\displaystyle\sum_{i=1}^{8} 2 \cdot 3^i = 19,680.$

6. $a_1 = 30,000, \; r = 1.06$

$$S_n = \frac{a_1(1-r^n)}{1-r}$$

$$S_{30} = \frac{30,000\left(1-(1.06)^{30}\right)}{1-1.06} \approx 2,371,746$$

The total lifetime salary is \$2,371,746.

7. $A = P\dfrac{\left(1+\frac{r}{n}\right)^{nt} - 1}{\frac{r}{n}}$

$$P = 3000, \; r = 0.10, \; n = 1, \; t = 40$$

$$A = 3000\frac{(1+0.10)^{40} - 1}{0.10} \approx 1,327,778$$

The value of the IRA will be \$1,327,778.

8. $3 + 2 + \dfrac{4}{3} + \dfrac{8}{9} + \cdots$

$$a_1 = 3, \; r = \frac{2}{3}$$

$$S = \frac{a_1}{1-r}$$

$$S = \frac{3}{1-\frac{2}{3}} = \frac{3}{\frac{1}{3}} = 9$$

The sum of this infinite geometric series is 9.

9. $0.\overline{9} = 0.9999\cdots = \dfrac{9}{10} + \dfrac{9}{100} + \dfrac{9}{1000} + \cdots$

$$a_1 = \frac{9}{10}, r = \frac{1}{10}$$

$$S = \frac{\frac{9}{10}}{1-\frac{1}{10}} = \frac{\frac{9}{10}}{\frac{9}{10}} = 1$$

An equivalent fraction for $0.\overline{9}$ is 1.

10. $a_1 = 1000(0.8) = 800, \; r = 0.8$

$$S = \frac{800}{1-0.8} = 4000$$

The total amount spent is \$4000.

Exercise Set 8.3

1. $a_1 = 5, \; r = 3$

The first five terms are 5, 15, 45, 135, and 405.

3. $a_1 = 20$, $r = \dfrac{1}{2}$

The first five terms are $20,\ 10,\ 5,\ \dfrac{5}{2}$,

and $\dfrac{5}{4}$.

5. $a_n = -4a_{n-1}$, $a_1 = 10$

The first five terms are $10, -40, 160, -640$, and 2560.

7. $a_n = -5a_{n-1}$, $a_1 = -6$

The first five terms are $-6, 30, -150, 750$, and -3750.

9. $a_1 = 6$, $r = 2$

$a_n = 6 \cdot 2^{n-1}$

$a_8 = 6 \cdot 2^7 = 768$

11. $a_1 = 5$, $r = -2$

$a_n = 5 \cdot (-2)^{n-1}$

$a_{12} = 5 \cdot (-2)^{11} = -10,240$

13.

$a_1 = 1000$, $r = -\dfrac{1}{2}$

$a_n = 1000 \left(-\dfrac{1}{2}\right)^{n-1}$

$a_{40} = 1000 \left(-\dfrac{1}{2}\right)^{39}$

≈ 0.000000002

15. $a_1 = 1,000,000$, $r = 0.1$

$a_n = 1,000,000 (0.1)^{n-1}$

$a_8 = 1,000,000 (0.1)^7 = 0.1$

17. $3, 12, 48, 192, \ldots$

$r = \dfrac{12}{3} = 4$

$a_n = 3(4)^{n-1}$

$a_7 = 3(4)^6 = 12,288$

19. $19, 6, 2, \dfrac{2}{3}, \cdots$ $r = \dfrac{6}{18} = \dfrac{1}{3}$

$a_n = 18 \left(\dfrac{1}{3}\right)^{n-1}$

$a_7 = 18 \left(\dfrac{1}{3}\right)^6 = \dfrac{2}{81}$

21. $1.5, -3, 6, -12, \ldots$

$r = \dfrac{6}{-3} = -2$

$a_n = 1.5(-2)^{n-1}$

$a_7 = 1.5(-2)^6 = 96$

23. $0.0004, -0.004, 0.04, -0.4, \ldots$

$r = \dfrac{-0.004}{0.0004} = -10$

$a_n = 0.0004(-10)^{n-1}$

$a_7 = 0.0004(-10)^6 = 400$

25. $2, 6, 18, 54, \ldots$

$r = \dfrac{6}{2} = 3$

$S_{12} = \dfrac{2\left(1 - 3^{12}\right)}{1 - 3} = \dfrac{2(-531,440)}{-2} = 531,440$

27. $3, -6, 12, -24, \ldots$

$r = \dfrac{-6}{3} = -2$

$S_{11} = \dfrac{3\left[1 - (-2)^{11}\right]}{1 - (-2)} = \dfrac{3(2049)}{3} = 2049$

29. $-\dfrac{3}{2}, 3, -6, 12, \cdots$

$r = \dfrac{3}{\frac{-3}{2}} = -2$

$S_{14} = \dfrac{-\frac{3}{2}\left[1-(-2)^{14}\right]}{1-(-2)} = \dfrac{-\frac{3}{2}(-16,383)}{3} = \dfrac{16,383}{2}$

31. $\displaystyle\sum_{i=1}^{8} 3^i$

$r = 3, \quad a_1 = 3$

$S_8 = \dfrac{3\left(1-3^8\right)}{1-3} = \dfrac{3\left(-6560\right)}{-2} = 9840$

33. $\displaystyle\sum_{i=1}^{10} 5\cdot 2^i$

$r = 2, \quad a_1 = 10$

$S_{10} = \dfrac{10\left(1-2^{10}\right)}{1-2} = \dfrac{10\left(-1023\right)}{-1} = 10,230$

35. $\displaystyle\sum_{i=1}^{6} \left(\dfrac{1}{2}\right)^{i+1}$

$r = \dfrac{1}{2}, \quad a_1 = \dfrac{1}{4}$

$S_6 = \dfrac{\dfrac{1}{4}\left(1-\left(\dfrac{1}{2}\right)^6\right)}{1-\dfrac{1}{2}} = \dfrac{\dfrac{1}{4}\left(\dfrac{63}{64}\right)}{\dfrac{1}{2}} = \dfrac{63}{128}$

37. $r = \dfrac{1}{3}$

$S_\infty = \dfrac{1}{1-\frac{1}{3}} = \dfrac{1}{\frac{2}{3}} = \dfrac{3}{2}$

39. $r = \dfrac{1}{4}$

$S_\infty = \dfrac{3}{1-\frac{1}{4}} = \dfrac{3}{\frac{3}{4}} = 4$

41. $r = -\dfrac{1}{2}$

$S_\infty = \dfrac{1}{1-\left(-\dfrac{1}{2}\right)} = \dfrac{1}{\frac{3}{2}} = \dfrac{2}{3}$

43. $r = -0.3$

$S_\infty = \dfrac{8}{1-(-0.3)} = \dfrac{8}{1.3} \approx 6.15385$

45. $r = \dfrac{1}{10}$

$S_\infty = \dfrac{\frac{5}{10}}{1-\frac{1}{10}} = \dfrac{\frac{5}{10}}{\frac{9}{10}} = \dfrac{5}{9}$

47. $r = \dfrac{1}{100}$

$S_\infty = \dfrac{\frac{47}{100}}{1-\frac{1}{100}} = \dfrac{\frac{47}{100}}{\frac{99}{100}} = \dfrac{47}{99}$

49. $0.\overline{257} = \dfrac{257}{1000} + \dfrac{257}{10^6} + \dfrac{257}{10^9} + \cdots$

$r = \dfrac{1}{1000}$

$S_\infty = \dfrac{\frac{257}{1000}}{1-\frac{1}{1000}} = \dfrac{\frac{257}{1000}}{\frac{999}{1000}} = \dfrac{257}{999}$

51. $a_n = n + 5$

arithmetic, $d = 1$

53. $a_n = 2^n$

geometric, $r = 2$

55. $a_n = n^2 + 5$

neither

57. $1, 2, 4, 8, \ldots$

$r = 2$

$a_n = 2^{n-1}$

$a_{15} = 2^{14} = \$16,384$

59. $a_1 = 3,000,000$

$r = 1.04$

$a_n = 3,000,000(1.04)^{n-1}$

$a_7 = 3,000,000(1.04)^6 = \$3,795,957$

61. a. $\dfrac{30.15}{29.76} \approx 1.013$

$\dfrac{30.54}{30.15} \approx 1.013$

$\dfrac{30.94}{30.54} \approx 1.013$

The population is increasing geometrically with $r \approx 1.013$.

b. $a_n = 29.76 \cdot 1.013^{n-1}$

c. $2000 - 1989 = 11$

$a_{11} = 29.76 \cdot 1.013^{11-1} = 33.86$

In 2000, the model predicts California population will be 33.86. This is very close to the actual population.

63. $1, 2, 4, 8, \ldots$

$r = 2$

$S_{15} = \dfrac{1(1 - 2^{15})}{1 - 2} = 32,767$

The total savings is \$32,767.

65. $a_1 = 24,000, \ r = 1.05$

$S_{20} = \dfrac{24,000\left[1 - (1.05)^{20}\right]}{1 - 1.05} = 793,582.90$

The total salary is \$793,583.

67. $r = 0.9$

$S_{10} = \dfrac{20(1 - 0.9^{10})}{1 - 0.9} \approx 130.26$

The total length is 130.26 inches.

69. $A = 2500 \dfrac{\left(1 + 0.09\right)^{40} - 1}{0.09} \approx 844,706.11$

In 40 years, the value is \$844,706.

71. $A = 600 \dfrac{\left(1 + \frac{0.08}{4}\right)^{72} - 1}{\frac{0.08}{4}} \approx 94,834.21$

After 18 years, the value is \$94,834.

73. $r = 0.6$

$S_\infty = \dfrac{6(0.6)}{1 - 0.6} = 9$

The total economic impact is \$9 million.

75. $r = \frac{1}{4}$

$S_\infty = \dfrac{\frac{1}{4}}{1 - \frac{1}{4}} = \dfrac{1}{4} \cdot \dfrac{4}{3} = \dfrac{1}{3}$

77.–85. Answers may vary.

87. $f(x) = \dfrac{2\left[1 - \left(\frac{1}{3}\right)^x\right]}{1 - \frac{1}{3}}$

Horizontal asymptote at $y = 3$

$\displaystyle\sum_{n=0}^{\infty} 2\left(\tfrac{1}{3}\right)^n = \dfrac{2}{1 - \frac{1}{3}} = 3$

89. a. False; there is no common ratio.

   b. False; the sum can be calculated exactly, since the series is geometric $\left(r = \tfrac{1}{2}\right)$.

   c. False; $10 - 5 + \dfrac{5}{2} - \dfrac{5}{4} \cdots = \dfrac{10}{1 + \dfrac{1}{2}}$

   d. True; $r = 0.5 = \tfrac{1}{2}$

   (d) is true.

91. $1,000,000 = P\dfrac{\left(1 + \dfrac{0.1}{12}\right)^{360} - 1}{\dfrac{0.1}{12}}$

   $1,000,000 \approx 2260.49P$

   $P \approx 442.38$
   You must deposit \$442 monthly.

Section 8.4

Check Point Exercises

1. a. $S_1: 2 = 1(1+1)$

       $S_k: 2 + 4 + 6 + \cdots 2k = k(k+1)$

       $S_{k+1}: 2 + 4 + 6 + \cdots 2(k+1) = (k+1)(k+2)$

  b. $S_1 = 1^3 = \dfrac{1^2(1+1)^2}{4}$

       $S_k = 1^3 + 2^3 + 3^3 + \cdots + k^3 = \dfrac{k^2(k+1)^2}{4}$

       $S_{k+1} = 1^3 + 2^3 + 3^3 + \cdots + (k+1)^3 = \dfrac{(k+1)^2(k+2)^2}{4}$

2. $S_1: 2 = 1(1+1)$

       $2 = 2$ is true.

   $S_k: 2 + 4 + 6 + \cdots + 2k = k(k+1)$

   $S_{k+1}: 2 + 4 + 6 + \cdots + 2k + 2(k+1) = (k+1)(k+2)$

Add $2(k+1)$ to both sides of S_k:

$2 + 4 + 6 + \cdots + 2k + 2(k+1) = k(k+1) + 2(k+1)$

Simplify the right-hand side:

$k(k+1) + 2(k+1) = (k+1)(k+2)$

If S_k is true, then S_{k+1} is true. The statement is true for all n.

3. $S_1: 1^3 = \dfrac{1^2(1+1)^2}{4}$

       $1 = \dfrac{4}{4}$

       $1 = 1$ is true.

       $S_k: 1^3 + 2^3 + 3^3 + \cdots + k^3 = \dfrac{k^2(k+1)^2}{4}$

       $S_{k+1}: 1^3 + 2^3 + 3^3 + \cdots + k^3 + (k+1)^3 = \dfrac{(k+1)^2(k+2)^2}{4}$

Add $(k+1)^3$ to both sides of S_k:

$1^3 + 2^3 + 3^3 + \cdots + k^3 + (k+1)^3 = \dfrac{k^2(k+1)^2}{4} + (k+1)^3$

Simplify the right hand side:

$$\frac{k^2(k+1)^2}{4}+(k+1)^3=\frac{k^2(k+1)^2+4(k+1)^3}{4}=\frac{(k+1)^2\left[k^2+4(k+1)\right]}{4}=\frac{(k+1)^2(k^2+4k+4)}{4}$$

$$=\frac{(k+1)^2(k+2)^2}{4}$$

If S_k is true, then S_{k+1} is true. The statement is true for all n.

4. S_1: 2 is a factor of $1^2+1=2$, since $2=2\cdot 1$.

     S_k: 2 is a factor of k^2+k

S_{k+1}: 2 is a factor of $(k+1)^2+(k+1)$

Simplify:

$$(k+1)^2+(k+1)=k^2+2k+1+k+1$$
$$=k^2+3k+2$$
$$=k^2+k+2k+2$$
$$=(k^2+k)+2(k+1)$$

Because we assume S_k is true, we know 2 is a factor of k^2+k. Since 2 is a factor of $2(k+1)$, we conclude 2 is a factor of the sum $(k^2+k)+2(k+1)$. If S_k is true, then S_{k+1} is true. The statement is true for all n.

Exercise Set 8.4

1. $S_n=1+3+5+\cdots+(n-1)=n^2$

   $S_1:1=1^2$

     $1=1$ true

   $S_2:\ 1+3=2^2$

       $4=4$ true

   $S_3:\ 1+3+5=3^2$

        $9=9$ true

3. S_n: 2 is a factor of n^2-n

   S_1: 2 is a factor of $1^2-1=0$

     $0=0\cdot 2$ so 2 is a factor of 0 is true.

   S_2: 2 is a factor of $2^2-2=2$

     $2=1\cdot 2$ so 2 is a factor of 2 is true.

   S_3: 2 is a factor of $3^2-3=6$

     $6=3\cdot 2$ so 2 is a factor of 6 is true.

5. $S_n : 4 + 8 + 12 + \cdots + 4n = 2n(n+1)$

       $S_k : 4 + 8 + 12 + \cdots + 4k = 2k(k+1)$

    $S_{k+1} : 4 + 8 + 12 + \cdots + 4(k+1) = 2(k+1)(k+1+1)$

         $4 + 8 + 12 + \cdots + 4(k+1) = 2(k+1)(k+2)$

7. $S_n : 3 + 7 + 11 + \cdots + (4n-1) = n(2n+1)$

       $S_k : 3 + 7 + 11 + \cdots + (4k-1) = k(2k+1)$

    $S_{k+1} : 3 + 7 + 11 + \cdots + [4(k+1)-1] = (k+1)[2(k+1)+1]$

         $3 + 7 + 11 + \cdots + (4k+3) = (k+1)(2k+3)$

9. $S_n :$ 2 is a factor of $n^2 - n + 2$

      $S_k :$ 2 is a factor of $k^2 - k + 2$

   $S_{k+1} :$ 2 is a factor of $\left(k+1\right)^2 - \left(k+1\right) + 2$

        $k^2 + 2k + 1 - k - 1 + 2 = k^2 + k + 2$

   $S_{k+1} :$ 2 is a factor of $k^2 + k + 2.$

11. $S_1 : 4 = 2(1)(1+1)$

       $4 = 2(2)$

       $4 = 4$ is true.

   $S_k : 4 + 8 + 12 + \cdots + 4k = 2k(k+1)$

   $S_{k+1} : 4 + 8 + 12 + \cdots 4(k+1) = 2(k+1)(k+1+1)$

Add $4(k+1)$ to both sides of S_k:

$4 + 8 + 12 + \cdots + 4(k+1) = 2k(k+1) + 4(k+1)$

Simplify the right-hand side:

$= 2k(k+1) + 4(k+1) = (2k+4)(k+1)$

$= 2(k+2)(k+1)$

$= 2(k+1)(k+1+1)$

If S_k is true, then S_{k+1} is true. The statement is true for all n.

13. $S_1 : 1 = 1^2$

       $1 = 1$ is true.

    $S_k : 1 + 3 + 5 + \cdots + (2k-1) = k^2$

  $S_{k+1} : 1 + 3 + 5 + \cdots + (2k-1) + [2(k+1)-1] = (k+1)^2$

         $1 + 3 + 5 + \cdots + (2k-1) + (2k+1) = (k+1)^2$

Add $(2k+1)$ to both sides of S_k:

$1 + 3 + 5 + \cdots + (2k-1) + (2k+1) = k^2 + (2k+1)$

Simplify the right-hand side:

$= k^2 + (2k+1)$

$= (k + 1)^2$

If S_k is true, then S_{k+1} is true. The statement is true for all n.

15. S_1: $3 = 1[2(1) + 1)]$

        $3 = 3$ is true.

    S_k: $3 + 7 + 11 + \cdots + (4k - 1) = k(2k + 1)$

   S_{k+1}: $3 + 7 + 11 + \cdots + (4k - 1) + [4(k + 1) - 1] = (k + 1)[2(k + 1) + 1]$

         $3 + 7 + 11 + \cdots + (4k - 1) + (4k + 3) = (k + 1)(2k + 3)$

Add $(4k + 3)$ to both sides of S_k:

$3 + 7 + 11 + \ldots + (4k - 1) + (4k + 3) = k(2k + 1) + 4(k + 3)$

Simplify the right-hand side:

$= k(2k + 1) + (4k + 3) = 2k^2 + k + 4k + 3$

$= 2k^2 + 5k + 3$

$= (k + 1)(2k + 3)$

If S_k is true, then S_{k+1} is true. The statement is true for all n.

17. S_1: $1 = 2^1 - 1$

        $1 = 1$ is true.

    S_k: $1 + 2 + 2^2 + \cdots + 2^{k-1} = 2^k - 1$

   S_{k+1}: $1 + 2 + 2^2 + \cdots + 2^{k-1} + 2^{k+1-1} = 2^{k+1} - 1$

    $1 + 2 + 2^2 + \cdots + 2^{k-1} + 2^k = 2^{k+1} - 1$

Add 2^k to both sides of S_k:

$1 + 2 + 2^2 + \cdots + 2^{k-1} + 2^k = 2^k + 2^k - 1$

Simplify the right-hand side:

$= 2^k + 2^k - 1 = 2(2^k) - 1$

$= 2^{k+1} - 1$

If S_k is true, then S_{k+1} is true. The statement is true for all n.

19. S_1: $2 = 2^{1+1} - 2$

         $2 = 4 - 2$

         $2 = 2$ is true.

    S_k: $2 + 4 + 8 + \cdots + 2^k = 2^{k+1} - 2$

   S_{k+1}: $2 + 4 + 8 + \cdots + 2^k + 2^{k+1} = 2^{k+2} - 2$

Add 2^{k+1} to both sides of S_k:

    $2 + 4 + 8 + \cdots + 2^k + 2^{k+1} = 2^{k+1} + 2^{k+1} - 2$

Simplify the right-hand side:

$$= 2^{k+1} + 2^{k+1} - 1 = 2\left(2^{k+1}\right) - 2$$

$$= 2^{k+2} - 2$$

If S_k is true, then S_{k+1} is true. The statement is true for all n.

21. S_1: $1 \cdot 2 = \dfrac{1(1+1)(1+2)}{3}$

             $2 = \dfrac{6}{3}$

             $2 = 2$ is true.

$$S_k : 1 \cdot 2 + 2 \cdot 3 + 3 \cdot 4 + \cdots + k(k+1) = \frac{k(k+1)(k+2)}{3}$$

$$S_{k+1} : 1 \cdot 2 + 2 \cdot 3 + 3 \cdot 4 + \cdots + k(k+1) + (k+1)(k+2) = \frac{(k+1)(k+2)(k+3)}{3}$$

Add $(k+1)(k+2)$ to both sided of S_k:

$$1 \cdot 2 + 2 \cdot 3 + 3 \cdot 4 + \cdots + k(k+1) + (k+1)(k+2) = \frac{k(k+1)(k+2)}{3} + (k+1)(k+2)$$

Simplify the right-hand side:

$$= \frac{k(k+1)(k+2)}{3} + (k+1)(k+2) = \frac{k(k+1)(k+2) + 3(k+1)(k+2)}{3}$$

$$= \frac{(k+1)(k+2)(k+3)}{3}$$

If S_k is true, then S_{k+1} is true. The statement is true for all n.

23. S_1: $\dfrac{1}{1 \cdot 2} = \dfrac{1}{1+1}$

             $\dfrac{1}{2} = \dfrac{1}{2}$ is true.

$$S_k : \frac{1}{1 \cdot 2} + \frac{1}{2 \cdot 3} + \frac{1}{3 \cdot 4} + \cdots + \frac{1}{k(k+1)} = \frac{k}{k+1}$$

$$S_{k+1} : \frac{1}{1 \cdot 2} + \frac{1}{2 \cdot 3} + \frac{1}{3 \cdot 4} + \cdots + \frac{1}{k(k+1)} + \frac{1}{(k+1)(k+2)} = \frac{k+1}{k+2}$$

Add $\dfrac{1}{(k+1)(k+2)}$ to both sides of S_k:

$$\frac{1}{1 \cdot 2} + \frac{1}{2 \cdot 3} + \frac{1}{3 \cdot 4} + \cdots + \frac{1}{k(k+1)} + \frac{1}{(k+1)(k+2)} = \frac{k}{k+1} + \frac{1}{(k+1)(k+2)}$$

Simplify the right-hand side:

$$\frac{k}{\left(k+1\right)} + \frac{1}{\left(k+1\right)\left(k+2\right)} = \frac{k\left(k+2\right)+1}{\left(k+1\right)\left(k+2\right)}$$

$$= \frac{k^2 + 2k + 1}{\left(k+1\right)\left(k+2\right)}$$

$$= \frac{(k+1)(k+1)}{(k+1)(k+2)}$$

$$= \frac{k+1}{k+2}$$

If S_k is true, then S_{k+1} is true. The statement is true for all n.

25. S_1: 2 is a factor of $1^2 - 1 = 0$, since $0 = 2 \cdot 0$.

   S_k: 2 is a factor of $k^2 - k$

S_{k+1}: 2 is a factor of $\left(k+1\right)^2 - \left(k+1\right)$

$(k+1)^2 - (k-1) = k^2 + 2k + 1 - k - 1$

$$= k^2 + k$$

$$= k^2 - k + 2k$$

$$= (k^2 - k) + 2k$$

Because we assume S_k is true, we know 2 as a factor of $k^2 - k$. Since 2 is a factor of $2k$, we conclude 2 is factor of the sum $(k^2 + k) + 2k$. If S_k is true, then S_{k+1} is true. The statement is true for all n.

27. S_1: 6 is a factor of $1(1+1)(1+2) = 6$, since $6 = 6 \cdot 1$.

   S_k: 6 is a factor of $k(k+1)(k+2)$

S_{k+1}: 6 is a factor of $(k+1)(k+2)(k+3)$

   $(k+1)(k+2)(k+3) = k(k+1)(k+2) + 3(k+1)(k+2)$

Because we assume S_k is true, we know 6 as a factor of $k(k+1)(k+2)$. Since either $k+1$ or $k+2$ must be even, the product $(k+1)(k+2)$ is even. Thus 2 is a factor of $(k+1)(k+2)$, and we can conclude that 6 is factor of $3(k+1)(k+2)$ If S_k is true, then S_{k+1} is true.
The statement is true for all n.

29. $S_1: \left(ab\right)^1 = a^1 b^1$

$ab = ab$ is true.

$S_k: \left(ab\right)^k = a^k b^k$

$S_{k+1}: \left(ab\right)^{k+1} = a^{k+1} b^{k+1}$

Multiply both sides of S_k by ab:

$\left(ab\right)^k \left(ab\right) = a^k b^k \left(ab\right)$

$\left(ab\right)^{k+1} = a^{k+1} b^{k+1}$

If S_k is true, then S_{k+1} is true.
The statement is true for all n.

31. Answers may vary.

33. $n^2 > 2n + 1$ for $n \geq 3$

$S_3: 3^2 > 2 \cdot 3 + 1$

$\qquad 9 > 7$

$S_k: k^2 > 2k + 1$ for $k \geq 3$

$S_{k+1}: (k+1)^2 > 2k + 3$.

Add $2k + 1$ to both sides of S_k.

$k^2 + (2k+1) > 2k + 1 + (2k+1)$

Write the left side of the inequalities as the square of a binomial and simplify the right side. $(k+1)^2 > 4k + 2$

Since $4k + 2 > 2k + 3$ for $k \geq 3$, we can conclude that $(k+1)^2 > 4k + 2 > 2k + 3$.

By the transitive property,

$(k+1)^2 > 2k + 3$

$(k+1)^2 > 2(k+1) + 1$

If S_k is true, then S_{k+1} is true.
The statement is true for all n.

35. $S_1: \dfrac{1}{4} = \dfrac{1}{4}$

$S_2: \dfrac{1}{4} + \dfrac{1}{12} = \dfrac{1}{3}$

$S_3: \dfrac{1}{4} + \dfrac{1}{12} + \dfrac{1}{24} = \dfrac{3}{8}$

$S_4: \dfrac{1}{4} + \dfrac{1}{12} + \dfrac{1}{24} + \dfrac{1}{40} = \dfrac{2}{5}$

$S_5: \dfrac{1}{4} + \dfrac{1}{12} + \dfrac{1}{24} + \dfrac{1}{40} + \dfrac{1}{60} = \dfrac{5}{12}$

$S_n: \dfrac{1}{4} + \dfrac{1}{12} + \dfrac{1}{24} + \cdots + \dfrac{1}{2n(n+1)} = \dfrac{n}{2n+2}$

$S_k: \dfrac{1}{4} + \dfrac{1}{12} + \dfrac{1}{24} + \cdots + \dfrac{1}{2k(k+1)} = \dfrac{k}{2k+2}$

$S_{k+1}: \dfrac{1}{4} + \dfrac{1}{12} + \dfrac{1}{24} + \cdots + \dfrac{1}{2k(k+1)} + \dfrac{1}{2(k+1)(k+2)}$

$= \dfrac{k+1}{2k+4}$

Add $\dfrac{1}{2(k+1)(k+2)}$ to both sides of S_k:

$\dfrac{1}{4} + \dfrac{1}{12} + \dfrac{1}{24} + \cdots + \dfrac{1}{2k(k+1)} + \dfrac{1}{2(k+1)(k+2)}$

$= \dfrac{k}{2k+2} + \dfrac{1}{2(k+1)(k+2)}$

Simplify the right-hand side:

$\dfrac{k}{2k+2} + \dfrac{1}{2(k+1)(k+2)}$

$= \dfrac{k(k+2) + 1}{2(k+1)(k+2)}$

$= \dfrac{k^2 + 2k + 1}{2(k+1)(k+2)}$

$= \dfrac{(k+1)^2}{2(k+1)(k+2)}$

$= \dfrac{k+1}{2k+4}$

If S_k is true, then S_{k+1} is true.
The conjecture is proven.

Section 8.5

Check Point Exercises

1. a. $\dbinom{6}{3} = \dfrac{6!}{3!\,(6-3)!} = \dfrac{6!}{3!\,3!} = \dfrac{5 \cdot 4}{1} = 20$

    b. $\dbinom{6}{0} = \dfrac{6!}{0!\,(6-0)!} = \dfrac{6!}{6!} = 1$

    c. $\dbinom{8}{2} = \dfrac{8!}{2!\,(8-2)!} = \dfrac{8!}{2!\,6!} = \dfrac{8 \cdot 7}{2} = 28$

    d. $\dbinom{3}{3} = \dfrac{3!}{3!\,(3-3)!} = \dfrac{3!}{3!\,0!} = \dfrac{3!}{3!} = 1$

2. $(x+1)^4 = \dbinom{4}{0}x^4 + \dbinom{4}{1}x^3 + \dbinom{4}{2}x^2 + \dbinom{4}{1}x + \dbinom{4}{0} = x^4 + 4x^3 + 6x^2 + 4x + 1$

3. $(x-2y)^5$

    $= \dbinom{5}{0}x^5(-2y)^0 + \dbinom{5}{1}x^4(-2y)^1 + \dbinom{5}{2}x^3(-2y)^2 + \dbinom{5}{3}x^2(-2y)^3 + \dbinom{5}{4}x(-2y)^4 + \dbinom{5}{5}x^0(-2y)^5$

    $= x^5 - 5x^4(2y) + 10x^3(4y^2) - 10x^2(8y^3) + 5x(16y^4) - 32y^5$

    $= x^5 - 10x^4y + 40x^3y^2 - 80x^2y^3 + 80xy^4 - 32y^5$

4. $(2x+y)^9$

    fifth term $= \dbinom{9}{4}(2x)^5 y^4 = \dfrac{9!}{4!\,5!}(32x^5)y^4 = 4032x^5y^4$

Exercise Set 8.5

1. $\dbinom{8}{3} = \dfrac{8!}{3!\,(8-3)!} = \dfrac{8 \cdot 7 \cdot 6}{3 \cdot 2 \cdot 1} = 56$

3. $\dbinom{12}{1} = \dfrac{12!}{1!\,11!} = 12$

5. $\dbinom{6}{6} = \dfrac{6!}{0!\,6!} = 1$

7. $\begin{pmatrix} 100 \\ 2 \end{pmatrix} = \dfrac{100!}{2!\,98!} = \dfrac{100 \cdot 99}{2} = 4950$

9. $(x+2)^3 = \begin{pmatrix} 3 \\ 0 \end{pmatrix} x^3 + \begin{pmatrix} 3 \\ 1 \end{pmatrix} 2x^2 + \begin{pmatrix} 3 \\ 2 \end{pmatrix} 4x + \begin{pmatrix} 3 \\ 3 \end{pmatrix} 8$

$\qquad = x^3 + 3x^2 \cdot 2 + 3x \cdot 4 + 8$

$\qquad = x^3 + 6x^2 + 12x + 8$

11. $(3x+y)^3 = \begin{pmatrix} 3 \\ 0 \end{pmatrix} 27x^3 + \begin{pmatrix} 3 \\ 1 \end{pmatrix} 9x^2 y + \begin{pmatrix} 3 \\ 2 \end{pmatrix} 3xy^2 + \begin{pmatrix} 3 \\ 3 \end{pmatrix} y^3$

$\qquad = 27x^3 + 27x^2 y + 9xy^2 + y^3$

13. $(5x-1)^3 = \begin{pmatrix} 3 \\ 0 \end{pmatrix} 125x^3 - \begin{pmatrix} 3 \\ 1 \end{pmatrix} 25x^2 + \begin{pmatrix} 3 \\ 2 \end{pmatrix} 5x - \begin{pmatrix} 3 \\ 3 \end{pmatrix}$

$\qquad = 125x^3 - 75x^2 + 15x - 1$

15. $(2x+1)^4 = \begin{pmatrix} 4 \\ 0 \end{pmatrix} 16x^4 - \begin{pmatrix} 4 \\ 1 \end{pmatrix} 8x^3 + \begin{pmatrix} 4 \\ 2 \end{pmatrix} 4x^2 + \begin{pmatrix} 4 \\ 3 \end{pmatrix} 2x + \begin{pmatrix} 4 \\ 4 \end{pmatrix}$

$\qquad = 16x^4 + 32x^3 + 24x^2 + 8x + 1$

17. $(x^2+2y)^4 = \begin{pmatrix} 4 \\ 0 \end{pmatrix} (x^2)^4 + \begin{pmatrix} 4 \\ 1 \end{pmatrix} (x^2)^3 (2y) + \begin{pmatrix} 4 \\ 2 \end{pmatrix} (x^2)^2 (2y)^2 + \begin{pmatrix} 4 \\ 3 \end{pmatrix} (x^2)^1 (2y)^3 + \begin{pmatrix} 4 \\ 4 \end{pmatrix} (2y)^4$

$\qquad = 1(x^8) + 4(x^6)(2y) + 6(x^4)(4y^2) + 4x^2(8y^3) + 1(16y^4)$

$\qquad = x^8 + 8x^6 y + 24x^4 y^2 + 32x^2 y^3 + 16y^4$

19. $(y-3)^4 = \begin{pmatrix} 4 \\ 0 \end{pmatrix} y^4 + \begin{pmatrix} 4 \\ 1 \end{pmatrix} y^3 (-3) + \begin{pmatrix} 4 \\ 2 \end{pmatrix} y^2 (-3)^2 + \begin{pmatrix} 4 \\ 3 \end{pmatrix} y(-3)^3 + \begin{pmatrix} 4 \\ 4 \end{pmatrix} (-3)^4$

$\qquad = y^4 + 4(y^3)(-3) + 6(y^2)(9) + 4(y)(-27) + 81$

$\qquad = y^4 - 12y^3 + 54y^2 - 108y + 81$

21. $(2x^3-1)^4 = \begin{pmatrix} 4 \\ 0 \end{pmatrix} (2x^3)^4 + \begin{pmatrix} 4 \\ 1 \end{pmatrix} (2x^3)^3 (-1) + \begin{pmatrix} 4 \\ 2 \end{pmatrix} (2x^3)^2 (-1)^2 + \begin{pmatrix} 4 \\ 3 \end{pmatrix} (2x^3)(-1)^3 + \begin{pmatrix} 4 \\ 4 \end{pmatrix} (-1)^4$

$\qquad = 16x^{12} - 4(8x^9) + 6(4x^6) - 4(2x^3) + 1$

$\qquad = 16x^{12} - 32x^9 + 24x^6 - 8x^3 + 1$

23. $(c+2)^5 = \binom{5}{0}c^5 + \binom{5}{1}c^4(2) + \binom{5}{2}c^3(2^2) + \binom{5}{3}c^2(2^3) + \binom{5}{4}c(2^4) + \binom{5}{5}(2^5)$

$\quad = c^5 + 5c^4(2) + 10c^3(4) + 10c^2(8) + 5c(16) + 32$

$\quad = c^5 + 10c^4 + 40c^3 + 80c^2 + 80c + 32$

25. $(x-1)^5 = \binom{5}{0}x^5 - \binom{5}{1}x^4 + \binom{5}{2}x^3 - \binom{5}{3}x^2 + \binom{5}{4}x - \binom{5}{5}$

$\quad = x^5 - 5x^4 + 10x^3 - 10x^2 + 5x - 1$

27. $(3x-y)^5 = \binom{5}{0}(3x)^5 - \binom{5}{1}(3x)^4 y + \binom{5}{2}(3x)^3 y^2 - \binom{5}{3}(3x)^2 y^3 + \binom{5}{4}3xy^4 - \binom{5}{5}y^5$

$\quad = (1)243x^5 - 5(81x^4)y + 10(27x^3)y^2 - 10(9x^2)y^3 + 5(3x)y^4 - (1)y^5$

$\quad = 243x^5 - 405x^4 y + 270x^3 y^2 - 90x^2 y^3 + 15xy^4 - y^5$

29. $(2a+b)^6 = \binom{6}{0}(2a)^6 + \binom{6}{1}(2a)^5 b + \binom{6}{2}(2a)^4 b^2 + \binom{6}{3}(2a)^3 b^3 + \binom{6}{4}(2a)^2 b^4 + \binom{6}{5}(2a)b^5 + \binom{6}{6}b^6$

$\quad = 64a^6 + 6(32a^5)b + 15(16a^4)b^2 + 20(8a^3)b^3 + 15(4a^2)b^4 + 6(2a)b^5 + b^6$

$\quad = 64a^6 + 192a^5 b + 240a^4 b^2 + 160a^3 b^3 + 60a^2 b^4 + 12ab^5 + b^6$

31.

$(x+2)^8 = \binom{8}{0}x^8 + \binom{8}{1}x^7 2 + \binom{8}{3}x^6(2)^2 + \cdots$

$\quad = x^8 + 16x^7 + 112x^6 + \cdots$

33.

$(x-2y)^{10} = \binom{10}{0}x^{10} - \binom{10}{1}x^9(2y) + \binom{10}{2}x^8(2y)^2 - \cdots$

$\quad = x^{10} - 20x^9 y + 180x^8 y^2 - \cdots$

35.

$(x^2+1)^{16} = \binom{16}{0}(x^2)^{16} + \binom{16}{1}(x^2)^{15} + \binom{16}{2}(x^2)^{14} + \cdots$

$\quad = x^{32} + 16x^{30} + 120x^{28} + \cdots$

37.

$(y^3-1)^{20} = \binom{20}{0}(y^3)^{20} - \binom{20}{1}(y^3)^{19} + \binom{20}{2}(y^3)^{18} - \cdots$

$\quad = y^{60} - 20y^{57} + 190y^{54} - \cdots$

39. $(2x+y)^6$

$\quad \text{third term} = \binom{6}{2}(2x)^4(y)^2 = 15(16x^4 y^2) = 240x^4 y^2$

41. $(x-1)^9$

fifth term $= \begin{pmatrix} 9 \\ 4 \end{pmatrix} x^5 (-1)^4 = 126x^5$

43. $\left(x^2 + y^3\right)^8$

sixth term $= \begin{pmatrix} 8 \\ 5 \end{pmatrix} \left(x^2\right)^3 \left(y^3\right)^5 = 56x^6 y^{15}$

45. $\left(x - \frac{1}{2}\right)^9$

fourth term $= \begin{pmatrix} 9 \\ 3 \end{pmatrix} x^6 \left(-\frac{1}{2}\right)^3 = 84x^6 \left(-\frac{1}{8}\right) = -\frac{21}{2} x^6$

47. $\begin{pmatrix} 22 \\ 14 \end{pmatrix} (x^2)^8 y^{14} = 319770 x^{16} y^{14}$

49. $(x+h)^4 = \begin{pmatrix} 4 \\ 0 \end{pmatrix} x^4 + \begin{pmatrix} 4 \\ 1 \end{pmatrix} x^3 h + \begin{pmatrix} 4 \\ 2 \end{pmatrix} x^2 h^2 + \begin{pmatrix} 4 \\ 3 \end{pmatrix} x h^3 + \begin{pmatrix} 4 \\ 4 \end{pmatrix} h^4$

$= x^4 + 4x^3 h + 6x^2 h^2 + 4x h^3 + h^4$

$$\frac{(x+h)^4 - x^4}{h} = \frac{x^4 + 4x^3 h + 6x^2 h^2 + 4x h^3 + h^4 - x^4}{h} = \frac{4x^3 h + 6x^2 h^2 + 4x h^3 + h^4}{h}$$

$$= 4x^3 + 6x^2 h + 4x h^2 + h^3$$

51.   **a.** $g(x) = 0.12(x+3)^3 - (x+3)^2 + 3(x+3) + 15$

$= 0.12(x^3 + 9x^2 + 27x + 27) - (x^2 + 6x + 9) + 3x + 9 + 15$

$= 0.12x^3 + 1.08x^2 + 3.24x + 3.24 - x^2 - 6x - 9 + 3x + 24$

$= 0.12x^3 + 0.08x^2 + 0.24x + 18.24$

   b. $f(5) = 0.12(5)^3 - 5^2 + 3(5) + 15 = 20$

$g(2) = 0.12(2)^3 + 0.08(2)^2 + 0.24(2) + 18.24 = 20$

Both models give 20 and the graph also gives 20.

53.–63. Answers may vary.

65. $f_1(x) = (x+1)^4$

$f_2(x) = x^4$

$f_3(x) = x^4 + 4x^3$

$f_4(x) = x^4 + 4x^3 + 6x^2$

$f_5(x) = x^4 + 4x^3 + 6x^2 + 4x$

$f_6(x) = x^4 + 4x^3 + 6x^2 + 4x + 1$

f_2, f_3, f_4, and f_5 are approaching $f_1 = f_6$.

67. $f_1(x) = (x-2)^4$

$$= \binom{4}{0}x^4 + \binom{4}{1}x^3(-2) + \binom{4}{2}x^2(-2)^2 + \binom{4}{3}x(-2)^3 + \binom{4}{4}(-2)^4$$

$$= x^4 + 4x^3(-2) + 6x^2(4) + 4x(-8) + 16$$

$$= x^4 - 8x^3 + 24x^2 - 32x + 16$$

69. Answers may vary.

71.

$$\left(x^2 + x + 1\right)^3 = \left[x^2 + (x+1)\right]^3$$

$$= \binom{3}{0}\left(x^2\right)^3 + \binom{3}{1}\left(x^2\right)^2(x+1) + \binom{3}{2}x^2(x+1)^2 + \binom{3}{3}(x+1)^3$$

$$= x^6 + 3x^4(x+1) + 3x^2\left(x^2 + 2x + 1\right) + x^3 + 3x^2 + 3x + 1$$

$$= x^6 + 3x^5 + 3x^4 + 3x^4 + 6x^3 + 3x^2 + x^3 + 3x^2 + 3x + 1$$

$$= x^6 + 3x^5 + 6x^4 + 7x^3 + 6x^2 + 3x + 1$$

73. $\binom{n}{r} = \dfrac{n!}{r!(n-r)!}$

$$\binom{n}{n-r} = \frac{n!}{(n-r)!\left[n-(n-r)\right]!} = \frac{n!}{(n-r)!\,r!} = \binom{n}{r}$$

75. a. $S_1: (a+b)^1 = \binom{1}{0}a^1 + \binom{1}{1}a^{1-1}b = a+b$

444

b. $S_k: (a+b)^k = \binom{k}{0}a^k + \binom{k}{1}a^{k-1}b + \binom{k}{2}a^{k-2}b^2 + \cdots + \binom{k}{k-1}ab^{k-1} + \binom{k}{k}b^k$

$S_{k+1}: (a+b)^{k+1} = \binom{k+1}{0}a^{k+1} + \binom{k+1}{1}a^k b + \binom{k+1}{2}a^{k-1}b^2 + \cdots + \binom{k+1}{k}ab^k + \binom{k+1}{k+1}b^{k+1}$

c. $(a+b)(a+b)^k$

$(a+b)^{k+1} = \binom{k}{0}a^{k+1} + \binom{k}{0}a^k b + \binom{k}{1}a^k b + \binom{k}{1}a^{k-1}b^2 + \binom{k}{2}a^{k-1}b^2 + \binom{k}{2}a^{k-2}b^3 + \cdots$

$= \binom{k}{k-1}a^2 b^{k-1} + \binom{k}{k-1}ab^k + \binom{k}{k}ab^k + \binom{k}{k}b^{k+1}$

d. $(a+b)^{k+1} = \binom{k}{0}a^{k+1} + \left[\binom{k}{0} + \binom{k}{1}\right]a^k b + \left[\binom{k}{1} + \binom{k}{2}\right]a^{k-1}b^2 + \left[\binom{k}{2} + \binom{k}{3}\right]a^{k-2}b^3 + \cdots$

$+ \left[\binom{k}{k-1} + \binom{k}{k}\right]ab^k + \binom{k}{k}b^{k+1}$

e. $(a+b)^{k+1} = \binom{k}{0}a^{k+1} + \binom{k+1}{1}a^k b + \binom{k+1}{2}a^{k-1}b^2 + \binom{k+1}{3}a^{k-2}b^3 + \cdots + \binom{k+1}{k}ab^k + \binom{k}{k}b^{k+1}$

f. $\binom{k}{0} = \binom{k+1}{0}$ because both equal 1. $\binom{k}{k} = \binom{k+1}{k+1}$ also because both equal 1.

$S_{k+1}: (a+b)^{k+1} = \binom{k+1}{0}a^{k+1} + \binom{k+1}{1}a^k b + \binom{k+1}{2}a^{k-1}b^2 + \cdots + \binom{k+1}{k}ab^k + \binom{k+1}{k+1}b^{k+1}$

Section 8.6

Check Point Exercises

1. We use the Fundamental Counting Principal to find the number of ways a one-topping pizza can be ordered. Multiply the number of choices for each of the three groups.
$3 \cdot 4 \cdot 6 = 72$ pizzas
There are 72 different ways of ordering a one-topping pizza.

2. We use the Fundamental Counting Principal to find the number of ways we can answer the questions. Multiply the number of choices, 3, for each of the six questions.
$3 \cdot 3 \cdot 3 \cdot 3 \cdot 3 \cdot 3 = 3^6 = 729$ ways
There are 729 ways of answering the questions.

3. We use the Fundamental Counting Principal to find the number of different license plates that can be manufactured. Multiply the number of different letters, 26, for the first two places and the number of different digits, 10, for the next three places.
$26 \cdot 26 \cdot 10 \cdot 10 \cdot 10 = 26^2 \cdot 1000 = 676,000$ plates
There are 676,000 different license plates possible.

4. Your group is choosing $r = 4$ officers from a group of $n = 7$ people. The order in which the officers
are chosen matters because the four officers to be chosen have different responsibilities. Thus, we are looking for the number of permutations of 7 things taken 4 at a time.
We use the formula $_nP_r = \dfrac{n!}{(n-r)!}$ with $n = 7$ and $r = 4$. $_7P_4 = \dfrac{7!}{(7-4)!} = \dfrac{7!}{3!} = 840.$
Thus, there are 840 different ways of filling the four offices.

5. Because you are using all six of your books in every possible arrangement, you are arranging $r = 6$ books from a group of $n = 6$ books. Thus, we are looking for the number of permutations of 6 things taken 6 at a time. We use the formula
$_nP_r = \dfrac{n!}{(n-r)!}$ with $n = 6$ and $r = 6$.
$_6P_6 = \dfrac{6!}{(6-6)!} = \dfrac{6!}{0!} = 6! = 720.$
There are 720 different possible permutations. Thus, you can arrange the books in 720 ways.

6. **a.** The order does not matter; this is a combination.

   b. Since what place each runner finishes matters, this is a permutation.

7. The order in which the four people are selected does not matter. This is a problem of selecting $r = 4$ people from a group of $n = 10$ people. We are looking for the number of combinations of 10 things taken 4 at a time. We use the formula
$_nC_r = \dfrac{n!}{(n-r)! \, r!}$ with $n = 10$ and $r = 4$.
$_{10}C_4 = \dfrac{10!}{(10-4)! \, 4!} = \dfrac{10!}{6! \, 4!} = \dfrac{10 \cdot 9 \cdot 8 \cdot 7 \cdot 6!}{6! \cdot 4 \cdot 3 \cdot 2 \cdot 1}$
$= \dfrac{10 \cdot 9 \cdot 8 \cdot 7}{4 \cdot 3 \cdot 2 \cdot 1} = 210$
Thus, 210 committees of 4 people each can be found from 10 people at the conference on acupuncture.

8. Because the order in which the 4 cards are dealt does not matter, this is a problem involving combinations. We are looking for the number of combinations of $n = 16$ cards drawn $r = 4$ at a time. We use the formula
$_nC_r = \dfrac{n!}{(n-r)! \, r!}$ with $n = 16$ and $r = 4$.

$$_{16}C_4 = \frac{16!}{(16-4)!\,4!} = \frac{16!}{12!\,4!} = \frac{16 \cdot 15 \cdot 14 \cdot 13 \cdot 12!}{12! \cdot 4 \cdot 3 \cdot 2 \cdot 1}$$
$$= 1820$$

Thus, there are 1820 different 4-card hands possible.

Exercise Set 8.6

1. $_9P_4 = \dfrac{9!}{5!} = 3024$

3. $_8P_5 = \dfrac{8!}{3!} = 8 \cdot 7 \cdot 6 \cdot 5 \cdot 4 = 6720$

5. $_6P_6 = \dfrac{6!}{0!} = 720$

7. $_8P_0 = \dfrac{8!}{8!} = 1$

9. $_9C_5 = \dfrac{9!}{4!\,5!} = \dfrac{9 \cdot 8 \cdot 7 \cdot 6}{4 \cdot 3 \cdot 2 \cdot 1} = \dfrac{3 \cdot 7 \cdot 6}{1} = 126$

11. $_{11}C_4 = \dfrac{11!}{7!\,4!} = \dfrac{11 \cdot 10 \cdot 9 \cdot 8}{4 \cdot 3 \cdot 2 \cdot 1} = \dfrac{11 \cdot 10 \cdot 3}{1} = 330$

13. $_7C_7 = \dfrac{7!}{0!\,7!} = 1$

15. $_5C_0 = \dfrac{5!}{5!\,0!} = 1$

17. combination; The order in which the volunteers are chosen does not matter.

19. permutation; The order of the letters matters because ABCD is not the same as BADC.

21. $9 \cdot 3 = 27$ ways

23. $2 \cdot 4 \cdot 5 = 40$ ways

25. $3^5 = 243$ ways

27. $8 \cdot 2 \cdot 9 = 144$ area codes

29. $5 \cdot 4 \cdot 3 \cdot 2 \cdot 1 \cdot 1 = 120$ ways

31. $1 \cdot 3 \cdot 2 \cdot 1 \cdot 1 = 6$ paragraphs

33. $_{10}P_3 = \dfrac{10!}{7!\,3!} = 10 \cdot 9 \cdot 8 = 720$ ways

35. $_{13}P_7 = \dfrac{13!}{6!} = 13 \cdot 12 \cdot 11 \cdot 10 \cdot 9 \cdot 8 \cdot 7$
$$= 8,648,640 \text{ ways}$$

37. $_6P_3 = \dfrac{6!}{3!} = 6 \cdot 5 \cdot 4 = 120$ ways

39. $_9P_5 = \dfrac{9!}{4!} = 9 \cdot 8 \cdot 7 \cdot 6 \cdot 5 = 15,120$ lineups

41. $_6C_3 = \dfrac{6!}{3!\,3!} = \dfrac{6 \cdot 5 \cdot 4}{3 \cdot 2 \cdot 1} = 20$ ways

43. $_{12}C_4 = \dfrac{12!}{8!\,4!} = \dfrac{12 \cdot 11 \cdot 10 \cdot 9}{4 \cdot 3 \cdot 2 \cdot 1}$
$$= 495 \text{ collections}$$

45. $_{17}C_8 = \dfrac{17!}{9!\,8!} = \dfrac{17 \cdot 16 \cdot 15 \cdot 14 \cdot 13 \cdot 12 \cdot 11 \cdot 10}{8 \cdot 7 \cdot 6 \cdot 5 \cdot 4 \cdot 3 \cdot 2 \cdot 1}$
$$= 24,310 \text{ groups}$$

47. $_{53}C_6 = \dfrac{53!}{47!\,6!} = 22,957,480$ selections

49. $_6P_4 = \dfrac{6!}{2!} = 6 \cdot 5 \cdot 4 \cdot 3 = 360$ ways

51. $_{13}C_6 = \dfrac{13!}{7!\,6!} = \dfrac{13 \cdot 12 \cdot 11 \cdot 10 \cdot 9 \cdot 8}{6 \cdot 5 \cdot 4 \cdot 3 \cdot 2 \cdot 1}$
$$= 1716 \text{ ways}$$

53. $_{20}C_3 = \dfrac{20!}{17!\,3!} = \dfrac{20 \cdot 19 \cdot 18}{3 \cdot 2 \cdot 1} = 1140$ ways

55. $_7P_4 = \dfrac{7!}{3!} = 840$ passwords

57. $_{15}P_3 = \dfrac{15!}{12!} = 15 \cdot 14 \cdot 13 = 2730$ cones

59.–67. Answers may vary.

69. a. False; the number of ways is $_{10}C_4$.

　b. False;

$$_nP_r = \frac{n!}{(n-r)!} > \frac{n!}{(n-r)!\,r!} = {_n}C_{r \text{ if } r>1}.$$

　c. True; $_7P_3 = \dfrac{7!}{4!} = 3!\,\dfrac{7!}{4!\,3!} = 3!\,{_7}C_3$

　d. False;
　　the number of ways is $20 \cdot 19 = {_{20}}P_2$.
　(c) is true.

71. $2 \cdot 6 \cdot 6 \cdot 2 = 144$ numbers

Section 8.7

Check Point Exercises

1. $\dfrac{.69}{3.00} = 0.23 = 23\%$

The empirical probability of randomly selecting an Arab American who is a Muslim is 23%.

2. The sample space of equally likely outcomes is $S = \{1, 2, 3, 4, 5, 6\}$. There are six outcomes in the sample space, so $n(S) = 6$. The event of getting a number greater than 4 can be represented by $E = \{5, 6\}$. There are two outcomes in this event, so $n(E) = 2$. The probability of rolling a number greater than 4 is

$$P(E) = \frac{n(E)}{n(S)} = \frac{2}{6} = \frac{1}{3}.$$

3. We have $n(S) = 36$. The phrase "getting a sum of 5" describes the event $E = \{(1,4),(2,3),(3,2),(4,1)\}$. This event has 4 outcomes, so $n(E) = 4$. Thus, the probability of getting a sum of 5 is

$$P(E) = \frac{n(E)}{n(S)} = \frac{4}{36} = \frac{1}{9}.$$

4. Let E be the event of being dealt a king. Because there are 4 kings in the deck, the event of being dealt a king can occur in 4 ways, i.e., $n(E) = 4$. With 52 cards in the deck, $n(S) = 52$. The probability of being dealt a king is $P(E) = \dfrac{n(E)}{n(S)} = \dfrac{4}{52} = \dfrac{1}{13}$.

5. Because the order of the six numbers does not matter, this is a situation involving combinations. With one lottery ticket, there is only one way of winning so $n(E) = 1$. Using the combinations formula

$$_nC_r = \frac{n!}{(n-r)!\,r!} \text{ to find the number of}$$

outcomes in the sample space, we are selecting $r = 6$ numbers from a collection of $n = 49$ numbers.

$$_{49}C_6 = \frac{49!}{43! \cdot 6!} = 13{,}983{,}816$$

So $n(S) = 13{,}983{,}816$.
If a person buys one lottery ticket, the probability of winning is

$$P(E) = \frac{n(E)}{n(S)} = \frac{1}{13{,}983{,}816}$$

The probability of winning the state lottery is 0.0000000715.

6. $P(\text{not dying})$

$$= 1 - P(\text{dying}) = 1 - \frac{1}{1000} = \frac{999}{1000}$$

The probability of not dying is 0.999

7. We find the probability that either of these mutually exclusive events will occur by adding their individual probabilities.

$P(4 \text{ or } 5) = P(4) + P(5)$

$$= \frac{1}{6} + \frac{1}{6} = \frac{2}{6} = \frac{1}{3}$$

The probability of selecting a 4 or a 5 is $\frac{1}{3}$.

8. It is possible for the pointer to land on a number that is odd and less than 5. Two of the numbers , 1 and 3, are odd and less than 5. These events are not mutually exclusive. The probability of landing on a number that is odd and less than 5 is

P (odd or less than 5)

$= P$ (odd) $+ P$ (less than 5)

$- P$ (odd and less than 5)

$$= \frac{4}{8} + \frac{4}{8} - \frac{2}{8}$$

$$= \frac{6}{8} = \frac{3}{4}$$

The probability that the pointer will stop on an odd number or a number less than 5 is $\frac{3}{4}$.

9. P(Muslim or African American)

$= P$(Muslim) $+ P$(African American) $-$ P(both)

$$\frac{20}{40} + \frac{26}{40} - \frac{14}{40} = \frac{32}{40} = \frac{4}{5}$$

10. The wheel has 38 equally likely outcomes and 2 are green. Thus, the probability of a green occurring on a play is $\frac{2}{38}$, or $\frac{1}{19}$. The result that occurs on each play is independent of all previous results. Thus, P (green and green)

$= P$ (green) $\cdot P$ (green)

$$= \frac{1}{19} \cdot \frac{1}{19} = \frac{1}{361}$$

$\approx 0.003.$

The probability of green occurring on two consecutive plays is $\frac{1}{361}$.

11. If two or more events are independent, we can find the probability of them all occurring by multiplying the probabilities.

The probability of a baby boy is $\frac{1}{2}$, so the probability of having four boys in a row is P (4 boys in a row)

$$= \frac{1}{2} \cdot \frac{1}{2} \cdot \frac{1}{2} \cdot \frac{1}{2}$$

$$= \frac{1}{16}.$$

Exercise Set 8.7

1. $P(\text{weight training}) = \dfrac{320}{2000} = \dfrac{4}{25} = 0.16$

3. $P(\text{biking}) = \dfrac{240}{2000} = \dfrac{3}{25} = 0.12$

5. $P(\text{African}) = \dfrac{784,400,000}{6,054,900,000} \approx 0.13$

7. $P(\text{North American}) = \dfrac{309,600,000}{6,054,900,000} \approx 0.051$

9. $P(R) = \dfrac{n(E)}{n(S)} = \dfrac{1}{6}$

11. $P(E) = \dfrac{n(E)}{n(S)} = \dfrac{3}{6} = \dfrac{1}{2}$

13. $P(E) = \dfrac{n(E)}{n(S)} = \dfrac{2}{6} = \dfrac{1}{3}$

15. $P(E) = \dfrac{n(E)}{n(S)} = \dfrac{4}{52} = \dfrac{1}{13}$

17. $P(E) = \dfrac{n(E)}{n(S)} = \dfrac{12}{52} = \dfrac{3}{13}$

19. $P(E) = \dfrac{n(E)}{n(S)} = \dfrac{1}{4}$

21. $P(E) = \dfrac{n(E)}{n(S)} = \dfrac{7}{8}$

23. $P(E) = \dfrac{n(E)}{n(S)} = \dfrac{3}{36} = \dfrac{1}{12}$

25. Buying 1 ticket:

$P(E) = \dfrac{n(E)}{n(S)} = \dfrac{1}{{}_{51}C_6} = \dfrac{1}{18,009,460}$

Buying 100 tickets:

$P(E) = \dfrac{100}{18,009,460} = \dfrac{5}{900,473}$

27. $0.00140 \times 18,009,460 = 25,213$ A 20-year old male is 25,213 times more likely to die than to win the lottery.

29. a. ${}_{52}C_5 = \dfrac{52!}{47!\,5!}$

$= \dfrac{52 \cdot 51 \cdot 50 \cdot 49 \cdot 48}{5 \cdot 4 \cdot 3 \cdot 2 \cdot 1} = 2,598,960$

    b. ${}_{13}C_5 = \dfrac{13!}{8!\,5!} = \dfrac{13 \cdot 12 \cdot 11 \cdot 10 \cdot 9}{5 \cdot 4 \cdot 3 \cdot 2 \cdot 1} = 1287$

    c. $P(E) = \dfrac{n(E)}{n(S)} = \dfrac{1287}{2,598,960} \approx 0.0005$

31. a. 0.1

    b. $1 - 0.1 = 0.9$

33. $\dfrac{4}{52} + \dfrac{4}{52} = \dfrac{8}{52} = \dfrac{2}{13} \approx 0.154$

35. $\dfrac{2}{52} + \dfrac{2}{52} = \dfrac{4}{52} = \dfrac{1}{13} \approx 0.076$

37. $P(E) = P(\text{even}) + P(\text{less than 5})$
$\qquad - P(\text{even and less than 5})$

$= \dfrac{3}{6} + \dfrac{4}{6} - \dfrac{2}{6} = \dfrac{5}{6}$

39. $P(E) = P(7) + P(\text{red}) - P(\text{red 7})$

$= \dfrac{4}{52} + \dfrac{26}{52} - \dfrac{2}{52} = \dfrac{28}{52} = \dfrac{7}{13}$

41. $P(E) = P(\text{odd}) + P(\text{less than 6})$
$\qquad - P(\text{odd and less than 6})$

$= \dfrac{4}{8} + \dfrac{5}{8} - \dfrac{3}{8} = \dfrac{6}{8} = \dfrac{3}{4}$

43. $P(E)$
$= P(\text{professor}) + P(\text{male}) - P(\text{male professor})$

$= \dfrac{19}{40} + \dfrac{22}{40} - \dfrac{8}{40} = \dfrac{33}{40}$

45. $P(E) = P(2) \cdot P(3) = \dfrac{1}{6} \cdot \dfrac{1}{6} = \dfrac{1}{36}$

47. $P(E) = P(\text{even}) \cdot P(\text{greater than 2})$

$= \dfrac{3}{6} \cdot \dfrac{4}{6} = \dfrac{1}{2} \cdot \dfrac{2}{3} = \dfrac{1}{3}$

49. $P(E) = \left(\dfrac{1}{2}\right)^6 = \dfrac{1}{64}$

51. $0.22^4 \approx 0.00234$

53. a. $P(E) = \dfrac{1}{16} \cdot \dfrac{1}{16} = \dfrac{1}{256}$

    b. $P(E) = \left(\dfrac{1}{16}\right)^3 = \dfrac{1}{4096}$

    c. $P(E) = \left(\dfrac{15}{16}\right)^{10}$

    d. $1 - \left(\dfrac{15}{16}\right)^{10}$

55.–65. Answers may vary.

Review Exercises

1.　$a_n = 7n - 4$

　　$a_1 = 7 - 4 = 3$

　　$a_2 = 14 - 4 = 10$

　　$a_3 = 21 - 4 = 17$

　　$a_4 = 28 - 4 = 24$

　　The first four terms are 3, 10, 17, and 24.

2.　$a_n = (-1)^n \dfrac{n+2}{n+1}$

　　$a_1 = (-1)^1 \dfrac{1+2}{1+1} = -\dfrac{3}{2}$

　　$a_2 = (-1)^2 \dfrac{2+2}{2+1} = \dfrac{4}{3}$

　　$a_3 = (-1)^3 \dfrac{3+2}{3+1} = -\dfrac{5}{4}$

　　$a_4 = (-1)^4 \dfrac{4+2}{4+1} = \dfrac{6}{5}$

　　The first four terms are

　　$-\dfrac{3}{2}, \dfrac{4}{3}, -\dfrac{5}{4},$ and $\dfrac{6}{5}.$

3.　$a_n = \dfrac{1}{(n-1)!}$

　　$a_1 = \dfrac{1}{0!} = 1$

　　$a_2 = \dfrac{1}{1!} = 1$

　　$a_3 = \dfrac{1}{2!} = \dfrac{1}{2}$

　　$a_4 = \dfrac{1}{3!} = \dfrac{1}{6}$

　　The first four terms are 1, 1, $\dfrac{1}{2}$, and $\dfrac{1}{6}$.

4.　$a_n = \dfrac{(-1)^{n+1}}{2^n}$

　　$a_1 = \dfrac{(-1)^2}{2^1} = \dfrac{1}{2}$

　　$a_2 = \dfrac{(-1)^3}{2^2} = -\dfrac{1}{4}$

　　$a_3 = \dfrac{(-1)^4}{2^3} = \dfrac{1}{8}$

　　$a_4 = \dfrac{(-1)^5}{2^4} = -\dfrac{1}{16}$

　　The first four terms are

　　$\dfrac{1}{2}, -\dfrac{1}{4}, \dfrac{1}{8},$ and $-\dfrac{1}{16}.$

5.　$a_1 = 9$ and $a_n = \dfrac{2}{3a_{n-1}}$

　　$a_1 = 9$

　　$a_2 = \dfrac{2}{3 \cdot 9} = \dfrac{2}{27}$

　　$a_3 = \dfrac{2}{3} \cdot \dfrac{27}{2} = \dfrac{54}{6} = 9$

　　$a_4 = \dfrac{2}{3 \cdot 9} = \dfrac{2}{27}$

　　The first four terms are 9, $\dfrac{2}{27}$, 9, and $\dfrac{2}{27}$.

6.　$a_1 = 4$ and $a_n = 2a_{n-1} + 3$

　　$a_1 = 4$

　　$a_2 = 2 \cdot 4 + 3 = 8 + 3 = 11$

　　$a_3 = 2 \cdot 11 + 3 = 22 + 3 = 25$

　　$a_4 = 2 \cdot 25 + 3 = 50 + 3 = 53$

　　The first four terms are 4, 11, 25, and 53.

7.　$\dfrac{40!}{4! \cdot 38!} = \dfrac{40 \cdot 39 \cdot 38!}{4 \cdot 3 \cdot 2 \cdot 1 \cdot 38!} = 65$

8. $\displaystyle\sum_{i=1}^{5}\left(2i^2-3\right)=(2-3)+\left(2\cdot2^2-3\right)+\left(2\cdot3^2-3\right)+\left(2\cdot4^2-3\right)+\left(2\cdot5^2-3\right)$

$$=-1+5+15+29+47$$
$$=95$$

9. $\displaystyle\sum_{i=0}^{4}(-1)^{i+1}i!=(-1)^1 0!+(-1)^2 1!+(-1)^3 3!+(-1)^4 4!$

$$=-1+1-2+6-24$$
$$=-20$$

10. $\dfrac{1}{3}+\dfrac{2}{4}+\dfrac{3}{5}+\cdots+\dfrac{15}{17}=\displaystyle\sum_{i=1}^{15}\dfrac{i}{i+2}$

11. $4^3+5^3+6^3+\cdots+13^3=\displaystyle\sum_{i=1}^{10}\left(i+3\right)^3$

12. $a_1=7$, $d=4$

The first six terms are 7, 11, 15, 19, 23, and 27.

13. $a_1=-4$, $d=-5$

The first six terms are $-4, -9, -14, -19, -24,$ and -29.

14. $a_1=\dfrac{3}{2}$, $d=-\dfrac{1}{2}$

The first six terms are $\dfrac{3}{2}, 1, \dfrac{1}{2}, 0, -\dfrac{1}{2},$ and -1.

15. $a_{n+1}=a_n+5$, $a_1=-2$

The first six terms are $-2, 3, 8, 13, 18,$ and 23.

16. $a_1=5$, $d=3$

$a_n=5+(n-1)3$

$a_6=5+(5)3=20$

17. $a_1=-8$, $d=-2$

$a_n=-8+(n-1)(-2)$

$a_{12}=-8+11(-2)=-30$

18. $a_1=14$, $d=-4$

$a_n=14+(n-1)(-4)$

$a_{14}=14+(13)(-4)=-38$

19. $-7, -3, 1, 5, \ldots$

$d = -3 - (-7) = 4$

$a_n = -7 + (n-1)(4)$

$a_n = 4n - 11$

$a_{20} = 4(20) - 11$

$a_{20} = 69$

20. $a_1 = 200,\ d = -20$

$a_n = 200 + (n-1)(-20)$

$a_n = 220 - 20n$

$a_{20} = 220 - 20(20)$

$a_{20} = -180$

21. $a_n = a_{n-1} - 5,\ a_1 = 3$

$d = -5$

$a_n = 3 + (n-1)(-5) = 3 - 5n + 5$

$a_n = 8 - 5n$

$a_{20} = 8 - 5(20) = -92$

22. $5, 12, 19, 26, \ldots$

$d = 7$

$a_n = 5 + (n-1)(7)$

$a_{22} = 5 + 21(7) = 152$

$S_{22} = \dfrac{22}{2}(5 + 152) = 1727$

23. $-6, -3, 0, 3, \ldots$

$d = 3$

$a_n = -6 + (n-1)3$

$a_{15} = -6 + (14)3 = 36$

$S_{15} = \dfrac{15}{2}(-6 + 36) = 225$

24. $3 + 6 + 9 + \ldots + 300$

$S_{100} = \dfrac{100}{2}(3 + 300) = 15,150$

25. $\displaystyle\sum_{i=1}^{16}(3i + 2)$

$a_1 = 3 + 2 = 5$

$a_{16} = 3(16) + 2 = 50$

$S_{16} = \dfrac{16}{2}(5 + 50) = 440$

26. $\displaystyle\sum_{i=1}^{25}(-2i + 6)$

$a_1 = -2 + 6 = 4$

$a_{25} = -2(25) + 6 = -44$

$S_{25} = \dfrac{25}{2}(4 - 44) = -500$

27. $\displaystyle\sum_{i=1}^{30} -5i$

$a_1 = -5$

$a_{30} = -5(30) = -150$

$S_{30} = \dfrac{30}{2}(-5 - 150) = -2325$

28. **a.** $a_n = 20 + 0.52(n-1)$

    b. $n = 2010 - 1900 = 110$

$a_{110} = 20 + 0.52(109) = 76.68$

In 2010, 76.68% of the labor force will be white-collar.

29. $a_n = 31,500 + (n-1)2300$

$a_{10} = 31,500 + (9)2300 = 52,200$

$S_{10} = \dfrac{10}{2}(31,500 + 52,200) = 418,500$

The total salary is \$418, 500.

30. $a_n = 25 + (n-1)$

$a_{35} = 25 + 34 = 59$

$S_{35} = \dfrac{35}{2}(25 + 59) = 1470$

There are 1470 seats.

31. $a_1 = 3$, $r = 2$

The first five terms are 3, 6, 12, 24, and 48.

32. $a_1 = \dfrac{1}{2}$, $r = \dfrac{1}{2}$

The first five terms are

$\dfrac{1}{2}, \dfrac{1}{4}, \dfrac{1}{8}, \dfrac{1}{16}$, and $\dfrac{1}{32}$.

33. $a_1 = 16$, $r = -\dfrac{1}{2}$

The first five terms are

16, -8, 4, -2, and 1.

34. $a_n = -5a_{n-1}$, $a_1 = -1$

The first five terms are -1, 5, -25, 125, and -625.

35. $a_1 = 2$, $r = 3$

$a_n = 2 \cdot 3^{n-1}$

$a_7 = 2 \cdot 3^6 = 1458$

36. $a_1 = 16$, $r = \dfrac{1}{2}$

$a_n = 16 \left(\dfrac{1}{2} \right)^{n-1}$

$a_6 = 16 \left(\dfrac{1}{2} \right)^5 = \dfrac{16}{32} = \dfrac{1}{2}$

37. $a_1 = -3$, $r = 2$

$a_n = -3 \cdot 2^{n-1}$

$a_5 = -3 \cdot 2^4 = -48$

38. 1, 2, 4, 8, ...

$a_1 = 1$, $r = \dfrac{2}{1} = 2$

$a_n = 2^{n-1}$

$a_8 = 2^7 = 128$

39. 100, 10, 1, $\dfrac{1}{10}$, ...

$a_1 = 100$, $r = \dfrac{10}{100} = \dfrac{1}{10}$

$a_n = 100 \left(\dfrac{1}{10} \right)^{n-1}$

$a_8 = 100 \left(\dfrac{1}{10} \right)^7 = \dfrac{1}{100,000}$

40. $12, -4, \dfrac{4}{3}, -\dfrac{4}{9} \cdots$

$a_1 = 12$, $r = -\dfrac{4}{12} = -\dfrac{1}{3}$

$a_n = 12 \left(-\dfrac{1}{3} \right)^{n-1}$

$a_8 = 12 \left(-\dfrac{1}{3} \right)^7 = -\dfrac{4}{729}$

41. 5, -15, 45, -135, ...

$r = \dfrac{-15}{5} = -3$

$S_{15} = \dfrac{5 \left[1 - (-3)^{15} \right]}{1 - (-3)} = 17,936,135$

42. $r = \dfrac{1}{2}$, $a_1 = 8$

$S_{78} = \dfrac{8 \left[1 - \left(\dfrac{1}{2} \right)^7 \right]}{1 - \dfrac{1}{2}} = -16 \left(1 - \dfrac{1}{128} \right)$

$= -16 \left(-\dfrac{127}{128} \right) = \dfrac{127}{8} = 15\dfrac{7}{8}$

43. $S_6 = \dfrac{5 \left(1 - 5^6 \right)}{1 - 5} = \dfrac{5(-15624)}{-4} = 19,530$

454

44. $\displaystyle\sum_{i=1}^{7} 3(-2)^i$

$a_1 = -6,\ r = -2$

$$S_7 = \frac{-6\left[1-(-2)^7\right]}{1-(-2)} = \frac{-6(129)}{3} = -258$$

45. $\displaystyle\sum_{i=1}^{5} 2\left(\tfrac{1}{4}\right)^{i-1}$

$a_1 = 2,\ r = \dfrac{1}{4}$

$$S_5 = \frac{2\left[1-\left(\tfrac{1}{4}\right)^5\right]}{1-\tfrac{1}{4}} = \frac{2\left(\tfrac{1023}{1024}\right)}{\tfrac{3}{4}} = \frac{341}{128}$$

46. $a_1 = 9,\ r = \dfrac{1}{3}$

$$S_\infty = \frac{9}{1-\tfrac{1}{3}} = \frac{9}{\tfrac{2}{3}} = 9 \cdot \frac{3}{2} = \frac{27}{2}$$

47. $a_1 = 2,\ r = -\dfrac{1}{2}$

$$S_\infty = \frac{2}{1-\left(-\tfrac{1}{2}\right)} = \frac{2}{\tfrac{3}{2}} = \frac{4}{3}$$

48. $a_1 = -6,\ r = -\dfrac{2}{3}$

$$S_\infty = \frac{-6}{1-\left(-\tfrac{2}{3}\right)} = \frac{-6}{\tfrac{5}{3}} = -\frac{18}{5}$$

49. $r = 0.8$

$$S_\infty = \frac{4}{1-0.8} = 20$$

50. $0.\overline{6} = 0.6 + 0.06 + 0.006 + \cdots$

$a_1 = \dfrac{6}{10},\ r = \dfrac{1}{10}$

$$S_\infty = \frac{\tfrac{6}{10}}{1-\tfrac{1}{10}} = \frac{\tfrac{6}{10}}{\tfrac{9}{10}} = \frac{6}{9} = \frac{2}{3}$$

51. $0.\overline{47} = 0.47 + 0.0047 + 0.000047 + \cdots$

$a_1 = \dfrac{47}{100},\ r = \dfrac{1}{100}$

$$S_\infty = \frac{\tfrac{47}{100}}{1-\tfrac{1}{100}} = \frac{\tfrac{47}{100}}{\tfrac{99}{100}} = \frac{47}{99}$$

52. a. $\dfrac{21.36}{20.6} = 1.04$

$\dfrac{22.19}{21.36} = 1.04$

$\dfrac{23.02}{22.19} = 1.04$

b. $a_n = 20.6 + (n-1)1.04$

c. $a_{11} = 20.6 + (11-1)1.04 = 31$

Iraq's population will be approximately 31 million in 2005.

53. $a_1 = 32,000,\ r = 1.06$

$a_6 = 32,000(1.06)^5 \approx 42,823.22$

The sixth year salary is $42,823.22.

$$S_6 = \frac{32,000\left(1-1.06^6\right)}{1-1.06}$$

$$= \frac{32,000\left(1-1.06^6\right)}{-0.06}$$

$$\approx 223,210.19$$

The total salary paid is $223,210.

54. $A = 200\,\dfrac{\left(1+\tfrac{0.1}{12}\right)^{18\cdot12}-1}{\tfrac{0.1}{12}} \approx 120,112.64$

You will save $120,112.64.

55. $4(0.7) + 4(0.7)^2 + \cdots;\ r = 0.7$

$$S_\infty = \frac{4(0.7)}{1-0.7} = 9.\overline{3}$$

The total spending is $9\dfrac{1}{3}$ million.

56. $S_1: 5 = \dfrac{5(1)(1+1)}{2}$

$\quad\quad 5 = \dfrac{5(2)}{2}$

$\quad\quad 5 = 5$ is true.

$S_k: 5 + 10 + 15 + \cdots + 5k = \dfrac{5k(k+1)}{2}$

$S_{k+1}: 5 + 10 + 15 + \cdots + 5k + 5(k+1)$

$\quad\quad = \dfrac{5(k+1)(k+2)}{2}$

Add $5(k+1)$ to both sides of S_k:

$5 + 10 + 15 + \cdots + 5k + 5(k+1)$

$\quad\quad = \dfrac{5k(k+1)}{2} + 5k(k+1)$

Simplify the right-hand side:

$\dfrac{5k(k+1)}{2} + 5(k+1) = \dfrac{5k(k+1) + 10(k+1)}{2}$

$\quad\quad\quad\quad\quad\quad\quad\quad = \dfrac{(5k+10)(k+1)}{2}$

$\quad\quad\quad\quad\quad\quad\quad\quad = \dfrac{5(k+1)(k+2)}{2}$

If S_k is true, then S_{k+1} is true.
The statement is true for all n.

57. $S_1: 1 = \dfrac{4^1 - 1}{3}$

$\quad\quad 1 = \dfrac{3}{3}$

$\quad\quad 1 = 1$ is true.

$S_k: 1 + 4 + 4^2 + \cdots + 4^{k-1} = \dfrac{4^k - 1}{3}$

$S_{k+1}: 1 + 4 + 4^2 + \cdots + 4^{k-1} + 4^k = \dfrac{4^{k+1} - 1}{3}$

Add 4^k to both sides of S_k:

$S_k: 1 + 4 + 4^2 + \cdots + 4^{k-1} = \dfrac{4^k - 1}{3}$

$1 + 4 + 4^2 + \cdots + 4^{k-1} + 4^k = \dfrac{4^k - 1}{3} + 4^k$

Simplify the right-hand side:

$\dfrac{4^k - 1}{3} + 4^k = \dfrac{4^k - 1 + 3 \cdot 4^k}{3}$

$\quad\quad\quad\quad\quad = \dfrac{4 \cdot 4^k - 1}{3}$

$\quad\quad\quad\quad\quad = \dfrac{4^{k+1} - 1}{3}$

If S_k is true, then S_{k+1} is true.
The statement is true for all n.

58. $S_1: 2 = 2(1)^2$

$\quad\quad 2 = 2$ is true.

$S_k: 2 + 6 + 10 + \cdots + (4k - 2) = 2k^2$

$S_{k+1}: 2 + 6 + 10 + \cdots + (4k - 2) + (4k + 2) = 2(k+1)^2$

Add $(4k + 2)$ to both sides of S_k:

$2 + 6 + 10 + \cdots + (4k - 2) + (4k + 2) = 2k^2 + (4k + 2)$

Simplify the right-hand side:

$2k^2 + 4k + 2 = 2(k^2 + 2k + 1)$

$\quad\quad\quad\quad\quad = 2(k+1)^2$

If S_k is true, then S_{k+1} is true. The
statement is true for all n.

59. $S_1: 1 \cdot 3 = \dfrac{1(1+1)[2(1)+7]}{6}$

$3 = \dfrac{2 \cdot 9}{6}$

$3 = \dfrac{18}{6}$

$3 = 3$ is true.

$S_k: 1 \cdot 3 + 2 \cdot 4 + 3 \cdot 5 + \cdots + k(k+2) = \dfrac{k(k+1)(2k+7)}{6}$

$S_{k+1}: 1 \cdot 3 + 2 \cdot 4 + 3 \cdot 5 + \cdots + k(k+2) + (k+1)(k+3) = \dfrac{(k+1)(k+2)(2k+9)}{6}$

Add $(k+1)(k+3)$ to both sides of S_k:

$1 \cdot 3 + 2 \cdot 4 + 3 \cdot 5 + \cdots + k(k+2) + (k+1)(k+3) = \dfrac{k(k+1)(2k+7)}{6} + (k+1)(k+3)$

Simplify the right-hand side:

$= \dfrac{k(k+1)(2k+7)}{6} + (k+1)(k+3)$

$= \dfrac{k(k+1)(2k+7) + 6(k+1)(k+3)}{6}$

$= \dfrac{(k+1)[k(2k+7) + 6(k+3)]}{6}$

$= \dfrac{(k+1)(2k^2 + 13k + 18)}{6}$

$= \dfrac{(k+1)(k+2)(2k+9)}{6}$

If S_k is true, then S_{k+1} is true. The statement is true for all n.

60. $S_1:$ 2 is a factor of $1^2 + 5(1) = 6$ since $6 = 2 \cdot 3$.

$S_k:$ 2 is a factor of $k^2 + 5k$.

$S_{k+1}:$ 2 is a factor of $(k+1)^2 + 5(k+1)$.

$(k+1)^2 + 5(k+1) = k^2 + 2k + 1 + 5k + 5$

$\qquad = k^2 + 7k + 6$

$\qquad = k^2 + 5k + 2(k+3)$

$\qquad = \left(k^2 + 5k\right) + 2(k+3)$

Because we assume S_k is true, we know 2 is a factor of $k^2 + 5k$. Since 2 is a factor of $2(k+3)$, we conclude 2 is a factor of the sum $\left(k^2 + 5k\right) + 2(k+3)$. If S_k is true, then S_{k+1} is true. The statement is true for all n.

61. $\dbinom{11}{8} = \dfrac{11!}{3!\,8!} = \dfrac{11 \cdot 10 \cdot 9}{3 \cdot 2 \cdot 1} = 165$

62. $\dbinom{90}{2} = \dfrac{90!}{88!\,2!} = \dfrac{90 \cdot 89}{2 \cdot 1} = 4005$

63. $(2x+1)^3 = \dbinom{3}{0}(2x)^3 + \dbinom{3}{1}(2x)^2 \cdot 1 + \dbinom{3}{2}(2x)1^2 + \dbinom{3}{3}1^3$

$\qquad = 8x^3 + 3\left(4x^2\right) + 3(2x) + 1$

$\qquad = 8x^3 + 12x^2 + 6x + 1$

64. $\left(x^2 - 1\right)^4 = \dbinom{4}{0}\left(x^2\right)^4 + \dbinom{4}{1}\left(x^2\right)^3(-1) + \dbinom{4}{2}\left(x^2\right)^2(-1)^2 + \dbinom{4}{3}x^2(-1)^3 + \dbinom{4}{4}(-1)^4$

$\qquad = x^8 - 4x^6 + 6x^4 - 4x^2 + 1$

65. $(x+2y)^5 = \dbinom{5}{0}x^5 + \dbinom{5}{1}x^4(2y) + \dbinom{5}{2}x^3(2y)^2 + \dbinom{5}{3}x^2(2y)^3 + \dbinom{5}{4}x(2y)^4 + \dbinom{5}{5}(2y)^5$

$\qquad = x^5 + 5(2)x^4y + 10(4)x^3y^2 + 10(8)x^2y^3 + 5(16)xy^4 + 32y^5$

$\qquad = x^5 + 10x^4y + 40x^3y^2 + 80x^2y^3 + 80xy^4 + 32y^5$

66. $(x-2)^6 = \dbinom{6}{0}x^6 + \dbinom{6}{1}x^5(-2) + \dbinom{6}{2}x^4(-2)^2 + \dbinom{6}{3}x^3(-2)^3 + \dbinom{6}{4}x^2(-2)^4 + \dbinom{6}{5}x(-2)^5 \dbinom{6}{6}(-2)^6$

$\qquad = x^6 + 6x^5(-2) + 15x^4(4) + 20x^3(-8) + 15x^2(16) + 6x(-32) + 64$

$\qquad = x^6 - 12x^5 + 60x^4 - 160x^3 + 240x^2 - 192x + 64$

67. $(x^2+3)^8 = \dbinom{8}{0}(x^2)^8 + \dbinom{8}{1}(x^2)^7 3 + \dbinom{8}{2}(x^2)^6 3^2 + \cdots$

$\qquad = x^{16} + 8x^{14}3 + 28x^{12}9 + \cdots$

$\qquad = x^{16} + 24x^{14} + 252x^{12} + \cdots$

68.

$(x-3)^9 = \dbinom{9}{0}x^9 + \dbinom{9}{1}x^8(-3) + \dbinom{9}{2}x^7(-3)^2 + \cdots$

$\qquad = x^9 + 9(-3)x^8 + 36(9)x^7 + \cdots$

$\qquad = x^9 - 27x^8 + 324x^7 + \cdots$

69. $(x+2)^5$

fourth term $= \dbinom{5}{3} x^2 (2)^3$

$= 10(8)x^2 = 80x^2$

70. $(2x-3)^6$

fifth term $= \dbinom{6}{4} (2x)^2 (-3)^4$

$= 15(4x^2)(81) = 4860x^2$

71. $_8P_3 = \dfrac{8!}{5!} = 8 \cdot 7 \cdot 6 = 336$

72. $_9P_5 = \dfrac{9!}{4!} = 9 \cdot 8 \cdot 7 \cdot 6 \cdot 5 = 15{,}120$

73. $_8C_3 = \dfrac{8!}{5!\,3!} = \dfrac{8 \cdot 7 \cdot 6}{3 \cdot 2 \cdot 1} = 56$

74. $_{13}C_{11} = \dfrac{13!}{2!\,11!} = \dfrac{13 \cdot 12}{2 \cdot 1} = 78$

75. $4 \cdot 5 = 20$ choices

76. $3^5 = 243$ possibilities

77. $_{15}P_4 = \dfrac{15!}{11!} = 15 \cdot 14 \cdot 13 \cdot 12 = 32{,}760$ ways

78. $_{20}C_4 = \dfrac{20!}{16!\,4!} = \dfrac{20 \cdot 19 \cdot 18 \cdot 17}{4 \cdot 3 \cdot 2 \cdot 1} = 4845$ ways

79. $_{20}C_3 = \dfrac{20!}{17!\,3!} = \dfrac{20 \cdot 19 \cdot 18}{3 \cdot 2 \cdot 1} = 1140$ sets

80. $_{20}P_4 = \dfrac{20!}{16!}$

$= 20 \cdot 19 \cdot 18 \cdot 17$

$= 116{,}280$ ways

81. $5! = 120$ ways

82. $P(E) = \dfrac{10{,}966{,}556}{33{,}871{,}648} \approx 0.324$

83. $P(E) = \dfrac{6{,}669{,}666}{20{,}851{,}820} \approx 0.320$

84. $P(E) = \dfrac{n(E)}{n(S)} = \dfrac{4}{6} = \dfrac{2}{3}$

85. $P(E) = \dfrac{2}{6} + \dfrac{2}{6} = \dfrac{4}{6} = \dfrac{2}{3}$

86. $P(E) = \dfrac{4}{52} + \dfrac{4}{52} = \dfrac{8}{52} = \dfrac{2}{13}$

87. $P(E) = \dfrac{4}{52} + \dfrac{26}{52} - \dfrac{2}{52} = \dfrac{28}{52} = \dfrac{7}{13}$

88. $P(\text{not yellow}) = 1 - P(\text{yellow}) = 1 - \dfrac{1}{6} = \dfrac{5}{6}$

89. $P(E) = \dfrac{3}{6} + \dfrac{3}{6} - \dfrac{1}{6} = \dfrac{5}{6}$

90. a. $P(E) = \dfrac{n(E)}{n(S)} = \dfrac{1}{_{20}C_5} = \dfrac{1}{15{,}504}$

b. $P(E) = \dfrac{100}{15{,}504} = \dfrac{25}{3876}$

91. $P(E) = \dfrac{70}{200} + \dfrac{140}{200} - \dfrac{50}{200} = \dfrac{160}{200} = \dfrac{4}{5}$

92. $P(E) = \dfrac{60}{200} + \dfrac{130}{200} - \dfrac{40}{200} = \dfrac{150}{200} = \dfrac{3}{4}$

93. $0.303 + 0.230 = 0.533$

94. $P(E) = \left(\dfrac{1}{2}\right)^5 = \dfrac{1}{32}$

95. a. $(0.2)^2 = 0.04$

b. $(0.2)^3 = 0.008$

c. $(1-0.2)^4 = (0.8)^4 = 0.4096$

Chapter 8 Test

1. $a_n = \dfrac{(-1)^{n+1}}{n^2}$

$a_1 = \dfrac{(-1)^2}{1^2} = 1$

$a_2 = \dfrac{(-1)^3}{2^2} = -\dfrac{1}{4}$

$a_3 = \dfrac{(-1)^4}{3^2} = \dfrac{1}{9}$

$a_4 = \dfrac{(-1)^5}{4^2} = -\dfrac{1}{16}$

$a_5 = \dfrac{(-1)^6}{5^2} = \dfrac{1}{25}$

The first five terms are

$1, -\dfrac{1}{4}, \dfrac{1}{9}, -\dfrac{1}{16},$ and $\dfrac{1}{25}$.

2. $\displaystyle\sum_{i=1}^{5}\left(i^2+10\right) = 11+14+19+26+35 = 105$

3. $\displaystyle\sum_{i=1}^{20}\left(3i-4\right)$

$a_1 = 3-4 = -1$

$d = 3$

$a_n = -1+(n-1)3$

$a_{20} = -1+(19)3 = 56$

$S_{20} = \dfrac{20}{2}(-1+56) = 550$

4. $\displaystyle\sum_{i=1}^{15}(-2)^i$

$a_1 = -2,\ r = -2$

$S_{15} = \dfrac{-2\left[1-(-2)^{15}\right]}{1-(-2)} = -21,846$

5. $\dbinom{9}{2} = \dfrac{9!}{7!\,2!} = \dfrac{9\cdot 8}{2\cdot 1} = 36$

6. $_{10}P_3 = \dfrac{10!}{7!} = 10\cdot 9\cdot 8 = 720$

7. $_{10}C_3 = \dfrac{10!}{7!\,3!} = \dfrac{10\cdot 9\cdot 8}{3\cdot 2\cdot 1} = 120$

8. $\dfrac{2}{3}+\dfrac{3}{4}+\dfrac{4}{5}+\cdots+\dfrac{21}{22} = \displaystyle\sum_{i=1}^{20}\dfrac{i+1}{i+2}$

9. $4, 9, 14, 19, \ldots$

$a_1 = 4,\ d = 5$

$a_n = 4+(n-1)\cdot 5 = 4+5n-1$

$a_n = 5n-1$

$a_{12} = 5(12)-1 = 59$

10. $16, 4, 1, \dfrac{1}{4}, \cdots$

$a_1 = 16,\ r = \dfrac{1}{4}$

$a_n = 16\left(\dfrac{1}{4}\right)^{n-1}$

$a_{12} = 16\left(\dfrac{1}{4}\right)^{11} = \dfrac{1}{262,144}$

11. $7, -14, 28, -56, \ldots$

$a_1 = 7,\ r = -2$

$S_{10} = \dfrac{7\left[1-(-2)^{10}\right]}{1-(-2)} = \dfrac{7(-1023)}{3} = -2387$

12. $-7, -14, -21, -28, \ldots$

$a_1 = -7, \ d = -7$

$a_n = -7 + (n-1)(-7)$

$a_{10} = -7 + 9(-7) = -70$

$S_{10} = \dfrac{10}{2}(-7 - 70) = -385$

13. $4 + \dfrac{4}{2} + \dfrac{4}{2^2} + \dfrac{4}{2^3} + \cdots$

$r = \dfrac{1}{2}$

$S_\infty = \dfrac{4}{1 - \dfrac{1}{2}} = 8$

14. $a_1 = 30,000, \ r = 1.04$

$S_8 = \dfrac{30,000 \left[1 - (1.04)^8 \right]}{1 - 1.04} \approx 276,426.79$

The total salary is \$276,427.

15. $S_1 : 1 = \dfrac{1[3(1) - 1]}{2}$

$1 = \dfrac{2}{2}$

$1 = 1$ is true.

$S_k : 1 + 4 + 7 + \cdots + (3k - 2) = \dfrac{k(3k - 1)}{2}$

$S_{k+1} : 1 + 4 + 7 + \cdots + (3k - 2) + (3k + 1) = \dfrac{(k+1)(3k+2)}{2}$

Add $(3k + 1)$ to both sides of S_k:

$1 + 4 + 7 + \cdots + (3k - 2) + (3k + 1) = \dfrac{k(3k - 1)}{2} + (3k + 1)$

Simplify the right-hand side:

$\dfrac{k(3k - 1)}{2} + (3k + 1) = \dfrac{k(3k - 1) + 2(3k + 1)}{2}$

$= \dfrac{3k^2 + 5k + 2}{2}$

$= \dfrac{(k + 1)(3k + 2)}{2}$

If S_k is true, then S_{k+1} is true. The statement is true for all n.

16. $\left(x^2 - 1\right)^5 = \binom{5}{0}\left(x^2\right)^5 + \binom{5}{1}\left(x^2\right)^4(-1) + \binom{5}{2}\left(x^2\right)^3(-1)^2 + \binom{5}{3}\left(x^2\right)^2(-1)^3 + \binom{5}{4}x^2(-1)^4 + \binom{5}{5}(-1)^5$

$= x^{10} - 5x^8 + 10x^6 - 10x^4 + 5x^2 - 1$

17. $_{11}P_3 = \dfrac{11!}{8!} = 11 \cdot 10 \cdot 9 = 990$ ways

18. $_{10}C_4 = \dfrac{10!}{6!\,4!} = \dfrac{10 \cdot 9 \cdot 8 \cdot 7}{4 \cdot 3 \cdot 2 \cdot 1} = 210$ sets

19. Four digits are open: $10^4 = 10,000$

20. $_{15}C_6 = \dfrac{15!}{9!\,6!} = \dfrac{15 \cdot 14 \cdot 13 \cdot 12 \cdot 11 \cdot 10}{6 \cdot 5 \cdot 4 \cdot 3 \cdot 2} = 5005$

$P(E) = \dfrac{50}{5005} = \dfrac{10}{1001}$

21. $P(E) = \dfrac{26}{52} + \dfrac{12}{52} - \dfrac{6}{52} = \dfrac{32}{52} = \dfrac{8}{13}$

22. $P(E) = \dfrac{25}{50} + \dfrac{20}{50} - \dfrac{15}{50} = \dfrac{30}{50} = \dfrac{3}{5}$

23. $P(E) = \left(\dfrac{1}{4}\right)^4 = \dfrac{1}{256}$

24. $P(E) = \dfrac{2}{8} \cdot \dfrac{2}{8} = \dfrac{1}{16}$

Cumulative Review Exercises (Chapters 1–8)

1. $-2(x - 5) + 10 = 3(x + 2)$

$-2x + 10 + 10 = 3x + 6$

$14 = 5x$

$x = \dfrac{14}{5}$

The solution set is $\left\{\dfrac{14}{5}\right\}$.

2. $3x^2 - 6x + 2 = 0$

$x = \dfrac{6 \pm \sqrt{36 - 24}}{6}$

$= \dfrac{6 \pm \sqrt{12}}{6}$

$= \dfrac{6 \pm 2\sqrt{3}}{6}$

$= \dfrac{3 \pm \sqrt{3}}{3}$

The solution set is $\left\{\dfrac{3 + \sqrt{3}}{3}, \dfrac{3 - \sqrt{3}}{3}\right\}$.

3. $\log_2 x + \log_2 (2x - 3) = 1$

$\log_2 x(2x - 3) = 1$

$x(2x - 3) = 2$

$2x^2 - 3x - 2 = 0$

$(2x + 1)(x - 2) = 0$

$2x + 1 = 0 \quad$ or $\quad x - 2 = 0$

$x = -\dfrac{1}{2} \qquad\qquad x = 2$

$x = -\dfrac{1}{2}$ does not check since $\log_2\left(-\dfrac{1}{2}\right)$

does not exist.

The solution set is $\{2\}$.

4. $x^{1/2} - 6x^{1/4} + 8 = 0$

Let $t = x^{1/4}$.

$t^2 - 6t + 8 = 0$

$(t - 2)(t - 4) = 0$

$t - 2 = 0 \quad$ or $\quad t - 4 = 0$

$t = 2 \qquad\qquad t = 4$

$x^{1/4} = 2 \qquad\qquad x^{1/4} = 4$

$x = 16 \qquad\qquad x = 256$

The solution set is $\{16, 256\}$.

5. $\sqrt{2x+4} - \sqrt{x+3} - 1 = 0$

$$\left(\sqrt{2x+4}\right)^2 = \left(\sqrt{x+3} + 1\right)^2$$

$$2x+4 = (x+3) + 2\sqrt{x+3} + 1$$

$$x = 2\sqrt{x+3}$$

$$x^2 = 4(x+3)$$

$$x^2 - 4x - 12 = 0$$

$$(x-6)(x+2) = 0$$

$x - 6 = 0$ or $x + 2 = 0$

$x = 6 \qquad\quad x = -2$

$\qquad\qquad x = -2$ does not check.

The solution set is $\{6\}$.

6. $|2x + 1| \le 1$

$-1 \le 2x + 1 \le 1$

$-2 \le 2x \le 0$

$-1 \le x \le 0$ or $[-1, 0]$

The solution set is

$\{x | -1 \le x \le 0\}$ or $[-1, 0]$.

7. $\qquad 6x^2 - 6 < 5x$

$6x^2 - 5x - 6 < 0$

$6x^2 - 5x - 6 = 0$

$(3x + 2)(2x - 3) = 0$

$3x + 2 = 0$ or $2x - 3 = 0$

$x = -\dfrac{2}{3} \qquad x = \dfrac{3}{2}$

The test intervals are $\left(-\infty, -\frac{2}{3}\right), \left(-\frac{2}{3}, \frac{3}{2}\right),$

and $\left(\frac{3}{2}, \infty\right)$. Testing a point in each interval

shows that the solution is $\left(-\frac{2}{3}, \frac{3}{2}\right)$.

8. $\dfrac{x-1}{x+3} \le 0$

The test intervals are $(-\infty, -3), (-3, 1)$ and

$(1, \infty)$.

Testing a point in each interval shows that

the solution is $(-3, 1]$.

9. $30e^{0.7x} = 240$

$e^{0.7x} = 8$

$\ln e^{0.7x} = \ln 8$

$0.7x = \ln 8$

$x = \dfrac{\ln 8}{0.7}$

The solution set is $\left\{\dfrac{\ln 8}{0.7}\right\}$, approximately

2.9706.

10. $2x^3 + 3x^2 - 8x + 3 = 0$

$p: \pm 1, \ \pm 3$

$q: \pm 1, \ \pm 2$

$\dfrac{p}{q}: \pm 1, \ \pm 3, \ \pm\dfrac{1}{2}, \ \pm\dfrac{3}{2}$

1	2	3	−8	3
		2	5	−3
	2	5	−3	0

$(x - 1)(2x^2 + 5x - 3) = 0$

$(x - 1)(2x - 1)(x + 3) = 0$

$x = 1$ or $x = \dfrac{1}{2}$ or $x = -3$

The solution set is $\left\{-3, \dfrac{1}{2}, 1\right\}$.

11. $4x^2 + 3y^2 = 48$

$3x^2 + 2y^2 = 35$

Multiply equation 1 by −2.

Multiply equation 2 by 3.

$$-8x^2 - 6y^2 = -96$$

$$9x^2 + 6y^2 = 105$$

Add: $\qquad\qquad x^2 = 9$

$\qquad\qquad\qquad x = \pm 3$

Let $x = -3$:

$$4(-3)^2 + 3y^2 = 48$$
$$36 + 3y^2 = 48$$
$$3y^2 = 12$$
$$y^2 = 4$$
$$y = \pm 2$$

Let $x = 3$:
$$4(3)^2 + 3y^2 = 48$$
$$36 + 3y^2 = 48$$
$$3y^2 = 12$$
$$y^2 = 4$$
$$y = \pm 2$$

The solution set is
$\{(3, 2), (3, -2), (-3, 2), (-3, -2)\}$.

12.
$$x - 2y + z = 16$$
$$2x - y - z = 14$$
$$3x + 5y - 4z = -10$$

$$\begin{bmatrix} 1 & -2 & 1 & | & 16 \\ 0 & -1 & -1 & | & 14 \\ 3 & 5 & -4 & | & -10 \end{bmatrix} \begin{matrix} \\ -2R_1 + R_2 \\ -3R_1 + R_3 \end{matrix}$$

$$\begin{bmatrix} 1 & -2 & 1 & | & 16 \\ 0 & 3 & -3 & | & -18 \\ 0 & 11 & -7 & | & -58 \end{bmatrix} \tfrac{1}{3}R_2$$

$$\begin{bmatrix} 1 & -2 & 1 & | & 16 \\ 0 & 1 & -1 & | & -6 \\ 0 & 11 & -7 & | & -58 \end{bmatrix} \begin{matrix} \\ 2R_2 + R_1 \\ -11R_2 + R_3 \end{matrix}$$

$$\begin{bmatrix} 1 & 0 & -1 & | & 4 \\ 0 & 1 & -1 & | & -6 \\ 0 & 0 & 4 & | & 8 \end{bmatrix} \tfrac{1}{4}R_3$$

$$\begin{bmatrix} 1 & 0 & -1 & | & 4 \\ 0 & 1 & -1 & | & -6 \\ 0 & 0 & 1 & | & 2 \end{bmatrix} \begin{matrix} R_3 + R_1 \\ R_2 + R_1 \\ \end{matrix}$$

$$\begin{bmatrix} 1 & 0 & 0 & | & 6 \\ 0 & 1 & 0 & | & -4 \\ 0 & 0 & 1 & | & 2 \end{bmatrix} \begin{matrix} R_3 + R_1 \\ R_2 + R_1 \\ \end{matrix}$$

The solution set is $\{(6, -4, 2)\}$.

13.
$$x - y = 1$$
$$x^2 - x - y = 1$$

Multiply $x - y = 1$ by -1, then add
$$-x + y = -1$$
$$\overline{x^2 - x - y = 1}$$
$$x^2 - 2x = 0$$
$$x(x - 2) = 0$$
$x = 0$ or $x = 2$
If $x = 0$, $-y = 1$ so $y = -1$.
If $x = 2$, $2 - y = 1$ so $y = 1$.
The solution set is $\{(0, -1), (2, 1)\}$.

14. $100x^2 + y^2 = 25$
$$4x^2 + \frac{y^2}{25} = 1$$
$$\frac{x^2}{\left(\frac{1}{4}\right)} + \frac{y^2}{25} = 1$$

Ellipse
Foci on the y-axis
$a^2 = 25$ and $b^2 = \dfrac{1}{4}$, so $\dfrac{1}{4} = 25 - c^2$.
$$c^2 = \frac{99}{4}$$
$$c = \frac{3\sqrt{11}}{2}$$
Foci: $\left(0, -\dfrac{3\sqrt{11}}{2}\right), \left(0, \dfrac{3\sqrt{11}}{2}\right)$

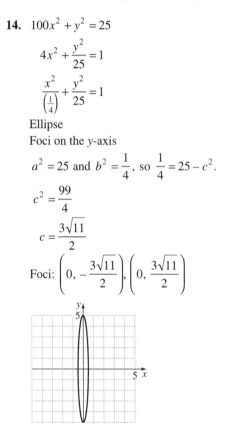

15.

$$4x^2 - 9y^2 - 16x + 54y - 29 = 0$$

$$4(x^2 - 4x) - 9(y^2 - 6y) = 29$$

$$4(x^2 - 4x + 4) - 9(y^2 - 6y + 9) = 16 - 81 + 29$$

$$4(x - 2)^2 - 9(y - 3)^2 = -36$$

$$\frac{(y - 3)^2}{4} - \frac{(x - 2)^2}{9} = 1$$

Hyperbola with center at (2, 3)

Transverse axis vertical

$a^2 = 4$ and $b^2 = 9$, so $9 = c^2 - 4$.

$c^2 = 13$

$c = \sqrt{13}$

Foci: $\left(2,\ 3 - \sqrt{13}\right), \left(2,\ 3 + \sqrt{13}\right)$

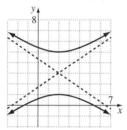

16.

$$f(x) = \frac{x^2 - 1}{x - 2}$$

Symmetry:

$$f(-x) = \frac{x^2 - 1}{-x - 2}$$

No symmetry since $f(-x) \neq f(x)$ and $f(-x) \neq -f(-x)$.

x-intercepts:

$$x^2 - 1 = 0$$

$$x = \pm 1$$

y-intercept:

$$f(0) = \frac{1}{2}$$

$$y = \frac{1}{2}$$

Vertical asymptote:

$$x - 2 = 0$$

$$x = 2$$

Horizontal asymptote:

$n > m$, so no horizontal asymptote.

Slant asymptote: $n = m + 1$

$$f(x) = x + 2 + \frac{3}{x - 2}$$

$$y = x + 2$$

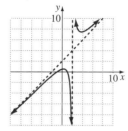

17. $2x - y \geq 4$

$x \leq 2$

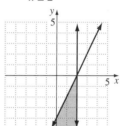

18. $f(x) = x^2 - 4x - 5$

$$x = \frac{-b}{2a} = \frac{4}{2} = 2$$

$f(2) = 2^2 - 8 - 5 = -9$

vertex: $(2, -9)$

x-intercepts:

$$x^2 - 4x - 5 = 0$$

$$(x - 5)(x + 1) = 0$$

$$x = 5, -1$$

y-intercept: $f(0) = -5$

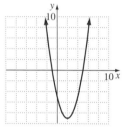

19. $y = \log_2 x$

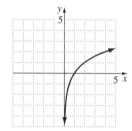

20.

$$f(x) = \sqrt[3]{x + 4}$$

$$y = \sqrt[3]{x + 4}$$

$$x = \sqrt[3]{y + 4}$$

$$x^3 = y + 4$$

$$y = x^3 - 4$$

$$f^{-1}(x) = x^3 - 4$$

21. $AB - 4A = \begin{bmatrix} 4 & 2 \\ 1 & -1 \\ 0 & 5 \end{bmatrix} \begin{bmatrix} 2 & 4 \\ 3 & 1 \end{bmatrix} - 4 \begin{bmatrix} 4 & 2 \\ 1 & 1 \\ 0 & 5 \end{bmatrix} = \begin{bmatrix} 14 & 18 \\ -1 & 3 \\ 15 & 5 \end{bmatrix} - \begin{bmatrix} 16 & 8 \\ 4 & -4 \\ 0 & 20 \end{bmatrix} = \begin{bmatrix} -2 & 10 \\ -5 & 7 \\ 15 & -15 \end{bmatrix}$

22.

$$\frac{2x^2 - 10x + 2}{(x - 2)(x^2 + 2x + 2)} = \frac{A}{x - 2} + \frac{Bx + C}{x^2 + 2x + 2}$$

$$2x^2 - 10x + 2 = A(x^2 + 2x + 2) + (Bx + C)(x - 2)$$

$$= Ax^2 + 2Ax + 2A + Bx^2 - 2Bx + Cx - 2C$$

$$= (A + B)x^2 + (2A - 2B + C)x + 2A - 2C$$

Thus we have the following system of equations.

$$A + B = 2$$
$$2A - 2B + C = -10$$
$$2A - 2C = 2$$

Add twice the first equation to the second equation.

$$2A + 2B = 4$$
$$\underline{2A - 2B + C = -10}$$
$$4A + C = -6$$

Add twice the resulting equation to the third equation.

$$8A + 2C = -12$$
$$\underline{2A - 2C = 2}$$
$$10A = -10$$
$$A = -1$$

Back-substitute to find B and C.
$$2(-1) - 2C = 2$$
$$-2 - 2C = 2$$
$$-2C = 4$$
$$C = -2$$
$$-1 + B = 2$$
$$B = 3$$
$$\frac{-1}{x-2} + \frac{3x-2}{x^2+2x+2}$$

23. $(x^3 + 2y)^5 = \binom{5}{0}(x^3)^5 + \binom{5}{1}(x^3)^4(2y) + \binom{5}{2}(x^3)^3(2y)^2 + \binom{5}{3}(x^3)^2(2y)^3 + \binom{5}{4}(x^3)(2y)^4 + \binom{5}{5}(2y)^5$

$$= x^{15} + 5x^{12}(2y) + 10x^9(4y^2) + 10x^6(8y^3) + 5x^3(16y^4) + 32y^5$$

$$= x^{15} + 10x^{12}y + 40x^9y^2 + 80x^6y^3 + 80x^3y^4 + 32y^5$$

24. $\displaystyle\sum_{i=1}^{50}\left(4i - 25\right)$

$$a_1 = 4(1) - 25 = -21$$
$$a_{50} = 4(50) - 25 = 175$$
$$S_{50} = \frac{50}{2}(-21 + 175) = 3850$$

25. a. $m = \dfrac{19.8 - 21}{52 - 50} = -0.6$ **b.** $y = -0.6x + 30 + 21$ **c.** $y = -0.6(54) + 51 = 18.6$

hours
$$y - 21 = -0.6(x - 50) \qquad\qquad y = -0.6x + 51$$

26. $200 + 0.05x = 0.15x$

$200 = 0.1x$

$2000 = x$

At \$2000 in sales, the two earnings will be the same.

27. $2L + 2W = 300$

$L = W + 50$

Rearrange the equations and add:

$L + W = 150$

$\underline{L - W = 50}$

$2L = 200$

$L = 100$

$W = 50$

length: 100 yards, width 50 yards

28. $10x + 12y = 42$

$5x + 10y = 29$

Multiply second equation by -2 and add:

$10x + 12y = 42$

$\underline{-10x - 20y = -58}$

$-8y = -16$

$y = 2$

Back substitute:

$5x + 10(2) = 29$

$5x = 9$

$x = 1.8$

pen: \$1.80, pad: \$2

29. $s(t) = -16t^2 + 80t + 96$

a. $-16t^2 + 80t + 96 = 0$

$t^2 - 5t - 6 = 0$

$(t + 1)(t - 6) = 0$

$t = -1$ or $t = 6$

The ball will strike the ground after 6 seconds.

b. $t = \dfrac{-b}{2a} = \dfrac{-80}{-32} = \dfrac{5}{2}$ or 2.5

$S(2.5) = -16(2.5)^2 + 80(2.5) + 96 = 196$

The ball reaches a maximum height of 196 feet, 2.5 seconds after it is thrown.

30. $I = \dfrac{k}{R}$

$5 = \dfrac{k}{22}$

$k = 110$

$I = \dfrac{110}{10} = 11$

11 amperes